Solutions Manual

for Chapters 11-16 and Appendix

CALCULUS

With Analytic Geometry

SECOND EDITION

ROBERT ELLIS
University of Maryland
at College Park

DENNY GULICK
University of Maryland
at College Park

HBJ

HARCOURT BRACE JOVANOVICH, INC.

New York San Diego Chicago San Francisco Atlanta
London Sydney Toronto

NOTE: Solutions for Chapters 1-10 are available in a separate manual.

ISBN: 0-15-505733-2

Printed in the United States of America

PREFACE

This Manual contains complete solutions to all exercises from Chapters 11-16 and the Appendix of Calculus With Analytic Geometry, Second Edition, by Robert Ellis and Denny Gulick. (The solutions for Chapters 1-10 appear in a separate Manual.) Our aim has been to provide all the details necessary for full understanding of the solutions and of the various techniques involved. In each solution we have included all important steps, so that the student can easily follow the line of reasoning. Where possible, solutions are patterned after the examples in the corresponding text section.

This Manual can be a valuable learning aid. We suggest that the student conscientiously attempt an exercise first, and only then refer to the Manual, both for the answer and for the method of obtaining it.

The solutions to the exercises have been carefully checked. We would be grateful to have any residual errors in either the Solutions Manual or the textbook brought to our attention.

Robert Ellis

Denny Gulick

CONTENTS

11

VECTORS, LINES, AND PLANES

Section 11.1

1. $|PQ| = \sqrt{3^2 + (-4)^2 + 10^2} = \sqrt{125} = 5\sqrt{5}$; $\overrightarrow{PQ} = 3\vec{i} - 4\vec{j} + 10\vec{k}$

2. $|PQ| = \sqrt{(3-1)^2 + (-1-(-3))^2 + (3-2)^2} = \sqrt{9} = 3$; $\overrightarrow{PQ} = 2\vec{i} + 2\vec{j} + \vec{k}$

3. $|PQ| = \sqrt{(3-0)^2 + (-1-1)^2 + (\sqrt{7}-0)^2} = \sqrt{20} = 2\sqrt{5}$; $\overrightarrow{PQ} = 3\vec{i} - 2\vec{j} + \sqrt{7}\,\vec{k}$

4. $|PQ| = \sqrt{(2-2)^2 + (1+\sqrt{2}-1)^2 + (1+\sqrt{3}-1)^2} = \sqrt{5}$; $\overrightarrow{PQ} = \sqrt{2}\,\vec{j} + \sqrt{3}\,\vec{k}$

5. $\vec{a} + \vec{b} = \vec{i} - 3\vec{j} + \vec{k}$; $\vec{a} - \vec{b} = 3\vec{i} - 7\vec{j} + 19\vec{k}$; $c\vec{a} = 4\vec{i} - 10\vec{j} + 20\vec{k}$

6. $\vec{a} + \vec{b} = \frac{3}{2}\vec{i} + \frac{1}{2}\vec{j} - 6\vec{k}$; $\vec{a} - \vec{b} = \frac{1}{2}\vec{i} + \frac{3}{2}\vec{j}$; $c\vec{a} = -\vec{i} - \vec{j} + 3\vec{k}$

7. $\vec{a} + \vec{b} = 2\vec{i} + \vec{j} + \vec{k}$; $\vec{a} - \vec{b} = 2\vec{i} - \vec{j} - \vec{k}$; $c\vec{a} = \frac{2}{3}\vec{i}$

8. $\vec{a} + \vec{b} = \vec{i} + \vec{k}$; $\vec{a} - \vec{b} = \vec{i} + 4\vec{j} - \vec{k}$; $c\vec{a} = \pi\vec{i} + 2\pi\vec{j}$

9. $\|\vec{a}\| = \sqrt{1^2 + (-1)^2 + 1^2} = \sqrt{3}$

10. $\|\vec{a}\| = \sqrt{2^2 + 1^2 + (-2)^2} = 3$

11. $\|\vec{b}\| = \sqrt{(-3)^2 + 4^2 + (-12)^2} = 13$

12. $\|\vec{b}\| = \sqrt{4^2 + (-8)^2 + 8^2} = 12$

13. $\|\vec{c}\| = \sqrt{(\sqrt{2})^2 + (-1)^2 + 1^2} = 2$

14. $\dfrac{\vec{a}}{\|\vec{a}\|} = \dfrac{\vec{a}}{\sqrt{3}} = \dfrac{1}{\sqrt{3}}\vec{i} + \dfrac{1}{\sqrt{3}}\vec{j} - \dfrac{1}{\sqrt{3}}\vec{k}$

15. $\dfrac{\vec{a}}{\|\vec{a}\|} = \dfrac{\vec{a}}{13} = -\dfrac{3}{13}\vec{i} + \dfrac{4}{13}\vec{j} - \dfrac{12}{13}\vec{k}$

16. $\dfrac{\vec{b}}{\|\vec{b}\|} = \dfrac{\vec{b}}{25} = \dfrac{7}{25}\vec{i} + \dfrac{12\sqrt{2}}{25}\vec{j} - \dfrac{12\sqrt{2}}{25}\vec{k}$

17. $\dfrac{\vec{b}}{\|\vec{b}\|} = \dfrac{\vec{b}}{\sqrt{13}} = \dfrac{2}{\sqrt{13}}\vec{i} - \dfrac{3}{\sqrt{13}}\vec{j}$

18. Let $P = (3, 0, 2)$, $Q = (1, -1, 5)$, and $R = (5, 1, -1)$. Then $|PQ| = \sqrt{(1-3)^2 + (-1-0)^2 + (5-2)^2} = \sqrt{14}$ and $|PR| = \sqrt{(5-3)^2 + (1-0)^2 + (-1-2)^2} = \sqrt{14}$. Thus P in equidistant from Q and R.

19. Let $P = (-1, 1, 2)$, $Q = (2, 0, 3)$, and $R = (3, 4, 5)$. The perimeter of the triangle is $|PQ| + |QR| + |RP| = \sqrt{(2-(-1))^2 + (0-1)^2 + (3-2)^2} + \sqrt{(3-2)^2 + (4-0)^2 + (5-3)^2} + \sqrt{(-1-3)^2 + (1-4)^2 + (2-5)^2}$ $= \sqrt{11} + \sqrt{21} + \sqrt{34}$

20. $(x-2)^2 + (y-1)^2 + (z+7)^2 = 25$

21. $(x+1)^2 + y^2 + (z-3)^2 = 2$

22. Completing the squares, we have $(x^2 - 2x + 1) + (y^2 - 4y + 4) + (z^2 + 6z + 9) = -10 + 1 + 4 + 9$, or $(x-1)^2 + (y-2)^2 + (z+3)^2 = 4$, which is an equation of a sphere with center $(1, 2, -3)$ and radius 2.

23. Completing the squares, we have $(x^2 + 6x + 9) + (y^2 + 8y + 16) + (z^2 - 4z + 4) = 9 + 16$, or $(x+3)^2 + (y+4)^2 + (z-2)^2 = 25$, which is an equation of a sphere with center $(-3, -4, 2)$ and radius 5.

24. $x^2 + (y+2)^2 + (z+3)^2 \le 36$

25. Let s be the length of the sides of the cube. Then $\overrightarrow{OB} + \overrightarrow{OD} + \overrightarrow{OF} = (s\vec{i} + s\vec{j}) + (s\vec{j} + s\vec{k}) + (s\vec{i} + s\vec{k}) = 2s\vec{i} + 2s\vec{j} + 2s\vec{k} = 2\,\overrightarrow{OG}$. Thus by Definition 11.4, $\overrightarrow{OB} + \overrightarrow{OD} + \overrightarrow{OF}$ is parallel to $\overrightarrow{OG}$.

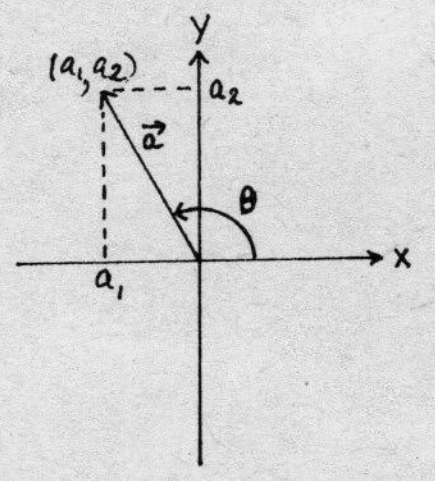

26. a. If we place the vector $\vec{a}$ in the xy plane with its initial point at the origin and let its terminal point be (a_1, a_2), then $\vec{a} = a_1\vec{i} + a_2\vec{j}$. By the definition of $\cos\theta$ and $\sin\theta$, we have $\cos\theta = \dfrac{a_1}{\|\vec{a}\|}$ and $\sin\theta = \dfrac{a_2}{\|\vec{a}\|}$. Thus

$$\vec{a} = a_1\vec{i} + a_2\vec{j} = \|\vec{a}\|(\cos\theta\,\vec{i} + \sin\theta\,\vec{j}).$$

b. Let θ be the angle between the positive x axis and $\vec{u}$. Since $\|\vec{u}\| = 1$, it follows from part (a) that $\vec{u} = \cos\theta\,\vec{i} + \sin\theta\,\vec{j}$.

27. a. The vector $\overrightarrow{PQ} = \vec{b} - \vec{a}$ points from P to Q. Thus $\frac{1}{2}(\vec{b} - \vec{a})$ points from P to the midpoint of PQ. Since $\vec{a}$ points from the origin to P, it follows that $\vec{c} = \vec{a} + \frac{1}{2}(\vec{b} - \vec{a}) = \vec{a} + \frac{1}{2}\vec{b} - \frac{1}{2}\vec{a} = \frac{1}{2}(\vec{a} + \vec{b})$.

b. By an argument similar to that in (a), we see that $\frac{2}{3}(\vec{b} - \vec{a})$ points from P to the point $\frac{2}{3}$ of the way from P to Q, so that $\vec{c} = \vec{a} + \frac{2}{3}(\vec{b} - \vec{a})$ $= \frac{1}{3}\vec{a} + \frac{2}{3}\vec{b}$.

28. Assume that the quadrilateral lies in the xy plane with P at the origin as in the figure, and let $\vec{a}$ and $\vec{b}$ be vectors along the two sides that contain the origin. Then $\vec{a} + \vec{b}$ and $\vec{a} - \vec{b}$ lie along the diagonals. Since the diagonals bisect each other, we have $\overrightarrow{SR} = \frac{1}{2}(\vec{a} - \vec{b}) + \frac{1}{2}(\vec{a} + \vec{b}) = \vec{a} = \overrightarrow{PQ}$ and $\overrightarrow{QR} = -\frac{1}{2}(\vec{a} - \vec{b}) + \frac{1}{2}(\vec{a} + \vec{b}) = \vec{b} = \overrightarrow{PS}$. Thus the opposite sides of the quadrilateral are parallel, so that the quadrilateral is a parallelogram.

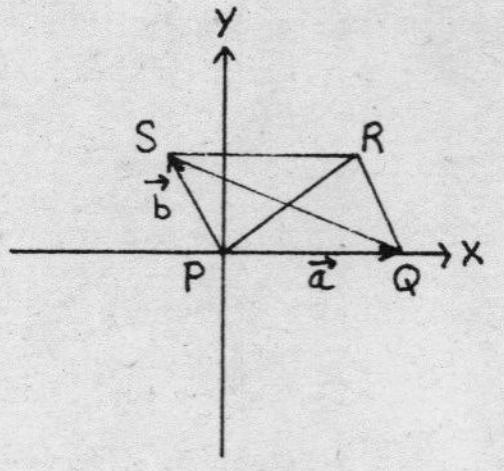

29. Let P, Q, R, and S be the midpoints of the sides of the quadrilateral, and $\vec{a}$, $\vec{b}$, $\vec{c}$, and $\vec{d}$ the vectors corresponding to the four sides, as in the figure. Our first goal is to show that the vector from P to the midpoint of PR is the same as the vector from P to the midpoint of QS. To begin with, the vector from P to the midpoint of PR is $\frac{1}{2}\overrightarrow{PR} = \frac{1}{2}(-\frac{1}{2}\vec{a} + \vec{b} + \frac{1}{2}\vec{c}) = -\frac{1}{4}\vec{a} + \frac{1}{2}\vec{b} + \frac{1}{4}\vec{c}$. Next, the vector from Q to the midpoint of QS is $\frac{1}{2}(-\frac{1}{2}\vec{b} + \vec{a} + \frac{1}{2}\vec{d}) = -\frac{1}{4}\vec{b} + \frac{1}{2}\vec{a} + \frac{1}{4}\vec{d}$. Since $\vec{a} + \vec{d} = \vec{b} + \vec{c}$, this means that $\vec{d} = \vec{b} + \vec{c} - \vec{a}$, so that $-\frac{1}{4}\vec{b} + \frac{1}{2}\vec{a} + \frac{1}{4}\vec{d}$ $= -\frac{1}{4}\vec{b} + \frac{1}{2}\vec{a} + \frac{1}{4}(\vec{b} + \vec{c} - \vec{a}) = \frac{1}{4}\vec{a} + \frac{1}{4}\vec{c}$. Thus the vector from P to the midpoint of QS is $-\frac{1}{2}\vec{a} + \frac{1}{2}\vec{b} + \frac{1}{2}\overrightarrow{QS} = -\frac{1}{2}\vec{a} + \frac{1}{2}\vec{b} + (\frac{1}{4}\vec{a} + \frac{1}{4}\vec{c})$ $= -\frac{1}{4}\vec{a} + \frac{1}{2}\vec{b} + \frac{1}{4}\vec{c}$, which is the same as the vector from P to the midpoint of PR. As a result, PR and QS bisect each other. By Exercise 28, the quadrilateral PQRS is a parallelogram.

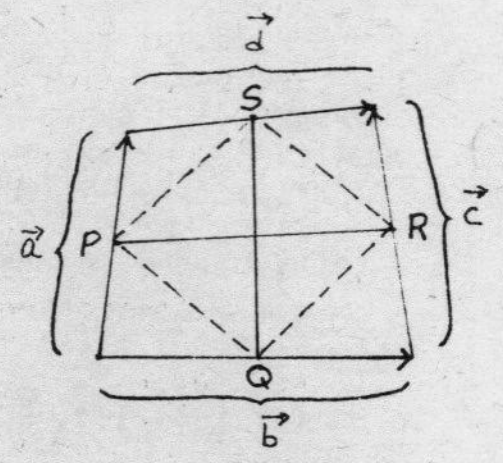

30. The force $\vec{F}_1$ exerted by the child at P is given by $\vec{F}_1 = -20\,\vec{j}$, and the force $\vec{F}_2$ exerted by the child at Q is given by $\vec{F}_2 = 100\,(\cos\frac{\pi}{3}\vec{i} + \sin\frac{\pi}{3}\vec{j})$ $= 50\,(\vec{i} + \sqrt{3}\,\vec{j})$. If $\vec{F}$ is the force exerted by the third child at R, and θ the angle $\vec{F}$ makes with the positive x axis, then $\vec{F} = \|\vec{F}\|\,(\cos\theta\,\vec{i} + \sin\theta\,\vec{j})$. If the total force exerted on the ball is to be $\vec{0}$, then $\vec{F}_1 + \vec{F}_2 + \vec{F} = \vec{0}$, so that $-20\,\vec{j} + 50\,(\vec{i} + \sqrt{3}\,\vec{j}) + \|\vec{F}\|\,(\cos\theta\,\vec{i} + \sin\theta\,\vec{j})$ $= \vec{0}$. Combining coefficients of $\vec{i}$ and $\vec{j}$, we find that

$$50 + \|\vec{F}\|\cos\theta = 0 \quad\text{and}\quad -20 + 50\sqrt{3} + \|\vec{F}\|\sin\theta = 0$$

so that

$$\|\vec{F}\|\cos\theta = -50 \text{ and } \|\vec{F}\|\sin\theta = 20 - 50\sqrt{3}$$

Therefore

$$\tan\theta = \frac{\sin\theta}{\cos\theta} = \frac{20 - 50\sqrt{3}}{-50} = \frac{5\sqrt{3} - 2}{5}$$

and

$$\vec{F} = \|\vec{F}\|\,(\cos\theta\,\vec{i} + \sin\theta\,\vec{j}) = \|\vec{F}\|\cos\theta\,\vec{i} + \|\vec{F}\|\sin\theta\,\vec{j}$$

$$= -50\,\vec{i} + (20 - 50\sqrt{3})\,\vec{j}$$

31. Consider a coordinate system having its x axis along the line ℓ. Let $\vec{F}_1$ be the force exerted by the tugboat at A and $\vec{F}_2$ for force exerted by the tugboat at B. Then $\vec{F}_1 = 1000\,(\cos\frac{\pi}{6}\vec{i} + \sin\frac{\pi}{6}\vec{j}) = 500\,(\sqrt{3}\,\vec{i} + \vec{j})$ and $\vec{F}_2 = \|\vec{F}_2\|\,(\cos\frac{\pi}{4}\vec{i} - \sin\frac{\pi}{4}\vec{j}) = \frac{\|\vec{F}_2\|}{2}(\sqrt{2}\,\vec{i} - \sqrt{2}\,\vec{j})$. If the freighter is to move along ℓ, then $\vec{F}_1 + \vec{F}_2 = c\vec{i}$ for some number c, so that $500\,(\sqrt{3}\,\vec{i} + \vec{j}) + \frac{\|\vec{F}_2\|}{2}(\sqrt{2}\,\vec{i} - \sqrt{2}\,\vec{j}) = c\vec{i}$. Equating the $\vec{j}$-components of both sides, we find that $500 - \frac{\|\vec{F}_2\|}{2}\sqrt{2} = 0$, or $\|\vec{F}_2\|$ $= 500\sqrt{2}$ (pounds).

32. Let $\vec{v}$ be the velocity of the airplane with respect to the ground, $\vec{v}_1$ the velocity of the airplane with respect to the air, and $\vec{v}_2$ the velocity of the air with respect to the ground. By the hint, $\vec{v} = \vec{v}_1 + \vec{v}_2 = 300 \cdot (\cos\frac{\pi}{6}\vec{i} + \sin\frac{\pi}{6}\vec{j}) + 20\,\vec{j} = 150\sqrt{3}\,\vec{i} + 170\,\vec{j}$. Thus $\|\vec{v}\|$ $= \sqrt{(150\sqrt{3})^2 + (170)^2} = \sqrt{96{,}400} \approx 310.483$ (miles per hour).

33. Consider a coordinate system with the positive y axis pointing north, in the direction the boat travels. Let $\vec{v}$ be the velocity of the boat with respect to the ground, $\vec{v}_1$ the velocity of the boat with respect to the air, and $\vec{v}_2$ the velocity of the air with respect to the ground. Then $\vec{v} = 8\vec{j}$, $\vec{v}_1 = c_1(\vec{i} - \vec{j})$, and $\vec{v}_2 = c_2\vec{i}$, for appropriate constants c_1 and c_2. By the hint to Exercise 32, $8\vec{j} = \vec{v} = \vec{v}_1 + \vec{v}_2 = c_1(\vec{i} - \vec{j}) + c_2\vec{i}$ $= (c_1 + c_2)\vec{i} - c_1\vec{j}$. Equating coefficients of $\vec{i}$ and $\vec{j}$, we find that $0 = c_1 + c_2$ and $8 = -c_1$, so that $c_1 = -8$ and $c_2 = 8$. Then the speed $\|\vec{v}_2\|$ of the wind is given by $\|\vec{v}_2\| = \|8\vec{i}\| = 8$ (miles per hour).

34. If we let $q_1 = 1.6 \times 10^{-19}$, $\vec{u}_1 = \dfrac{-\vec{j} - \vec{k}}{\sqrt{2}}$, $r_1 = 10^{-11}\sqrt{2}$, $q_2 = -1.6 \times 10^{-19}$, $\vec{u}_2 = \dfrac{-\vec{i} - \vec{j}}{\sqrt{2}}$, and $r_2 = 10^{-12}\sqrt{2}$, then

$$\vec{F} = \frac{q_1(1)}{4\pi\varepsilon_0 r_1^2}\vec{u}_1 + \frac{q_2(1)}{4\pi\varepsilon_0 r_2^2}\vec{u}_2 = \frac{1.6 \times 10^{-19}}{4\pi\varepsilon_0(2 \times 10^{-22})}\left(\frac{-\vec{j} - \vec{k}}{\sqrt{2}}\right)$$

$$+ \frac{-1.6 \times 10^{-19}}{4\pi\varepsilon_0(2 \times 10^{-24})}\left(\frac{-\vec{i} - \vec{j}}{\sqrt{2}}\right) = \frac{100\sqrt{2}}{\pi\varepsilon_0}(-\vec{j} - \vec{k} + 100\vec{i} + 100\vec{j})$$

$$= \frac{100\sqrt{2}}{\pi\varepsilon_0}(100\vec{i} + 99\vec{j} - \vec{k}).$$

35. If we let $q_1 = 1.6 \times 10^{-19}$, $\vec{u}_1 = -\vec{j}$, $r_1 = 10^{-11}$, $q_2 = -1.6 \times 10^{-19}$, $\vec{u}_2 = \dfrac{\vec{j} - \vec{k}}{\sqrt{2}}$, and $r_2 = 10^{-11}\sqrt{2}$, then

$$\vec{F} = \frac{q_1(1)}{4\pi\varepsilon_0 r_1^2}\vec{u}_1 + \frac{q_2(1)}{4\pi\varepsilon_0 r_2^2}\vec{u}_2 = \frac{1.6 \times 10^{-19}}{4\pi\varepsilon_0(10^{-22})}(-\vec{j}) + \frac{-1.6 \times 10^{-19}}{4\pi\varepsilon_0(2 \times 10^{-22})}\cdot$$

$$\left(\frac{\vec{j} - \vec{k}}{\sqrt{2}}\right) = \frac{400}{\pi\varepsilon_0}\left[-\left(1 + \frac{1}{2\sqrt{2}}\right)\vec{j} + \frac{1}{2\sqrt{2}}\vec{k}\right]$$

36. Let $m = m_1 + m_2 + \ldots + m_n$. By writing the vectors in terms of the corresponding components, we find that

$$m_1\overrightarrow{PP}_1 + m_2\overrightarrow{PP}_2 + \ldots + m_n\overrightarrow{PP}_n = [m_1(x_1 - \bar{x})\vec{i} + m_1(y_1 - \bar{y})\vec{j}]$$

$$+ [m_2(x_2 - \bar{x})\vec{i} + m_2(y_2 - \bar{y})\vec{j}] + \ldots + [m_n(x_n - \bar{x})\vec{i} + m_n(y_n - \bar{y})\vec{j}]$$

$$= [m_1(x_1 - \bar{x}) + m_2(x_2 - \bar{x}) + \ldots + m_n(x_n - \bar{x})]\vec{i} + [m_1(y_1 - \bar{y})$$

$$+ m_2(y_2 - \bar{y}) + \ldots m_n(y_n - \bar{y})]\vec{j} = [(m_1x_1 + m_2x_2 + \ldots + m_nx_n)$$

$$- (m_1 + m_2 + \ldots m_n)\bar{x}]\vec{i} + [(m_1y_1 + m_2y_2 + \ldots + m_ny_n) - (m_1 + m_2$$

$$+ \ldots + m_n)\bar{y}]\vec{j} = [(m_1x_1 + m_2x_2 + \ldots + m_nx_n) - m\bar{x}]\vec{i} + [(m_1y_1$$

$+ m_2y_2 + \ldots + m_ny_n) - m\bar{y}]\vec{j}$. By (3) of Section 8.7, the coefficients of $\vec{i}$ and $\vec{j}$ are 0, so that $m_1\overrightarrow{PP}_1 + m_2\overrightarrow{PP}_2 + \ldots + m_n\overrightarrow{PP}_n = \vec{0}$.

37. a. Let $\vec{b} = b_1\vec{i} + b_2\vec{j} + b_3\vec{k}$. Since a ray and its reflection travel in a plane, we find that $b_1\vec{i} + b_2\vec{j}$ is parallel to $a_1\vec{i} + a_2\vec{j}$, so that $b_1 = ca_1$ and $b_2 = ca_2$ for an appropriate positive value of c. Since the angle of incidence θ and the angle of reflection are equal, and since $\vec{a}$ and $\vec{b}$ are unit vectors, $-a_3 = \sin\theta = b_3$. Thus $\vec{b} = ca_1\vec{i} + ca_2\vec{j} - a_3\vec{k}$. Since $\sqrt{c^2(a_1^2 + a_2^2) + a_3^2} = \|\vec{b}\| = 1 = \|\vec{a}\| = \sqrt{a_1^2 + a_2^2 + a_3^2}$, it follows that $c = 1$, so that $\vec{b} = a_1\vec{i} + a_2\vec{j} - a_3\vec{k}$.

b. Consider a coordinate system such that the mirrors correspond to the three coordinate planes, and assume that the ray is reflected first by the xy plane, then by the yz plane, and finally by the xz plane, in the first octant. If $a_1\vec{i} + a_2\vec{j} + a_3\vec{k}$ denotes the incident ray, then after reflection in the xy plane, the ray becomes $a_1\vec{i} + a_2\vec{j} - a_3\vec{k}$ by part (a). After reflection in the yz plane, this ray becomes $a_1\vec{i}$ $- a_2\vec{j} - a_3\vec{k}$, and after reflection in the xz plane this ray becomes $-a_1\vec{i} - a_2\vec{j} - a_3\vec{k}$, which is parallel to the original incident ray.

$500\sqrt{3}i + 500j + \frac{\|F\|}{2}\sqrt{2}i - \frac{\|F\|\sqrt{2}}{2}j = ci$

Section 11.2

1. $\vec{a} \cdot \vec{b} = (1)(2) + (1)(-3) + (-1)(4) = -5$; $\cos\theta = \dfrac{\vec{a} \cdot \vec{b}}{\|\vec{a}\|\ \|\vec{b}\|}$

$= \dfrac{-5}{\sqrt{3}\ \sqrt{29}} = \dfrac{-5}{\sqrt{87}}$

2. $\vec{a} \cdot \vec{b} = (\frac{1}{2})(2) + (\frac{1}{3})(-2) + (-2)(1) = -\frac{5}{3}$; $\cos\theta = \dfrac{\vec{a} \cdot \vec{b}}{\|\vec{a}\|\ \|\vec{b}\|}$

$= \dfrac{-\frac{5}{3}}{\frac{\sqrt{157}}{6} \cdot 3} = \dfrac{-10}{3\sqrt{157}}$

3. $\vec{a} \cdot \vec{a} = (2)(2) + (3)(3) + (-1)(-1) = 14$; $\cos\theta = \dfrac{\vec{a} \cdot \vec{a}}{\|\vec{a}\|\ \|\vec{a}\|}$

$= \dfrac{\|\vec{a}\|^2}{\|\vec{a}\|^2} = 1$

4. $\vec{a} \cdot \vec{b} = (\sqrt{2})(-\sqrt{2}) + (4)(-\sqrt{3}) + (\sqrt{3})(2) = -2 - 2\sqrt{3}$; $\cos\theta = \dfrac{\vec{a} \cdot \vec{b}}{\|\vec{a}\|\ \|\vec{b}\|}$

$= \dfrac{-2 - 2\sqrt{3}}{\sqrt{21} \cdot 3} = -\dfrac{2(1 + \sqrt{3})}{3\sqrt{21}}$

5. $\vec{a} \cdot \vec{b} = 4(-\frac{1}{2}) + (-2)(-1) + (0)(\sqrt{3}) = 0$; $\cos\theta = \dfrac{\vec{a} \cdot \vec{b}}{\|a\|\ \|b\|} = 0$

6. $\vec{a} \cdot \vec{b} = (1)(0) + (0)(1) = 0$; they are perpendicular.

7. $\vec{a} \cdot \vec{b} = (1)(1) + (-1)(1) = 0$; they are perpendicular.

8. $\vec{a} \cdot \vec{b} = (-4)(\frac{1}{2}) + (2)(6) + (-5)(2) = 0$; they are perpendicular.

9. $\vec{a} \cdot \vec{b} = (\sqrt{2})(-1) + (3)(\sqrt{2}) + (1)(5) = 2\sqrt{2} + 5 \neq 0$; they are not perpendicular.

10. Since $(2\vec{i} + \vec{j} - \vec{k}) \cdot (3\vec{i} + 7\vec{j} + 13\vec{k}) = 6 + 7 - 13 = 0$, $(2\vec{i} + \vec{j} - \vec{k}) \cdot (20\vec{i} - 29\vec{j} + 11\vec{k}) = 40 - 29 - 11 = 0$, and $(3\vec{i} + 7\vec{j} + 13\vec{k}) \cdot (20\vec{i} - 29\vec{j} + 11\vec{k}) = 60 - 203 + 143 = 0$, the three vectors are mutually perpendicular.

11. $\text{pr}_{\vec{a}}\vec{b} = \dfrac{\vec{a} \cdot \vec{b}}{\|\vec{a}\|^2}\vec{a} = \frac{2}{9}(2\vec{i} - \vec{j} + 2\vec{k}) = \frac{4}{9}\vec{i} - \frac{2}{9}\vec{j} + \frac{4}{9}\vec{k}$

12. $\text{pr}_{\vec{a}}\vec{b} = \dfrac{\vec{a} \cdot \vec{b}}{\|\vec{a}\|^2}\vec{a} = \frac{-2}{1}\vec{i} = -2\vec{i}$

13. $\text{pr}_{\vec{a}}\vec{b} = \dfrac{\vec{a} \cdot \vec{b}}{\|\vec{a}\|^2}\vec{a} = \frac{1}{2}(\vec{i} + \vec{j})$

14. $\text{pr}_{\vec{a}}\vec{b} = \dfrac{\vec{a} \cdot \vec{b}}{\|\vec{a}\|^2}\vec{a} = \dfrac{4\sqrt{3} - 8}{16}(\sqrt{3}\,\vec{i} + 2\vec{j} - 3\vec{k}) = \dfrac{\sqrt{3} - 2}{4}(\sqrt{3}\,\vec{i}$

$+ 2\vec{j} - 3\vec{k})$

15. $\vec{a} \cdot \vec{a}' = 0 + 2 - 2 = 0$. Thus $\vec{a}$ and $\vec{a}'$ are perpendicular.

$\text{pr}_{\vec{a}}\vec{b} = \dfrac{\vec{a} \cdot \vec{b}}{\|\vec{a}\|^2}\vec{a} = \frac{18}{6}\vec{a} = 3\vec{a} = 3(\vec{i} + 2\vec{j} - \vec{k})$; $\text{pr}_{\vec{a}'}\vec{b} = \vec{b} - \text{pr}_{\vec{a}}\vec{b}$

$= 3\vec{i} + \vec{j} - 13\vec{k} - 3(\vec{i} + 2\vec{j} - \vec{k}) = -5\vec{j} - 10\vec{k} = -5\vec{a}'$. Thus

$\vec{b} = 3\vec{a} - 5\vec{a}'$.

16. $\vec{a} \cdot \vec{a}' = 2 - 3 + 1 = 0$. Thus $\vec{a}$ and $\vec{a}'$ are perpendicular.

$\text{pr}_{\vec{a}}\vec{b} = \dfrac{\vec{a} \cdot \vec{b}}{\|\vec{a}\|^2}\vec{a} = \frac{-6}{3}\vec{a} = -2\vec{a} = -2(\vec{i} + \vec{j} - \vec{k})$; $\text{pr}_{\vec{a}'}\vec{b} = \vec{b} - \text{pr}_{\vec{a}}\vec{b}$

$= -5\vec{j} + \vec{k} + 2(\vec{i} + \vec{j} - \vec{k}) = 2\vec{i} - 3\vec{j} - \vec{k} = \vec{a}'$. Thus $\vec{b} = -2\vec{a} + \vec{a}'$.

17. $\vec{a} \cdot \vec{a}' = 4 - 24 + 20 = 0$. Thus $\vec{a}$ and $\vec{a}'$ are perpendicular. $\text{pr}_{\vec{a}}\vec{b}$

$= \dfrac{\vec{a} \cdot \vec{b}}{\|\vec{a}\|^2}\vec{a} = \dfrac{-45}{45}\vec{a} = -\vec{a} = -(2\vec{i} - 4\vec{j} + 5\vec{k})$; $\text{pr}_{\vec{a}'}\vec{b} = \vec{b} - \text{pr}_{\vec{a}}\vec{b}$

$= \vec{i} + 13\vec{j} + \vec{k} + (2\vec{i} - 4\vec{j} + 5\vec{k}) = 3\vec{i} + 9\vec{j} + 6\vec{k} = \frac{3}{2}\vec{a}'$. Thus

$\vec{b} = -\vec{a} + \frac{3}{2}\vec{a}'$.

18. Let $\vec{a} = \vec{i}$, $\vec{b} = \vec{j}$, and $\vec{c} = \vec{k}$. Then $\vec{a} \cdot \vec{b} = 0 = \vec{a} \cdot \vec{c}$, but $\vec{b} \neq \vec{c}$.

19. $\vec{a} \cdot \vec{a} = (a_1)(a_1) + (a_2)(a_2) + (a_3)(a_3) = a_1^2 + a_2^2 + a_3^2 = \|\vec{a}\|^2$.

20. $\vec{a} \cdot \vec{b} = (a_1)(b_1) + (a_2)(b_2) + (a_3)(b_3) = (b_1)(a_1) + (b_2)(a_2) + (b_3)(a_3)$ $= \vec{b} \cdot \vec{a}$.

21. a. $\vec{a}\cdot(\vec{b}+\vec{c}) = \vec{a}\cdot[(b_1+c_1)\vec{i} + (b_2+c_2)\vec{j} + (b_3+c_3)\vec{k}]$

$= a_1(b_1+c_1) + a_2(b_2+c_2) + a_3(b_3+c_3) = (a_1b_1 + a_2b_2 + a_3b_3)$

$+ (a_1c_1 + a_2c_2 + a_3c_3) = \vec{a}\cdot\vec{b} + \vec{a}\cdot\vec{c}.$

b. If $\vec{a}$ is perpendicular to $\vec{b}$ and $\vec{c}$, then $\vec{a}\cdot\vec{b} = 0 = \vec{a}\cdot\vec{c}$, so that by (a), $\vec{a}\cdot(\vec{b}+\vec{c}) = \vec{a}\cdot\vec{b} + \vec{a}\cdot\vec{c} = 0 + 0 = 0$, which implies that $\vec{a}$ is perpendicular to $\vec{b}+\vec{c}$.

22. $(c\vec{a})\cdot\vec{b} = (c\,a_1\vec{i} + c\,a_2\vec{j} + c\,a_3\vec{k})\cdot\vec{b} = (c\,a_1)b_1 + (c\,a_2)b_2$

$+ (c\,a_3)b_3 = c(a_1b_1 + a_2b_2 + a_3b_3) = c(\vec{a}\cdot\vec{b}).$

23. a. $|\vec{a}\cdot\vec{b}| = \|\vec{a}\|\,\|\vec{b}\|\,|\cos\theta| \le \|\vec{a}\|\,\|\vec{b}\|$

b. By part (a), $(a_1b_1 + a_2b_2 + a_3b_3)^2 = (\vec{a}\cdot\vec{b})^2 = |\vec{a}\cdot\vec{b}|^2$

$\le \|\vec{a}\|^2\,\|\vec{b}\|^2 = (a_1^2 + a_2^2 + a_3^2)(b_1^2 + b_2^2 + b_3^2)$

c. Taking $b_1 = b_2 = b_3 = 1$ in part (b), we have $(a_1 + a_2 + a_3)^2$

$\le 3(a_1^2 + a_2^2 + a_3^2)$, so that $\left(\dfrac{a_1 + a_2 + a_3}{3}\right)^2 \le \dfrac{a_1^2 + a_2^2 + a_3^2}{3}$

24. The first four steps follow, in order, from Exercises 19, 21(a), 19 and 20, and 23(a). The last step follows from the algebraic identity $x^2 + 2xy + y^2 = (x+y)^2$.

25. $\|\vec{PQ}\| = \|\vec{PR} + \vec{RQ}\| \le \|\vec{PR}\| + \|\vec{RQ}\|.$

26. a. $\|\vec{a}+\vec{b}\|^2 + \|\vec{a}-\vec{b}\|^2 = (\vec{a}+\vec{b})\cdot(\vec{a}+\vec{b})$

$+ (\vec{a}-\vec{b})\cdot(\vec{a}-\vec{b}) = (\vec{a}\cdot\vec{a} + \vec{a}\cdot\vec{b} + \vec{b}\cdot\vec{a} + \vec{b}\cdot\vec{b}) + (\vec{a}\cdot\vec{a}$

$- \vec{a}\cdot\vec{b} - \vec{b}\cdot\vec{a} + \vec{b}\cdot\vec{b}) = 2(\vec{a}\cdot\vec{a}) + 2(\vec{b}\cdot\vec{b}) = 2\|\vec{a}\|^2 +$

$2\|\vec{b}\|^2.$

b. $\|\vec{a}+\vec{b}\|^2 - \|\vec{a}-\vec{b}\|^2 = (\vec{a}+\vec{b})\cdot(\vec{a}+\vec{b})$

$- (\vec{a}-\vec{b})\cdot(\vec{a}-\vec{b}) = \vec{a}\cdot\vec{a} + \vec{a}\cdot\vec{b} + \vec{b}\cdot\vec{a} + \vec{b}\cdot\vec{b}$

$- \vec{a}\cdot\vec{a} + \vec{a}\cdot\vec{b} + \vec{b}\cdot\vec{a} - \vec{b}\cdot\vec{b} = 2\vec{a}\cdot\vec{b} + 2\vec{b}\cdot\vec{a} = 4\vec{a}\cdot\vec{b}.$

c. Let $\vec{a}$ and $\vec{b}$ be vectors along two adjacent sides of the parallelogram, as in Figure 11.34. If the diagonals have equal length, then $\|\vec{a}+\vec{b}\| = \|\vec{a}-\vec{b}\|$, so that by part (b), $\vec{a}\cdot\vec{b} = 0$. Thus the sides are perpendicular, which means that the parallelogram is a rectangle. Conversely, if the parallelogram is a rectangle, then $\vec{a}$ and $\vec{b}$ are perpendicular, so that $\vec{a}\cdot\vec{b} = 0$, and thus by part (b), $\|\vec{a}+\vec{b}\|^2 - \|\vec{a}-\vec{b}\|^2 = 0$, or $\|\vec{a}+\vec{b}\|^2 = \|\vec{a}-\vec{b}\|^2$. This means that the diagonals have equal length.

27. If $\vec{a}$ and $\vec{b}$ are vectors along two adjacent sides of the rhombus, then $\vec{a}+\vec{b}$ and $\vec{a}-\vec{b}$ lie along the diagonals, and by hypothesis $\|\vec{a}\| = \|\vec{b}\|$. Thus $(\vec{a}+\vec{b})\cdot(\vec{a}-\vec{b}) = \vec{a}\cdot\vec{a} - \vec{a}\cdot\vec{b} + \vec{b}\cdot\vec{a} - \vec{b}\cdot\vec{b} = \|\vec{a}\|^2 - \|\vec{b}\|^2 = 0$, which means that the diagonals are perpendicular.

28. Let θ be the angle between $\vec{a}$ and $\vec{c}$, and φ the angle between $\vec{c}$ and $\vec{b}$. If $\vec{c} \ne \vec{0}$, then $\cos\theta = \dfrac{\vec{a}\cdot\vec{c}}{\|\vec{a}\|\,\|\vec{c}\|} = \dfrac{\vec{a}\cdot(\|\vec{b}\|\,\vec{a} + \|\vec{a}\|\,\vec{b})}{\|\vec{a}\|\,\|\vec{c}\|}$

$= \dfrac{\|\vec{b}\|\,\vec{a}\cdot\vec{a} + \|\vec{a}\|\,\vec{a}\cdot\vec{b}}{\|\vec{a}\|\,\|\vec{c}\|} = \dfrac{\|\vec{b}\|\,\|\vec{a}\|^2 + \|\vec{a}\|\,\vec{a}\cdot\vec{b}}{\|\vec{a}\|\,\|\vec{c}\|}$

$= \dfrac{\|\vec{b}\|\,\|\vec{a}\| + \vec{a}\cdot\vec{b}}{\|\vec{c}\|}$, and $\cos\varphi = \dfrac{\vec{c}\cdot\vec{b}}{\|\vec{c}\|\,\|\vec{b}\|} = \dfrac{(\|\vec{b}\|\,\vec{a} + \|\vec{a}\|\,\vec{b})\cdot\vec{b}}{\|\vec{c}\|\,\|\vec{b}\|}$

$= \dfrac{\|\vec{b}\|\,\vec{a}\cdot\vec{b} + \|\vec{a}\|\,\vec{b}\cdot\vec{b}}{\|\vec{c}\|\,\|\vec{b}\|} = \dfrac{\|\vec{b}\|\,\vec{a}\cdot\vec{b} + \|\vec{a}\|\,\|\vec{b}\|^2}{\|\vec{c}\|\,\|\vec{b}\|}$

$= \dfrac{\vec{a}\cdot\vec{b} + \|\vec{a}\|\,\|\vec{b}\|}{\|\vec{c}\|}.$

Thus $\cos\theta = \cos\varphi$. Since $0 \le \theta \le \pi$ and $0 \le \varphi \le \pi$, this means that $\theta = \varphi$. Thus $\vec{c}$ bisects the angle formed by $\vec{a}$ and $\vec{b}$.

29. Assume that the sled travels along the x axis from P = (0, 0) to Q = (100, 0), and the force $\vec{F}$ acts in the xy plane with the positive y axis pointing upward. It follows that $\vec{PQ} = 100\,\vec{i}$ and $\vec{F} = 5\left(\cos\frac{\pi}{4}\vec{i} + \sin\frac{\pi}{4}\vec{j}\right) = \frac{5}{2}\sqrt{2}\,(\vec{i}+\vec{j})$. Consequently $W = \vec{F}\cdot\vec{PQ} = \left(\frac{5}{2}\sqrt{2}\right)100 = 250\sqrt{2}$ (foot-pounds).

30. Using the same terminology as that in Example 7, we find that $\overrightarrow{PQ} = 500\,\vec{i}$ and $\vec{F} = 100\,(\cos\frac{\pi}{6}\vec{i} + \sin\frac{\pi}{6}\vec{j}) = 50\sqrt{3}\,\vec{i} + 50\,\vec{j}$. Therefore $W = \vec{F}\cdot\overrightarrow{PQ} = (50\sqrt{3})\,500 = 25{,}000\sqrt{3}$ (foot-pounds).

31. Consider a coordinate system with the origin at the base of the ramp, as in the figure. Then $\overrightarrow{PQ} = 15\cdot(\cos\frac{\pi}{6}\,\vec{i} + \sin\frac{\pi}{6}\,\vec{j}) = \frac{15}{2}(\sqrt{3}\,\vec{i} + \vec{j})$ and $\vec{F} = 20\,\vec{i}$. Thus $W = \vec{F}\cdot\overrightarrow{PQ} = 20\,(\frac{15}{2}\sqrt{3}) = 150\sqrt{3}$ (foot-pounds).

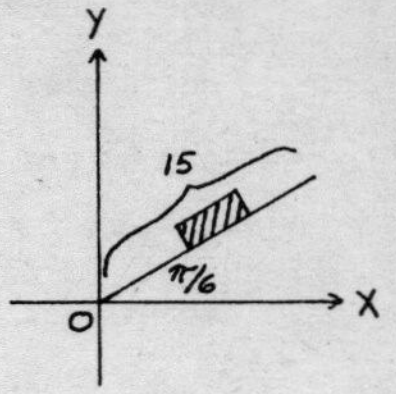

Section 11.3

1. $\vec{a}\times\vec{b} = \begin{vmatrix}\vec{i} & \vec{j} & \vec{k}\\ 1 & 1 & 0\\ 0 & 1 & 1\end{vmatrix} = \vec{i} - \vec{j} + \vec{k}$

Thus $\vec{c}\cdot(\vec{a}\times\vec{b}) = (-1)(1) + (-3)(-1) + (4)(1) = 6$.

2. $\vec{a}\times\vec{b} = \begin{vmatrix}\vec{i} & \vec{j} & \vec{k}\\ 1 & 1 & 1\\ 1 & 0 & -1\end{vmatrix} = -\vec{i} + 2\vec{j} - \vec{k}$

Thus $\vec{c}\cdot(\vec{a}\times\vec{b}) = (1)(-1) + (1)(2) + (-1)(-1) = 2$.

3. $\vec{a}\times\vec{b} = \begin{vmatrix}\vec{i} & \vec{j} & \vec{k}\\ 2 & 3 & -1\\ -1 & 4 & 5\end{vmatrix} = 19\,\vec{i} - 9\,\vec{j} + 11\,\vec{k}$

Thus $\vec{c}\cdot(\vec{a}\times\vec{b}) = (2)(19) + (3)(-9) + (4)(11) = 55$.

4. $\vec{a}\times\vec{b} = \begin{vmatrix}\vec{i} & \vec{j} & \vec{k}\\ 3 & 4 & 12\\ 3 & 4 & -12\end{vmatrix} = -96\,\vec{i} + 72\,\vec{j}$

Thus $\vec{c}\cdot(\vec{a}\times\vec{b}) = (\frac{1}{8})(-96) + (-\frac{1}{12})(72) + (\frac{1}{16})(0) = -18$.

5. $\vec{a}\times\vec{b} = \begin{vmatrix}\vec{i} & \vec{j} & \vec{k}\\ 3 & 4 & 12\\ 3 & 4 & 12\end{vmatrix} = 0\,\vec{i} + 0\,\vec{j} + 0\,\vec{k} = \vec{0}$

Thus $\vec{c}\cdot(\vec{a}\times\vec{b}) = (1)(0) + (1)(0) + (0)(0) = 0$

6. $\sin\theta = \dfrac{\|\vec{a}\times\vec{b}\|}{\|\vec{a}\|\,\|\vec{b}\|} = \dfrac{\sqrt{(-96)^2 + (72)^2}}{\sqrt{3^2 + 4^2 + 12^2}\,\sqrt{3^2 + 4^2 + (-12)^2}} = \dfrac{120}{(13)(13)} = \dfrac{120}{169}$

7. $\vec{a}\times\vec{b} = (a_2 b_3 - a_3 b_2)\,\vec{i} + (a_3 b_1 - a_1 b_3)\,\vec{j} + (a_1 b_2 - a_2 b_1)\,\vec{k}$

$= -(b_2 a_3 - b_3 a_2)\,\vec{i} - (b_3 a_1 - b_1 a_3)\,\vec{j} - (b_1 a_2 - b_2 a_1)\,\vec{k}$

$= -\vec{b}\times\vec{a}$

8. $\vec{a} \times (\vec{b} + \vec{c}) = [a_2 (b_3 + c_3) - a_3 (b_2 + c_2)]\vec{i} + [a_3 (b_1 + c_1)$
$- a_1 (b_3 + c_3)]\vec{j} + [a_1 (b_2 + c_2) - a_2 (b_1 + c_1)]\vec{k} = [(a_2 b_3 - a_3 b_2)$
$+ (a_2 c_3 - a_3 c_2)]\vec{i} + [(a_3 b_1 - a_1 b_3) + (a_3 c_1 - a_1 c_3)]\vec{j}$
$+ [(a_1 b_2 - a_2 b_1) + (a_1 c_2 - a_2 c_1)]\vec{k} = [(a_2 b_3 - a_3 b_2)\vec{i}$
$+ (a_3 b_1 - a_1 b_3)\vec{j} + (a_1 b_2 - a_2 b_1)\vec{k}] + [(a_2 c_3 - a_3 c_2)\vec{i}$
$+ (a_3 c_1 - a_1 c_3)\vec{j} + (a_1 c_2 - a_2 c_1)\vec{k}] = \vec{a} \times \vec{b} + \vec{a} \times \vec{c}.$

9. $\vec{0} = \vec{a} \times \vec{0} = \vec{a} \times (\vec{a} + \vec{b} + \vec{c}) = (\vec{a} \times \vec{a}) + (\vec{a} \times \vec{b}) + (\vec{a} \times \vec{c}) = (\vec{a} \times \vec{b}) + (\vec{a} \times \vec{c})$. Thus $\vec{a} \times \vec{b} = -(\vec{a} \times \vec{c}) = \vec{c} \times \vec{a}$ by Exercise 7. Similarly, $\vec{0} = \vec{b} \times \vec{0} = \vec{b} \times (\vec{a} + \vec{b} + \vec{c}) = (\vec{b} \times \vec{a}) + (\vec{b} \times \vec{b}) + (\vec{b} \times \vec{c}) = (\vec{b} \times \vec{a}) + (\vec{b} \times \vec{c})$. Thus $\vec{b} \times \vec{c} = -(\vec{b} \times \vec{a}) = \vec{a} \times \vec{b}$ by Exercise 7.

10. By Theorem 11.10(a), the cross product $(\vec{i} - 3\vec{j} + 2\vec{k}) \times (-2\vec{i} + \vec{j} - 5\vec{k})$ is such a vector. This cross product is

$$\begin{vmatrix} \vec{i} & \vec{j} & \vec{k} \\ 1 & -3 & 2 \\ -2 & 1 & -5 \end{vmatrix} = 13\vec{i} + \vec{j} - 5\vec{k}.$$

11. If $\vec{a} = 2\vec{i} - 3\vec{j} + 4\vec{k}$, $\vec{b} = \vec{i} + \vec{j} - \vec{k}$, and $\vec{c} = 4\vec{i} - \vec{j} - \vec{k}$, then the volume is $|\vec{a} \cdot (\vec{b} \times \vec{c})|$. Since

$$\vec{a} \cdot (\vec{b} \times \vec{c}) = \begin{vmatrix} 2 & -3 & 4 \\ 1 & 1 & -1 \\ 4 & -1 & -1 \end{vmatrix} = (-2 + 12 - 4) - (16 + 3 + 2) = -15$$

the volume is 15.

12. Let $a = \vec{i}$, $b = 2\vec{i}$, and $c = 3\vec{i}$. Then $\vec{a} \times \vec{b} = \vec{0} = \vec{a} \times \vec{c}$, but $\vec{b} \neq \vec{c}$.

13. We have $\vec{a} \cdot (\vec{b} - \vec{c}) = \vec{a} \cdot \vec{b} - \vec{a} \cdot \vec{c} = 0$ and $\vec{a} \times (\vec{b} - \vec{c}) = \vec{a} \times \vec{b} - \vec{a} \times \vec{c} = \vec{0}$. If $\vec{b}$ and $\vec{c}$ were not equal, then $\vec{b} - \vec{c}$ would be nonzero and it would follow from the preceding calculations and the fact that $\vec{a} \neq \vec{0}$ that $\vec{a}$ is both perpendicular to and parallel to $\vec{b} - \vec{c}$, which is impossible. Thus it does follow that $\vec{b} = \vec{c}$.

14. If $\vec{a} = \vec{0}$ or $\vec{b} = \vec{0}$, the equation is trivially valid. Otherwise
$\|\vec{a} \times \vec{b}\|^2 = \|\vec{a}\|^2 \|\vec{b}\|^2 \sin^2\theta = \|\vec{a}\|^2 \|\vec{b}\|^2 (1 - \cos^2\theta)$
$= \|\vec{a}\|^2 \|\vec{b}\|^2 - (\|\vec{a}\| \|\vec{b}\| \cos\theta)^2 = \|\vec{a}\|^2 \|\vec{b}\|^2 - (\vec{a} \cdot \vec{b})^2$

15. $$\vec{b} \times \vec{c} = \begin{vmatrix} \vec{i} & \vec{j} & \vec{k} \\ \frac{1}{2} & 1 & -1 \\ 4 & -5 & 6 \end{vmatrix} = \vec{i} - 7\vec{j} - \frac{13}{2}\vec{k}$$

$$\vec{a} \times (\vec{b} \times \vec{c}) = \begin{vmatrix} \vec{i} & \vec{j} & \vec{k} \\ 2 & -3 & 4 \\ 1 & -7 & \frac{-13}{2} \end{vmatrix} = \frac{95}{2}\vec{i} + 17\vec{j} - 11\vec{k}$$

$\vec{a} \times (\vec{b} \times \vec{c}) = \vec{b}(\vec{a} \cdot \vec{c}) - \vec{c}(\vec{a} \cdot \vec{b}) = 47\vec{b} + 6\vec{c} = \frac{95}{2}\vec{i} + 17\vec{j} - 11\vec{k}$

16. $$\vec{b} \times \vec{c} = \begin{vmatrix} \vec{i} & \vec{j} & \vec{k} \\ 3 & -7 & 2 \\ 2 & -5 & 0 \end{vmatrix} = 10\vec{i} + 4\vec{j} - \vec{k}$$

$$\vec{a} \times (\vec{b} \times \vec{c}) = \begin{vmatrix} \vec{i} & \vec{j} & \vec{k} \\ 1 & -4 & 2 \\ 10 & 4 & -1 \end{vmatrix} = -4\vec{i} + 21\vec{j} + 44\vec{k}$$

$\vec{a} \times (\vec{b} \times \vec{c}) = \vec{b}(\vec{a} \cdot \vec{c}) - \vec{c}(\vec{a} \cdot \vec{b}) = 22\vec{b} - 35\vec{c} = -4\vec{i} + 21\vec{j}$
$+ 44\vec{k}$

17. Since $\vec{b} \times \vec{c} = (b_2 c_3 - b_3 c_2)\vec{i} + (b_3 c_1 - b_1 c_3)\vec{j} + (b_1 c_2 - b_2 c_1)\vec{k}$,
we have $\vec{a} \times (\vec{b} \times \vec{c}) = [a_2 (b_1 c_2 - b_2 c_1) - a_3 (b_3 c_1 - b_1 c_3)]\vec{i}$
$+ [a_3 (b_2 c_3 - b_3 c_2) - a_1 (b_1 c_2 - b_2 c_1)]\vec{j} + [a_1 (b_3 c_1 - b_1 c_3)$
$- a_2 (b_2 c_3 - b_3 c_2)]\vec{k} = [(a_1 c_1 + a_2 c_2 + a_3 c_3) b_1$
$- (a_1 b_1 + a_2 b_2 + a_3 b_3) c_1]\vec{i} + [(a_1 c_1 + a_2 c_2 + a_3 c_3) b_2$
$- (a_1 b_1 + a_2 b_2 + a_3 b_3) c_2]\vec{j} + [(a_1 c_1 + a_2 c_2 + a_3 c_3) b_3$
$- (a_1 b_1 + a_2 b_2 + a_3 b_3) c_3]\vec{k} = [(\vec{a} \cdot \vec{c}) b_1 - (\vec{a} \cdot \vec{b}) c_1]\vec{i}$
$+ [(\vec{a} \cdot \vec{c}) b_2 - (\vec{a} \cdot \vec{b}) c_2]\vec{j} + [(\vec{a} \cdot \vec{c}) b_3 - (\vec{a} \cdot \vec{b}) c_3]\vec{k}$
$= (\vec{a} \cdot \vec{c})\vec{b} - (\vec{a} \cdot \vec{b})\vec{c} = \vec{b}(\vec{a} \cdot \vec{c}) - \vec{c}(\vec{a} \cdot \vec{b}).$

18. By the bac - cab rule,

$\vec{a} \times (\vec{b} \times \vec{c}) + \vec{b} \times (\vec{c} \times \vec{a}) + \vec{c} \times (\vec{a} \times \vec{b}) = [\vec{b}\ (\vec{a} \cdot \vec{c}) - \vec{c}\ (\vec{a} \cdot \vec{b})]$

$+ [\vec{c}\ (\vec{b} \cdot \vec{a}) - \vec{a}\ (\vec{b} \cdot \vec{c})] + [\vec{a}\ (\vec{c} \cdot \vec{b}) - \vec{b}\ (\vec{c} \cdot \vec{a})]$

$= \vec{b}\ (\vec{a} \cdot \vec{c} - \vec{c} \cdot \vec{a}) + \vec{c}\ (-\vec{a} \cdot \vec{b} + \vec{b} \cdot \vec{a}) + \vec{a}\ (-\vec{b} \cdot \vec{c} + \vec{c} \cdot \vec{b}) = \vec{0}.$

19. Using the bac-cab rule, we have

$(\vec{a} \times \vec{b}) \times \vec{c} = -\vec{c} \times (\vec{a} \times \vec{b}) = -[\vec{a}\ (\vec{c} \cdot \vec{b}) - \vec{b}\ (\vec{c} \cdot \vec{a})] = (\vec{a} \cdot \vec{c})\ \vec{b}$

$- (\vec{b} \cdot \vec{c})\ \vec{a}$.

20. Using the coordinate system shown in Figure 11.37, with the stapler in the yz plane, we have $\overrightarrow{PQ} = \frac{3}{2}(\cos \frac{\pi}{6}\ \vec{j} + \sin \frac{\pi}{6}\ \vec{k}) = \frac{3}{2}(\frac{\sqrt{3}}{2}\ \vec{j} + \frac{1}{2}\ \vec{k})$

$= \frac{3}{4}(\sqrt{3}\ \vec{j} + \vec{k})$ and $\vec{F} = -32\ \vec{k}$. Thus $\vec{M} = \overrightarrow{PQ} \times \vec{F} = -24\sqrt{3}\ \vec{i}$.

21. Using the coordinate system shown in the figure, we have $\overrightarrow{PQ} = 4\ (\cos \frac{\pi}{4}\ \vec{j} + \cos \frac{\pi}{4}\ \vec{k})$

$= 4\ (\frac{\sqrt{2}}{2}\ \vec{j} + \frac{\sqrt{2}}{2}\ \vec{k}) = 2\sqrt{2}\ (\vec{j} + \vec{k})$ and

$\vec{F} = -5\ \vec{k}$. Thus $\vec{M} = \overrightarrow{PQ} \times \vec{F} = -10\sqrt{2}\ \vec{i}$.

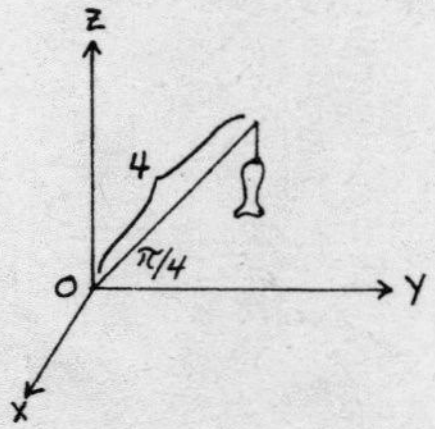

Section 11.4

1. $\vec{r}_0 = -2\ \vec{i} + \vec{j}$, so that a vector equation of the line is $\vec{r} = (-2 + 3t)\ \vec{i}$ $+ (1 - t)\ \vec{j} + 5t\vec{k}$; a = 3, b = -1, c = 5, so that symmetric equations of the line are $\frac{x + 2}{3} = \frac{y - 1}{-1} = \frac{z}{5}$.

2. $\vec{r}_0 = \vec{0}$, so that a vector equation of the line is $\vec{r} = 11\ t\vec{i} - 13t\vec{j} - 15t\vec{k}$; a = 11, b = -13, c = -15, so that symmetric equations of the line are $\frac{x}{11} = \frac{y}{-13} = \frac{z}{-15}$.

3. $\vec{r}_0 = 3\vec{i} + 4\vec{j} + 5\vec{k}$, so that a vector equation of the line is $\vec{r}$ $= (3 + \frac{1}{2}t)\ \vec{i} + (4 - \frac{1}{3}t)\ \vec{j} + (5 + \frac{1}{6}t)\ \vec{k}$; $a = \frac{1}{2}$, $b = -\frac{1}{3}$, $c = \frac{1}{6}$, so that symmetric equations of the line are $\frac{x - 3}{\frac{1}{2}} = \frac{y - 4}{-\frac{1}{3}} = \frac{z - 5}{\frac{1}{6}}$.

4. $\vec{r}_0 = -3\vec{i} + 6\vec{j} + 2\vec{k}$, so that a vector equation of the line is $\vec{r}$ $= (-3 + t)\ \vec{i} + (6 - t)\ \vec{j} + 2\vec{k}$; a = 1, b = -1, c = 0, so that symmetric equations of the line are $\frac{x + 3}{1} = \frac{y - 6}{-1}$ and z = 2.

5. $\vec{r}_0 = 2\vec{i} + 5\vec{k}$, so that a vector equation of the line is $\vec{r} = 2\vec{i} + 2t\vec{j}$ $+ (5 + 3t)\ \vec{k}$; a = 0, b = 2, z = 3, so that symmetric equations of the line are x = 2 and $\frac{y}{2} = \frac{z - 5}{3}$.

6. $\vec{r}_0 = 7\vec{i} - \vec{j} + 2\vec{k}$, so that a vector equation of the line is $\vec{r} = 7\vec{i} - \vec{j}$ $+ (2 + t)\ \vec{k}$; a = 0 = b, c = 1, so that symmetric equations of the line are x = 7 and y = -1.

7. $\vec{r}_0 = 4\vec{i} + 2\vec{j} - \vec{k}$, so that a vector equation of the line is $\vec{r} = 4\vec{i}$ $+ (2 + t)\ \vec{j} - \vec{k}$; a = 0 = c, b = 1, so that symmetric equations of the line are x = 4 and z = -1.

8. $x_0 = 3$, $y_0 = -1$, $z_0 = 2$, $a = 4$, $b = 2$, $c = 1$, so that parametric equations for the line are $x = 3 + 4t$, $y = -1 + 2t$, $z = 2 + t$.

9. $x_0 = -1$, $y_0 = 1$, $z_0 = 0$, $a = -2 - (-1) = -1$, $b = 5 - 1 = 4$, $c = 7 - 0 = 7$, so that parametric equations for the line are $x = -1 - t$, $y = 1 + 4t$, $z = 7t$.

10. $x_0 = -1$, $y_0 = 1$, $z_0 = 0$, $a = -1 - (-1) = 0$, $b = 5 - 1 = 4$, $c = 7 - 0 = 7$, so that parametric equations for the line are $x = -1$, $y = 1 + 4t$, $z = 7t$.

11. $x_0 = -1$, $y_0 = 1$, $z_0 = 0$, $a = 0$, $b = 0$, $c = 7$, so that symmetric equations for the line are $x = -1$ and $y = 1$.

12. The line through (1, 7, 5) and (3, 2, -1) is parallel to $\vec{L}_1$, where $\vec{L}_1 = (3 - 1)\vec{i} + (2 - 7)\vec{j} + (-1 - 5)\vec{k} = 2\vec{i} - 5\vec{j} - 6\vec{k}$. The line through (2, -2, 5) and (-2, 8, 17) is parallel to $\vec{L}_2$, where $\vec{L}_2 = (-2 - 2)\vec{i} + (8 + 2)\vec{j} + (17 - 5)\vec{k} = -4\vec{i} + 10\vec{j} + 12\vec{k}$. Now $\vec{L}_1$ and $\vec{L}_2$ are parallel since $\vec{L}_2 = -2\vec{L}_1$. Thus the two lines are parallel.

13. The line through (2, -1, 3) and (0, 7, 9) is parallel to $\vec{L}_1$, where $\vec{L}_1 = (0 - 2)\vec{i} + (7 + 1)\vec{j} + (9 - 3)\vec{k} = -2\vec{i} + 8\vec{j} + 6\vec{k}$. The line through (-1, 0, 4) and (2, 3, 1) is parallel to $\vec{L}_2$, where $\vec{L}_2 = (2 + 1)\vec{i} + (3 - 0)\vec{j} + (1 - 4)\vec{k} = 3\vec{i} + 3\vec{j} - 3\vec{k}$. Since $\vec{L}_1 \cdot \vec{L}_2 = (-2)(3) + (8)(3) + (6)(-3) = 0$, $\vec{L}_1$ and $\vec{L}_2$ are perpendicular. Consequently the two lines are perpendicular.

14. The line through (5, 7, 9) and (4, 11, 9) is parallel to $\vec{L}_1$, where $\vec{L}_1 = (4 - 5)\vec{i} + (11 - 7)\vec{j} + (9 - 9)\vec{k} = -\vec{i} + 4\vec{j}$. The line with equations $\frac{x - 1}{-3} = \frac{y - 2}{12}$, $z = 5$ is parallel to $\vec{L}_2$, where $\vec{L}_2 = -3\vec{i} + 12\vec{j}$. Since $\vec{L}_2 = 3\vec{L}_1$, the two lines are parallel.

15. The line through (0, 0, 5) and (1, -1, 4) is parallel to $\vec{L}_1$, where $\vec{L}_1 = (1 - 0)\vec{i} + (-1 - 0)\vec{j} + (4 - 5)\vec{k} = \vec{i} - \vec{j} - \vec{k}$. The line with equations $\frac{x}{7} = \frac{y - 3}{4} = \frac{z + 9}{3}$ is parallel to $\vec{L}_2$, where $\vec{L}_2 = 7\vec{i} + 4\vec{j} + 3\vec{k}$. Since $\vec{L}_1 \cdot \vec{L}_2 = (1)(7) + (-1)(4) + (-1)(3) = 0$, $\vec{L}_1$ and $\vec{L}_2$ are perpendicular. Consequently the two lines are perpendicular.

16. The point $P_0 = (1, -2, -1)$ is on the line, and the line is parallel to $\vec{i} - 2\vec{j} + 3\vec{k}$. If $P_1 = (5, 0, -4)$, then P_1 is not on the line, and $\overrightarrow{P_0P_1} = 4\vec{i} + 2\vec{j} - 3\vec{k}$, so by (5) the distance D is given by

$$D = \frac{\|(\vec{i} - 2\vec{j} + 3\vec{k}) \times (4\vec{i} + 2\vec{j} - 3\vec{k})\|}{\sqrt{1^2 + (-2)^2 + 3^2}} = \frac{\|15\vec{j} + 10\vec{k}\|}{\sqrt{14}} = 5\sqrt{\frac{13}{14}}$$

17. The point $P_0 = (-2, 0, 1)$ is on the line, and the line is parallel to $\vec{j} + \vec{k}$. If $P_1 = (2, 1, 0)$, then P_1 is not on the line, and $\overrightarrow{P_0P_1} = 4\vec{i} + \vec{j} - \vec{k}$, so by (5) the distance D is given by

$$D = \frac{\|(\vec{j} + \vec{k}) \times (4\vec{i} + \vec{j} - \vec{k})\|}{\sqrt{1^2 + 1^2}} = \frac{\|-2\vec{i} + 4\vec{j} - 4\vec{k}\|}{\sqrt{2}} = 3\sqrt{2}$$

18. The line has a vector equation $\vec{r} = (-3 + 2t)\vec{i} + (-3 - 3t)\vec{j} + (3 + 5t)\vec{k}$, and if $P_1 = (0, 0, 0)$, then P_1 is not on the line. Let $P_0 = (-3, -3, 3)$, and let $\vec{L} = 2\vec{i} - 3\vec{j} + 5\vec{k}$, so that $\vec{r}$ and $\vec{L}$ are parallel. Then $\overrightarrow{P_0P_1} = 3\vec{i} + 3\vec{j} - 3\vec{k}$, and by (5) the distance D from P_1 to the given line is given by

$$D = \frac{\|(2\vec{i} - 3\vec{j} + 5\vec{k}) \times (3\vec{i} + 3\vec{j} - 3\vec{k})\|}{\sqrt{2^2 + (-3)^2 + 5^2}} = \frac{3\,\|-2\vec{i} + 7\vec{j} + 5\vec{k}\|}{\sqrt{38}} = 3\sqrt{\frac{39}{19}}.$$

19. $\sqrt{(x - x)^2 + (y - 0)^2 + (z - 0)^2} = 3$, or $y^2 + z^2 = 9$.

20. $\sqrt{(x - 0)^2 + (y - y)^2 + (z - 0)^2} = \sqrt{2}$, or $x^2 + z^2 = 2$.

21. Let $P_1 = (x, y, z)$ be on the cylinder, and let $\vec{L} = \vec{i} + \vec{j} + \vec{k}$, so that $\vec{L}$ is parallel to the axis of the cylinder. Using Theorem 11.12 with $P_0 = (0, 0, 0)$ we find that the distance D from P_1 to the axis of the cylinder is 5 if

$$5 = D = \frac{\|(\vec{i} + \vec{j} + \vec{k}) \times (x\vec{i} + y\vec{j} + z\vec{k})\|}{\sqrt{1^2 + 1^2 + 1^2}}$$

$= \dfrac{\|(z - y)\vec{i} + (x - z)\vec{j} + (y - x)\vec{k}\|}{\sqrt{3}} = \dfrac{\sqrt{(z - y)^2 + (x - z)^2 + (y - x)^2}}{\sqrt{3}}$

so that $(z - y)^2 + (x - z)^2 + (y - x)^2 = 75$.

22. a. By (3), the parametric equations have the form $x = x_0 + at$, $y = y_0 + bt$, $z = z_0 + ct$. Since P_1 corresponds to $t = 0$ and P_2 corresponds to $t = 1$, we have

$$-1 = x_0 + a \cdot 0 \;,\quad -2 = y_0 + b \cdot 0 \;,\quad -3 = z_0 + c \cdot 0$$
$$2 = x_0 + a \;,\quad -1 = y_0 + b \;,\quad 0 = z_0 + c$$

Thus $x_0 = -1$, $y_0 = -2$, $z_0 = -3$, so $a = 2 - x_0 = 3$, $b = -1 - y_0 = 1$, $c = -z_0 = 3$. Thus the parametric equations are $x = -1 + 3t$, $y = -2 + t$, $z = -3 + 3t$.

b. As in (a), the parametric equations have the form $x = x_0 + at$, $y = y_0 + bt$, $z = z_0 + ct$. Since P_1 corresponds to $t = 0$ and P_2 corresponds to $t = 2$, we have

$$-1 = x_0 + a \cdot 0 \;,\quad -2 = y_0 + b \cdot 0 \;,\quad -3 = z_0 + c \cdot 0$$
$$2 = x_0 + 2a \;,\quad -1 = y_0 + 2b \;,\quad 0 = z_0 + 2c$$

Thus $x_0 = -1$, $y_0 = -2$, $z_0 = -3$, so that $a = \frac{1}{2}(2 - x_0) = \frac{3}{2}$, $b = \frac{1}{2}(-1 - y_0) = \frac{1}{2}$, $c = -\frac{1}{2}z_0 = \frac{3}{2}$. Thus the parametric equations are $x = -1 + \frac{3}{2}t$, $y = -2 + \frac{1}{2}t$, $z = -3 + \frac{3}{2}t$.

c. As in (a), the parametric equations have the form $x = x_0 + at$, $y = y_0 + bt$, $z = z_0 + ct$. Since P_1 corresponds to $t = -1$ and P_2 corresponds to $t = 4$, we have

$$-1 = x_0 - a,\quad -2 = y_0 - b,\quad -3 = z_0 - c$$
$$2 = x_0 + 4a,\quad -1 = y_0 + 4b,\quad 0 = z_0 + 4c$$

Subtracting the equations vertically, we find that $a = \frac{3}{5}$, $b = \frac{1}{5}$, $c = \frac{3}{5}$, so that $x_0 = -1 + a = -\frac{2}{5}$, $y_0 = -2 + b = -\frac{9}{5}$, $z_0 = -3 + c = -\frac{12}{5}$. Thus the parametric equations are $x = -\frac{2}{5} + \frac{3}{5}t$, $y = -\frac{9}{5} + \frac{1}{5}t$, $z = -\frac{12}{5} + \frac{3}{5}t$.

23. The line through (1, 4, 2) and (4, -3, -5) is parallel to $3\vec{i} - 7\vec{j} - 7\vec{k}$, and the line through (1, 4, 2) and (-5, -10, -8) is parallel to $-6\vec{i} - 14\vec{j} - 10\vec{k}$. Since these two vectors are not parallel, the three points do not lie on the same line.

24. The points (2, 5, 7) and (0, 3, 2) lie on a line parallel to $-2\vec{i} - 2\vec{j} - 5\vec{k}$, and thus parametric equations of the line are $x = 2 - 2t$, $y = 5 - 2t$, $z = 7 - 5t$. If $(x, y, 1)$ is to be on the line, then $1 = 7 - 5t$, so that $t = \frac{6}{5}$. Therefore $x = 2 - 2\left(\frac{6}{5}\right) = -\frac{2}{5}$ and $y = 5 - 2\left(\frac{6}{5}\right) = \frac{13}{5}$.

25. Notice that $\vec{a} - \vec{b}$ lies on ℓ, so is parallel to $\vec{L}$. Thus $\vec{L} \times (\vec{a} - \vec{b}) = \vec{0}$. Since $\vec{0} = \vec{L} \times (\vec{a} - \vec{b}) = (\vec{L} \times \vec{a}) - (\vec{L} \times \vec{b})$, it follows that $\vec{L} \times \vec{a} = \vec{L} \times \vec{b}$.

Section 11.5

1. $x_0 = -1$, $y_0 = 2$, $z_0 = 3$, $a = -4$, $b = 15$, $c = -\frac{1}{2}$; $-4(x + 1) + 15(y - 2) - \frac{1}{2}(z - 3) = 0$, or $8x - 30y + z = -65$.

2. $x_0 = \pi$, $y_0 = 0$, $z_0 = -\pi$, $a = 2$, $b = 3$, $c = -4$; $2(x - \pi) + 3(y - 0) - 4(z + \pi) = 0$, or $2x + 3y - 4z = 6\pi$.

3. $x_0 = 9$, $y_0 = 17$, $z_0 = -7$, $a = 2$, $b = 0$, $c = -3$; $2(x - 9) + 0(y - 17) - 3(z + 7) = 0$, or $2x - 3z = 39$.

4. $x_0 = -1$, $y_0 = -1$, $z_0 = -1$, $a = \frac{1}{\sqrt{2}} = b$, $c = -\frac{1}{\sqrt{2}}$; $\frac{1}{\sqrt{2}}(x + 1) + \frac{1}{\sqrt{2}}(y + 1) - \frac{1}{\sqrt{2}}(z + 1) = 0$, or $x + y - z = -1$.

5. $x_0 = 2$, $y_0 = 3$, $z_0 = -5$, $a = 0$, $b = 1$, $c = 0$, $0(x - 2) + 1(y - 3) + 0(z + 5) = 0$, or $y = 3$.

6. Let $P_0 = (2, -1, 4)$, $P_1 = (5, 3, 5)$, and $P_2 = (2, 4, 3)$. Then $\overrightarrow{P_0P_1} = 3\vec{i} + 4\vec{j} + \vec{k}$ and $\overrightarrow{P_0P_2} = 5\vec{j} - \vec{k}$. Since $\overrightarrow{P_0P_1}$ and $\overrightarrow{P_0P_2}$ are not parallel, P_0, P_1 and P_2 determine a plane, and the normal $\vec{N}$ we take is given by $\vec{N} = \overrightarrow{P_0P_1} \times \overrightarrow{P_0P_2} = (3\vec{i} + 4\vec{j} + \vec{k}) \times (5\vec{j} - \vec{k}) = -9\vec{i} + 3\vec{j} + 15\vec{k}$. An equation of the plane is $-9(x - 2) + 3(y + 1) + 15(z - 4) = 0$, or $-9x + 3y + 15z = 39$.

7. The point $P_0 = (-2, -1, -5)$ is on the line, and hence on the plane. Let $P_1 = (1, -1, 2)$, so that $\overrightarrow{P_0P_1} = 3\vec{i} + 7\vec{k}$. The vector $\vec{i} + \vec{j} + 2\vec{k}$ is parallel to the line but not parallel to $\overrightarrow{P_0P_1}$. For a normal to the plane we take $\vec{N} = \overrightarrow{P_0P_1} \times (\vec{i} + \vec{j} + 2\vec{k}) = (3\vec{i} + 7\vec{k}) \times (\vec{i} + \vec{j} + 2\vec{k}) = -7\vec{i} + \vec{j} + 3\vec{k}$. An equation of the plane is $-7(x + 2) + 1(y + 1) + 3(z + 5) = 0$, or $7x - y - 3z = 2$.

8. Let $P_0 = (1, -1, 5)$ and $P_1 = (-3, 4, 0)$, so that P_0 and P_1 are on the plane. Then $\overrightarrow{P_0P_1} = -4\vec{i} + 5\vec{j} - 5\vec{k}$ and $3\vec{i} + 2\vec{j} + 4\vec{k}$ are not parallel. Thus a normal to the plane is given by $\vec{N} = \overrightarrow{P_0P_1} \times (3\vec{i} + 2\vec{j} + 4\vec{k}) = (-4\vec{i} + 5\vec{j} - 5\vec{k}) \times (3\vec{i} + 2\vec{j} + 4\vec{k}) = 30\vec{i} + \vec{j} - 23\vec{k}$. An equation of the plane is $30(x - 1) + 1(y + 1) - 23(z - 5) = 0$, or $30x + y - 23z = -86$.

9. A normal to the plane is given by $\vec{N} = 2\vec{i} + 5\vec{j} + 9\vec{k}$, so an equation of the plane is $2(x - 2) + 5(y - \frac{1}{2}) + 9(z - \frac{1}{3}) = 0$, or $4x + 10y + 18z = 19$.

10. The line is parallel to $2\vec{i} - 3\vec{j} + 4\vec{k}$, and thus parametric equations for the line are $x = 2 + 2t$, $y = -1 - 3t$, $z = 4t$.

11. a. The line ℓ is perpendicular to the vectors $2\vec{i} - 3\vec{j} + 4\vec{k}$ and $\vec{i} - \vec{k}$, which are normal to the two planes. Thus ℓ is parallel to $(2\vec{i} - 3\vec{j} + 4\vec{k}) \times (\vec{i} - \vec{k}) = 3\vec{i} + 6\vec{j} + 3\vec{k}$ and hence to $\vec{i} + 2\vec{j} + \vec{k}$. Since $(1, 0, 0)$ is on the intersection of the two planes, a vector equation of ℓ is $\vec{r} = \vec{i} + t(\vec{i} + 2\vec{j} + \vec{k}) = (1 + t)\vec{i} + 2t\vec{j} + t\vec{k}$.

    b. A normal to the plane is given by $\vec{N} = \vec{i} + 2\vec{j} + \vec{k}$, so that an equation of the plane is $1(x + 9) + 2(y - 12) + 1(z - 14) = 0$, or $x + 2y + z = 29$.

12. a. From the equations for ℓ we find that $\frac{x + 1}{2} = -z$, so that $x = -2z - 1$ and $\frac{y + 3}{3} = -z$, so that $y = -3z - 3$. Substituting for x and y in the equation for P, we obtain $3(-2z - 1) - 2(-3z - 3) + 4z = -1$, so that $z = -1$. Therefore $x = -2(-1) - 1 = 1$ and $y = -3(-1) - 3 = 0$, so that $P_0 = (1, 0, -1)$.

    b. A normal for P is given by $\vec{N} = 2\vec{i} + 3\vec{j} - \vec{k}$, so that an equation for P is $2(x - 1) + 3(y - 0) - 1(z + 1) = 0$, or $2x + 3y - z = 3$.

    c. Since the vector $3\vec{i} - 2\vec{j} + 4\vec{k}$ is parallel to the line and passes through $P_0 = (1, 0 -1)$, symmetric equations of the line are $\frac{x - 1}{3} = \frac{y}{-2} = \frac{z + 1}{4}$.

13. The point $P_1 = (3, -1, 4)$ is not on the plane, whereas $P_0 = (0, 0, 5)$ is on the plane. Then $\overrightarrow{P_0P_1} = 3\vec{i} - \vec{j} - \vec{k}$. If $\vec{N} = 2\vec{i} - \vec{j} + \vec{k}$, then $\vec{N}$ is normal to the plane, and by Theorem 11.13 the distance D from P_1 to the plane is given by

$$D = \frac{|\vec{N} \cdot \overrightarrow{P_0P_1}|}{\|\vec{N}\|} = \frac{|(2\vec{i} - \vec{j} + \vec{k}) \cdot (3\vec{i} - \vec{j} - \vec{k})|}{\sqrt{2^2 + (-1)^2 + 1^2}} = \frac{6}{\sqrt{6}} = \sqrt{6}$$

14. If the plane passes through the origin, then $d = 0$, so that the distance from the origin to the plane and the number $\frac{|d|}{\sqrt{a^2 + b^2 + c^2}}$ are both 0. If the plane does not pass through the origin, let $P_1 = (0, 0, 0)$. Also assume that $c \neq 0$, and let $P_0 = (0, 0, \frac{d}{c})$, so that P_0 is on the plane. By Theorem 11.13, the distance D from P_1 to the plane is given by

$$D = \frac{|(a\vec{i} + b\vec{j} + c\vec{k}) \cdot \overrightarrow{P_0P_1}|}{\sqrt{a^2 + b^2 + c^2}} = \frac{|(a\vec{i} + b\vec{j} + c\vec{k}) \cdot (\frac{d}{c}\vec{k})|}{\sqrt{a^2 + b^2 + c^2}}$$

$$= \frac{|d|}{\sqrt{a^2 + b^2 + c^2}}$$

The same result follows if $a \neq 0$, or if $b \neq 0$.

15. The planes are perpendicular if and only if their normals, $a_1\vec{i} + b_1\vec{j} + c_1\vec{k}$ and $a_2\vec{i} + b_2\vec{j} + c_2\vec{k}$, are perpendicular, which happens if and only if $a_1a_2 + b_1b_2 + c_1c_2 = (a_1\vec{i} + b_1\vec{j} + c_1\vec{k}) \cdot (a_2\vec{i} + b_2\vec{j} + c_2\vec{k}) = 0$.

16. Normals to the two planes are $2\vec{i} - 3\vec{j} + 4\vec{k}$ and $4\vec{i} - 6\vec{j} + 8\vec{k}$ respectively. Since these normals are parallel, so are the planes. To find the distance between the planes, let $P_0 = (1, -1, 0)$, which is on the first plane, and $P_1 = (-\frac{1}{4}, 0, 0)$, which is on the second plane. Then $\overrightarrow{P_0P_1} = -\frac{5}{4}\vec{i} + \vec{j}$, and by Theorem 11.13 the distance D from P_1 to the first plane is given by

$$D = \frac{|(2\vec{i} - 3\vec{j} + 4\vec{k}) \cdot (-\frac{5}{4}\vec{i} + \vec{j})|}{\sqrt{2^2 + (-3)^2 + 4^2}} = \frac{11\sqrt{29}}{58}$$

17. Let (x, y, z) be on the plane. Then $\sqrt{(x - 3)^2 + (y - 1)^2 + (z - 5)^2} = \sqrt{(x - 5)^2 + (y + 1)^2 + (z - 3)^2}$. Squaring both sides, we obtain $(x - 3)^2 + (y - 1)^2 + (z - 5)^2 = (x - 5)^2 + (y + 1)^2 + (z - 3)^2$. Simplifying, we obtain $x - y - z = 0$.

18. The vector $a\vec{i} - b\vec{j}$ lies along the line joining (a, 0, 0) and (0, b, 0), and the vector $b\vec{j} - c\vec{k}$ lies along the line joining (0, b, 0) and (0, 0, c). Thus $\vec{N} = (a\vec{i} - b\vec{j}) \times (b\vec{j} - c\vec{k}) = bc\vec{i} + ac\vec{j} + ab\vec{k}$ is normal to the plane containing (a, 0, 0), (0, b, 0), and (0, 0, c). Thus an equation of the plane is $bc(x - a) + acy + abz = 0$, or $bcx + acy + abz = abc$, or $\frac{x}{a} + \frac{y}{b} + \frac{z}{c} = 1$.

19. Let $P_0 = (2, 3, 2)$, $P_1 = (1, -1, -3)$, and $P_2 = (1, 0, -1)$. Then $\overrightarrow{P_0P_1} = -\vec{i} - 4\vec{j} - 5\vec{k}$ and $\overrightarrow{P_0P_2} = -\vec{i} - 3\vec{j} - 3\vec{k}$. Thus a normal $\vec{N}$ to the plane containing the three points is given by

$$\vec{N} = \overrightarrow{P_0P_1} \times \overrightarrow{P_0P_2} = (-\vec{i} - 4\vec{j} - 5\vec{k}) \times (-\vec{i} - 3\vec{j} - 3\vec{k}) = -3\vec{i} + 2\vec{j} - \vec{k}.$$

Therefore an equation of the plane is $-3(x - 2) + 2(y - 3) - 1(z - 2) = 0$, or $3x - 2y + z = 2$. Since $3 \cdot 5 - 2 \cdot 9 + 5 = 2$, the fourth point (5, 9, 5) lies on the plane, so that all four given points lie on the same plane.

20. Let $t = \frac{x - 1}{2} = \frac{y + 1}{3} = \frac{z + 5}{7}$, so that $x = 1 + 2t$, $y = -1 + 3t$, and $z = -5 + 7t$. Let $P_1 = (1 + 2t, -1 + 3t, -5 + 7t)$ and $P_0 = (1, -3, 0)$, so that P_1 is not on the plane (unless $t = -3$) and P_0 is on the plane, and $\overrightarrow{P_0P_1} = 2t\vec{i} + (2 + 3t)\vec{j} + (-5 + 7t)\vec{k}$. The normal $\vec{N}$ to the plane is given by $\vec{N} = 2\vec{i} + 2\vec{j} - \vec{k}$. By Theorem 11.13 the distance from P_1 to the

plane is given by

$$D = \frac{|\vec{N} \cdot \overrightarrow{P_0P_1}|}{\|\vec{N}\|} = \frac{|(2\vec{i} + 2\vec{j} - \vec{k}) \cdot [2t\vec{i} + (2 + 3t)\vec{j} + (-5 + 7t)\vec{k}]|}{\sqrt{2^2 + 2^2 + (-1)^2}}$$

$= \frac{|3t + 9|}{3} = |t + 3|$. Now $D = 3$ if $|t + 3| = 3$, which means $t = 0$ or $t = -6$. If $t = 0$, then $P_1 = (1, -1, -5)$ and if $t = -6$, then $P_1 = (-11, -19, -47)$. These two points are both distance 3 from the plane.

21. Since $(\vec{a} \times \vec{b}) \times (\vec{c} \times \vec{d})$ is perpendicular to $(\vec{a} \times \vec{b})$ and $(\vec{c} \times \vec{d})$, which are normal to P_1 and P_2 respectively, $(\vec{a} \times \vec{b}) \times (\vec{c} \times \vec{d})$ is parallel to all vectors that lie in both P_1 and P_2, and thus is parallel to the intersection of P_1 and P_2.

22. Normals of the planes in (a) - (d) are $\vec{i} + 2\vec{j} - 3\vec{k}$, $15\vec{i} - 9\vec{j} + \vec{k}$, $-2\vec{i} - 4\vec{j} + 6\vec{k}$, and $5\vec{i} - 3\vec{j} + \frac{1}{3}\vec{k}$ respectively. Since the first and third, and the second and fourth are multiples of each other, the planes in (a) and (c) are parallel, and the planes in (b) and (d) are parallel. Since the equation in (c) can be obtained from the one in (a) by multiplying by -2 and rearranging, the planes in (a) and (c) are identical.

23. Normals of the planes in (a) - (d) are $\vec{i} + \vec{j} - \vec{k}$, $\vec{i} - \vec{j}$, $\vec{j} - \vec{k}$, and $\vec{i} + \vec{j}$. Since none of these is a multiple of another, no two planes are identical or parallel. Since $(\vec{i} + \vec{j} - \vec{k}) \cdot (\vec{i} - \vec{j}) = 0$ and $(\vec{i} - \vec{j}) \cdot (\vec{i} + \vec{j}) = 0$, the planes in (a) and (b) are perpendicular, as are the planes in (b) and (d).

24. a. The vector $\vec{k}$ is normal to the xy plane, so an equation of the plane is $1(z - 3) = 0$, or $z = 3$.
    b. The vector $\vec{i}$ is normal to the plane, so an equation of the plane is $1(x + 1) = 0$, or $x = -1$.
    c. The vector $\vec{j}$ is normal to the plane, so an equation of the plane is $1(y - 2) = 0$, or $y = 2$.

25. a. The vector $\vec{i}$ is normal to the plane, so an equation of the plane is $1(x + 4) = 0$, or $x = -4$.
    b. The vector $\vec{j}$ is normal to the plane, so an equation of the plane is $1(y + 5) = 0$, or $y = -5$.
    c. The vector $\vec{k}$ is normal to the plane, so an equation of the plane is $1(z + 3) = 0$, or $z = -3$.

26. The points $(-2, 1, 4)$ and $(0, 3, 1)$ determine the vector $2\vec{i} + 2\vec{j} - 3\vec{k}$, and $(2\vec{i} + 2\vec{j} - 3\vec{k}) \times (2\vec{i} - 4\vec{j} + 6\vec{k}) = -18\vec{j} - 12\vec{k}$. Thus an equation of the plane is $0(x + 2) - 18(y - 1) - 12(z - 4) = 0$, or $18y + 12z = -66$.

27. From the first and second equations, $x = 1 - y$ and $z = 2 - y$. Substituting in the third equation, we find that $3 = x + z = (1 - y) + (2 - y) = 3 - 2y$, so that $y = 0$. Thus $x = 1$ and $z = 2$. The point of interesection is $(1, 0, 2)$.

28. From the first and third equations, $2 - y = x - z = y$, so that $y = 1$. Then the first and second equations become $x - z = 1$ and $-x - z = 1$, so that $1 + z = x = -1 - z$. Thus $z = -1$, so that $x = 0$. The point is $(0, 1, -1)$.

29. Adding the first and second equations, we obtain $3x = -1$, so that $x = -\frac{1}{3}$. The second equation becomes $3y + z = -\frac{5}{3}$. Subtracting the third equation from this equation, we obtain $y = -\frac{11}{6}$. Therefore $z = \frac{23}{6}$. The point is $(-\frac{1}{3}, -\frac{11}{6}, \frac{23}{6})$.

30. Since the third equation can be obtained from the first equation by multiplying by $\frac{1}{2}$, the two corresponding planes are identical. Multiplying the second equation by 2 and adding it to the third, we obtain $3x - 5z = 6$, so that $z = \frac{3x - 6}{5}$. Multiplying the second equation by 3 and subtracting the third equation from it, we obtain $2x - 5y - 4 = 0$, so that $y = \frac{2x - 4}{5}$. If $x = t$, then the points of intersection form a line having the parametric equations $x = t$, $y = -\frac{4}{5} + \frac{2}{5}t$, $z = -\frac{6}{5} + \frac{3}{5}t$.

31. The two planes are parallel. Let $P_0 = (0, 0, 2)$ and $P_1 = (0, 0, \frac{1}{3})$, which are on the first and second planes, respectively. Then $\overrightarrow{P_0P_1} = -\frac{5}{3}\vec{k}$, and a normal $\vec{N}$ to either plane is given by $\vec{N} = \vec{i} - \vec{j} + \vec{k}$. By Theorem 11.13, the distance D is given by

$$D = \frac{|\vec{N} \cdot \overrightarrow{P_0P_1}|}{\|\vec{N}\|} = \frac{\frac{5}{3}}{\sqrt{1^2 + (-1)^2 + 1^2}} = \frac{5\sqrt{3}}{9}$$

32. The two planes are parallel. Let $P_0 = (0, 4, 0)$ and $P_1 = (0, -1, 1)$, which are on the first and second planes, respectively. Then $P_0P_1 = -5\vec{j} + \vec{k}$ and a normal $\vec{N}$ to either plane is given by $\vec{N} = \vec{j} - 2\vec{k}$. By Theorem 11.13, the distance D is given by

$$D = \frac{|\vec{N} \cdot \overrightarrow{P_0P_1}|}{\|\vec{N}\|} = \frac{7}{\sqrt{1^2 + (-2)^2}} = \frac{7\sqrt{5}}{5}$$

33. The two planes are parallel. The z axis is perpendicular to the two planes and intersects them in the points (0, 0, 6) and (0, 0, -4). Thus the distance between the planes is 6 - (-4) = 10.

Chapter 11 - Review

1. $2\vec{a} + \vec{b} - 3\vec{c} = 5\vec{i} - 10\vec{j} + 11\vec{k}$; $\vec{a} \times \vec{b} = \begin{vmatrix} \vec{i} & \vec{j} & \vec{k} \\ 2 & -3 & 1 \\ 1 & -1 & 0 \end{vmatrix} = \vec{i} + \vec{j} + \vec{k}$;

$\vec{c} \cdot (\vec{a} \times \vec{b}) = (\vec{j} - 3\vec{k}) \cdot (\vec{i} + \vec{j} + \vec{k}) = -2$; $\vec{a} \times (\vec{b} \times \vec{c}) = \vec{b}(\vec{a} \cdot \vec{c}) - \vec{c}(\vec{a} \cdot \vec{b}) = -6\vec{b} - 5\vec{c} = -6\vec{i} + \vec{j} + 15\vec{k}$

2. $2\vec{a} + \vec{b} - 3\vec{c} = 9\vec{j} - 8\vec{k}$; $\vec{a} \times \vec{b} = \begin{vmatrix} \vec{i} & \vec{j} & \vec{k} \\ \frac{1}{2} & -1 & 2 \\ 2 & -4 & 6 \end{vmatrix} = 2\vec{i} + \vec{j}$; $\vec{c} \cdot (\vec{a} \times \vec{b})$

$= (\vec{i} - 5\vec{j} + 6\vec{k}) \cdot (2\vec{i} + \vec{j}) = -3$; $\vec{a} \times (\vec{b} \times \vec{c}) = \vec{b}(\vec{a} \cdot \vec{c}) - \vec{c}(\vec{a} \cdot \vec{b})$

$= \frac{35}{2}\vec{b} - 17\vec{c} = 18\vec{i} + 15\vec{j} + 3\vec{k}$

3. $2\vec{a} + \vec{b} - 3\vec{c} = 11\vec{i} - 9\vec{j} + 6\vec{k}$; $\vec{a} \times \vec{b} = \begin{vmatrix} \vec{i} & \vec{j} & \vec{k} \\ 3 & -2 & 1 \\ 5 & -2 & 1 \end{vmatrix} = 2\vec{j} + 4\vec{k}$;

$\vec{c} \cdot (\vec{a} \times \vec{b}) = (\vec{j} - \vec{k}) \cdot (2\vec{j} + 4\vec{k}) = -2$; $\vec{a} \times (\vec{b} \times \vec{c}) = \vec{b}(\vec{a} \cdot \vec{c}) - \vec{c}(\vec{a} \cdot \vec{b}) = -3\vec{b} - 20\vec{c} = -15\vec{i} - 14\vec{j} + 17\vec{k}$

4. $\cos\theta = \dfrac{(3\vec{i} - 4\vec{j} + 12\vec{k}) \cdot (\vec{i} - \vec{k})}{\|3\vec{i} - 4\vec{j} + 12\vec{k}\| \, \|\vec{i} - \vec{k}\|} = \dfrac{-9}{13\sqrt{2}}$

5. Let $Q = (b_1, b_2, b_3)$. Then $\overrightarrow{PQ} = (b_1 - 1)\vec{i} + (b_2 + 2)\vec{j} + (b_3 - 3)\vec{k}$, so that $\overrightarrow{PQ} = \vec{a}$ if $b_1 - 1 = 2$, $b_2 + 2 = -2$, $b_3 - 3 = 1$, that is, if $b_1 = 3$, $b_2 = -4$, $b_3 = 4$. Thus Q = (3, - 4, 4).

6. Let $\vec{b} = 2\vec{i} - \vec{j} - \vec{k}$, $\vec{a} = 2\vec{j} + \vec{k}$, and $\vec{a}' = -20\vec{i} - 2\vec{j} + 4\vec{k}$. Note that $\vec{a} \cdot \vec{a}' = -4 + 4 = 0$, so that $\vec{a}$ and $\vec{a}'$ are perpendicular. $\text{pr}_{\vec{a}}\vec{b} = \dfrac{\vec{a} \cdot \vec{b}}{\|\vec{a}\|^2}\vec{a}$

$= \frac{-3}{5}\vec{a} = \frac{-3}{5}(2\vec{j} + \vec{k})$; $\text{pr}_{\vec{a}'}\vec{b} = \vec{b} - \text{pr}_{\vec{a}}\vec{b} = 2\vec{i} - \vec{j} - \vec{k} + \frac{3}{5}(2\vec{j} + \vec{k})$

$= 2\vec{i} + \frac{1}{5}\vec{j} - \frac{2}{5}\vec{k} = -\frac{1}{10}\vec{a}'$. Thus $\vec{b} = -\frac{3}{5}\vec{a} - \frac{1}{10}\vec{a}'$.

7. Let P = (1, 1, 1), Q = (2, 3, 5), and R = (-1, 3, 1). The area of the triangle with vertices P, Q, and R is $\frac{1}{2}\ \|\overrightarrow{PQ} \times \overrightarrow{PR}\|$. Since $\overrightarrow{PQ} = \vec{i} + 2\vec{j} + 4\vec{k}$ and $\overrightarrow{PR} = -2\vec{i} + 2\vec{j}$, it follows that

$$\overrightarrow{PQ} \times \overrightarrow{PR} = \begin{vmatrix} \vec{i} & \vec{j} & \vec{k} \\ 1 & 2 & 4 \\ -2 & 2 & 0 \end{vmatrix} = -8\vec{i} - 8\vec{j} + 6\vec{k}.$$

Thus the area is $\frac{1}{2}\ \|\overrightarrow{PQ} \times \overrightarrow{PR}\| = \frac{1}{2}\sqrt{164} = \sqrt{41}$.

8. Let the triangle have vertices P, Q, and R, and the vectors $\vec{a}$, $\vec{b}$, and $\vec{c}$ point from the vertices to the midpoints of the opposite sides, as in the figure.

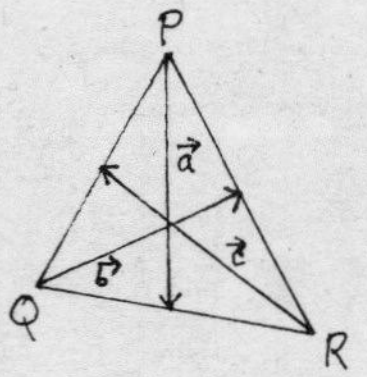

Then $\vec{a} = \overrightarrow{PR} + \frac{1}{2}\overrightarrow{RQ}$, $\vec{b} = \overrightarrow{QP} + \frac{1}{2}\overrightarrow{PR}$, and $\vec{c} = \overrightarrow{RQ} + \frac{1}{2}\overrightarrow{QP}$, so that $\vec{a} + \vec{b} + \vec{c} = (\overrightarrow{PR} + \frac{1}{2}\overrightarrow{RQ}) + (\overrightarrow{QP} + \frac{1}{2}\overrightarrow{PR}) + (\overrightarrow{RQ} + \frac{1}{2}\overrightarrow{QP}) = \frac{3}{2}\overrightarrow{PR} + \frac{3}{2}\overrightarrow{RQ} + \frac{3}{2}\overrightarrow{QP} = \frac{3}{2}\overrightarrow{PP} = \vec{0}$.

9. a. Since $\vec{a} \cdot \vec{c} = \vec{b} \cdot \vec{c}$ for all $\vec{c}$, we let $\vec{c} = \vec{a} - \vec{b}$ and find that

$$\|\vec{a} - \vec{b}\|^2 = (\vec{a} - \vec{b}) \cdot (\vec{a} - \vec{b}) = (\vec{a} - \vec{b}) \cdot \vec{c} = \vec{a} \cdot \vec{c} - \vec{b} \cdot \vec{c} = 0.$$

Thus $\vec{a} - \vec{b} = 0$, so that $\vec{a} = \vec{b}$.

b. If $\vec{a} \neq \vec{b}$, then $\vec{a} - \vec{b} \neq \vec{0}$, so we let $\vec{c}$ be a nonzero vector perpendicular to $\vec{a} - \vec{b}$. It follows that $\vec{0} = (\vec{a} \times \vec{c}) - (\vec{b} \times \vec{c}) = (\vec{a} - \vec{b}) \times \vec{c}$. Therefore $\|\vec{a} - \vec{b}\|\,\|\vec{c}\| = 0$, which is impossible since $\|\vec{a} - \vec{b}\| \neq 0$ and $\|\vec{c}\| \neq \vec{0}$. Thus $\vec{a} = \vec{b}$.

10. Let $c = -\dfrac{\vec{a} \cdot \vec{b}}{\|\vec{b}\|^2}$. Then $\|\vec{a} + c\vec{b}\|^2 = (\vec{a} + c\vec{b}) \cdot (\vec{a} + c\vec{b})$

$= \vec{a} \cdot \vec{a} + 2c\vec{a} \cdot \vec{b} + c^2\vec{b} \cdot \vec{b} = \|\vec{a}\|^2 - \dfrac{2(\vec{a} \cdot \vec{b})^2}{\|\vec{b}\|^2} + \dfrac{(\vec{a} \cdot \vec{b})^2}{\|\vec{b}\|^4}\|\vec{b}\|^2$

$= \|\vec{a}\|^2 - \dfrac{(\vec{a} \cdot \vec{b})^2}{\|\vec{b}\|^2}$. Therefore $\|\vec{a}\| \leq \|\vec{a} + c\vec{b}\|$ for every number c only if $\dfrac{(\vec{a} \cdot \vec{b})^2}{\|\vec{b}\|^2} = 0$, that is, if $\vec{a} \cdot \vec{b} = 0$, or $\vec{a}$ and $\vec{b}$ are perpendicular.

Conversely, if $\vec{a}$ and $\vec{b}$ are perpendicular, then for any number c, $\|\vec{a}\|^2 \leq \|\vec{a}\|^2 + c^2\|\vec{b}\|^2 = \vec{a} \cdot \vec{a} + 2c\vec{a} \cdot \vec{b} + c^2\vec{b} \cdot \vec{b} = \|\vec{a} + c\vec{b}\|^2$, so that $\|\vec{a}\| \leq \|\vec{a} + c\vec{b}\|$ for all numbers c.

11. Letting $\vec{a} = \cos x\,\vec{i} + \sin x\,\vec{j}$ and $\vec{b} = \cos y\,\vec{i} - \sin y\,\vec{j}$, we find that $\vec{a} \cdot \vec{b} = \cos x \cos y - \sin x \cdot \sin y$. But by the definitions of $\vec{a}$ and $\vec{b}$, the angle between $\vec{a}$ and $\vec{b}$ is x + y, (see figure), so that $\vec{a} \cdot \vec{b} = \|\vec{a}\|\,\|\vec{b}\| \cos(x + y) = \cos(x + y)$. Thus $\cos(x + y) = \cos x \cos y - \sin x \sin y$.

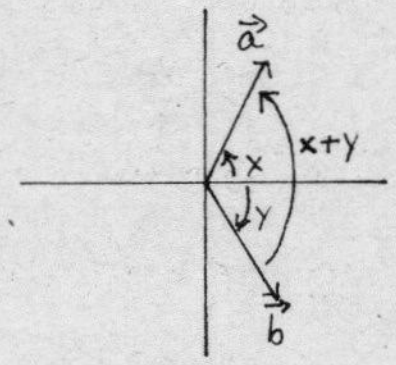

12. a. $\|\vec{a} + \vec{b}\|^2\,\|\vec{a} - \vec{b}\|^2 = [(\vec{a} + \vec{b}) \cdot (\vec{a} + \vec{b})]\,[(\vec{a} - \vec{b}) \cdot (\vec{a} - \vec{b})]$

$= [\|\vec{a}\|^2 + 2\vec{a} \cdot \vec{b} + \|\vec{b}\|^2] \cdot [\|\vec{a}\|^2 - 2\vec{a} \cdot \vec{b} + \|\vec{b}\|^2]$

$= (\|\vec{a}\|^4 + 2\|\vec{a}\|^2\|\vec{b}\|^2 + \|\vec{b}\|^4) - 4(\vec{a} \cdot \vec{b})^2 = (\|\vec{a}\|^2 + \|\vec{b}\|^2)^2 - 4(\vec{a} \cdot \vec{b})^2$

b. Since $-4(\vec{a} \cdot \vec{b})^2 \leq 0$, we infer that $\|\vec{a} + \vec{b}\|^2\,\|\vec{a} - \vec{b}\|^2 \leq (\|\vec{a}\|^2 + \|\vec{b}\|^2)^2$, so that $\|\vec{a} + \vec{b}\|\,\|\vec{a} - \vec{b}\| \leq \|\vec{a}\|^2 + \|\vec{b}\|^2$.

13. Using the fact that $\vec{a}$, $\vec{b}$, and $\vec{c}$ are pairwise perpendicular, we have $\|\vec{d}\|^2 = \vec{d} \cdot \vec{d} = (a\vec{a} + b\vec{b} + c\vec{c}) \cdot (a\vec{a} + b\vec{b} + c\vec{c}) = a^2(\vec{a} \cdot \vec{a}) + b^2(\vec{b} \cdot \vec{b}) + c^2(\vec{c} \cdot \vec{c})$. Since $\vec{a}$, $\vec{b}$, and $\vec{c}$ are unit vectors, $\vec{a} \cdot \vec{a} = \vec{b} \cdot \vec{b} = \vec{c} \cdot \vec{c} = 1$, so that $a^2(\vec{a} \cdot \vec{a}) + b^2(\vec{b} \cdot \vec{b}) + c^2(\vec{c} \cdot \vec{c}) = a^2 + b^2 + c^2$, and thus $\|\vec{d}\| = \sqrt{a^2 + b^2 + c^2}$.

14. If $P_0 = (\frac{1}{2}, \frac{1}{3}, 0)$, $P_1 = (1, 1, -1)$, and $P_2 = (-2, -3, 5)$, then $\overrightarrow{P_0P_1} = \frac{1}{2}\vec{i} + \frac{2}{3}\vec{j} - \vec{k}$, whereas $\overrightarrow{P_1P_2} = -3\vec{i} - 4\vec{j} + 6\vec{k}$. Thus $-6\,\overrightarrow{P_0P_1} = \overrightarrow{P_1P_2}$, so that the three points are collinear. Symmetric equations of the line are

$$\frac{x-1}{-3} = \frac{y-1}{-4} = \frac{z+1}{6}.$$

15. Let $P_0 = (-1, 1, 1)$, $P_1 = (0, 2, 1)$, and $P_2 = (0, 0, \frac{3}{2})$. Then $\overrightarrow{P_0P_1} = \vec{i} + \vec{j}$ and $\overrightarrow{P_0P_2} = \vec{i} - \vec{j} + \frac{1}{2}\vec{k}$. Thus a normal $\vec{N}$ to the plane containing the three points is given by

$$\vec{N} = \overrightarrow{P_0P_1} \times \overrightarrow{P_0P_2} = \frac{1}{2}\vec{i} - \frac{1}{2}\vec{j} - 2\vec{k}$$

Therefore an equation of the plane is $\frac{1}{2}(x + 1) - \frac{1}{2}(y - 1) - 2(z - 1) = 0$, or $\frac{1}{2}x - \frac{1}{2}y - 2z = -3$. Since $\frac{1}{2}(13) - \frac{1}{2}(-1) - 2(5) = -3$, the fourth point $(13, -1, 5)$ lies on the plane, so that all four points lie on the same plane.

16. The line is parallel to $2\vec{i} - 3\vec{j} + 4\vec{k}$, which is normal to the plane. Since $\vec{r}_0 = -3\vec{i} - 3\vec{j} + \vec{k}$, a vector equation of the line is $\vec{r} = (-3 + 2t)\vec{i} + (-3 - 3t)\vec{j} + (1 + 4t)\vec{k}$.

17. Let $P_0 = (1, 0, -1)$, $P_1 = (-5, 3, 2)$, and $P_2 = (2, -1, 4)$. Then $\overrightarrow{P_0P_1} = -6\vec{i} + 3\vec{j} + 3\vec{k}$ and $\overrightarrow{P_0P_2} = \vec{i} - \vec{j} + 5\vec{k}$. Thus a normal $\vec{N}$ to the plane containing the three points is given by

$$\vec{N} = \overrightarrow{P_0P_1} \times \overrightarrow{P_0P_2} = 18\vec{i} + 33\vec{j} + 3\vec{k}$$

Therefore an equation of the plane is $18(x - 1) + 33(y - 0) + 3(z + 1) = 0$, or $6x + 11y + z = 5$.

18. Since a normal $\vec{N}$ of the plane is perpendicular to the z axis, $\vec{N} = a\vec{i} + b\vec{j}$ for appropriate choices of a and b. Then an equation of the plane is $a(x - 3) + b(y + 1) + 0(z - 5) = 0$, or $ax + by = 3a - b$. Since $(7, 9, 4)$ is on the plane, $7a + 9b = 3a - b$, so that $4a = -10b$, or $a = \frac{-5}{2}b$. Thus an equation of the plane is $-\frac{5}{2}bx + by = -\frac{15}{2}b - b$, or $5x - 2y = 17$.

19. The line is parallel to $7\vec{i} + 9\vec{j} + 45\vec{k}$, and the vector $9\vec{i} - 2\vec{j} - \vec{k}$ is perpendicular to the plane. Since $(7\vec{i} + 9\vec{j} + 45\vec{k}) \cdot (9\vec{i} - 2\vec{j} - \vec{k}) = 0$, these two vectors are perpendicular, so that the line and the plane are parallel.

20. The point $P_1 = (1, -2, 5)$ is not on the plane, whereas $P_0 = (1, -2, 0)$ is on the plane. Then $\overrightarrow{P_0P_1} = 5\vec{k}$. If $\vec{N} = 3\vec{i} - 4\vec{j} + 12\vec{k}$, then $\vec{N}$ is normal to the plane, and the distance D from P_1 to the plane is given by

$$D = \frac{|\vec{N} \cdot \overrightarrow{P_0P_1}|}{\|\vec{N}\|} = \frac{|(3\vec{i} - 4\vec{j} + 12\vec{k}) \cdot (5\vec{k})|}{\sqrt{3^2 + (-4)^2 + (12)^2}} = \frac{60}{13}$$

21. The point $P_1 = (1, -2, 5)$ is not on the line, and the line is parallel to $3\vec{i} - 4\vec{j} + 12\vec{k}$. The point $P_0 = (1, -2, 0)$ is on the line, and $\overrightarrow{P_0P_1} = 5\vec{k}$. Therefore the distance D from P_1 to the line is given by

$$D = \frac{\|(3\vec{i} - 4\vec{j} + 12\vec{k}) \times (5\vec{k})\|}{\sqrt{3^2 + (-4)^2 + (12)^2}} = \frac{\|-20\vec{i} - 15\vec{j}\|}{13} = \frac{25}{13}$$

22. a. Letting $y = 4$ and $z = 1$ in the first equation, we obtain $3x - 4 + 1 = 2$, or $x = \frac{5}{3}$. Thus the three planes have the point $(\frac{5}{3}, 4, 1)$ in common.

b. If (x, y, z) is on the first two planes, then $2x + y - 2z - 1 = 0 = 3x + y - z - 2$, so that $-z = x - 1$, or $x = 1 - z$. If (x, y, z) is on on the first and third planes, then $2x + y - 2z - 1 = 0 = 2x - 2y + 2z$, so that $3y - 1 = 4z$, or $y = \frac{4z + 1}{3}$. Thus if (x, y, z) is on all three planes, then $0 = x - y + z = (1 - z) - (\frac{4z + 1}{3}) + z$, so that $z = \frac{1}{2}$. Thus $x = \frac{1}{2}$ and $y = 1$. Thus the planes have the point $(\frac{1}{2}, 1, \frac{1}{2})$ in common.

c. If (x, y, z) is on the first two planes, then $2x - 11y + 6z + 2 = 0 = 2x - 3y + 2z - 2$, or $z + 1 = 2y$. If (x, y, z) is on the first and third planes. Then $2x - 11y + 6z + 2 = 0 = 2x - 9y + 5z + 1$, or $z + 1 = 2y$. Thus $z = 2y - 1$. Substituting $z = 2y - 1$ into the equation $2x - 3y + 2z = 2$, we obtain $2x - 3y + 2(2y - 1) = 2$, or $2x + y = 4$. Thus $x = -\frac{1}{2}y + 2$. If we let $y = t$, then $x = -\frac{1}{2}t + 2$, $y = t$, $z = 2t - 1$ are parametric equations of the line common to the three planes.

23. Symmetric equations of the line are $\frac{x - a}{a} = \frac{y - b}{b} = \frac{z - c}{c}$. If we substitute 0 for x, y, and z in these equations, then the equations become $-1 = -1 = -1$. Thus (0, 0, 0) lies on the line.

24. An equation of the required plane is $a(x - a) + b(y - b) + c(z - c) = 0$, or $ax + by + cz = a^2 + b^2 + c^2$.

25. Consider a coordinate system with the forces applied at the origin, the 500 pound force $\vec{F}_1$ above the positive x axis and the 300 pound force along the line at an angle of $\pi/3$ with the positive x axis. Then $\vec{F}_1 = 500\vec{i}$ and $\vec{F}_2 = 300\left(\cos\frac{\pi}{3}\vec{i} + \sin\frac{\pi}{3}\vec{j}\right) = 150\vec{i} + 150\sqrt{3}\,\vec{j}$. Thus the resultant force $\vec{F} = \vec{F}_1 + \vec{F}_2 = 500\vec{i} + (150\vec{i} + 150\sqrt{3}\,\vec{j}) = 650\vec{i} + 150\sqrt{3}\,\vec{j}$. Therefore the magnitude of $\vec{F}$ is given by $\|\vec{F}\| = \sqrt{(650)^2 + (150)^2(3)} = 700$ (pounds). For the cosine of the angle θ between $\vec{F}$ and $\vec{F}_1$ we obtain $\cos\theta = \frac{\vec{F}\cdot\vec{F}_1}{\|\vec{F}\|\,\|\vec{F}_1\|} = \frac{650 \cdot 500}{700 \cdot 500} = \frac{13}{14}$.

26. Let $\vec{F}_1$ and $\vec{F}_2$ be the forces pointing downward and upward, respectively. Then $\vec{F}_1 = 5(\cos\theta\,\vec{i} - \sin\theta\,\vec{j})$ and $\vec{F}_2 = 5(\cos\theta\,\vec{i} + \sin\theta\,\vec{j})$. We must choose θ so that $\vec{F}_1 + \vec{F}_2 = 5\vec{i}$. But $\vec{F}_1 + \vec{F}_2 = 5(\cos\theta\,\vec{i} - \sin\theta\,\vec{j}) + 5(\cos\theta\,\vec{i} - \sin\theta\,\vec{j}) = 10\cos\theta\,\vec{i}$, so that $\vec{F}_1 + \vec{F}_2 = 5\vec{i}$ if and only if $10\cos\theta = 5$, or $\cos\theta = \frac{1}{2}$. Thus $\theta = \frac{\pi}{3}$.

27. Consider a coordinate system with the river flowing in the direction of the negative x axis and the motorboat traveling with increasing values of y. Let $\vec{v}_1$ be the velocity of the motorboat with respect to the water, and $\vec{v}_2$ the velocity of the river, so that $\vec{v}_1 + \vec{v}_2$ is the velocity of the motorboat with respect to the ground. Notice that $\vec{v}_2 = -5\vec{i}$ and $\vec{v}_1 = 10(\cos\theta\,\vec{i} + \sin\theta\,\vec{j})$, with θ to be chosen so that $\vec{v}_1 + \vec{v}_2 = c\vec{j}$ for an appropriate positive value of c. But $\vec{v}_1 + \vec{v}_2 = 10(\cos\theta\,\vec{i} + \sin\theta\,\vec{j}) - 5\vec{i} = (10\cos\theta - 5)\,\vec{i} + 10\sin\theta\,\vec{j}$, so that $10\cos\theta - 5 = 0$ and $10\sin\theta = c > 0$ if $\theta = \frac{\pi}{3}$. Thus the boat should be pointed at an angle of $\frac{\pi}{3}$ with respect to the shore. Also $\vec{v}_1 + \vec{v}_2 = 10\sin\frac{\pi}{3}\,\vec{j} = 5\sqrt{3}\,\vec{j}$. Therefore the $\frac{1}{2}$ mile width of the river is traveled at a speed of $5\sqrt{3}$ miles per hour in $\frac{1}{10\sqrt{3}}$ hours, or approximately 3.46410 minutes.

28. Let $\vec{v}$ be the velocity of the jet with respect to the ground, $\vec{v}_1$ the velocity of the jet with respect to the air, and $\vec{v}_2$ the velocity of the air (jet stream). Then $\vec{v} = \vec{v}_1 + \vec{v}_2 = 500\vec{j} + 100\vec{i}$. The ground speed of the jet is $\|\vec{v}\|$, and $\|\vec{v}\| = \sqrt{500^2 + 100^2} = 100\sqrt{26} \approx 509.902$ miles per hour.

29. If we let $q_1 = 3.2 \times 10^{-19}$, $\vec{u}_1 = -\vec{i}$, $r_1 = 10^{-12}$, $q_2 = -6.4 \times 10^{-19}$, $\vec{u}_2 = -\vec{j}$, $r_2 = 2 \times 10^{-12}$, $q_3 = 4.8 \times 10^{-19}$, $\vec{u}_3 = -\vec{k}$, and $r_3 = 3 \times 10^{-12}$, then

$$\vec{F} = \frac{q_1(1)}{4\pi\varepsilon_0 r_1^2}\vec{u}_1 + \frac{q_2(1)}{4\pi\varepsilon_0 r_2^2}\vec{u}_2 + \frac{q_3(1)}{4\pi\varepsilon_0 r_3^2}\vec{u}_3 = \frac{3.2 \times 10^{-19}}{4\pi\varepsilon_0\, 10^{-24}}(-\vec{i}) + \frac{-6.4 \times 10^{-19}}{4\pi\varepsilon_0(4 \times 10^{-24})}(-\vec{j}) + \frac{4.8 \times 10^{-19}}{4\pi\varepsilon_0(9 \times 10^{-24})}(-\vec{k}) = \frac{10^4}{\pi\varepsilon_0}\left(-8\vec{i} + 4\vec{j} - \frac{4}{3}\vec{k}\right).$$

12

VECTOR-VALUED FUNCTIONS

Section 12.1

1. domain: $(-\infty, \infty)$; $f_1(t) = t$, $f_2(t) = t^2$, $f_3(t) = t^3$

2. domain: $[1, \infty)$; $f_1(t) = \sqrt{t + 1}$, $f_2(t) = \sqrt{t - 1}$, $f_3(t) = 1$

3. tanh t is defined for all t; domain: $(-\infty, -2)$, and $(-2, 2)$ and $(2, \infty)$; $f_1(t) = \tanh t$, $f_2(t) = 0$, $f_3(t) = \dfrac{-1}{t^2 - 4}$

4. $\vec{F}(t) = (\frac{1}{t} \ln t - e^{-5t} \cot t)\,\vec{i} + [(4 - t^2) \cot t - \frac{1}{t}(t^2 - 1)]\,\vec{j} + [e^{-5t}(t^2 - 1) - (4 - t^2) \ln t]\,\vec{k}$. Thus the domain consists of all intervals of the form $(n\pi, (n + 1)\pi)$ for any nonnegative integer n. Also $f_1(t) = \frac{1}{t} \ln t - e^{-5t} \cot t$, $f_2(t) = (4 - t^2) \cot t - \frac{1}{t}(t^2 - 1)$, and $f_3(t) = e^{-5t}(t^2 - 1) - (4 - t^2) \ln t$.

5. $\vec{F}(t) = 2\sqrt{t}\,\vec{i} - 2t^{3/2}\,\vec{j} - (t^3 + 1)\,\vec{k}$. Thus the domain is $[0, \infty)$. Also $f_1(t) = 2\sqrt{t}$, $f_2(t) = -2t^{3/2}$, and $f_3(t) = -(t^3 + 1)$.

6. $(\vec{F} - \vec{G})(t) = (2t - e^t)\,\vec{i} + (t^2 - e^{-t})\,\vec{j} + (-\ln t - 2t)\,\vec{k}$. Thus the domain is $(0, \infty)$. Also $f_1(t) = 2t - e^t$, $f_2(t) = t^2 - e^{-t}$, and $f_3(t) = -\ln t - 2t$.

7. $(2\vec{F} - 3\vec{G})(t) = (2t - 3\cos t)\,\vec{i} + (2t^2 - 3\sin t)\,\vec{j} + (2t^3 - 3)\,\vec{k}$. Thus the domain is $(-\infty, \infty)$. Also $f_1(t) = 2t - 3\cos t$, $f_2(t) = 2t^2 - 3\sin t$, and $f_3(t) = 2t^3 - 3$.

8. $(\vec{F} \times \vec{G})(t) = (t^2 - t^3 \sin t)\,\vec{i} + (t^3 \cos t - t)\,\vec{j} + (t \sin t - t^2 \cos t)\,\vec{k}$. Thus the domain is $(-\infty, \infty)$. Also $f_1(t) = t^2 - t^3 \sin t$, $f_2(t) = t^3 \cos t - t$, and $f_3(t) = t \sin t - t^2 \cos t$.

9. $(\vec{F} \times \vec{G})(t) = \frac{1}{\sqrt{t}}(1 - \cos t)\,\vec{i} - \frac{1}{\sqrt{t}}(t - \sin t)\,\vec{j} - t(t - \sin t)\,\vec{k}$. Thus the domain is $(0, \infty)$. Also $f_1(t) = \frac{1}{\sqrt{t}}(1 - \cos t)$, $f_2(t) = -\frac{1}{\sqrt{t}}(t - \sin t)$, and $f_3(t) = -t(t - \sin t)$.

10. $(f\vec{F})(t) = \sqrt{t} \ln t\,\vec{i} - 4\sqrt{t}\,e^{2t}\,\vec{j} + (\sqrt{t}\,\sqrt{t - 1}/t)\,\vec{k}$. Thus the domain is $[1, \infty)$. Also $f_1(t) = \sqrt{t} \ln t$, $f_2(t) = -4\sqrt{t}\,e^{2t}$, and $f_3(t) = \sqrt{t - 1}/\sqrt{t}$.

11. $(\vec{F} \circ g)(t) = \cos t^{1/3}\,\vec{i} + \sin t^{1/3}\,\vec{j} + \sqrt{t^{1/3} + 2}\,\vec{k}$. Thus the domain consists of all t for which $t^{1/3} + 2 \geq 0$, and hence is $[-8, \infty)$. Also $f_1(t) = \cos t^{1/3}$, $f_2(t) = \sin t^{1/3}$, and $f_3(t) = \sqrt{t^{1/3} + 2}$.

12. $(\vec{F} \circ g)(t) = e^{-2 \ln t}\,\vec{i} + e^{(\ln t)^2}\,\vec{j} + (\ln t)^3\,\vec{k} = \frac{1}{t^2}\,\vec{i} + e^{(\ln t)^2}\,\vec{j} + (\ln t)^3\,\vec{k}$. Thus the domain is $(0, \infty)$. Also $f_1(t) = \frac{1}{t^2}$, $f_2(t) = e^{(\ln t)^2}$, and $f_3(t) = (\ln t)^3$.

13.

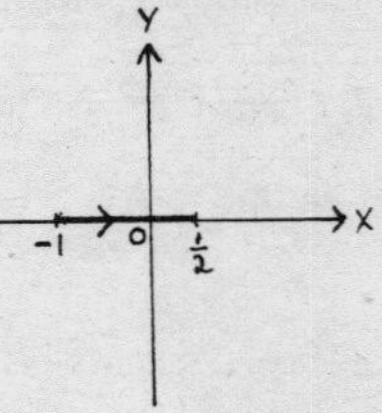

14.

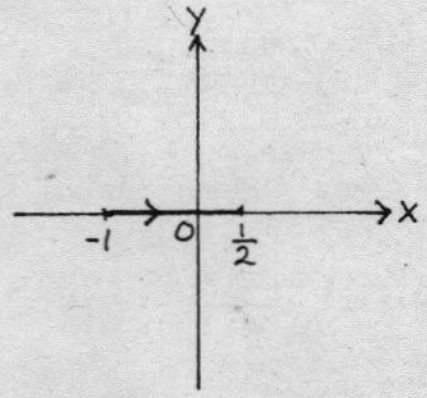

15.

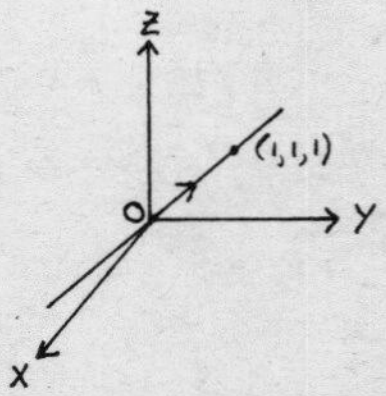

16.

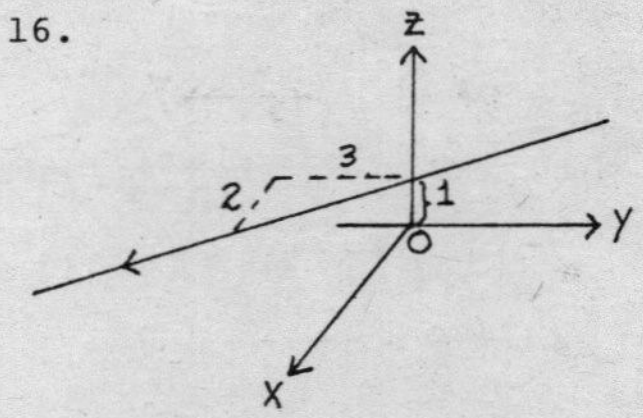

17.

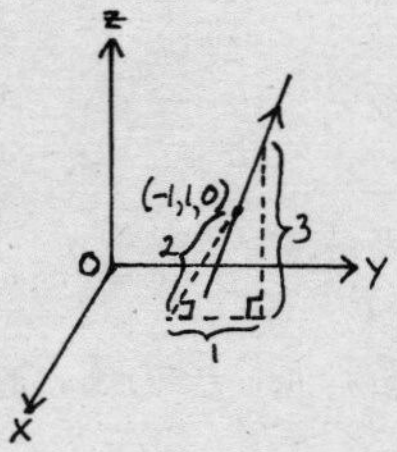

18.

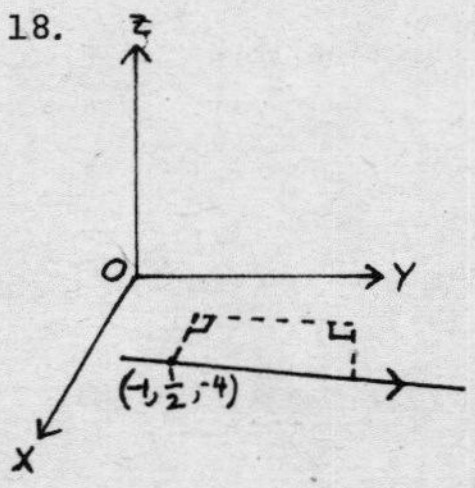

19.

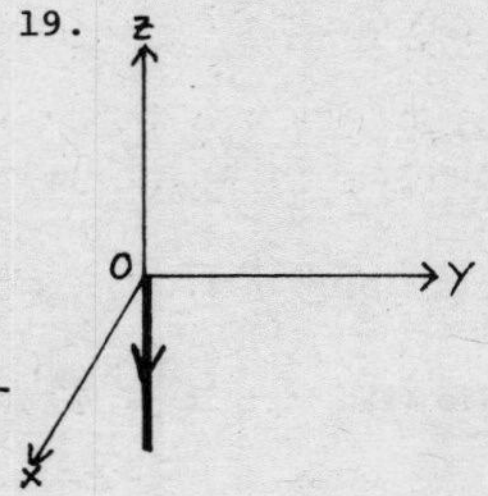

20.

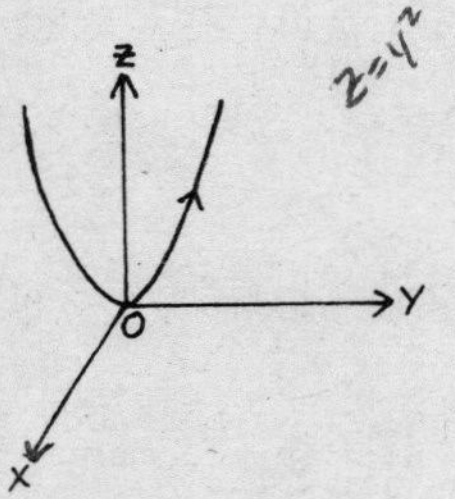

21.

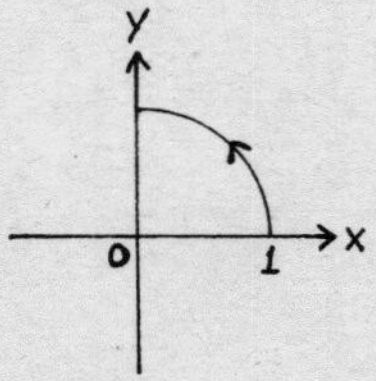

22.

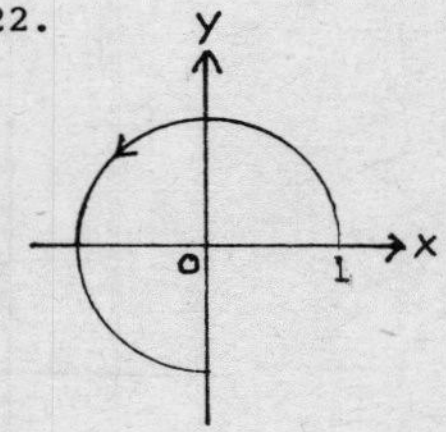

23.

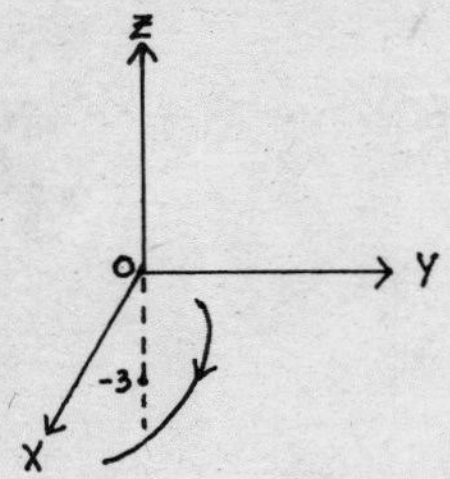

24.

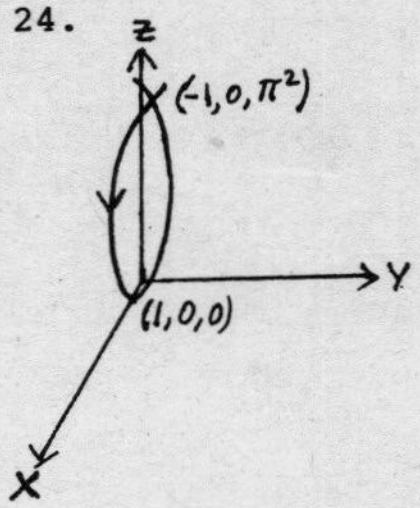

25.

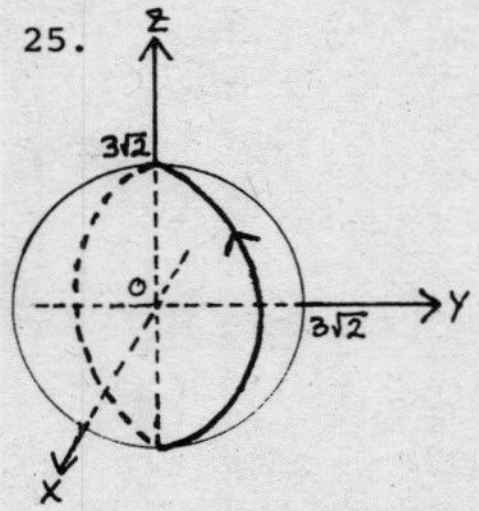

26.

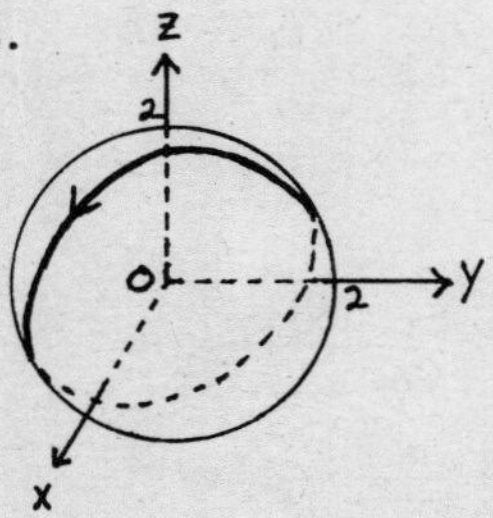

27. a. $(\vec{F} - \vec{G})(t) = (t - 1)\,\vec{i} + (-2t + 3)\,\vec{j} - 4t\,\vec{k}$, so parametric equations are $x = t - 1$, $y = -2t + 3$, and $z = -4t$.

b. $(\vec{F} + 3\vec{G})(t) = (5t + 3)\,\vec{i} + (10t - 5)\,\vec{j}$, so parametric equations are $x = 5t + 3$, $y = 10t - 5$, and $z = 0$.

c. $(\vec{F} \circ g)(t) = 2\cos t\,\vec{i} + (\cos t + 1)\,\vec{j} - 3\cos t\,\vec{k}$. Then $x = 2\cos t$, $y = \cos t + 1$, and $z = 3\cos t$ for all real t, which yields the line segment parameterized by $x = 2t$, $y = t + 1$, $z = -3t$ for $-1 \le t \le 1$.

28. If (x, y, z) is on the curve, then $x = t\cos \pi t$, $y = t \sin \pi t$, and $z = t$. If in addition (x, y, z) is on the cylinder $x^2 + y^2 = 4$, then $(t\cos \pi t)^2 + (t \sin \pi t)^2 = 4$, so that $t^2(\cos^2 \pi t + \sin^2 \pi t) = 4$, or $t^2 = 4$, or $t = \pm 2$. If $t = 2$, then $(x, y, z) = (2\cos 2\pi, 2\sin 2\pi, 2) = (2, 0, 2)$, and if $t = -2$, then $(x, y, z) = (-2\cos(-2\pi), -2\sin(-2\pi), -2) = (-2, 0, -2)$. The points of intersection are therefore $(2, 0, 2)$ and $(-2, 0, -2)$.

29. If (x, y, z) is on the curve, then $x = \cos \pi t$, $y = \sin \pi t$, and $z = t$. If in addition (x, y, z) is on the sphere $x^2 + y^2 + z^2 = 10$, then $(\cos \pi t)^2 + (\sin \pi t)^2 + t^2 = 10$, so that $t^2 = 9$, and thus $t = \pm 3$. If $t = 3$, then $(x, y, z) = (\cos 3\pi, \sin 3\pi, 3) = (-1, 0, 3)$, and if $t = -3$, then $(x, y, z) = (\cos(-3\pi), \sin(-3\pi), -3) = (-1, 0, -3)$. The points of intersection are therefore $(-1, 0, 3)$ and $(-1, 0, -3)$.

30. $\vec{F}(t)$ can be written $\vec{a} + \vec{b}$, where $\vec{a}$ describes the motion of the center of the circle and $\vec{b}$ describes the motion of P around the center. As in Example 7, $\vec{a} = rt\vec{i} + r\vec{j}$. Also, if C is the center of the circle, then t represents the number of radians through which $\overrightarrow{CP}$ has rotated since time 0. At that time $\overrightarrow{CP}$ makes an angle of $(3\pi/2 - t)$ radians with the positive x axis, so $\vec{b} = \overrightarrow{CP} = b\cos(3\pi/2 - t)\,\vec{i} + b\sin(3\pi/2 - t)\,\vec{j} = -b\sin t\,\vec{i} - b\cos t\,\vec{j}$. Consequently $\vec{F}(t) = \vec{a} + \vec{b} = (rt\vec{i} + r\vec{j}) + (-b\sin t\,\vec{i} - b\cos t\,\vec{j}) = (rt - b\sin t)\,\vec{i} + (r - b\cos t)\,\vec{j}$.

31. $\vec{F}(t)$ can be written $\vec{a} + \vec{b}$, where $\vec{a}$ describes the motion of the center C of the circle and $\vec{b}$ describes the motion of P around the center. First of all, $\vec{a} = (r + b) \cos t\, \vec{i} + (r + b) \sin t\, \vec{j}$. The number t represents the number of radians through which $\overrightarrow{OC}$ has rotated since time 0. Notice that an angle of t radians on the fixed circle corresponds to an arc of length rt, which in turn corresponds to an arc of length rt on the rolling circle. If the corresponding angle on the rolling circle has α radians, then the arc has length $b\alpha$, so that $b\alpha = rt$, or $\alpha = \frac{r}{b}t$. Thus by time t the angle OCP has $\frac{r}{b}t$ radians, so that $\overrightarrow{CP}$ makes an angle of $\frac{r}{b} t + t$ radians with a line parallel to the negative x axis, and hence an angle of $\pi + \frac{r}{b} t + t$ radians with a line parallel to the positive x axis. Therefore $\vec{b} = \overrightarrow{CP} = b \cos (\pi + \frac{r}{b} t + t)\, \vec{i} + b \sin (\pi + \frac{r}{b} t + t)\, \vec{j}$

$= - b \cos (\frac{r}{b} t + t)\, \vec{i} - b \sin (\frac{r}{b} t + t)\, \vec{j}$. Consequently $\vec{F}(t) = \vec{a} + \vec{b}$

$= \left[(r + b) \cos t\, \vec{i} + (r + b) \sin t\, \vec{j}\right] + \left[- b \cos (\frac{r}{b} t + t)\, \vec{i}\right.$

$\left.- b \sin (\frac{r}{b} t + t)\, \vec{j}\right] = \left[(r + b) \cos t - b \cos (\frac{r + b}{b} t)\right] \vec{i} + \left[(r + b) \sin t\right.$

$\left.- b \sin (\frac{r + b}{b} t)\right] \vec{j}$.

32. Place the coordinate system so that the axis of the cylinder is the z axis, and the base of the staircase lies on the positive x axis. Let $0 \le t \le 2\pi$, and let $\vec{F}(t)$ be the vector from the origin to the point on the staircase whose $\vec{i}$ and $\vec{j}$ components are $50 \cos t$ and $50 \sin t$, respectively. Then $\vec{F}(t) = 50 \cos t\, \vec{i} + 50 \sin t\, \vec{j} + at\vec{k}$, for $0 \le t \le 2\pi$, where a is chosen so that one revolution yields a height of 200 feet, that is, $a(2\pi) = 200$. This means that $a = \frac{200}{2\pi} = \frac{100}{\pi}$, so that $\vec{F}(t)$

$= 50 \cos t\, \vec{i} + 50 \sin t\, \vec{j} + \frac{100}{\pi} t\vec{k}$ for $0 \le t \le 2\pi$.

Section 12.2

1. $\lim_{t\to 4} (\vec{i} - \vec{j} + \vec{k}) = \vec{i} - \vec{j} + \vec{k}$

2. $\lim_{t\to -1} (3\vec{i} + t\vec{j} + t^5\vec{k}) = (\lim_{t\to -1} 3)\, \vec{i} + (\lim_{t\to -1} t)\, \vec{j} + (\lim_{t\to -1} t^5)\, \vec{k} = 3\vec{i} - \vec{j} - \vec{k}$

3. $\lim_{t\to \pi} (\tan t\vec{i} + 3t\vec{j} - 4\vec{k}) = (\lim_{t\to\pi} \tan t)\, \vec{i} + (\lim_{t\to\pi} 3t)\, \vec{j} + (\lim_{t\to\pi} (-4))\, \vec{k}$

$= 0\vec{i} + 3\pi\vec{j} - 4\vec{k} = 3\pi\vec{j} - 4\vec{k}$

4. $\lim_{t\to 0} (\frac{\sin t}{t}\vec{i} + e^t\vec{j} + (t + \sqrt{2})\, \vec{k}) = (\lim_{t\to 0} \frac{\sin t}{t})\, \vec{i} + (\lim_{t\to 0} e^t)\, \vec{j}$

$+ (\lim_{t\to 0} (t + \sqrt{2}))\vec{k} = \vec{i} + \vec{j} + \sqrt{2}\, \vec{k}$.

5. $\lim_{t\to 2^-} \vec{F}(t) = \lim_{t\to 2^-} (5\vec{i} - \sqrt{2t^2 + 2t + 4}\, \vec{j} + e^{-(t - 2)}\vec{k}) = (\lim_{t\to 2^-} 5)\, \vec{i}$

$+ (\lim_{t\to 2^-} - \sqrt{2t^2 + 2t + 4})\, \vec{j} + (\lim_{t\to 2^-} e^{-(t - 2)})\, \vec{k} = 5\vec{i} - 4\vec{j} + \vec{k}$, whereas

$\lim_{t\to 2^+} \vec{F}(t) = \lim_{t\to 2^+} (t^2 + 1)\, \vec{i} + (4 - t^3)\, \vec{j} + \vec{k} = (\lim_{t\to 2^+} (t^2 + 1))\, \vec{i}$

$+ (\lim_{t\to 2^+} (4 - t^3))\, \vec{j} + (\lim_{t\to 2^+} 1)\, \vec{k} = 5\vec{i} - 4\vec{j} + \vec{k}$. Since $\lim_{t\to 2^-} \vec{F}(t) = \lim_{t\to 2^+} \vec{F}(t)$

$= 5\vec{i} - 4\vec{j} + \vec{k}$, it follows that $\lim_{t\to 2} \vec{F}(t)$ exists and that $\lim_{t\to 2} \vec{F}(t) = 5\vec{i} - 4\vec{j} + \vec{k}$.

6. $\lim_{t\to 0} \vec{F}(t) = \lim_{t\to 0} (t\vec{i} + e^{-1/t^2}\, \vec{j} + t^2\vec{k}) = 0\vec{i} + 0\vec{j} + 0\vec{k} = \vec{0}$

7. $\lim_{t\to 0} (\vec{F} - \vec{G})\, (t) = \lim_{t\to 0} \left[(e^{-1/t^2} + \pi)\, \vec{i} + (\cos t - \frac{1 + \cos t}{t})\, \vec{j} + t^3\, \vec{k}\right]$. Since

$\lim_{t\to 0} \frac{1 + \cos t}{t}$ and hence $\lim_{t\to 0} (\cos t - \frac{1 + \cos t}{t})$ does not exist, Theorem 12.4 implies that $\lim_{t\to 0} (\vec{F} - \vec{G})\, (t)$ does not exist.

8. $\lim_{t\to 1} (\vec{F} \cdot \vec{G})\, (t) = \lim_{t\to 1} \left[\vec{F}(t) \cdot \vec{G}(t)\right] = \lim_{t\to 1} \left[(t^2 + 1)\, \frac{\sin (t - 1)}{t - 1} - 1\right.$

$\left.- \sqrt{t^2 + 1}\, \cos \pi t\right]$. Since $\lim_{t\to 1} \frac{\sin (t - 1)}{t - 1} = \lim_{u\to 0} \frac{\sin u}{u} = 1$, we find that

$\lim_{t\to 1} (\vec{F} \cdot \vec{G})\, (t) = 2 - 1 + \sqrt{2} = 1 + \sqrt{2}$.

9. $\lim_{t\to 3} \left(\frac{t^2 - 5t + 6}{t - 3}\vec{i} + \frac{t^2 - 2t - 3}{t - 3}\vec{j} + \frac{t^2 + 4t - 21}{t - 3}\vec{k}\right) = \lim_{t\to 3}\left[(t - 2)\vec{i} + (t + 1)\vec{j} + (t + 7)\vec{k}\right] = \left(\lim_{t\to 3}(t - 2)\right)\vec{i} + \left(\lim_{t\to 3}(t + 1)\right)\vec{j} + \left(\lim_{t\to 3}(t + 7)\right)\vec{k} = \vec{i} + 4\vec{j} + 10\vec{k}$

10. Since $\lim_{t\to 1}\frac{t^2 + 1}{t - 1}$ does not exist, the given limit does not exist, by virtue of Theorem 12.4.

11. $(-\infty,\infty)$

12. $(-\infty,\infty)$

13. Since $\sqrt{2t}$ is continuous on $[0,\infty)$, so is $\vec{F}$.

14. $\lim_{t\to 0^-}\vec{F}(t) = \lim_{t\to 0^-}\left(\frac{\sin t}{t}\vec{i} + \vec{j} + \vec{k}\right) = \vec{i} + \vec{j} + \vec{k}$, and $\lim_{t\to 0^+}\vec{F}(t) = \lim_{t\to 0^+}\left[(t^2+1)\vec{i} + \ln(t + 3)\vec{j} + \vec{k}\right] = \left(\lim_{t\to 0^+}(t^2 + 1)\right)\vec{i} + \left(\lim_{t\to 0^+}\ln(t + 3)\right)\vec{j} + \left(\lim_{t\to 0^+} 1\right)\vec{k} = \vec{i} + \ln 3\,\vec{j} + \vec{k}$. Thus $\vec{F}$ is not continuous at 0. However, $\frac{\sin t}{t}\vec{i} + \vec{j} + \vec{k}$ is continuous on $(-\infty, 0)$ and $(t^2 + 1)\vec{i} + \ln(t + 3)\vec{j} + \vec{k}$ is continuous on $[0,\infty)$. Thus $\vec{F}$ is continuous on $(-\infty, 0)$ and $[0,\infty)$.

15. $\lim_{t\to -3^-}\vec{F}(t) = \lim_{t\to -3^-}\left[(2t + 1)\vec{i} + (2t - 1)\vec{j} + 4t\vec{k}\right] = \left(\lim_{t\to -3^-}(2t + 1)\right)\vec{i} + \left(\lim_{t\to -3^-}(2t - 1)\right)\vec{j} + \left(\lim_{t\to -3^-}4t\right)\vec{k} = -5\vec{i} - 7\vec{j} - 12\vec{k}$, and $\lim_{t\to -3^+}\vec{F}(t) = \lim_{t\to -3^+}\left[(t - 2)\vec{i} - (t + 10)\vec{j} + (2t - 9)\vec{k}\right] = \left(\lim_{t\to -3^+}(t - 2)\right)\vec{i} + \left(\lim_{t\to -3^+} -(t + 10)\right)\vec{j} + \left(\lim_{t\to -3^+}(2t - 9)\right)\vec{k} = -5\vec{i} - 7\vec{j} - 15\vec{k}$. Thus $\vec{F}$ is not continuous at -3. However, $(2t + 1)\vec{i} + (2t - 1)\vec{j} + 4t\vec{k}$ is continuous on $(-\infty, -3)$ and $(t - 2)\vec{i} - (t + 10)\vec{j} + (2t - 9)\vec{k}$ is continuous on $[-3,\infty)$. Thus $\vec{F}$ is continuous on $(-\infty, -3)$ and $[-3,\infty)$.

16. a. Let $\vec{F}$ be defined at each point in some open interval (t_0, t_1). A vector $\vec{L}$ is the limit of $\vec{F}(t)$ as t approaches t_0 from the right if for every $\varepsilon > 0$ there is a number $\delta > 0$ such that

if $0 < t - t_0 < \delta$, then $\|\vec{F}(t) - \vec{L}\| < \varepsilon$.

In this case we write $\lim_{t\to t_0^+}\vec{F}(t) = \vec{L}$. To prove that such limits can be computed componentwise, we can use the statement and proof of Theorem 12.4, with "$\lim_{t\to t_0}$" replaced by "$\lim_{t\to t_0^+}$", and "$0 < |t - t_0| < \delta$" replaced by "$0 < t - t_0 < \delta$".

b. Let $\vec{F}$ be defined at each point in some open interval (t_1, t_0). A vector $\vec{L}$ is the limit of $\vec{F}(t)$ as t approaches t_0 from the left if for every $\varepsilon > 0$ there is a number $\delta > 0$ such that

if $-\delta < t - t_0 < 0$, then $\|\vec{F}(t) - \vec{L}\| < \varepsilon$.

In this case we write $\lim_{t\to t_0^-}\vec{F}(t) = \vec{L}$. To prove that such limits can be computed componentwise, use the statement and proof of Theorem 12.4, with "$\lim_{t\to t_0}$" replaced by "$\lim_{t\to t_0^-}$" and "$0 < |t - t_0| < \delta$" replaced by "$-\delta < t - t_0 < 0$".

17. a. Since $\lim_{t\to 0^+}\frac{-\ln t}{t}$ does not exist, neither does the given limit.

b. $\lim_{t\to 1^+}\left[e^{1/(1 - t)}\vec{i} + \sqrt{t - 1}\,\vec{j} + \ln t\,\vec{k}\right] = \left(\lim_{t\to 1^+}e^{1/(1-t)}\right)\vec{i} + \left(\lim_{t\to 1^+}\sqrt{t - 1}\right)\vec{j} + \left(\lim_{t\to 1^+}\ln t\right)\vec{k} = 0\vec{i} + 0\vec{j} + 0\vec{k} = \vec{0}$.

c. $\lim_{t\to 1^-}\left[\sqrt{1 - t}\,\vec{i} - (1 - t)\ln(1 - t)\vec{j}\right] = \left(\lim_{t\to 1^-}\sqrt{1 - t}\right)\vec{i} + \left(\lim_{t\to 1^-} -(1 - t)\ln(1 - t)\right)\vec{j}$. Since $\lim_{t\to 1^-}(1 - t)\ln(1 - t) = \lim_{u\to 0^+}u\ln u = \lim_{u\to 0^+}\frac{\ln u}{1/u} = \lim_{u\to 0^+}\frac{1/u}{-1/u^2} = \lim_{u\to 0^+}(-u) = 0$ by l'Hôpital's

Rule, we find that $(\lim_{t\to 1^-} \sqrt{1-t})\vec{i} + (\lim_{t\to 1^-} -(1-t)\ \ln(1-t))\vec{j}$ $= 0\,\vec{i} + 0\,\vec{j} = \vec{0}$. Thus $\lim_{t\to 1^-} (\sqrt{1-t}\,\vec{i} - (1-t)\ln(1-t)\,\vec{j})) = \vec{0}$.

18. a. Let $\vec{F}$ be defined at each point in an interval of the form (t_0,∞). A vector $\vec{L}$ is the limit of $\vec{F}(t)$ as t approaches ∞ if for every $\varepsilon > 0$ there is a number M such that

if $t > M$, then $\|\vec{F}(t) - \vec{L}\| < \varepsilon$

In this case we write $\lim_{t\to\infty} \vec{F}(t) = \vec{L}$. To prove that such limits can be computed componentwise, use the statement and proof of Theorem 12.4, with "$\lim_{t\to t_0}$" replaced by "$\lim_{t\to\infty}$", "$\delta > 0$" by "M", and "$0 < |t - t_0| < \delta$" by "$t > M$".

b. $\lim_{t\to\infty} (\frac{1}{t}\vec{i} + \frac{t-1}{t+1}\vec{j} + \frac{\sin t^3}{t^2})\vec{k} = (\lim_{t\to\infty}\frac{1}{t})\vec{i} + (\lim_{t\to\infty}\frac{t-1}{t+1})\vec{j}$ $+ (\lim_{t\to\infty}\frac{\sin t^3}{t^2})\vec{k}$. Since $\left|\frac{\sin t^3}{t^2}\right| \le \frac{1}{t^2}$, we have $\lim_{t\to\infty}\frac{\sin t^3}{t^2} = 0$. Thus

$(\lim_{t\to\infty}\frac{1}{t})\vec{i} + (\lim_{t\to\infty}\frac{t-1}{t+1})\vec{j} + (\lim_{t\to\infty}\frac{\sin t^3}{t^2})\vec{k} = 0\,\vec{i} + \vec{j} + 0\,\vec{k} = \vec{j}$.

19. a. By Theorem 12.5(a), $\lim_{t\to t_0} (\vec{F} + \vec{G})(t) = \lim_{t\to t_0} \vec{F}(t) + \lim_{t\to t_0} \vec{G}(t) = \vec{F}(t_0)$ $+ \vec{G}(t_0) = (\vec{F} + \vec{G})(t_0)$, so that $\vec{F} + \vec{G}$ is continuous at t_0.

b. By Theorem 12.5(c) with $f(t) = c$ for all t, $\lim_{t\to t_0} (c\vec{F})(t) = \lim_{t\to t_0} c \cdot$ $\cdot \lim_{t\to t_0} \vec{F}(t) = c(\vec{F}(t_0)) = (c\vec{F})(t_0)$, so that $c\vec{F}$ is continuous at t_0.

c. Let f_1, f_2, and f_3 be the component functions of $\vec{F}$. Then $\|\vec{F}(t)\|$ $= \sqrt{(f_1(t))^2 + (f_2(t))^2 + (f_3(t))^2}$. Since f_1, f_2, and f_3 are continuous at t_0 by Theorem 12.7, and since the square root function is continuous on $(0,\infty)$, it follows that $\|\vec{F}\|$ is continuous at t_0.

d. By Theorem 12.5(d), $\lim_{t\to t_0} (\vec{F}\cdot\vec{G})(t) = \lim_{t\to t_0} \vec{F}(t) \cdot \lim_{t\to t_0} \vec{G}(t) = F(t_0)\cdot G(t_0)$ $= (\vec{F}\cdot\vec{G})(t_0)$, so that $\vec{F}\cdot\vec{G}$ is continuous at t_0.

e. By Theorem 12.5(e), $\lim_{t\to t_0} (\vec{F}\times\vec{G})(t) = \lim_{t\to t_0} \vec{F}(t) \times \lim_{t\to t_0} \vec{G}(t)$ $= \vec{F}(t_0)\times\vec{G}(t_0) = (\vec{F}\times\vec{G})(t_0)$, so that $\vec{F}\times\vec{G}$ is continuous at t_0.

Section 12.3

1. $\vec{F}'(t) = \vec{j} + 5t^4\,\vec{k}$

2. $\vec{F}'(t) = (2t + 1)\,\vec{j} - \vec{k}$

3. $\vec{F}'(t) = \frac{3}{2}\,(1 + t)^{1/2}\,\vec{i} + \frac{3}{2}\,(1 - t)^{1/2}\,\vec{j} + \frac{3}{2}\,\vec{k}$

4. $\vec{F}'(t) = (2t \cos t - t^2 \sin t)\,\vec{i} + (3t^2 \sin t + t^3 \cos t)\,\vec{j} + 4t^3\,\vec{k}$

5. $\vec{F}'(t) = \sec^2 t\,\vec{i} + \sec t \tan t\,\vec{k}$

6. $\vec{F}'(t) = (e^t \cos t - e^t \sin t)\,\vec{i} - (e^t \sin t + e^t \cos t)\,\vec{k}$

7. $F'(t) = \sinh t\,\vec{i} + \cosh t\,\vec{j} - \frac{1}{2\sqrt{t}}\,\vec{k}$

8. $\vec{F}'(t) = \frac{4}{\sqrt{1 - 16t^2}}\,\vec{i} - \frac{6}{1 + (2t - 1)^2}\,\vec{j} + \frac{14}{t}\,\vec{k}$

9. $(4\vec{F} - 2\vec{G})(t) = (8 \sec t - 6t)\,\vec{i} + (2t^2 - 12)\,\vec{j} + 12 \csc t\,\vec{k}$, so that $(4\vec{F} - 2\vec{G})'(t) = (8 \sec t \tan t - 6)\,\vec{i} + 4t\,\vec{j} - 12 \csc t \cot t\,\vec{k}$

10. $(\vec{F} \cdot \vec{G})(t) = 6t \sec t + 3t^2 - 4 \csc^2 t$; $(\vec{F} \cdot \vec{G})'(t) = (6 \sec t + 6t \sec t \tan t) + 6t + 8 \csc^2 t \cot t$

11. $(\vec{F} \times \vec{G})(t) = (-3 \ln t)\,\vec{i} - (2 \sec t \ln t)\,\vec{j}$; $(\vec{F} \times \vec{G})'(t) = \left(\frac{-3}{t}\right)\vec{i} - \left(2 \sec t \tan t \ln t + \frac{2}{t} \sec t\right)\vec{k}$

12. $(\vec{F} \cdot \vec{G})(t) = 3 + e^{-t}$ for $t \neq 0$; $(\vec{F} \cdot \vec{G})'(t) = -e^{-t}$ for $t \neq 0$

13. $(\vec{F} \times \vec{G})(t) = (t - \frac{3}{t} e^{-t})\,\vec{k}$; $(\vec{F} \times \vec{G})'(t) = (1 + \frac{3}{t^2} e^{-t} + \frac{3}{t} e^{-t})\,\vec{k}$

14. $(\vec{F} \cdot \vec{G})(t) = \frac{4t + 8t^3}{(1 + t^2)^3} - \frac{4t + 8t^3}{(1 + t^2)^3} = 0$; $(\vec{F} \cdot \vec{G})'(t) = 0$

15. $(\vec{F} \circ g)'(t) = \vec{F}'(g(t))\,g'(t) = \left(\frac{1}{\sqrt{t}}\,\vec{i} - 8e^{2\sqrt{t}}\,\vec{j} + \frac{1}{(\sqrt{t})^2}\,\vec{k}\right)\frac{1}{2\sqrt{t}} = \frac{1}{2t}\,\vec{i} - \frac{4e^{2\sqrt{t}}}{\sqrt{t}}\,\vec{j} + \frac{1}{2} t^{-3/2}\,\vec{k}$

16. $(\vec{F} \circ g)'(t) = \vec{F}'(g(t))\,g'(t) = \left(3 \cos^2 t\,\vec{i} - \sqrt{3}\,\vec{j} - \frac{2}{\cos^3 t}\,\vec{k}\right)(-\sin t) = -3 \sin t \cos^2 t\,\vec{i} + \sqrt{3} \sin t\,\vec{j} + 2 \sin t \sec^3 t\,\vec{k}$

17. $\int \left(t^2\,\vec{i} - (3t - 1)\,\vec{j} - \frac{1}{t^3}\,\vec{k}\right) dt = \frac{t^3}{3}\,\vec{i} - \left(\frac{3}{2} t^2 - t\right)\vec{j} + \frac{1}{2t^2}\,\vec{k} + \vec{C}$

18. By parts we find that $\int t \cos t\, dt = t \sin t - \int \sin t\, dt = t \sin t + \cos t + C$ and $\int t \sin t\, dt = -t \cos t + \int \cos t\, dt = -t \cos t + \sin t + C$. Thus $\int (t \cos t\,\vec{i} + t \sin t\,\vec{j} + 3t^4\,\vec{k})\, dt = (t \sin t + \cos t)\,\vec{i} + (-t \cos t + \sin t)\,\vec{j} + \frac{3}{5} t^5\,\vec{k} + \vec{C}$.

19. $\int_0^1 (e^t\,\vec{i} + e^{-t}\,\vec{j} + 2t\,\vec{k})\, dt = e^t \Big|_0^1\,\vec{i} - e^{-t} \Big|_0^1\,\vec{j} + t^2 \Big|_0^1\,\vec{k} = (e - 1)\,\vec{i} + (1 - e^{-1})\,\vec{j} + \vec{k}$

20. $\int_0^1 (\cosh t\,\vec{i} + \sinh t\,\vec{j} + \vec{k})\, dt = \sinh t \Big|_0^1\,\vec{i} + \cosh t \Big|_0^1\,\vec{j} + t \Big|_0^1\,\vec{k} = (\sinh 1)\,\vec{i} + (\cosh 1 - 1)\,\vec{j} + \vec{k}$

21. $\int_{-1}^1 \left[(1 + t)^{3/2}\,\vec{i} + (1 - t)^{3/2}\,\vec{j}\right] dt = \frac{2}{5}\,(1 + t)^{5/2} \Big|_{-1}^1\,\vec{i} - \frac{2}{5}\,(1 - t)^{5/2} \Big|_{-1}^1\,\vec{j} = \frac{8}{5}\,\sqrt{2}\,(\vec{i} + \vec{j})$

22. $\vec{v}(t) = 3\,\vec{i} + 2\,\vec{j} - 32t\,\vec{k}$, $\|\vec{v}(t)\| = \sqrt{9 + 4 + (-32t)^2} = \sqrt{13 + 1024t^2}$, $\vec{a}(t) = -32\,\vec{k}$

23. $\vec{v}(t) = -\sin t\,\vec{i} + \cos t\,\vec{j} - 32t\,\vec{k}$, $\|\vec{v}(t)\| = \sqrt{(-\sin t)^2 + \cos^2 t + (-32t)^2} = \sqrt{1 + 1024t^2}$, $\vec{a}(t) = -\cos t\,\vec{i} - \sin t\,\vec{j} - 32\,\vec{k}$

24. $\vec{v}(t) = -e^{-t}\,\vec{i} - e^{-t}\,\vec{j}$, $\|\vec{v}(t)\| = \sqrt{(-e^{-t})^2 + (-e^{-t})^2} = e^{-t}\sqrt{2}$, $\vec{a}(t) = e^{-t}\,\vec{i} + e^{-t}\,\vec{j}$

25. $\vec{v}(t) = 2\,\vec{i} + 2t\,\vec{j} + \frac{1}{t}\,\vec{k}$, $\|\vec{v}(t)\| = \sqrt{4 + 4t^2 + \frac{1}{t^2}} = \frac{2t^2 + 1}{t}$, $\vec{a}(t) = 2\,\vec{j} - \frac{1}{t^2}\,\vec{k}$

26. $\vec{v}(t) = \sinh t\,\vec{i} + \cosh t\,\vec{j} + \vec{k}$, $\|\vec{v}(t)\| = \sqrt{\sinh^2 t + \cosh^2 t + 1} = \sqrt{2 \cosh^2 t} = \sqrt{2} \cosh t$, $\vec{a}(t) = \cosh t\,\vec{i} + \sinh t\,\vec{j}$

27. $\vec{v}(t) = (e^t \sin t + e^t \cos t)\,\vec{i} + (e^t \cos t - e^t \sin t)\,\vec{j} + e^t\,\vec{k}$, $\|\vec{v}(t)\|$

$= \sqrt{(e^{2t}\sin^2 t + 2e^{2t}\sin t\cos t + e^{2t}\cos^2 t) + [e^{2t}\cos^2 t - 2e^{2t}(\sin t)\cdot(\cos t) + e^{2t}\sin^2 t] + e^{2t}} = e^t\sqrt{3}$, $\vec{a}(t) = 2e^t \cos t\,\vec{i} - 2e^t \sin t\,\vec{j} + e^t\,\vec{k}$

28. $\vec{v}(t) = \int \vec{a}(t)\,dt = \int -32\,\vec{k}\,dt = -32t\,\vec{k} + \vec{C}$; $\vec{r}(t) = \int \vec{v}(t)\,dt = \int (-32t\,\vec{k} + \vec{C})\,dt$ $= -16t^2\,\vec{k} + \vec{C}t + \vec{C}_1$. Since $\vec{v}(0) = \vec{v}_0 = \vec{0}$, we have $\vec{C} = \vec{0}$, so that $\vec{v}(t)$ $= -32t\,\vec{k}$. Since $\vec{r}(0) = \vec{r}_0 = \vec{0}$, we have $\vec{C}_1 = \vec{0}$, so that $\vec{r}(t) = -16t^2\,\vec{k}$. Finally, $\|\vec{v}(t)\| = 32|t|$.

29. As in Exercise 28, $\vec{v}(t) = -32t\,\vec{k} + \vec{C}$ and $\vec{r}(t) = -16t^2\,\vec{k} + \vec{C}t + \vec{C}_1$. Since $\vec{v}(0) = \vec{v}_0 = \vec{i} + \vec{j}$, we have $\vec{C} = \vec{i} + \vec{j}$, so that $\vec{v}(t) = \vec{i} + \vec{j} - 32t\,\vec{k}$. Since $\vec{r}(0) = \vec{r}_0 = 0$, we have $\vec{C}_1 = 0$, so that $\vec{r}(t) = t\,\vec{i} + t\,\vec{j} - 16t^2\,\vec{k}$. Finally, $\|\vec{v}(t)\| = \sqrt{1 + 1 + (-32t)^2} = \sqrt{2 + 1024t^2}$.

30. As in Exercise 28, $\vec{v}(t) = -32t\,\vec{k} + \vec{C}$ and $\vec{r}(t) = -16t^2\,\vec{k} + \vec{C}t + \vec{C}_1$. Since $\vec{v}(0) = \vec{v}_0 = 3\,\vec{i} - 2\,\vec{j} + \vec{k}$, we have $\vec{C} = 3\,\vec{i} - 2\,\vec{j} + \vec{k}$, so that $\vec{v}(t) = 3\,\vec{i} - 2\,\vec{j} + (1 - 32t)\,\vec{k}$. Since $\vec{r}(0) = \vec{r}_0 = 5\,\vec{j} + 2\,\vec{k}$, we have $\vec{C}_1 = 5\,\vec{j} + 2\vec{k}$, so that $\vec{r}(t) = -16t^2\,\vec{k} + (3\,\vec{i} - 2\,\vec{j} + \vec{k})\,t + 5\,\vec{j} + 2\,\vec{k} = 3t\,\vec{i} + (5 - 2t)\,\vec{j} + (2 + t - 16t^2)\,\vec{k}$. Finally, $\|\vec{v}(t)\| = \sqrt{9 + 4 + (1 - 64t + 1024t^2)}$ $= \sqrt{14 - 64t + 1024t^2}$.

31. $\vec{v}(t) = \int \vec{a}(t)\,dt = \int(-\cos t\,\vec{i} - \sin t\,\vec{j})\,dt = -\sin t\,\vec{i} + \cos t\,\vec{j} + \vec{C}$; $\vec{r}(t)$ $= \int \vec{v}(t)\,dt = \int(-\sin t\,\vec{i} + \cos t\,\vec{j} + \vec{C})\,dt = \cos t\,\vec{i} + \sin t\,\vec{j} + \vec{C}t + \vec{C}_1$. Since $\vec{v}(0) = \vec{v}_0 = \vec{k}$, we have $\vec{k} = -\sin 0\,\vec{i} + \cos 0\,\vec{j} + \vec{C} = \vec{j} + \vec{C}$, so that $\vec{C} = \vec{k} - \vec{j}$, and thus $\vec{v}(t) = -\sin t\,\vec{i} + (\cos t - 1)\,\vec{j} + \vec{k}$. Since $\vec{r}(0)$ $= \vec{r}_0 = \vec{i}$, we have $\vec{i} = \cos 0\,\vec{i} + \sin 0\,\vec{j} + (\vec{k} - \vec{j})\,0 + \vec{C}_1 = \vec{i} + \vec{C}_1$, so that $\vec{C}_1 = \vec{0}$, and thus $\vec{r}(t) = \cos t\,\vec{i} + \sin t\,\vec{j} + t\,(\vec{k} - \vec{j}) = \cos t\,\vec{i} + (\sin t - t)\,\vec{j} + t\,\vec{k}$. Finally, $\|\vec{v}(t)\| = \sqrt{\sin^2 t + (\cos t - 1)^2 + 1} = \sqrt{3 - 2\cos t}$.

32. $\vec{v}(t) = \int \vec{a}(t)\,dt = \int(e^t\,\vec{i} + e^{-t}\,\vec{j})\,dt = e^t\,\vec{i} - e^{-t}\,\vec{j} + \vec{C}$; $\vec{r}(t) = \int \vec{v}(t)\,dt$ $= \int(e^t\,\vec{i} - e^{-t}\,\vec{j} + \vec{C})\,dt = e^t\,\vec{i} + e^{-t}\,\vec{j} + \vec{C}t + \vec{C}_1$. Since $\vec{v}(0) = \vec{v}_0 = \vec{i} - \vec{j} + \sqrt{2}\,\vec{k}$, we have $\vec{i} - \vec{j} + \sqrt{2}\,\vec{k} = e^0\,\vec{i} - e^{-0}\,\vec{j} + \vec{C} = \vec{i} - \vec{j} + \vec{C}$, so that $\vec{C} = \sqrt{2}\,\vec{k}$, and thus $\vec{v}(t) = e^t\,\vec{i} - e^{-t}\,\vec{j} + \sqrt{2}\,\vec{k}$. Since $\vec{r}(0) = \vec{r}_0 = \vec{i} + \vec{j}$, we have $\vec{i} + \vec{j} = e^0\,\vec{i} + e^{-0}\,\vec{j} + \sqrt{2}\,(0)\,\vec{k} + \vec{C}_1 = \vec{i} + \vec{j} + \vec{C}_1$, so that $\vec{C}_1$ $= \vec{0}$, and thus $\vec{r}(t) = e^t\,\vec{i} + e^{-t}\,\vec{j} + t\,(\sqrt{2}\,\vec{k}) + \vec{0} = e^t\,\vec{i} + e^{-t}\,\vec{j} + \sqrt{2}\,t\,\vec{k}$. Finally, $\|\vec{v}(t)\| = \sqrt{e^{2t} + e^{-2t} + 2} = e^t + e^{-t}$.

33. $\vec{F}(t) = (\int_0^t u\tan u^3\,du)\,\vec{i} + (\int_0^t \cos e^u\,du)\,\vec{j} + (\int_0^t e^{(u^2)}\,du)\,\vec{k}$, and thus $\vec{F}'(t) = t\tan t^3\,\vec{i} + \cos e^t\,\vec{j} + e^{(t^2)}\,\vec{k}$.

34. $\vec{G}(t) = (\int_0^{t^2} \cos u\,du)\,\vec{i} + (\int_0^{t^2} e^{-(u^2)}du)\,\vec{j} + (\int_0^{t^2} \tan u\,du)\,\vec{k}$, so that $\vec{G}'(t) = (\cos t^2)(2t)\,\vec{i} + (e^{-t^4})(2t)\,\vec{j} + (\tan t^2)(2t)\,\vec{k}$

35. $\|\vec{F}(t)\| = \sqrt{\dfrac{16t^2}{(1 + 4t^2)^2} + \dfrac{1 - 8t^2 + 16t^4}{(1 + 4t^2)^2}} = \sqrt{\dfrac{(1 + 4t^2)^2}{(1 + 4t^2)^2}} = 1$, so that by Corollary 12.11, $\vec{F}(t)\cdot\vec{F}'(t) = 0$ for all t.

36. $\vec{F}'(t) = -\sin t\,\vec{i} + \cos t\,\vec{j}$ and $\dfrac{\vec{F}(\pi) - \vec{F}(0)}{\pi - 0} = \dfrac{-\vec{i} - \vec{i}}{\pi - 0} = \dfrac{-2}{\pi}\,\vec{i}$. Now $\vec{F}'(\frac{\pi}{2})$ $= -\vec{i}$, so that $\vec{F}'(\frac{\pi}{2})$ is parallel to $\dfrac{\vec{F}(\pi) - \vec{F}(0)}{\pi - 0}$. But for any other value of t in $(0, \pi)$ the $\vec{j}$ component of $\vec{F}'(t)$ is nonzero, and hence $\vec{F}'(t)$ $\nparallel \dfrac{\vec{F}(\pi) - \vec{F}(0)}{\pi - 0}$. Consequently there is no value of t in $(0, \pi)$ such that $\vec{F}'(t) = \dfrac{\vec{F}(\pi) - \vec{F}(0)}{\pi - 0}$.

37. $\vec{F}'(t) = \cos t\,\vec{i} + \sin t\,\vec{j}$ and $\vec{F}''(t) = -\sin t\,\vec{i} + \cos t\,\vec{j} = -\vec{F}(t)$. Since $\|\vec{F}(t)\| = \|\vec{F}''(t)\| = 1$, it follows that $\vec{F}(t)$ and $\vec{F}''(t)$ are parallel but have opposite, and hence dissimilar, directions, for all t.

38. $\vec{F}'(t) = -2e^{-2t}\,\vec{i} + 2e^{2t}\,\vec{k}$ and $\vec{F}''(t) = 4e^{-2t}\,\vec{i} + 4e^{2t}\,\vec{k} = 4\vec{F}(t)$. Since $\|\vec{F}(t)\| = \sqrt{e^{-4t} + e^{4t}} \neq 0$, it follows that $\vec{F}(t)$ and $\vec{F}''(t)$ are not only parallel but have the same direction for all t.

39. By Theorem 12.10(e), $\frac{d}{dt}(\vec{F} \times \vec{F}')(t) = [\vec{F}'(t) \times \vec{F}'(t)] + [\vec{F}(t) \times \vec{F}''(t)]$ $= \vec{F}(t) \times \vec{F}''(t)$.

40. If $\vec{F}(t)$ is parallel to $\vec{F}''(t)$ for all t, then there is a constant c such that $\vec{F}''(t) = c\vec{F}(t)$ for all t. Then by Exercise 39 and properties of cross products, $\frac{d}{dt}(\vec{F} \times \vec{F}')(t) = \vec{F}(t) \times \vec{F}''(t) = c(\vec{F}(t) \times \vec{F}(t)) = \vec{0}$, so that by integration, $(\vec{F} \times \vec{F}')(t) = \vec{C}$ for some constant vector $\vec{C}$.

41. By using Theorem 12.10(d) and then Theorem 12.10(e), we find that

$$\frac{d}{dt}\left[\vec{F} \cdot (\vec{G} \times \vec{H})\right] = \frac{d\vec{F}}{dt} \cdot (\vec{G} \times \vec{H}) + \vec{F} \cdot \frac{d}{dt}(\vec{G} \times \vec{H}) = \frac{d\vec{F}}{dt} \cdot (\vec{G} \times \vec{H}) + \vec{F} \cdot \left[\left(\frac{d\vec{G}}{dt} \times \vec{H}\right) + \left(\vec{G} \times \frac{d\vec{H}}{dt}\right)\right] = \frac{d\vec{F}}{dt} \cdot (\vec{G} \times \vec{H}) + \vec{F} \cdot \left(\frac{d\vec{G}}{dt} \times \vec{H}\right) + \vec{F} \cdot \left(\vec{G} \times \frac{d\vec{H}}{dt}\right).$$

42. Let $K_1(t)$ and $K_2(t)$ be the kinetic energies of the mass at any time t during its first and second journeys, respectively. By Example 10, the first time the position is given by $\vec{r}_1(t) = (-16t^2 + 96)\,\vec{k}$, so that $\vec{r}_1(\sqrt{6}) = \vec{0}$, and thus the ball hits the ground when $t = \sqrt{6}$. Since $\vec{v}_1(t) = -32t\,\vec{k}$, and $K_1(t) = \frac{1}{2} m \|\vec{v}_1(t)\|^2$, we therefore have $K_1(\sqrt{6}) = \frac{1}{2} m \left| -32(\sqrt{6}) \right|^2 = 3072\text{ m}$. The second time the position is given by $\vec{r}_2(t) = (-16t^2 - 80t + 96)\,\vec{k} = -16(t^2 + 5t - 6)\,\vec{k} = -16(t + 6)(t - 1)\,\vec{k}$, so that $\vec{r}_2(1) = \vec{0}$, and thus the ball hits the ground when $t = 1$. Since $\vec{v}_2(t) = (-32t - 80)\,\vec{k}$, and $K_2(t) = \frac{1}{2} m \|\vec{v}_2(t)\|^2$, we have $K_2(1) = \frac{1}{2} m\,|-32 - 80|^2 = 6272\text{ m}$. Consequently $K_2(1) - K_1(\sqrt{6}) = 6272\text{ m} - 3072\text{ m} = 3200\text{ m}$, and this is how much larger the kinetic energy is at impact the second time.

43. a. Initial position: $\vec{r}_0 = \vec{0}$; velocity: $\vec{v}(t) = 90\sqrt{2}\,\vec{i} + 90\sqrt{2}\,\vec{j} + (64 - 32t)\,\vec{k}$; initial velocity: $\vec{v}_0 = 90\sqrt{2}\,\vec{i} + 90\sqrt{2}\,\vec{j} + 64\,\vec{k}$

b. $\vec{r}(4) = 360\sqrt{2}\,\vec{i} + 360\sqrt{2}\,\vec{j} + 0\,\vec{k}$, so the height is 0 when $t = 4$; distance from initial position: $\|\vec{r}(4) - \vec{r}(0)\| = \|360\sqrt{2}\,\vec{i} + 360\sqrt{2}\,\vec{j}\|$ $= 720$ (feet).

44. By Example 10 with $g = 32$, we have $\vec{r}(t) = -16t^2\,\vec{k} + t\vec{v}_0 + \vec{r}_0$. By hypothesis, $\vec{v}_0 = 2\,\vec{i} + 3\,\vec{k}$ and $\vec{r}_0 = \vec{k}$. Thus $\vec{r}(t) = -16t^2\,\vec{k} + t(2\,\vec{i} + 3\,\vec{k}) + \vec{k} = 2t\,\vec{i} + (1 + 3t - 16t^2)\,\vec{k}$.

45. Place the coordinate system so that the floor represents the xy plane and the ball rolls on a line directly above the negative x axis towards the edge, located at the point $(0, 0, 2.6)$. Then by Example 10, the position of the ball t seconds after it leaves the table is given by $\vec{r}(t) = -16t^2\,\vec{k} + t\vec{v}_0 + \vec{r}_0$. By assumption, $\vec{v}_0 = 2\,\vec{i}$ and $\vec{r}_0 = 2.6k$. Thus $\vec{r}(t) = -16t^2\,\vec{k} + 2t\,\vec{i} + 2.6\,\vec{k} = 2t\,\vec{i} + (2.6 - 16t^2)\,\vec{k}$.

a. The $\vec{k}$ component of $\vec{r}(t)$ is 0 if $2.6 = 16t^2$, or $t = \frac{\sqrt{2.6}}{4} \approx .403113$. Thus the ball hits the floor after approximately .403113 seconds.

b. $\vec{v}(t) = 2\,\vec{i} - 32t\,\vec{k}$, so that $\left\|\vec{v}\left(\frac{\sqrt{2.6}}{4}\right)\right\| = \left\|2\,\vec{i} - 32\left(\frac{\sqrt{2.6}}{4}\right)\vec{k}\right\|$ $= \sqrt{4 + 166.4} = \sqrt{170.4} \approx 13.0537$ (feet per second).

c. It would hit at the same time, because the $\vec{k}$ component of the position would be unchanged.

46. By (4) and the comments following it, the speed of the satellite and the radius of the orbit are related by $\frac{v_0^2}{r} \approx 32$, where the units are feet and seconds. A speed of 17,725 miles per hour equals $17{,}725 \times \frac{5280}{3600}$ feet per second. Thus $r \approx \frac{v_0^2}{32} = \frac{1}{32}\left(17{,}725 \times \frac{5280}{3600}\right)^2 \approx 21{,}119{,}583$ (feet), or 3999.92 (miles).

47. As in Exercise 46, $\frac{v_0^2}{r} \approx 32$. Since 4200 miles equals 22,176,000 feet, we find that $v_0 \approx \sqrt{32r} = \sqrt{(32)(22{,}176{,}000)} \approx 26{,}638.9$ (feet per second), or 18,162.9 (miles per hour).

48. The bobsled moves $60(\frac{5280}{3600})$ feet per second, so by (4), $\|\vec{a}(t)\| = \frac{v_0^2}{r}$

$= \frac{[60(\frac{5280}{3600})]^2}{100} = 77.44$ (feet per second per second).

49. a. By (4), $\|\vec{a}(t)\| = \frac{[(2.5) \times 10^5]^2}{1} = 6.25 \times 10^{10}$ (kilometers per second per second).

b. By (4), $\|\vec{a}(t)\| = \frac{[(2.9) \times 10^5]^2}{1} = 8.41 \times 10^{10}$ (kilometers per second per second).

Section 12.4

1. $\vec{r}'(t) = \vec{i} + 2t\,\vec{j} + 3t^2\,\vec{k}$; $\vec{r}'$ is continuous and is never $\vec{0}$, so $\vec{r}$ is smooth.

2. $\vec{r}'(t) = \vec{i} + \vec{j} + \vec{k}$; $\vec{r}'$ is constant and nonzero, so $\vec{r}$ is smooth.

3. $\vec{r}'(t) = \begin{cases} -\vec{i} + \vec{j} + \vec{k} & \text{for } t < 0 \\ \vec{i} + \vec{j} + \vec{k} & \text{for } t > 0 \end{cases}$, so $\vec{r}'$ is continuous and nonzero on $(-\infty, 0)$ and on $(0, \infty)$. Since the one-sided derivatives at 0 are $-\vec{i} + \vec{j} + \vec{k}$ and $\vec{i} + \vec{j} + \vec{k}$ respectively, we conclude that $\vec{r}$ is piecewise smooth but not smooth.

4. $\vec{r}'(t) = \frac{2}{3}t^{-1/3}\vec{i} + \vec{j} + 2t\vec{k}$. Since $\vec{r}'(0)$ does not exist, $\vec{r}$ is neither smooth nor piecewise smooth.

5. $\vec{r}'(t) = \frac{3}{2}(1 + t)^{1/2}\,\vec{i} - \frac{3}{2}(1 - t)^{1/2}\,\vec{j} + \frac{3}{2}\vec{k}$ for $-1 < t < 1$, and the one-sided derivatives exist and make $\vec{r}'$ continuous and nonzero on $[-1, 1]$. Thus $\vec{r}$ is smooth.

6. $\vec{r}'(t) = \cos t\,\vec{i} - \sin t\,\vec{j} + 2t\,\vec{k}$, and $\|\vec{r}'(t)\| = \sqrt{\cos^2 t + \sin^2 t + 4t^2} = \sqrt{1 + 4t^2} > 0$ for all t. Thus $\vec{r}'$ is continuous and nonzero, so $\vec{r}$ is smooth.

7. $\vec{r}'(t) = -2\cos t \sin t\,\vec{i} + 2\sin t \cos t\,\vec{j} + 2t\,\vec{k}$; $\vec{r}$ is continuous and $\vec{r}'(t) = \vec{0}$ only if $t = 0$. Thus $\vec{r}$ is piecewise smooth.

8. $\vec{r}'(t) = e^t\,\vec{i} - e^{-t}\,\vec{j} + 2\,\vec{k}$; $\vec{r}'$ is continuous and is never zero, so $\vec{r}$ is smooth.

9. $\vec{r}'(t) = (e^t - 1)\,\vec{i} + 2t\,\vec{j} + 3t^2\,\vec{k}$; $\vec{r}'$ is continuous and $\vec{r}'(t) = \vec{0}$ only if $t = 0$. Thus $\vec{r}$ is piecewise smooth.

10. $\vec{r}'(t) = 2\,\vec{i} + 2t\,\vec{j} + \frac{1}{t}\vec{k}$; $\vec{r}'$ is continuous on $(0, \infty)$ and is never zero, so $\vec{r}$ is smooth.

11. The line segment is parallel to $7\,\vec{i} - 2\,\vec{j} + 4\,\vec{k}$ and starts at $(-3, 2, 1)$. Thus a parameterization is $\vec{r}(t) = (-3 + 7t)\,\vec{i} + (2 - 2t)\,\vec{j} + (1 + 4t)\,\vec{k}$ for $0 \le t \le 1$, and $\vec{r}$ is smooth.

12. The line segment is parallel to $6\vec{i} - \frac{5}{2}\vec{j}$ and starts at $(0, 3, -2)$. Thus a parameterization is $\vec{r}(t) = 6t\,\vec{i} + (3 - \frac{5}{2}t)\,\vec{j} - 2\,\vec{k}$ for $0 \le t \le 1$, and $\vec{r}$ is smooth.

13. $\vec{r}(t) = 6\cos t\,\vec{i} + 6\sin t\,\vec{j}$ for $0 \le t \le 2\pi$ is one such smooth parameterization.

14. $\vec{r}(t) = (2\vec{i} + 4\vec{j} - \vec{k}) + \frac{5}{2}(\cos t\,\vec{i} + \sin t\,\vec{j}) = (2 + \frac{5}{2}\cos t)\,\vec{i} + (4 + \frac{5}{2}\sin t)\,\vec{j} - \vec{k}$ for $0 \le t \le 2\pi$ is one such smooth parameterization.

15. $\vec{r}(t) = \cos t\,\vec{i} + \sin t\,\vec{j}$ for $0 \le t \le \pi$ is one such smooth parameterization.

16. $\vec{r}(t) = \cos t\,\vec{i} - \sin t\,\vec{j}$ for $0 \le t \le \frac{\pi}{2}$ is one such smooth parameterization.

17. Notice that the quarter circle in the xy plane that extends from $(\sqrt{2}/2, \sqrt{2}/2)$ to $(\sqrt{2}/2, -\sqrt{2}/2)$ corresponds to the quarter circle from $(1, \frac{\pi}{4})$ to $(1, \frac{-\pi}{4})$ in polar coordinates. This leads us to $\vec{r}(t) = \cos t\,\vec{i} - \sin t\,\vec{j} + 4\,\vec{k}$ for $\frac{-\pi}{4} \le t \le \frac{\pi}{4}$, which is smooth.

18. $\vec{r}(t) = t\,\vec{i} + (t^2 + 1)\,\vec{j}$ is one such smooth parameterization.

19. $\vec{r}(t) = t\,\vec{i} + \tan t\,\vec{j}$ for $0 \le t \le \pi/4$ is one such smooth parameterization.

20. $\vec{r}(t) = t\,\vec{i} + (t^5 - t^2 + 5)\,\vec{j}$ for $-1 \le t \le 0$ is one such smooth parameterization.

21. $\vec{r}(t) = \begin{cases} 3t\,\vec{i} & \text{for } 0 \le t \le 1 \\ 3\,\vec{i} + 3(t - 1)\,\vec{j} & \text{for } 1 \le t \le 2 \\ 3(3 - t)\,\vec{i} + 3\,\vec{j} & \text{for } 2 \le t \le 3 \\ 3(4 - t)\,\vec{j} & \text{for } 3 \le t \le 4 \end{cases}$ is a piecewise smooth parameterization of the square, beginning with the vertex $(0, 0)$, and passing in turn through $(3, 0)$, $(3, 3)$, and $(0, 3)$, and ending with $(0, 0)$.

22. $\vec{r}(t) = \begin{cases} 2t\,\vec{i} & \text{for } 0 \le t \le 1 \\ 2(2 - t)\,\vec{i} + 2(t - 1)\,\vec{j} & \text{for } 1 \le t \le 2 \\ 2(3 - t)\,\vec{j} & \text{for } 2 \le t \le 3 \end{cases}$ is a piecewise smooth parameterization of the triangle, beginning with the vertex $(0, 0)$, and passing in turn through $(2, 0)$ and $(0, 2)$, and ending with $(0, 0)$.

23. $\vec{r}(t) = \begin{cases} 2t\,\vec{j} + (1 + 2t)\,\vec{k} & \text{for } 0 \le t \le 1 \\ 3(t - 1)\,\vec{i} + 2(2 - t)\,\vec{j} + (2 + t)\,\vec{k} & \text{for } 1 \le t \le 2 \end{cases}$ is a piecewise smooth parameterization of the polygonal line.

24. $\vec{r}(t) = \begin{cases} t\,\vec{i} + 2t\,\vec{j} & \text{for } 0 \le t \le 1 \\ \vec{i} + 2\,\vec{j} + (t - 1)\,\vec{k} & \text{for } 1 \le t \le 2 \\ (2t - 3)\,\vec{i} + (8 - 3t)\,\vec{j} + (t - 1)\,\vec{k} & \text{for } 2 \le t \le 3 \end{cases}$ is a piecewise smooth parameterization of the polygonal line.

25. $\mathcal{L} = \int_0^{2\pi} \sqrt{[3\cos^2 t\,(-\sin t)]^2 + [3\sin^2 t\cos t]^2}\,dt = \int_0^{2\pi} 3|\sin t\cos t|\,dt$
$= 12\int_0^{\pi/2} \sin t\cos t\,dt = 6\sin^2 t\,\Big|_0^{\pi/2} = 6$

26. $\mathcal{L} = \int_1^2 \sqrt{4 + 4t^2 + \frac{1}{t^2}}\,dt = \int_1^2 (2t + \frac{1}{t})\,dt = (t^2 + \ln t)\Big|_1^2 = 3 + \ln 2$

27. $\mathcal{L} = \int_{-1}^1 \sqrt{\frac{1}{4}(1 + t) + \frac{1}{4}(1 - t) + \frac{1}{4}}\,dt = \int_{-1}^1 \frac{1}{2}\sqrt{3}\,dt = \frac{1}{2}\sqrt{3}t\,\Big|_{-1}^1 = \sqrt{3}$

28. $\mathcal{L} = \int_0^1 \sqrt{\sinh^2 t + \cosh^2 t + 1}\,dt = \int_0^1 \sqrt{2\cosh^2 t}\,dt = \sqrt{2}\int_0^1 \cosh t\,dt$
$= \sqrt{2}\sinh t\,\Big|_0^1 = \sqrt{2}\sinh 1 = \frac{\sqrt{2}}{2}(e - e^{-1})$

29. $\mathcal{L} = \int_0^1 \sqrt{e^{2t} + e^{-2t} + 2}\,dt = \int_0^1 \sqrt{(e^t + e^{-t})^2}\,dt = \int_0^1 (e^t + e^{-t})\,dt$
$= (e^t - e^{-t})\,\Big|_0^1 = e - e^{-1}$

30. $\mathcal{L} = \int_0^{20/3} \sqrt{\sin^2 t + \cos^2 t + \frac{9}{4}t}\,dt = \int_0^{20/3} \sqrt{1 + \frac{9}{4}t}\,dt$
$= \frac{8}{27}(1 + \frac{9}{4}t)^{3/2}\,\Big|_0^{20/3} = \frac{56}{3}$

31. $\mathcal{L} = \int_0^{\sqrt{8}} \sqrt{[36t^2(t^2 - 1)] + 36t^2 + 36t^2}\,dt = \int_0^{\sqrt{8}} 6\sqrt{t^4 + t^2}\,dt$
$= \int_0^{\sqrt{8}} 6t\sqrt{t^2 + 1}\,dt = 2(t^2 + 1)^{3/2}\,\Big|_0^{\sqrt{8}} = 52$

32. $\mathcal{L} = \int_0^1 \sqrt{(9 - 18t^2 + 9t^4) + 36t^2 + (9 + 18t^2 + 9t^4)}\,dt$
$= \int_0^1 \sqrt{18(1 + 2t^2 + t^4)}\,dt = \int_0^1 3\sqrt{2}(1 + t^2)\,dt = 3\sqrt{2}(t + \frac{t^3}{3})\,\Big|_0^1$
$= 4\sqrt{2}$

33. $\frac{ds}{dt} = \sqrt{4\cos^2 2t + 4\sin^2 2t + t} = \sqrt{4 + t}$

34. $\frac{ds}{dt} = \sqrt{t^4 + 2t^2 + 1} = t^2 + 1$

35. $\frac{ds}{dt} = \sqrt{(\cos t - t\sin t)^2 + (\sin t + t\cos t)^2 + 1}$

$= \sqrt{\cos^2 t + \sin^2 t + t^2(\sin^2 t + \cos^2 t) + 1} = \sqrt{2 + t^2}$

36. $\frac{ds}{dt} = \sqrt{4 + 4t^2 + t^4} = 2 + t^2$

37. $\frac{ds}{dt} = \sqrt{(1 - \cos t)^2 + \sin^2 t + 1} = \sqrt{3 - 2\cos t}$

38. $\mathcal{L} = \int_{-\pi/2}^{\pi/2} \sqrt{(a\cos\theta)^2 + (-a\sin\theta)^2}\,d\theta = a\int_{-\pi/2}^{\pi/2} 1\,d\theta = \pi a$

39. $\mathcal{L} = \int_0^{\pi} \sqrt{(a\sin\theta)^2 + (a\cos\theta)^2}\,d\theta = a\int_0^{\pi} 1\,d\theta = \pi a$

40. $\mathcal{L} = \int_0^1 \sqrt{\theta^2 + 1}\,d\theta \overset{\theta = \tan u}{=} \int_0^{\pi/4} \sqrt{\tan^2 u + 1}\,\sec^2 u\,du = \int_0^{\pi/4} \sec^3 u\,du$

$= (\frac{1}{2}\sec u\tan u + \frac{1}{2}\ln|\sec u + \tan u|)\Big|_0^{\pi/4} = \frac{1}{2}\sqrt{2}, + \frac{1}{2}\ln(\sqrt{2} + 1)$

41. $\mathcal{L} = \int_{-1}^{1} \sqrt{\cos^2 t + \sin^2 t + t^4}\,dt = \int_{-1}^{1} \sqrt{1 + t^4}\,dt \approx \frac{2}{12}\left[\sqrt{2} + 4\sqrt{\frac{17}{16}}\right.$

$\left. + 2\cdot 1 + 4\sqrt{\frac{17}{16}} + \sqrt{2}\right] \approx 2.17911$

42. $\mathcal{L} = \int_0^2 \sqrt{4\sin^2 2t + 4\cos^2 2t + 4t^3}\,dt = 2\int_0^2 \sqrt{1 + t^3}\,dt \approx \frac{4}{12}\left[1 + 4\sqrt{\frac{9}{8}}\right.$

$\left. + 2\sqrt{2} + 4\sqrt{\frac{35}{8}} + 3\right] \approx 6.47922$

43. $\mathcal{L} = \int_{-1}^{1} \sqrt{1 + 4t^2 + 9t^4}\,dt \approx \frac{2}{12}\left[\sqrt{14} + 4\sqrt{\frac{41}{16}} + 2\cdot 1 + 4\sqrt{\frac{41}{16}} + \sqrt{14}\right] \approx 3.71493$

44. By (7) the arc length function is given by

$s(t) = \int_0^t \sqrt{[r(1 - \cos u)]^2 + (r\sin u)^2}\,du$

$= r\int_0^t \sqrt{2 - 2\cos u}\,du$ for $0 \le t \le 2\pi$

45. $\|\vec{r}(t)\| = \sqrt{\frac{(1 - t^2)^2}{(1 + t^2)^2} + \frac{4t^2}{(1 + t^2)^2}} = 1$ for all t, so $\vec{r}$ parameterizes a portion of the circle $x^2 + y^2 = 1$. Let $f_1(t)$ denote the $\vec{i}$ component of $\vec{r}$. Since $f_1(0) = 1$ and $\lim_{t\to-\infty} f_1(t) = \lim_{t\to\infty} f_1(t) = -1$, we conclude from the Intermediate Value Theorem that f_1 takes all values in the interval $(-1, 1]$. Since the $\vec{j}$ component of $\vec{r}$ is positive for $t > 0$ and negative for $t < 0$, it follows that $\vec{r}$ parameterizes all the points on the circle between $(1, 0)$ and $(-1, 0)$. Finally, $(-1, 0)$ is not included in the parameterization since $\frac{1 - t^2}{1 + t^2} \ne -1$ for all t and hence $\vec{r}(t) \ne -\vec{i}$ for all t.

46. Since $(\frac{t^2 + 1}{t^2 - 1})^2 - (\frac{2t}{t^2 - 1})^2 = \frac{(t^2 - 1)^2}{(t^2 - 1)^2} = 1$ for all $t \ne \pm 1$, it follows that $\vec{r}$ parameterizes a portion of the hyperbola $x^2 - y^2 = 1$. Notice that $\vec{r}(0) = -\vec{i}$, $\lim_{t\to-\infty} \vec{r}(t) = \vec{i}$, $\lim_{t\to\infty} \vec{r}(t) = \vec{i}$,

$\lim_{t\to -1^-} \|\vec{r}(t)\| = \lim_{t\to -1^+} \|\vec{r}(t)\| = \lim_{t\to 1^-} \|\vec{r}(t)\|$

$= \lim_{t\to 1^+} \|\vec{r}(t)\| = \infty$. Also, the $\vec{i}$ component of $\vec{r}(t)$ is positive if and only if $|t| > 1$, and the $\vec{j}$ component of $\vec{r}(t)$ is positive if and only if $-1 < t < 0$ or $t > 1$. These observations, along with 4 applications of the Intermediate Value Theorem (one for each quadrant), imply that $\vec{r}$ parameterizes all points on the hyperbola $x^2 - y^2 = 1$ except $(1, 0)$, which is not included because $\frac{t^2 + 1}{t^2 - 1} \ne 1$ for all t, and hence $\vec{r}(t) \ne \vec{i}$ for all t. The figure to the right indicates which portions of the hyperbola are parameterized for various values of t.

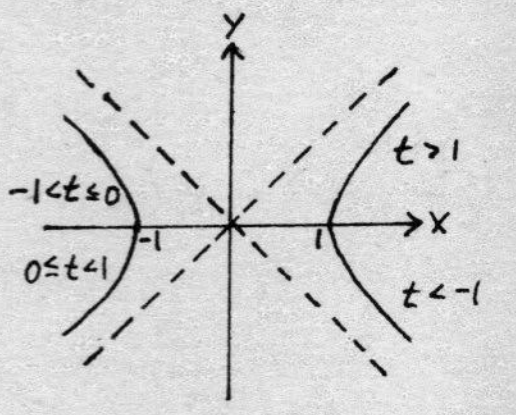

47. a. Assume that the radius of the circle is $r > 0$. Then $n = 8$ and $d = 2r$. Thus $\frac{\pi n d}{8} = \frac{\pi(8)(2r)}{8} = 2\pi r$ = circumference $\mathcal{L}$ of the circle.

b. $n = 18$, $d = \frac{1}{3}$, so $\mathcal{L} \approx \frac{\pi(18)(\frac{1}{3})}{8} = \frac{3\pi}{4} \approx 2.35619$

Section 12.5

1. $\vec{r}'(t) = 2t\,\vec{i} + 2\,\vec{j}$; $\|\vec{r}'(t)\| = \sqrt{(2t)^2 + 2^2} = 2\sqrt{t^2+1}$; $\vec{T}(t) = \dfrac{\vec{r}'(t)}{\|\vec{r}'(t)\|}$

$= \dfrac{2t\,\vec{i} + 2\,\vec{j}}{2\sqrt{t^2+1}} = \dfrac{t}{\sqrt{t^2+1}}\,\vec{i} + \dfrac{1}{\sqrt{t^2+1}}\,\vec{j}$; $\vec{T}'(t)$

$= \dfrac{\sqrt{t^2+1} - \dfrac{t^2}{\sqrt{t^2+1}}}{t^2+1}\,\vec{i} - \dfrac{t}{(t^2+1)^{3/2}}\,\vec{j} = \dfrac{1}{(t^2+1)^{3/2}}\,\vec{i} - \dfrac{t}{(t^2+1)^{3/2}}\,\vec{j}$;

$\|\vec{T}'(t)\| = \sqrt{\dfrac{1}{(t^2+1)^3} + \dfrac{t^2}{(t^2+1)^3}} = \dfrac{1}{t^2+1}$; $\vec{N}(t) = \dfrac{\vec{T}'(t)}{\|\vec{T}'(t)\|} = \dfrac{1}{\sqrt{t^2+1}}\,\vec{i}$

$- \dfrac{t}{\sqrt{t^2+1}}\,\vec{j}$; $\kappa(t) = \dfrac{\|\vec{T}'(t)\|}{\|\vec{r}'(t)\|} = \dfrac{\dfrac{1}{t^2+1}}{2\sqrt{t^2+1}} = \dfrac{1}{2(t^2+1)^{3/2}}$

2. $\vec{r}'(t) = 3\cos^2 t\,(-\sin t)\,\vec{i} + 3\sin^2 t\cos t\,\vec{j} = -3\sin t\cos^2 t\,\vec{i}$

$+ 3\sin^2 t\cos t\,\vec{j}$; $\|\vec{r}'(t)\| = 3\sin t\cos t\sqrt{(-\cos t)^2 + (\sin t)^2}$

$= 3\sin t\cos t$; $\vec{T}(t) = \dfrac{\vec{r}'(t)}{\|\vec{r}'(t)\|} = -\cos t\,\vec{i} + \sin t\,\vec{j}$; $\vec{T}'(t) = \sin t\,\vec{i}$

$+ \cos t\,\vec{j}$; $\|\vec{T}'(t)\| = \sqrt{\sin^2 t + \cos^2 t} = 1$; $\vec{N}(t) = \dfrac{\vec{T}'(t)}{\|\vec{T}'(t)\|} = \sin t\,\vec{i}$

$+ \cos t\,\vec{j}$; $\kappa(t) = \dfrac{\|\vec{T}'(t)\|}{\|\vec{r}'(t)\|} = \dfrac{1}{3\sin t\cos t}$

3. $\vec{r}'(t) = -\sin t\,\vec{i} - \sin t\,\vec{j} + \sqrt{2}\cos t\,\vec{k}$; $\|\vec{r}'(t)\|$

$= \sqrt{(-\sin t)^2 + (-\sin t)^2 + (\sqrt{2}\cos t)^2} = \sqrt{2}$; $\vec{T}(t) = \dfrac{\vec{r}'(t)}{\|\vec{r}'(t)\|}$

$= -\dfrac{\sin t}{\sqrt{2}}\,\vec{i} - \dfrac{\sin t}{\sqrt{2}}\,\vec{j} + \cos t\,\vec{k}$; $\vec{T}'(t) = -\dfrac{\cos t}{\sqrt{2}}\,\vec{i} - \dfrac{\cos t}{\sqrt{2}}\,\vec{j} - \sin t\,\vec{k}$;

$\|\vec{T}'(t)\| = \sqrt{\left(\dfrac{-\cos t}{\sqrt{2}}\right)^2 + \left(\dfrac{-\cos t}{\sqrt{2}}\right)^2 + (-\sin t)^2} = 1$; $\vec{N}(t) = \dfrac{\vec{T}'(t)}{\|\vec{T}'(t)\|}$

$= -\dfrac{\cos t}{\sqrt{2}}\,\vec{i} - \dfrac{\cos t}{\sqrt{2}}\,\vec{j} - \sin t\,\vec{k}$; $\kappa(t) = \dfrac{\|\vec{T}'(t)\|}{\|\vec{r}'(t)\|} = \dfrac{1}{\sqrt{2}}$

4. $\vec{r}'(t) = \dfrac{1}{2}(1+t)^{1/2}\,\vec{i} - \dfrac{1}{2}(1-t)^{1/2}\,\vec{j} + \dfrac{\sqrt{2}}{2}\,\vec{k}$; $\|\vec{r}'(t)\|$

$= \dfrac{1}{2}\sqrt{(1+t) + (1-t) + 2} = 1$; $\vec{T}(t) = \dfrac{\vec{r}'(t)}{\|\vec{r}'(t)\|} = \dfrac{1}{2}(1+t)^{1/2}\,\vec{i}$

$- \dfrac{1}{2}(1-t)^{1/2}\,\vec{j} + \dfrac{\sqrt{2}}{2}\,\vec{k}$; $\vec{T}'(t) = \dfrac{1}{4}(1+t)^{-1/2}\,\vec{i} + \dfrac{1}{4}(1-t)^{-1/2}\,\vec{j}$;

$\|\vec{T}'(t)\| = \dfrac{1}{4}\sqrt{(1+t)^{-1} + (1-t)^{-1}} = \dfrac{1}{4}\sqrt{\dfrac{1-t+1+t}{(1+t)(1-t)}} = \dfrac{1}{4}\sqrt{\dfrac{2}{1-t^2}}$;

$\vec{N}(t) = \dfrac{\vec{T}'(t)}{\|\vec{T}'(t)\|} = \sqrt{\dfrac{1-t}{2}}\,\vec{i} + \sqrt{\dfrac{1+t}{2}}\,\vec{j}$; $\kappa(t) = \dfrac{\|\vec{T}'(t)\|}{\|\vec{r}'(t)\|} = \dfrac{1}{4}\sqrt{\dfrac{2}{1-t^2}}$

5. $\vec{r}'(t) = 2\,\vec{i} + 2t\,\vec{j} + t^2\,\vec{k}$; $\|\vec{r}'(t)\| = \sqrt{2^2 + (2t)^2 + (t^2)^2}$

$= \sqrt{4 + 4t^2 + t^4} = 2 + t^2$; $\vec{T}(t) = \dfrac{\vec{r}'(t)}{\|\vec{r}'(t)\|} = \dfrac{2}{2+t^2}\,\vec{i} + \dfrac{2t}{2+t^2}\,\vec{j}$

$+ \dfrac{t^2}{2+t^2}\,\vec{k}$; $\vec{T}'(t) = \dfrac{-4t}{(2+t^2)^2}\,\vec{i} + \dfrac{2(2+t^2) - 4t^2}{(2+t^2)^2}\,\vec{j} + \dfrac{2t(2+t^2) - 2t^3}{(2+t^2)^2}\,\vec{k}$

$= \dfrac{-4t}{(2+t^2)^2}\,\vec{i} + \dfrac{4 - 2t^2}{(2+t^2)^2}\,\vec{j} + \dfrac{4t}{(2+t^2)^2}\,\vec{k}$; $\|\vec{T}'(t)\| =$

$= \dfrac{1}{(2+t^2)^2}\sqrt{(-4t)^2 + (4-2t^2)^2 + (4t)^2} = \dfrac{1}{(2+t^2)^2}\sqrt{16 + 16t^2 + 4t^4}$

$= \dfrac{2}{2+t^2}$; $\vec{N}(t) = \dfrac{\vec{T}'(t)}{\|\vec{T}'(t)\|} = \dfrac{-2t}{2+t^2}\,\vec{i} + \dfrac{2-t^2}{2+t^2}\,\vec{j} + \dfrac{2t}{2+t^2}\,\vec{k}$;

$\kappa(t) = \dfrac{\|\vec{T}'(t)\|}{\|\vec{r}'(t)\|} = \dfrac{\dfrac{2}{2+t^2}}{2+t^2} = \dfrac{2}{(2+t^2)^2}$

6. $\vec{r}'(t) = -\dfrac{4}{5}\sin t\,\vec{i} - \cos t\,\vec{j} + \dfrac{3}{5}\sin t\,\vec{k}$; $\|\vec{r}'(t)\|$

$= \sqrt{\left(\dfrac{-4}{5}\sin t\right)^2 + (-\cos t)^2 + \left(\dfrac{3}{5}\sin t\right)^2} = \sqrt{\sin^2 t + \cos^2 t} = 1$; $\vec{T}(t)$

$= \dfrac{\vec{r}'(t)}{\|\vec{r}'(t)\|} = -\dfrac{4}{5}\sin t\,\vec{i} - \cos t\,\vec{j} + \dfrac{3}{5}\sin t\,\vec{k}$; $\vec{T}'(t) = -\dfrac{4}{5}\cos t\,\vec{i}$

$+ \sin t\,\vec{j} + \dfrac{3}{5}\cos t\,\vec{k}$; $\|\vec{T}'(t)\| = \sqrt{\left(-\dfrac{4}{5}\cos t\right)^2 + \sin^2 t + \left(\dfrac{3}{5}\cos t\right)^2}$

$= \sqrt{\cos^2 t + \sin^2 t} = 1$; $\vec{N}(t) = \dfrac{\vec{T}'(t)}{\|\vec{T}'(t)\|} = -\dfrac{4}{5}\cos t\,\vec{i} + \sin t\,\vec{j}$

$$+ \frac{3}{5}\cos t\,\vec{k};\quad \kappa(t) = \frac{\|\vec{T}'(t)\|}{\|\vec{r}'(t)\|} = 1$$

7. $\vec{r}'(t) = e^t\,\vec{i} - e^{-t}\,\vec{j} + \sqrt{2}\,\vec{k};\quad \|\vec{r}'(t)\| = \sqrt{e^{2t} + e^{-2t} + 2} = e^t + e^{-t};$

$$\vec{T}(t) = \frac{\vec{r}'(t)}{\|\vec{r}'(t)\|} = \frac{e^t}{e^t + e^{-t}}\,\vec{i} - \frac{e^{-t}}{e^t + e^{-t}}\,\vec{j} + \frac{\sqrt{2}}{e^t + e^{-t}}\,\vec{k};$$

$$\vec{T}'(t) = \frac{e^t(e^t + e^{-t}) - e^t(e^t - e^{-t})}{(e^t + e^{-t})^2}\,\vec{i} - \frac{-e^{-t}(e^t + e^{-t}) - e^{-t}(e^t - e^{-t})}{(e^t + e^{-t})^2}\,\vec{j}$$

$$- \frac{\sqrt{2}\,(e^t - e^{-t})}{(e^t + e^{-t})^2}\,\vec{k} = \frac{2}{(e^t + e^{-t})^2}\,\vec{i} + \frac{2}{(e^t + e^{-t})^2}\,\vec{j} - \frac{\sqrt{2}\,(e^t - e^{-t})}{(e^t + e^{-t})^2}\,\vec{k};$$

$$\|\vec{T}'(t)\| = \frac{1}{(e^t + e^{-t})^2}\sqrt{2^2 + 2^2 + \left[\sqrt{2}\,(e^{-t} - e^t)\right]^2}$$

$$= \frac{\sqrt{2e^{-2t} + 4 + 2e^{2t}}}{(e^t + e^{-t})^2} = \frac{\sqrt{2}}{e^t + e^{-t}};\quad \vec{N}(t) = \frac{\vec{T}'(t)}{\|\vec{T}'(t)\|} = \frac{\sqrt{2}}{e^t + e^{-t}}\,\vec{i} + \frac{\sqrt{2}}{e^t + e^{-t}}\,\vec{j}$$

$$- \frac{e^t - e^{-t}}{e^t + e^{-t}}\,\vec{k};\quad \kappa(t) = \frac{\|\vec{T}'(t)\|}{\|\vec{r}'(t)\|} = \frac{\dfrac{\sqrt{2}}{e^t + e^{-t}}}{e^t + e^{-t}} = \frac{\sqrt{2}}{(e^t + e^{-t})^2}$$

8. $\vec{r}'(t) = \sinh t\,\vec{i} + \cosh t\,\vec{j} + \vec{k};\quad \|\vec{r}'(t)\| = \sqrt{\sinh^2 t + \cosh^2 t + 1}$

$$= \sqrt{2\cosh^2 t} = \sqrt{2}\cosh t;\quad \vec{T}(t) = \frac{\vec{r}'(t)}{\|\vec{r}'(t)\|} = \frac{\sinh t}{\sqrt{2}\cosh t}\,\vec{i} + \frac{1}{\sqrt{2}}\,\vec{j}$$

$$+ \frac{1}{\sqrt{2}\cosh t}\,\vec{k} = \frac{1}{\sqrt{2}}\tanh t\,\vec{i} + \frac{1}{\sqrt{2}}\,\vec{j} + \frac{1}{\sqrt{2}}\operatorname{sech} t\,\vec{k};\quad \vec{T}'(t) = \frac{1}{\sqrt{2}}\operatorname{sech}^2 t\,\vec{i}$$

$$- \frac{1}{\sqrt{2}}\operatorname{sech} t\tanh t\,\vec{k};\quad \|\vec{T}'(t)\| = \frac{1}{\sqrt{2}}\sqrt{\operatorname{sech}^4 t + \operatorname{sech}^2 t\tanh^2 t}$$

$$= \frac{1}{\sqrt{2}}\operatorname{sech} t\sqrt{\operatorname{sech}^2 t + \tanh^2 t} = \frac{1}{\sqrt{2}}\operatorname{sech} t;\quad \vec{N}(t) = \frac{\vec{T}'(t)}{\|\vec{T}'(t)\|} = \operatorname{sech} t\,\vec{i}$$

$$- \tanh t\,\vec{k};\quad \kappa(t) = \frac{\|\vec{T}'(t)\|}{\|\vec{r}'(t)\|} = \frac{\dfrac{1}{\sqrt{2}}\operatorname{sech} t}{\sqrt{2}\cosh t} = \frac{1}{2\cosh^2 t}$$

9. $\vec{r}'(t) = 2\,\vec{i} + 2t\,\vec{j} + \frac{1}{t}\,\vec{k};\quad \|\vec{r}'(t)\| = \sqrt{2^2 + (2t)^2 + (\frac{1}{t})^2}$

$$= \sqrt{4t^2 + 4 + \frac{1}{t^2}} = 2t + \frac{1}{t} = \frac{2t^2 + 1}{t};\quad \vec{T}(t) = \frac{\vec{r}'(t)}{\|\vec{r}'(t)\|} = \frac{2t}{2t^2 + 1}\,\vec{i}$$

$$+ \frac{2t^2}{2t^2 + 1}\,\vec{j} + \frac{1}{2t^2 + 1}\,\vec{k};\quad \vec{T}'(t) = \frac{2(2t^2 + 1) - 2t(4t)}{(2t^2 + 1)^2}\,\vec{i}$$

$$+ \frac{4t(2t^2 + 1) - 2t^2(4t)}{(2t^2 + 1)^2}\,\vec{j} - \frac{4t}{(2t^2 + 1)^2}\,\vec{k} = \frac{2 - 4t^2}{(2t^2 + 1)^2}\,\vec{i} + \frac{4t}{(2t^2 + 1)^2}\,\vec{j}$$

$$- \frac{4t}{(2t^2 + 1)^2}\,\vec{k};\quad \|\vec{T}'(t)\| = \frac{1}{(2t^2 + 1)^2}\sqrt{(2 - 4t^2)^2 + (4t)^2 + (-4t)^2}$$

$$= \frac{\sqrt{16t^4 + 16t^2 + 4}}{(2t^2 + 1)^2} = \frac{2}{2t^2 + 1};\quad \vec{N}(t) = \frac{\vec{T}'(t)}{\|\vec{T}'(t)\|} = \frac{1 - 2t^2}{2t^2 + 1}\,\vec{i} + \frac{2t}{2t^2 + 1}\,\vec{j}$$

$$- \frac{2t}{2t^2 + 1}\,\vec{k};\quad \kappa(t) = \frac{\|\vec{T}'(t)\|}{\|\vec{r}'(t)\|} = \frac{\dfrac{2}{2t^2 + 1}}{\dfrac{2t^2 + 1}{t}} = \frac{2t}{(2t^2 + 1)^2}$$

10. $\vec{r}'(t) = 9t^{7/2}\,\vec{i} + \frac{9}{2}\sqrt{2}\,t^2\,\vec{j} + \frac{9}{2}\sqrt{2}\,t^2\,\vec{k};$

$$\|\vec{r}'(t)\| = 9\sqrt{(t^{7/2})^2 + (\tfrac{\sqrt{2}}{2}t^2)^2 + (\tfrac{\sqrt{2}}{2}t^2)^2} = 9\sqrt{t^7 + t^4} = 9t^2\sqrt{t^3 + 1};$$

$$\vec{T}(t) = \frac{\vec{r}'(t)}{\|\vec{r}'(t)\|} = \frac{t^{3/2}}{\sqrt{t^3 + 1}}\,\vec{i} + \frac{\sqrt{2}}{2\sqrt{t^3 + 1}}\,\vec{j} + \frac{\sqrt{2}}{2\sqrt{t^3 + 1}}\,\vec{k};$$

$$\vec{T}'(t) = \frac{\frac{3}{2}t^{1/2}\sqrt{t^3 + 1} - t^{3/2}\,(\frac{1}{2})(t^3 + 1)^{-1/2}\,(3t^2)}{t^3 + 1}\,\vec{i} - \frac{3\sqrt{2}\,t^2}{4}(t^3 + 1)^{-3/2}\,\vec{j}$$

$$- \frac{3\sqrt{2}\,t^2}{4}(t^3 + 1)^{-3/2}\,\vec{k} = \frac{3t^{1/2}}{2(t^3 + 1)^{3/2}}\,\vec{i} - \frac{3\sqrt{2}\,t^2}{4(t^3 + 1)^{3/2}}\,\vec{j} - \frac{3\sqrt{2}\,t^2}{4(t^3 + 1)^{3/2}}\,\vec{k};$$

$$\|\vec{T}'(t)\| = \frac{3}{2(t^3 + 1)^{3/2}}\sqrt{(t^{1/2})^2 + (-\tfrac{\sqrt{2}\,t^2}{2})^2 + (-\tfrac{\sqrt{2}\,t^2}{2})^2} = \frac{3t^{1/2}}{2(t^3 + 1)};$$

$$\vec{N}(t) = \frac{\vec{T}'(t)}{\|\vec{T}'(t)\|} = \frac{1}{(t^3 + 1)^{1/2}}\,\vec{i} - \frac{\sqrt{2}\,t^{3/2}}{2(t^3 + 1)^{1/2}}\,\vec{j} - \frac{\sqrt{2}\,t^{3/2}}{2(t^3 + 1)^{1/2}}\,\vec{k};$$

$$\kappa(t) = \frac{\|\vec{T}'(t)\|}{\|\vec{r}'(t)\|} = \frac{\dfrac{3t^{1/2}}{2(t^3 + 1)}}{9t^2\sqrt{t^3 + 1}} = \frac{1}{6t^{3/2}\,(t^3 + 1)^{3/2}}$$

11. $\vec{v} = \frac{d\vec{r}}{dt} = 2\,\vec{i} + 2t\,\vec{j}$; $\|\vec{v}\| = \sqrt{2^2 + (2t)^2} = 2\sqrt{1 + t^2}$; $\vec{a} = \frac{d\vec{v}}{dt} = 2\,\vec{j}$; $\vec{v} \times \vec{a}$

$= \begin{vmatrix} \vec{i} & \vec{j} & \vec{k} \\ 2 & 2t & 0 \\ 0 & 2 & 0 \end{vmatrix} = 4\,\vec{k}$; $\|\vec{v} \times \vec{a}\| = 4$; $K = \frac{\|\vec{v} \times \vec{a}\|}{\|\vec{v}\|^3} = \frac{4}{(2\sqrt{1 + t^2})^3}$

$= \frac{1}{2(1 + t^2)^{3/2}}$

12. $\vec{v} = \frac{d\vec{r}}{dt} = (\cos t - t \sin t)\,\vec{i} + (\sin t + t \cos t)\,\vec{j}$; $\|\vec{v}\|$

$= \sqrt{(\cos t - t \sin t)^2 + (\sin t + t \cos t)^2}$

$= \sqrt{\cos^2 t - 2t \cos t \sin t + t^2 \sin^2 t + \sin^2 t + 2t \sin t \cos t + t^2 \cos^2 t}$

$= \sqrt{1 + t^2}$; $\vec{a} = \frac{d\vec{v}}{dt} = (-\sin t - \sin t - t \cos t)\,\vec{i} + (\cos t + \cos t$

$- t \sin t)\vec{j} = -(2 \sin t + t \cos t)\,\vec{i} + (2 \cos t - t \sin t)\,\vec{j}$;

$\vec{v} \times \vec{a} = \begin{vmatrix} \vec{i} & \vec{j} & \vec{k} \\ \cos t - t \sin t & \sin t + t \cos t & 0 \\ -(2 \sin t + t \cos t) & 2 \cos t - t \sin t & 0 \end{vmatrix} = (2 + t^2)\,\vec{k}$

$K = \frac{\|\vec{v} \times \vec{a}\|}{\|\vec{v}\|^3} = \frac{2 + t^2}{(1 + t^2)^{3/2}}$

13. $\vec{v} = \frac{d\vec{r}}{dt} = e^t (\sin t + \cos t)\,\vec{i} + e^t (\cos t - \sin t)\,\vec{j} + \vec{k}$; $\|\vec{v}\|$

$= \sqrt{e^{2t} (\sin t + \cos t)^2 + e^{2t} (\cos t - \sin t)^2 + 1}$

$= \sqrt{e^{2t} (\sin^2 t + 2 \sin t \cos t + \cos^2 t + \cos^2 t - 2 \cos t \sin t + \sin^2 t) + 1}$

$= \sqrt{2e^{2t} + 1}$; $\vec{a} = \frac{d\vec{v}}{dt} = [e^t (\sin t + \cos t) + e^t (\cos t - \sin t)]\,\vec{i}$

$+ [e^t (\cos t - \sin t) + e^t (-\sin t - \cos t)]\,\vec{j} = 2e^t \cos t\,\vec{i} - 2e^t \sin t\,\vec{j}$;

$\vec{v} \times \vec{a} = \begin{vmatrix} \vec{i} & \vec{j} & \vec{k} \\ e^t (\sin t + \cos t) & e^t (\cos t - \sin t) & 1 \\ 2e^t \cos t & -2e^t \sin t & 0 \end{vmatrix}$

$= 2e^t \sin t\,\vec{i} + 2e^t \cos t\,\vec{j} - 2e^{2t}\,\vec{k}$; $\|\vec{v} \times \vec{a}\|$

$= 2e^t\sqrt{\sin^2 t + \cos^2 t + (-e^t)^2} = 2e^t\sqrt{1 + e^{2t}}$;

$K = \frac{\|\vec{v} \times \vec{a}\|}{\|\vec{v}\|^3} = \frac{2e^t (1 + e^{2t})^{1/2}}{(2e^{2t} + 1)^{3/2}}$

14. $\vec{v} = \frac{d\vec{r}}{dt} = t(t^2 - 1)^{1/2}\,\vec{i} + \frac{\sqrt{2}}{2} t\,\vec{j} + \frac{\sqrt{2}}{2} t\,\vec{k}$;

$\|\vec{v}\| = \sqrt{t^2 (t^2 - 1) + \frac{1}{2} t^2 + \frac{1}{2} t^2} = t^2$; $\vec{a} = \left[(t^2 - 1)^{1/2} + \frac{t^2}{(t^2 - 1)^{1/2}}\right]\vec{i}$

$+ \frac{\sqrt{2}}{2}\,\vec{j} + \frac{\sqrt{2}}{2}\,\vec{k} = \frac{2t^2 - 1}{(t^2 - 1)^{1/2}}\,\vec{i} + \frac{\sqrt{2}}{2}\,\vec{j} + \frac{\sqrt{2}}{2}\,\vec{k}$; $\vec{v} \times \vec{a}$

$= \begin{vmatrix} \vec{i} & \vec{j} & \vec{k} \\ t(t^2 - 1)^{1/2} & \frac{\sqrt{2}}{2} t & \frac{\sqrt{2}}{2} t \\ \frac{2t^2 - 1}{(t^2 - 1)^{1/2}} & \frac{\sqrt{2}}{2} & \frac{\sqrt{2}}{2} \end{vmatrix} = \frac{\sqrt{2}\, t^3}{2(t^2 - 1)^{1/2}}\,\vec{j} - \frac{\sqrt{2}\, t^3}{2(t^2 - 1)^{1/2}}\,\vec{k}$;

$\|\vec{v} \times \vec{a}\| = \frac{|t^3|}{(t^2 - 1)^{1/2}}$; $K = \frac{\|\vec{v} \times \vec{a}\|}{\|\vec{v}\|^3} = \frac{\frac{|t^3|}{(t^2 - 1)^{1/2}}}{t^6} = \frac{1}{|t^3|(t^2 - 1)^{1/2}}$

15. $\vec{v} = \frac{d\vec{r}}{dt} = \cos t\,\vec{i} - \sin t\,\vec{j} + t^{1/2}\,\vec{k}$; $\|\vec{v}\| = \sqrt{\cos^2 t + \sin^2 t + t}$

$= \sqrt{1 + t}$; $\vec{a} = \frac{d\vec{v}}{dt} = -\sin t\,\vec{i} - \cos t\,\vec{j} + \frac{1}{2} t^{-1/2}\,\vec{k}$; $\vec{v} \times \vec{a}$

$= \begin{vmatrix} \vec{i} & \vec{j} & \vec{k} \\ \cos t & -\sin t & t^{1/2} \\ -\sin t & -\cos t & \frac{1}{2} t^{-1/2} \end{vmatrix} = (-\frac{1}{2} t^{-1/2} \sin t + t^{1/2} \cos t)\,\vec{i}$

$+ (-t^{1/2} \sin t - \frac{1}{2} t^{-1/2} \cos t)\,\vec{j} - \vec{k}$; $\|\vec{v} \times \vec{a}\|$

$= \sqrt{(-\frac{1}{2} t^{-1/2} \sin t + t^{1/2} \cos t)^2 + (-t^{1/2} \sin t - \frac{1}{2} t^{-1/2} \cos t)^2 + 1}$

$= \sqrt{\frac{1}{4} t^{-1} \sin^2 t - \sin t \cos t + t \cos^2 t + t \sin^2 t + \sin t \cos t}$

$\overline{+ \frac{1}{4} t^{-1} \cos^2 t + 1} = \sqrt{\frac{1}{4} t^{-1} + 1 + t} = \sqrt{\frac{1 + 4t + 4t^2}{4t}} = \frac{2t + 1}{2\sqrt{t}}$;

$K = \frac{\|\vec{v} \times \vec{a}\|}{\|\vec{v}\|^3} = \frac{\frac{2t + 1}{2\sqrt{t}}}{(\sqrt{1 + t})^3} = \frac{2t + 1}{2\sqrt{t}\,(1 + t)^{3/2}}$

16. $x = 2\cos t$, $\frac{dx}{dt} = -2\sin t$, $\frac{d^2x}{dt^2} = -2\cos t$; $y = 3\sin t$, $\frac{dy}{dt} = 3\cos t$,

$$\frac{d^2y}{dt^2} = -3\sin t; \quad K = \frac{\left|\frac{dx}{dt}\frac{d^2y}{dt^2} - \frac{d^2x}{dt^2}\frac{dy}{dt}\right|}{\left[\left(\frac{dx}{dt}\right)^2 + \left(\frac{dy}{dt}\right)^2\right]^{3/2}} = \frac{|6\sin^2 t + 6\cos^2 t|}{(4\sin^2 t + 9\cos^2 t)^{3/2}}$$

$$= \frac{6}{(4\sin^2 t + 9\cos^2 t)^{3/2}} = \frac{6}{(4 + 5\cos^2 t)^{3/2}}; \text{ for } t_0 = 0, \quad K = \frac{6}{9^{3/2}} = \frac{2}{9},$$

so that $\rho = \frac{1}{K} = \frac{9}{2}$.

17. By the solution of Exercise 16, $K = \frac{6}{(4 + 5\cos^2 t)^{3/2}}$; for $t_0 = \frac{\pi}{2}$,

$$K = \frac{6}{4^{3/2}} = \frac{3}{4}, \text{ so that } \rho = \frac{1}{K} = \frac{4}{3}.$$

18. $x = 2\cosh t$, $\frac{dx}{dt} = 2\sinh t$, $\frac{d^2x}{dt^2} = 2\cosh t$; $y = 3\sinh t$, $\frac{dy}{dt} = 3\cosh t$,

$$\frac{d^2y}{dt^2} = 3\sinh t; \quad K = \frac{\left|\frac{dx}{dt}\frac{d^2y}{dt^2} - \frac{d^2x}{dt^2}\frac{dy}{dt}\right|}{\left[\left(\frac{dx}{dt}\right)^2 + \left(\frac{dy}{dt}\right)^2\right]^{3/2}} = \frac{|6\sinh^2 t - 6\cosh^2 t|}{(4\sinh^2 t + 9\cosh^2 t)^{3/2}}$$

$$= \frac{6}{(4\sinh^2 t + 9\cosh^2 t)^{3/2}}; \text{ for } t_0 = 0, \quad K = \frac{6}{9^{3/2}} = \frac{2}{9}, \text{ so that } \rho = \frac{1}{K}$$

$$= \frac{9}{2}.$$

19. $x = t$, $\frac{dx}{dt} = 1$, $\frac{d^2x}{dt^2} = 0$; $y = \frac{1}{3}t^3$, $\frac{dy}{dt} = t^2$, $\frac{d^2y}{dt^2} = 2t$,

$$K = \frac{\left|\frac{dx}{dt}\frac{d^2y}{dt^2} - \frac{d^2x}{dt^2}\frac{dy}{dt}\right|}{\left[\left(\frac{dx}{dt}\right)^2 + \left(\frac{dy}{dt}\right)^2\right]^{3/2}} = \frac{2|t|}{(1 + t^4)^{3/2}}; \text{ for } t_0 = 1, \quad K = \frac{2}{2^{3/2}} = \frac{1}{\sqrt{2}}, \text{ so}$$

that $\rho = \frac{1}{K} = \sqrt{2}$.

20. $$\frac{dy}{dx} = \cos x, \quad \frac{d^2y}{dx^2} = -\sin x; \quad K = \frac{\left|\frac{d^2y}{dx^2}\right|}{\left[1 + \left(\frac{dy}{dx}\right)^2\right]^{3/2}} = \frac{\sin x}{(1 + \cos^2 x)^{3/2}}$$

21. $$\frac{dy}{dx} = \frac{1}{x}, \quad \frac{d^2y}{dx^2} = -\frac{1}{x^2}; \quad K = \frac{\left|\frac{d^2y}{dx^2}\right|}{\left[1 + \left(\frac{dy}{dx}\right)^2\right]^{3/2}} = \frac{\frac{1}{x^2}}{\left(1 + \frac{1}{x^2}\right)^{3/2}} = \frac{x}{(1 + x^2)^{3/2}}$$

22. $$\frac{dy}{dx} = \frac{1}{3}x^{-2/3}, \quad \frac{d^2y}{dx^2} = -\frac{2}{9}x^{-5/3}; \quad K = \frac{\left|\frac{d^2y}{dx^2}\right|}{\left[1 + \left(\frac{dy}{dx}\right)^2\right]^{3/2}} = \frac{\frac{2}{9}x^{-5/3}}{\left(1 + \frac{1}{9}x^{-4/3}\right)^{3/2}}$$

$$= \frac{6x^{1/3}}{(9x^{4/3} + 1)^{3/2}}$$

23. $$\frac{dy}{dx} = -\frac{1}{x^2}, \quad \frac{d^2y}{dx^2} = \frac{2}{x^3}; \quad K = \frac{\left|\frac{d^2y}{dx^2}\right|}{\left[1 + \left(\frac{dy}{dx}\right)^2\right]^{3/2}} = \frac{-\frac{2}{x^3}}{\left(1 + \frac{1}{x^4}\right)^{3/2}} = \frac{-2x^3}{(1 + x^4)^{3/2}}$$

24. $\vec{v} = r(1 - \cos t)\vec{i} + r\sin t\,\vec{j}$; $\|\vec{v}\| = \sqrt{r^2(1 - \cos t)^2 + r^2\sin^2 t}$

$$= \sqrt{2r^2(1 - \cos t)}; \quad a_{\vec{T}} = \frac{d\|\vec{v}\|}{dt} = \frac{r^2\sin t}{\sqrt{2r^2(1 - \cos t)}}; \quad \vec{a} = \frac{d\vec{v}}{dt} = r\sin t\,\vec{i}$$

$$+ r\cos t\,\vec{j}; \quad \|\vec{a}\|^2 = r^2\sin^2 t + r^2\cos^2 t = r^2; \quad a_{\vec{N}} = \sqrt{\|\vec{a}\|^2 - a_{\vec{T}}^2}$$

$$= \sqrt{r^2 - \frac{r^4\sin^2 t}{2r^2(1 - \cos t)}} = \sqrt{r^2 - \frac{r^2(1 - \cos^2 t)}{2(1 - \cos t)}} = \frac{|r|}{2}\sqrt{1 - \cos t}$$

25. $\vec{v} = -2\sin t\,\vec{i} + 3\cos t\,\vec{j}$; $\|\vec{v}\| = \sqrt{4\sin^2 t + 9\cos^2 t} = \sqrt{4 + 5\cos^2 t}$;

$$a_{\vec{T}} = \frac{d\|\vec{v}\|}{dt} = \frac{-5\cos t\sin t}{\sqrt{4 + 5\cos^2 t}}; \quad \vec{a} = -2\cos t\,\vec{i} - 3\sin t\,\vec{j}; \quad \|\vec{a}\|^2$$

$$= 4\cos^2 t + 9\sin^2 t = 4 + 5\sin^2 t; \quad a_{\vec{N}} = \sqrt{\|\vec{a}\|^2 - a_{\vec{T}}^2}$$

$= \sqrt{4 + 5 \sin^2 t - \frac{25 \cos^2 t \sin^2 t}{4 + 5 \cos^2 t}} = \sqrt{\frac{16 + 20 (\cos^2 t + \sin^2 t)}{4 + 5 \cos^2 t}}$

$= \frac{6}{\sqrt{4 + 5 \cos^2 t}}$

26. $\vec{v} = 2\vec{i} + 2t\vec{j} + t^2\vec{k}$; $\|\vec{v}\| = \sqrt{4 + 4t^2 + t^4} = 2 + t^2$; $a_{\vec{T}} = \frac{d\|\vec{v}\|}{dt} = 2t$;

$\vec{a} = 2\vec{j} + 2t\vec{k}$; $\|\vec{a}\|^2 = 4(1 + t^2)$; $a_{\vec{N}} = \sqrt{\|\vec{a}\|^2 - a_{\vec{T}}^2} = \sqrt{4(1 + t^2) - 4t^2}$

$= 2$.

27. $\vec{v} = -\frac{4}{5}\sin t\,\vec{i} - \cos t\,\vec{j} + \frac{3}{5}\sin t\,\vec{k}$; $\|\vec{v}\|$

$= \sqrt{\frac{16}{25}\sin^2 t + \cos^2 t + \frac{9}{25}\sin^2 t} = 1$; $a_{\vec{T}} = \frac{d\|\vec{v}\|}{dt} = 0$; $\vec{a} = -\frac{4}{5}\cos t\,\vec{i}$

$+ \sin t\,\vec{j} + \frac{3}{5}\cos t\,\vec{k}$; $\|\vec{a}\|^2 = \frac{16}{25}\cos^2 t + \sin^2 t + \frac{9}{25}\cos^2 t = 1$; $a_{\vec{N}}$

$= \sqrt{\|\vec{a}\|^2 - a_{\vec{T}}^2} = \sqrt{1 - 0} = 1$

28. $\vec{v} = e^t\vec{i} - e^{-t}\vec{j} + \sqrt{2}\,\vec{k}$; $\|\vec{v}\| = \sqrt{e^{2t} + e^{-2t} + 2} = e^t + e^{-t}$; $a_{\vec{T}} = \frac{d\|\vec{v}\|}{dt}$

$= e^t - e^{-t}$; $\vec{a} = e^t\vec{i} + e^{-t}\vec{j}$; $\|\vec{a}\|^2 = e^{2t} + e^{-2t}$; $a_{\vec{N}} = \sqrt{\|\vec{a}\|^2 - a_{\vec{T}}^2}$

$= \sqrt{(e^{2t} + e^{-2t}) - (e^t - e^{-t})^2} = \sqrt{2}$

29. $\vec{r}(t) = -2\vec{i} + (-2 + 3\cos t)\vec{j} - (1 + 3\sin t)\vec{k}$ for $0 \le t \le 2\pi$

30. $\vec{r}(t) = -4\sin t\,\vec{j} + 4\cos t\,\vec{k}$ for $0 \le t \le \pi$

31. $\vec{r}(t) = \begin{cases} t\,\vec{i} & \text{for } 0 \le t \le 1 \\ \cos\frac{\pi}{2}(t-1)\,\vec{i} + \sin\frac{\pi}{2}(t-1)\,\vec{j} & \text{for } 1 \le t \le 2 \\ (3-t)\,\vec{j} & \text{for } 2 \le t \le 3 \end{cases}$

32. $\vec{r}(t) = \begin{cases} t\,\vec{i} + t^2\,\vec{j} & \text{for } 0 \le t \le 1 \\ (2-t)\,\vec{i} + (2-t)\,\vec{j} & \text{for } 1 \le t \le 2 \end{cases}$

33. $\vec{r}(t) = \begin{cases} 4(1-t)\,\vec{i} + 3t\,\vec{j} & \text{for } 0 \le t \le 1 \\ 3(2-t)\,\vec{j} + 5(t-1)\,\vec{k} & \text{for } 1 \le t \le 2 \\ 4(t-2)\,\vec{i} + 5(3-t)\,\vec{k} & \text{for } 2 \le t \le 3 \end{cases}$

34. $\vec{r}(t) = \begin{cases} (t+1)\,\vec{i} & \text{for } 0 \le t \le 1 \\ 2\cos\frac{\pi}{2}(t-1)\,\vec{i} + 2\sin\frac{\pi}{2}(t-1)\,\vec{j} & \text{for } 1 \le t \le 2 \\ (4-t)\,\vec{j} & \text{for } 2 \le t \le 3 \\ \sin\frac{\pi}{2}(t-3)\,\vec{i} + \cos\frac{\pi}{2}(t-3)\,\vec{j} & \text{for } 3 \le t \le 4 \end{cases}$

35. Since $\vec{r}_1(0) = \vec{j} = \vec{r}_2(0)$, the two curves intersect at $(0, 1, 0)$. Since $\vec{r}_1{}'(t) = (t+1)\vec{i} + \vec{j} - \vec{k}$ and $\vec{r}_2{}'(t) = \cos t\,\vec{i} + e^t\vec{j} - \sec^2 t\,\vec{k}$, we have $\vec{r}_1{}'(0) = \vec{i} + \vec{j} - \vec{k}$ and $\vec{r}_2{}'(0) = \vec{i} + \vec{j} - \vec{k}$, so that the vectors tangent to the two curves at $(0, 1, 0)$ are parallel.

36. Since $\vec{r}_1(1) = \vec{i} + 2\vec{j} + \vec{k} = \vec{r}_2(-1)$, the two curves intersect at $(1, 2, 1)$. Since $\vec{r}_1{}'(t) = \vec{i} + 2\vec{j} + 2t\vec{k}$ and $\vec{r}_2{}'(t) = 2t\,\vec{i} - \vec{j} - 2t\,\vec{k}$, we have $\vec{r}_1{}'(1) = \vec{i} + 2\vec{j} + 2\vec{k}$ and $\vec{r}_2{}'(-1) = -2\vec{i} - \vec{j} + 2\vec{k}$. Thus $\vec{T}_1(1) = \frac{1}{3}(\vec{i} + 2\vec{j} + 2\vec{k})$ and $\vec{T}_2(-1) = \frac{1}{3}(-2\vec{i} - \vec{j} + 2\vec{k})$, so that $\vec{T}_1(1) \cdot \vec{T}_2(-1) = \frac{1}{9}(-2 - 2 + 4) = 0$. Thus the two tangent vectors are perpendicular.

37. $x = 3\cos t$, $\frac{dx}{dt} = -3\sin t$, $\frac{d^2x}{dt^2} = -3\cos t$; $y = 2\sin t$, $\frac{dy}{dt} = 2\cos t$,

$\frac{d^2y}{dt^2} = -2\sin t$; $\kappa = \frac{\left|\frac{dx}{dt}\frac{d^2y}{dt^2} - \frac{d^2x}{dt^2}\frac{dy}{dt}\right|}{\left[\left(\frac{dx}{dt}\right)^2 + \left(\frac{dy}{dt}\right)^2\right]^{3/2}} = \frac{|6\sin^2 t + 6\cos^2 t|}{(9\sin^2 t + 4\cos^2 t)^{3/2}}$

$= \frac{6}{(4 + 5\sin^2 t)^{3/2}}$. Evidently the curvature is maximum when the denominator is smallest (namely for $\sin t = 0$), and is minimum when the denominator is largest (namely for $\sin t = \pm 1$). Since $\sin t = 0$ if $t = 0$ or

$t = \pi$, and $\sin t = \pm 1$ if $t = \frac{\pi}{2}$ or $-\frac{\pi}{2}$, it follows that the curvature is maximum at the points $(3\cos 0, 2\sin 0) = (3, 0)$ and $(3\cos\pi, 2\sin\pi) = (-3, 0)$, and is minimum at the points $(3\cos\frac{\pi}{2}, 2\sin\frac{\pi}{2}) = (0, 2)$ and $(3\cos\frac{-\pi}{2}, 2\sin\frac{-\pi}{2}) = (0, -2)$.

38. $\frac{dy}{dx} = e^x = \frac{d^2y}{dx^2}$; $\kappa = \dfrac{\left|\frac{d^2y}{dx^2}\right|}{\left[1 + (\frac{dy}{dx})^2\right]^{3/2}} = \dfrac{e^x}{(1 + e^{2x})^{3/2}}$; $\frac{d\kappa}{dx}$

$= \dfrac{e^x(1 + e^{2x})^{3/2} - e^x(\frac{3}{2})(1 + e^{2x})^{1/2}(2e^{2x})}{(1 + e^{2x})^3} = \dfrac{e^x - 2e^{3x}}{(1 + e^{2x})^{5/2}}$

$= \dfrac{e^x(1 - 2e^{2x})}{(1 + e^{2x})^{5/2}}$; $\frac{d\kappa}{dx} = 0$ if $1 - 2e^{2x} = 0$, or $x = \frac{-1}{2}\ln 2$. Since $\frac{d\kappa}{dx} > 0$ for $x < \frac{-1}{2}\ln 2$, and $\frac{d\kappa}{dx} < 0$ for $x > \frac{-1}{2}\ln 2$, κ is maximum at $(\frac{-1}{2}\ln 2, \frac{\sqrt{2}}{2})$.

39. $\vec{v} = -\sin t\,\vec{i} + \cos t\,\vec{j} + \vec{k}$; $\|\vec{v}\| = \sqrt{\sin^2 t + \cos^2 t + 1} = \sqrt{2}$;

$\vec{a} = -\cos t\,\vec{i} - \sin t\,\vec{j}$; $\vec{v}\times\vec{a} = \begin{vmatrix} \vec{i} & \vec{j} & \vec{k} \\ -\sin t & \cos t & 1 \\ -\cos t & -\sin t & 0 \end{vmatrix} = \sin t\,\vec{i} - \cos t\,\vec{j}$

$+ \vec{k}$; $\|\vec{v}\times\vec{a}\| = \sqrt{\sin^2 t + \cos^2 t + 1} = \sqrt{2}$; $\kappa = \dfrac{\|\vec{v}\times\vec{a}\|}{\|\vec{v}\|^3} = \dfrac{\sqrt{2}}{(\sqrt{2})^3} = \frac{1}{2}$

40. Since $\frac{d^2y}{dx^2} = 0$ at any point of inflection, (13) implies that $\kappa = 0$ at any point of inflection.

41. a. By (9), $\left\|\frac{d\vec{T}}{dt}\right\| = \kappa\left\|\frac{d\vec{r}}{dt}\right\| = \kappa\|\vec{v}\|$, so that by (7), $a_{\vec{N}} = \|\vec{v}\|\left\|\frac{d\vec{T}}{dt}\right\|$

$= \kappa\|\vec{v}\|^2$.

b. Since the graph of the sine function has an inflection point at $(\pi, 0)$, Exercise 40 implies that $\kappa = 0$ at $(\pi, 0)$. Thus by part (a), $a_{\vec{N}} = 0$ at $(\pi, 0)$

42. $\frac{d}{dt}(\|\vec{v}\|^2) = \frac{d}{dt}(\vec{v}\cdot\vec{v}) = \frac{d\vec{v}}{dt}\cdot\vec{v} + \vec{v}\cdot\frac{d\vec{v}}{dt} = 2\vec{v}\cdot\vec{a} = 0$, so that $\|\vec{v}\|^2$, and hence $\|\vec{v}\|$, is constant.

43. Since $a_{\vec{T}} = \frac{d\|\vec{v}\|}{dt}$, it follows from Theorem 4.7 that $a_{\vec{T}} = 0$ only if $\|\vec{v}\|$ is constant.

44. Let $\vec{r}$ be a smooth parameterization of a curve lying on the sphere. Then $\|\vec{r}\| = c$ for some constant c, so that by Corollary 12.11, $\vec{r}\cdot\frac{d\vec{r}}{dt} = 0$. Since $\vec{T} = \dfrac{\frac{d\vec{r}}{dt}}{\left\|\frac{d\vec{r}}{dt}\right\|}$, it follows that $\vec{r}\cdot\vec{T} = \dfrac{1}{\left\|\frac{d\vec{r}}{dt}\right\|}(\vec{r}\cdot\frac{d\vec{r}}{dt}) = 0$, so that $\vec{r}$ and $\vec{T}$ are perpendicular.

45. $x = f(\theta)\cos\theta$, $\frac{dx}{d\theta} = f'(\theta)\cos\theta - f(\theta)\sin\theta$; $\frac{d^2x}{d\theta^2} = f''(\theta)\cos\theta - 2f'(\theta)\sin\theta - f(\theta)\cos\theta$; $y = f(\theta)\sin\theta$, $\frac{dy}{d\theta} = f'(\theta)\sin\theta + f(\theta)\cos\theta$, $\frac{d^2y}{d\theta^2} = f''(\theta)\sin\theta + 2f'(\theta)\cos\theta - f(\theta)\sin\theta$; $\kappa(\theta) = \dfrac{\left|\frac{dx}{d\theta}\frac{d^2y}{d\theta^2} - \frac{d^2x}{d\theta^2}\frac{dy}{d\theta}\right|}{\left[(\frac{dx}{d\theta})^2 + (\frac{dy}{d\theta})^2\right]^{3/2}}$

$= \dfrac{\left|2[f'(\theta)]^2(\cos^2\theta + \sin^2\theta) - f(\theta)f''(\theta)(\sin^2\theta + \cos^2\theta) + [f(\theta)]^2\cdot(\sin^2\theta + \cos^2\theta)\right|}{\left[(f'(\theta))^2(\cos^2\theta + \sin^2\theta) + (f(\theta))^2(\sin^2\theta + \cos^2\theta)\right]^{3/2}} = \dfrac{\left|2[f'(\theta)]^2 - f(\theta)f''(\theta) + [f(\theta)]^2\right|}{\left[(f'(\theta))^2 + (f(\theta))^2\right]^{3/2}}$

46. By Exercise 45, $\kappa(\theta) = \dfrac{\left|2(3\cos 3\theta)^2 - \sin 3\theta(-9\sin 3\theta) + \sin^2 3\theta\right|}{\left[(3\cos 3\theta)^2 + \sin^2 3\theta\right]^{3/2}}$

$= \dfrac{18\cos^2 3\theta + 10\sin^2 3\theta}{(9\cos^2 3\theta + \sin^2 3\theta)^{3/2}} = \dfrac{8\cos^2 3\theta + 10}{(8\cos^2 3\theta + 1)^{3/2}}$

47. By Exercise 45, $\kappa(\theta) = \dfrac{\left|2\sin^2\theta - (1-\cos\theta)\cos\theta + (1-\cos\theta)^2\right|}{\left[\sin^2\theta + (1-\cos\theta)^2\right]^{3/2}}$

$= \dfrac{3(1-\cos\theta)}{\left[2(1-\cos\theta)\right]^{3/2}} = \dfrac{3\sqrt{2}}{4(1-\cos\theta)^{1/2}}$

48. Using the results of Example 5, we have

$$\vec{B} = \vec{T}\times\vec{N} = \begin{vmatrix} \vec{i} & \vec{j} & \vec{k} \\ -\frac{2}{\sqrt{13}}\sin t & \frac{2}{\sqrt{13}}\cos t & \frac{3}{\sqrt{13}} \\ -\cos t & -\sin t & 0 \end{vmatrix} = \frac{3}{\sqrt{13}}\sin t\,\vec{i}$$

$- \dfrac{3}{\sqrt{13}}\cos t\,\vec{j} + \dfrac{2}{\sqrt{13}}\vec{k}$

49. a. $\theta'(t) = \kappa(t)$; $\vec{v} = \cos\theta(t)\,\vec{i} + \sin\theta(t)\,\vec{j}$; $\|\vec{v}\| = \sqrt{\cos^2\theta(t) + \sin^2\theta(t)}$

$= 1$; $\vec{a} = (-\sin\theta(t))\,\theta'(t)\,\vec{i} + (\cos\theta(t))\,\theta'(t)\,\vec{j} = -\kappa(t)\sin\theta(t)\,\vec{i}$

$+ \kappa(t)\cos\theta(t)\,\vec{j}$; $\quad \vec{v}\times\vec{a} = \begin{vmatrix} \vec{i} & \vec{j} & \vec{k} \\ \cos\theta(t) & \sin\theta(t) & 0 \\ -\kappa(t)\sin\theta(t) & \kappa(t)\cos\theta(t) & 0 \end{vmatrix}$

$= \kappa(t)\,\vec{k}$; $\quad \|\vec{v}\times\vec{a}\| = \kappa(t)$. Thus the curvature is $\dfrac{\|\vec{v}\times\vec{a}\|}{\|\vec{v}\|^3} = \kappa(t)$.

b. Taking $a = 0$ in part (a), we find that

$\theta(t) = \displaystyle\int_0^t \frac{1}{\sqrt{1-u^2}}\,du = \arcsin t$, so that

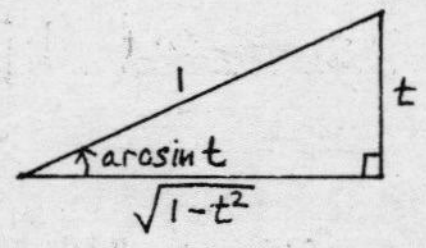

$\displaystyle\int_0^t \cos\theta(u)\,du = \int_0^t \cos(\arcsin u)\,du$

$= \displaystyle\int_0^t \sqrt{1-u^2}\,du \overset{u=\sin w}{=} \int_0^{\arcsin t} \sqrt{1-\sin^2 w}\,\cos w\,dw$

$= \displaystyle\int_0^{\arcsin t} \cos^2 w\,dw = \int_0^{\arcsin t} \left(\frac{1}{2} + \frac{1}{2}\cos 2w\right)dw$

$= \left(\frac{1}{2}w + \frac{1}{4}\sin 2w\right)\Big|_0^{\arcsin t} = \frac{1}{2}\arcsin t + \frac{1}{2}\sin(\arcsin t)\cos(\arcsin t)$

$= \dfrac{1}{2}\arcsin t + \dfrac{t}{2}\sqrt{1-t^2}$; $\displaystyle\int_0^t \sin\theta(u)\,du = \int_0^t \sin(\arcsin u)\,du$

$= \displaystyle\int_0^t u\,du = \frac{1}{2}t^2$. Thus the desired parameterization is $\vec{r}(t)$

$= \left(\frac{1}{2}\arcsin t + \frac{t}{2}\sqrt{1-t^2}\right)\vec{i} + \frac{1}{2}t^2\,\vec{j}$ for $-1 < t < 1$.

c. Taking $a = 0$ in part (a), we find that $\theta(t)$

$= \displaystyle\int_0^t \frac{1}{1+u^2}\,du = \arctan t$, so that

$\displaystyle\int_0^t \cos\theta(u)\,du = \int_0^t \cos(\arctan u)\,du$

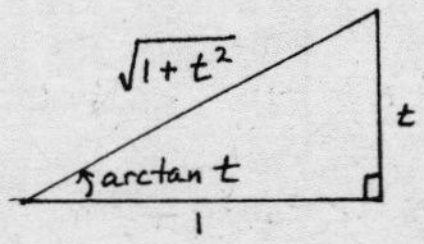

$= \displaystyle\int_0^t \frac{1}{\sqrt{1+u^2}}\,du$

$\overset{u=\tan w}{=} \displaystyle\int_0^{\arctan t} \frac{1}{\sqrt{1+\tan^2 w}}\,\sec^2 w\,dw$

$= \displaystyle\int_0^{\arctan t} \sec w\,dw = \ln|\sec w + \tan w|\,\Big|_0^{\arctan t}$

$= \ln|\sec(\arctan t) + \tan(\arctan t)| = \ln(t + \sqrt{1+t^2})$;

$\displaystyle\int_0^t \sin\theta(u)\,du = \int_0^t \sin(\arctan u)\,du = \int_0^t \frac{u}{\sqrt{1+u^2}}\,du = \sqrt{1+u^2}\,\Big|_0^t$

$= \sqrt{1+t^2} - 1$. Thus the desired parameterization is $\vec{r}(t)$

$= \ln(t + \sqrt{1+t^2})\,\vec{i} + (\sqrt{1+t^2} - 1)\,\vec{j}$

50. In each of the parameterizations, $y = 0$ for $t < 0$, so that $\kappa(t) = 0$ by (12). Thus $\lim_{t\to 0^-} \kappa(t) = 0$ in each case.

a. $x = t,\ y = t^2$ for $t > 0$. From (12), $\kappa(t) = \dfrac{|(1)(2) - 0(2t)|}{[1^2 + (2t)^2]^{3/2}}$

$= \dfrac{2}{(1 + 4t^2)^{3/2}}$, so that $\lim_{t\to 0^+} \kappa(t) = \dfrac{2}{(1+0)^{3/2}} = 2$. Thus the curvature is discontinuous at 0, and hence the function cannot trace out a railroad track.

b. $x = t,\ y = t^{7/3}$ for $t > 0$. From (12), $\kappa(t)$

$= \dfrac{\left|(1)(\frac{28}{9} t^{1/3}) - (0)(\frac{7}{3} t^{4/3})\right|}{[1^2 + (\frac{7}{3} t^{4/3})^2]^{3/2}} = \dfrac{\frac{28}{9} t^{1/3}}{[1 + \frac{49}{9} t^{8/3}]^{3/2}}$, so that $\lim_{t\to 0^+} \kappa(t)$

$= 0$. Also $\left.\dfrac{dx}{dt}\right|_{t=0} = 1$, $\left.\dfrac{d^2x}{dt^2}\right|_{t=0} = 0 = \left.\dfrac{dy}{dt}\right|_{t=0} = \left.\dfrac{d^2y}{dt^2}\right|_{t=0}$, so that by (12), $\kappa(0) = \dfrac{|1\cdot 0 - 0\cdot 0|}{(1^2 + 0^2)^{3/2}} = 0$. Thus the curvature is continuous at each point, including at 0, and hence the function could trace out a railroad track.

c. $x = t,\ y = t^3$ for $t > 0$. From (12), $\kappa(t)$

$= \dfrac{|(1)(6t) - (0)(3t^2)|}{[1^2 + (3t^2)^2]^{3/2}} = \dfrac{6t}{(1 + 9t^4)^{3/2}}$, so that $\lim_{t\to 0^+} \kappa(t) = 0$. Also

$\left.\dfrac{dx}{dt}\right|_{t=0} = 1$, $\left.\dfrac{d^2x}{dt^2}\right|_{t=0} = 0 = \left.\dfrac{dy}{dt}\right|_{t=0} = \left.\dfrac{d^2y}{dt^2}\right|_{t=0}$, so that by (12),

$\kappa(0) = \dfrac{|1\cdot 0 - 0\cdot 0|}{(1^2 + 0^2)^{3/2}} = 0$. Thus the curvature is continuous at each point, including at 0, and hence the function could trace out a railroad track.

51. $a_{\vec{T}} = \dfrac{d\|\vec{v}\|}{dt} = \dfrac{0-81}{9-0} = -9$. Since $\|\vec{v}(0)\| = 81$ and $\dfrac{d\|\vec{v}\|}{dt} = -9$, we have $\|\vec{v}\| = 81 - 9t$. Since the radius of the circle is 729, it follows that $\kappa = \dfrac{1}{\rho} = \dfrac{1}{729}$, so that by Exercise 41(a), $a_{\vec{N}} = \kappa\|\vec{v}\|^2 = \dfrac{1}{729}(81 - 9t)^2$

$= \dfrac{(9-t)^2}{9}$. Thus $\|\vec{a}\| = \sqrt{a_{\vec{T}}^2 + a_{\vec{N}}^2} = \sqrt{81 + \dfrac{(9-t)^4}{81}}$.

52. a. From (14) and (15), $\tan\theta = \dfrac{\|\vec{F}_n\| \sin\theta}{\|\vec{F}_n\| \cos} = \dfrac{\frac{m v_R^2}{\rho}}{mg} = \dfrac{v_R^2}{\rho g}$, so that $v_R^2 = \rho g \tan\theta$.

b. $v_R = \sqrt{\rho g \tan\theta} = \sqrt{500\,(32)\tan\frac{\pi}{12}} \approx 65.4766$ (feet per second), or 44.6431 (miles per hour).

c. If ρ' and $v_{R'}$ are the new radius and rated speed, respectively, then $v_{R'} = 2v_R$ if $\sqrt{\rho' g \tan\theta} = 2\sqrt{\rho g \tan\theta} = \sqrt{4\rho g \tan\theta}$, so that $\rho' = 4\rho$. Since $\rho = 500$, it follows that if $\rho' = 2000$ (feet), then the rated speed will be doubled.

53. $\vec{F} = \vec{F}_1 + \vec{F}_2 = -2\vec{k} - 2\vec{j} + 2\sqrt{3}\,\vec{k} = -2\vec{j} + 2(\sqrt{3} - 1)\vec{k}$, so that $\vec{a} = \dfrac{\vec{F}}{m} = 16\vec{F} = -32\vec{j} + 32(\sqrt{3} - 1)\vec{k}$. Since the path of the ball is circular, it follows from Example 3 that the normal vector points along the string toward the point of attachment. Thus $\vec{N} = \cos\frac{2\pi}{3}\,\vec{j} + \sin\frac{2\pi}{3}\,\vec{k} = -\frac{1}{2}\vec{j} + \frac{\sqrt{3}}{2}\vec{k}$. Then $a_{\vec{N}} = \vec{a}\cdot\vec{N} = (-32)(-\frac{1}{2}) + 32(\sqrt{3} - 1)\frac{\sqrt{3}}{2} = 16 + 16(\sqrt{3} - 1)\sqrt{3} = 64 - 16\sqrt{3}$. By Exercise 41(a), $\|\vec{v}\| = \sqrt{\dfrac{a_{\vec{N}}}{\kappa}} = \sqrt{\dfrac{64 - 16\sqrt{3}}{\frac{1}{3}}} = 4\sqrt{12 - 3\sqrt{3}} \approx 10.4337$ (feet per second).

Section 12.6

1\. a. Since $\vec{u}$ is a unit vector, $\vec{u}$ and $\frac{d\vec{u}}{dt}$ are perpendicular by Corollary 12.11. Thus by (6), $p = \|p\vec{k}\| = \left\|r^2(\vec{u} \times \frac{d\vec{u}}{dt})\right\| = r^2 \|\vec{u}\|\left\|\frac{d\vec{u}}{dt}\right\| \sin\frac{\pi}{2}$ $= r^2\left\|\frac{d\vec{u}}{dt}\right\|$.

b. Since $\frac{dr}{dt} = 0$ when r is minimum, (5) implies that $\frac{d\vec{r}}{dt} = r\frac{d\vec{u}}{dt}$ when r is minimum.

c. Since r_0 is the minimum value of r, and v_0 is the corresponding speed, it follows from (a) and (b) that $p = r_0^2\left\|\frac{d\vec{u}}{dt}\right\| = r_0\left\|r_0\frac{d\vec{u}}{dt}\right\|$ $= r_0\left\|\frac{d\vec{r}}{dt}\right\| = r_0v_0$.

2\. a. From (11) and Exercise 1(c) we find that

$$r = \frac{p^2}{GM + w\cos\theta} = \frac{r_0^2v_0^2}{GM + w\cos\theta}$$

b. From the solution of part (a) we see that r is minimum when $\cos\theta$ is maximum, that is, when $\cos\theta = 1$, or $\theta = 0$. Since the minimum value of r is r_0, we have $r_0 = \frac{r_0^2v_0^2}{GM + w}$, so that $r_0 = \frac{GM + w}{v_0^2}$.

c. If the orbit is elliptical, then by (14), $GM > w$. It then follows from the solution of part (a) that r is maximum when $\cos\theta$ is minimum, that is, when $\cos\theta = -1$, or $\theta = \pi$.

3\. If the orbit is circular, then r is constant, so that $r = r_0$. From (13) and Exercise 1(c) we have $r_0^2 = \frac{p^4}{G^2M^2} = \frac{r_0^4v_0^4}{G^2M^2}$. Solving for v_0, we find that $v_0 = \sqrt{\frac{GM}{r_0}}$.

4\. From Exercise 3, $v_0 = \sqrt{\frac{GM}{r_0}} = \sqrt{\frac{1.237 \times 10^{12}}{5000}} \approx 15{,}729.0$ (miles per hour).

5\. By (23), $T = \sqrt{\frac{4\pi^2a^3}{GM}} = \sqrt{\frac{4\pi^2(5000)^3}{1.237 \times 10^{12}}} \approx 1.99733$ (hours).

6\. For a circular orbit we have $r = a = r_0$. From (23) we have $a = \sqrt[3]{\frac{GMT^2}{4\pi^2}}$ $= \sqrt[3]{\frac{1.237 \times 10^{12} \times (23.9344)^2}{4\pi^2}} \approx 26{,}182.9$ (miles). Thus the distance of the satellite from the surface of the earth is approximately 26,182.9 - 3960 = 22,222.9 (miles). By Exercise 3, the velocity is given by $v_0 = \sqrt{\frac{GM}{r_0}}$ $= \sqrt{\frac{1.237 \times 10^{12}}{26{,}182.9}} \approx 6{,}873.47$ (miles per hour).

7\. By (22), $c = \sqrt{a^2 - b^2} = \sqrt{\frac{p^4G^2M^2}{(G^2M^2 - w^2)^2} - \frac{p^4}{G^2M^2 - w^2}} = \sqrt{\frac{G^2M^2}{G^2M^2 - w^2} - 1}$

$\frac{p^2}{\sqrt{G^2M^2 - w^2}} = \frac{w}{\sqrt{G^2M^2 - w^2}}\;\frac{p^2}{\sqrt{G^2M^2 - w^2}} = \frac{wp^2}{G^2M^2 - w^2}$. Since c is the distance from the center of the ellipse to either focus and since the center is $\left(-\frac{wp^2}{G^2M^2 - w^2}, 0\right)$ by (21), it follows that one focus is the origin, where the sun is located.

8\. By Exercise 2(b), $r = r_0$ when $\theta = 0$. Thus by Exercise 2(a), $r_0 = \frac{r_0^2v_0^2}{GM + w}$. Solving for w, we find that $w = r_0v_0^2 - GM$.

9\. a. Since $\frac{d\vec{r}}{dt}$ is perpendicular to $\vec{k}$, (9) implies that $\|GM\vec{u} + \vec{w}_1\|$ $= \left\|\frac{d\vec{r}}{dt} \times p\vec{k}\right\| = p\left\|\frac{d\vec{r}}{dt}\right\|\|\vec{k}\|\sin\frac{\pi}{2} = p\left\|\frac{d\vec{r}}{dt}\right\|$. Thus $\left\|\frac{d\vec{r}}{dt}\right\|$ $= \frac{1}{p}\|GM\vec{u} + \vec{w}_1\|$.

b. Since $\vec{w}_1 = w\vec{i}$ and $\vec{u} = \cos\theta\vec{i} + \sin\theta\vec{j}$, we have $\|GM\vec{u} + \vec{w}_1\|$ $= \|(GM\cos\theta + w)\vec{i} + GM\sin\theta\vec{j}\| = \sqrt{(GM\cos\theta + w)^2 + G^2M^2\sin^2\theta}$ $= \sqrt{G^2M^2 + w^2 + 2GMw\cos\theta}$. Thus $\|GM\vec{u} + \vec{w}_1\|$ is maximum when $\cos\theta = 1$, or $\theta = 0$, and the maximum value is GM + w. By Exercises 9(a), 8, and

1(c) we find that the maximum speed is $\frac{GM + w}{p} = \frac{r_0 v_0^2}{p} = \frac{r_0 v_0^2}{r_0 v_0} = v_0$.

10. a. $b = \sqrt{a^2 - c^2} = \sqrt{a^2 - a^2e^2} = a\sqrt{1 - e^2} \approx 92{,}955{,}821\sqrt{1 - (.016732)^2}$ $\approx 92{,}942{,}808$ (miles). By (20), $p = \frac{2\pi ab}{T}$ $\frac{2\pi(92{,}955{,}821)(92{,}942{,}808)}{24(365.256)}$ $\approx 6.19247\ \ 10^{12}$ (miles squared per hour).

b. $r_0 = a - c = a - ae = a(1 - e) \approx 92{,}955{,}821\ (1 - .016732) \approx 91{,}400{,}484$ (miles)

c. By Exercise 1(c) and the preceding results, $v_0 = \frac{p}{r_0} \approx \frac{6.19247 \times 10^{12}}{91{,}400{,}484} \approx$ 67,751.0 (miles per hour)

d. By (23) the mass M of the sun is given by

$$M = \frac{4\pi^2 a^3}{GT^2} \approx \frac{4\pi^2(92{,}955{,}821)^3}{3.024 \times 10^{-12}[24(365.256)]^2} \approx 1.36455 \times 10^{29} \quad \text{(slugs)}$$

11. a. We have $a - c = r_0 = 100 + 3960 = 4060$ and $2a = 3100 + 100 + 2(3960) = 11{,}120$, so that $a = 5560$ and $c = 5560 - 4060 = 1500$. Thus $b = \sqrt{a^2 - c^2} = \sqrt{5560^2 - 1500^2} \approx 5353.84$. By equations (20) and (23) we have $p = \frac{2\pi ab}{T} = 2\pi ab\sqrt{\frac{GM}{4\pi^2 a^3}} = b\sqrt{\frac{GM}{a}} \approx 5353.84\sqrt{\frac{1.237 \times 10^{12}}{5560}}$ $\approx 7.98570 \times 10^7$. By Exercise 1(c), $v_0 = \frac{p}{r_0} \approx \frac{7.98570 \times 10^7}{4060} \approx 19{,}669.2$ (miles per hour).

b. By Exercise 8, $w = r_0 v_0^2 - GM \approx 4060\ (19{,}669.2)^2 - 1.237 \times 10^{12}$ $\approx 3.33722 \times 10^{11}$. At aphelion $\vec{u} = -\vec{i}$ so that $\|GM\vec{u} + \vec{w}_1\| = \|-GM\vec{i} + w\vec{i}\| = GM - w$. Thus, by Exercise 9(a) the minimum velocity is given by $\left\|\frac{d\vec{r}}{dt}\right\| = \frac{1}{p}\|GM\vec{u} + \vec{w}_1\| = \frac{GM - w}{p} \approx \frac{1.237 \times 10^{12} - 3.33722 \times 10^{11}}{7.98570 \times 10^7}$ $\approx 11{,}311.2$ (miles per hour).

12. a. By Exercise 1(c), $p = r_0 v_0 = (100 + 3960)(20{,}000) = 8.12 \times 10^7$, and by Exercise 8, $w = r_0 v_0^2 - GM = (4060)(20{,}000)^2 - 1.237 \times 10^{12} = 3.87 \times 10^{11}$ Thus equation (14) becomes $[(1.237 \times 10^{12})^2 - (3.87 \times 10^{11})^2]x^2 + 2\,(3.87 \times 10^{11})(8.12 \times 10^7)^2\,x + (1.237 \times 10^{12})^2\,y^2 = (8.12 \times 10^7)^4$, or approximately $(1.38 \times 10^{24})x^2 + (5.10 \times 10^{27})x + (1.53 \times 10^{24})y^2 = 4.35 \times 10^{31}$.

b. By Exercise 2(c), $\cos\theta = -1$ at apogee. Thus by Exercise 2(a) and the values of r_0 and w found in part (a) of this exercise, $r = \frac{r_0^2 v_0^2}{GM - w}$ $\approx \frac{(4060)^2\ (20{,}000)^2}{1.237 \times 10^{12} - 3.87 \times 10^{11}} \approx 7756.99$ at apogee. Thus the distance from apogee to the surface of the earth is approximately $7756.99 - 3960 = 3796.99$ (miles).

c. By (23) and the values of p and w found in part (a) of this exercise,

$$T = \frac{2\pi p^3 GM}{(G^2M^2 - w^2)^{3/2}} \approx \frac{2\pi(8.12 \times 10^7)^3\ (1.237 \times 10^{12})}{[(1.237 \times 10^{12})^2 - (3.87 \times 10^{11})^2]^{3/2}} \approx 2.56573$$

(hours).

13. Since $GM = w$ for a parabolic orbit, it follows from Exercise 8 that $GM = w = r_0 v_0^2 - GM$, so that $v_0 = \sqrt{\frac{2GM}{r_0}}$.

14. $v_0 = \sqrt{2gr_0} = \sqrt{2(7.855 \times 10^4)(100 + 3960)} \approx 25{,}255.2$ (miles per hour).

15. Let F_e be the magnitude of the gravitational force exerted by the earth on the spacecraft, F_m the magnitude of the gravitational force exerted by the moon on the spacecraft, m the mass of the spacecraft, and M_m the mass of the moon. By Newton's Law of Gravitation,

$$\frac{F_e}{F_m} = \frac{\dfrac{GM_e m}{(240{,}000 - 4080)^2}}{\dfrac{GM_m m}{(4080)^2}} = \frac{(4080)^2}{\dfrac{M_m}{M_e}(235{,}920)^2} \approx \frac{(4080)^2}{(.0123)(235{,}920)^2} \approx .024316.$$

16. Let M_m be the mass of the moon and M_e the mass of the earth. Then $GM_m = GM_e \cdot \frac{M_m}{M_e} \approx (1.237 \times 10^{12})(.0123) = 1.52151 \times 10^{10}$.

a. By Exercise 3, $v_0 = \sqrt{\frac{GM_m}{r_0}} \approx \sqrt{\frac{1.52151 \times 10^{10}}{1200}} \approx 3560.79$ (miles per hour)

b. By Exercise 13, $v_0 = \sqrt{\frac{2GM_m}{r_0}} \approx \sqrt{\frac{2(1.52151 \times 10^{10})}{1200}} \approx 5035.72$ (miles per hour).

17. $\vec{L}'(t) = \frac{d}{dt}(\vec{r} \times m\vec{v}) = \frac{d}{dt}(\vec{r} \times m\frac{d\vec{r}}{dt}) = m\frac{d}{dt}(\vec{r} \times \frac{d\vec{r}}{dt})$. Thus by (3), $\vec{L}'(t) = \vec{0}$.

18. a. When the planet makes one revolution in a circular orbit about the sun, it travels a distance of $2\pi r$ at a constant speed v, and the length of time required is T. Thus $2\pi r = vT$, or $T = \frac{2\pi r}{v}$.

b. By (24), (25), and (26) in that order, $\|\vec{F}\| = \frac{mv^2}{r} = \frac{m}{r}(\frac{4\pi^2 r^2}{T^2}) = \frac{m}{r}(\frac{4\pi^2 r^2}{cr^3}) = \frac{4\pi^2}{c}\frac{m}{r^2}$.

Chapter 12 - Review

1.

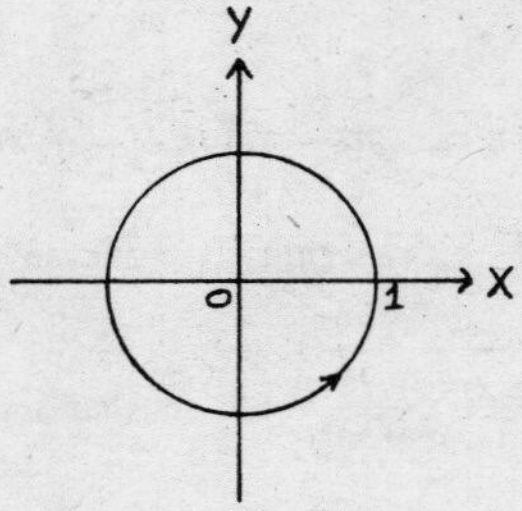

2.

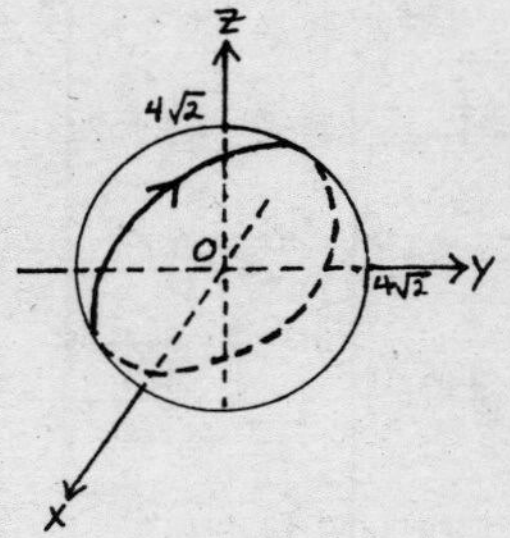

3. $(\vec{F} \times \vec{G})(t) = \begin{vmatrix} \vec{i} & \vec{j} & \vec{k} \\ t & 1 & 0 \\ 0 & 1 & t \end{vmatrix} = t\,\vec{i} - t^2\,\vec{j} + t\,\vec{k}$

$[(\vec{F} \times \vec{G}) \times \vec{H}](t) = \begin{vmatrix} \vec{i} & \vec{j} & \vec{k} \\ t & -t^2 & t \\ 0 & t & 0 \end{vmatrix} = -t^2\,\vec{i} + t^2\,\vec{k}$

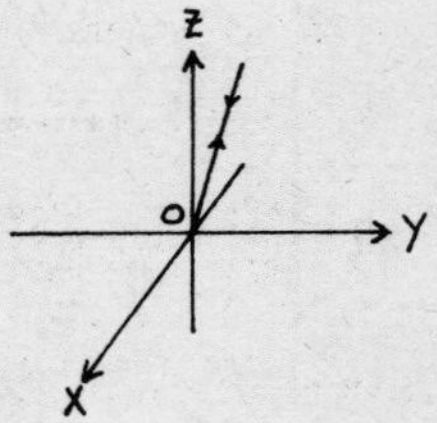

4. a. $(\vec{F} \cdot \vec{G})(t) = te^t + t^2e^{-t} + 1$; $(\vec{F} \cdot \vec{G})'(t) = e^t + te^t + 2te^{-t} - t^2e^{-t} = (1 + t)e^t + (2t - t^2)e^{-t}$

b. $(\vec{F} \times \vec{G})(t) = \begin{vmatrix} \vec{i} & \vec{j} & \vec{k} \\ e^t & t^2 & e^{-t} \\ t & e^{-t} & e^t \end{vmatrix} = (t^2e^t - e^{-2t})\,\vec{i} + (te^{-t} - e^{2t})\,\vec{j} + (1 - t^3)\,\vec{k}$; $(\vec{F} \times \vec{G})'(t) = (2te^t + t^2e^t + 2e^{-2t})\,\vec{i} + (e^{-t} - te^{-t} - 2e^{2t})\,\vec{j} - 3t^2\,\vec{k}$

5. a. $(\vec{F} \cdot \vec{G})(t) = t^3$; $(\vec{F} \cdot \vec{G})'(t) = 3t^2$

b. $(\vec{F} \times \vec{G})(t) = \begin{vmatrix} \vec{i} & \vec{j} & \vec{k} \\ \frac{1}{t} & t & 0 \\ 0 & t^2 & \frac{-1}{t^2} \end{vmatrix} = \frac{-1}{t}\,\vec{i} + \frac{1}{t^3}\,\vec{j} + t\,\vec{k}$; $(\vec{F} \times \vec{G})'(t) = \frac{1}{t^2}\,\vec{i} - \frac{3}{t^4}\,\vec{j} + \vec{k}$

6. $(\vec F \circ g)'(t) = \vec F'(g(t))\, g'(t) = \left[\frac{1}{e^{2t}}\vec i + (\ln\ e^{2t} + 1)\,\vec j - \frac{1}{e^{2t}}\vec k\right](2e^{2t})$

$= 2\,\vec i + 2e^{2t}\,(2t + 1)\,\vec j - 2\,\vec k$

7. $\int(\tan 2\pi t\,\vec i + \sec^2 2\pi t\,\vec j + \frac{4}{1 + t^2}\vec k)\,dt = (\int \tan 2\pi t\ dt)\,\vec i + (\int \sec^2 2\pi t\ dt)\,\vec j$

$+ (\int \frac{4}{1 + t^2}\,dt)\,\vec k = -\frac{1}{2\pi}\ln\left|\cos 2\pi t\right|\vec i + \frac{1}{2\pi}\tan 2\pi t\,\vec j + 4\arctan t\,\vec k + \vec C$

8. $\|\vec F(t)\| = \sqrt{\frac{4t^2}{(1 + t^2)^2} + \frac{(1 - t^2)^2}{(1 + t^2)^2}} = \sqrt{\frac{1 + 2t^2 + t^4}{(1 + t^2)^2}} = 1$, so that by Corollary 12.11, $\vec F(t) \cdot \vec F'(t) = 0$. Since $\vec F(t) \neq \vec 0$ for all t, it follows that $\vec F$ is perpendicular to $\vec F'$.

9. a. $\mathcal{L} = \int_0^{3\pi}\sqrt{(e^t\cos t - e^t\sin t)^2 + (e^t\sin t + e^t\cos t)^2}\,dt$

$= \int_0^{3\pi} e^t\sqrt{2}\,dt = e^t\sqrt{2}\,\Big|_0^{3\pi} = \sqrt{2}\,(e^{3\pi} - 1)$.

b. As in part (a) but with the limits of integration altered,

$\mathcal{L} = \int_{-2\pi}^{1} e^t\sqrt{2}\,dt = e^t\sqrt{2}\,\Big|_{-2\pi}^{1} = \sqrt{2}\,(e - e^{-2\pi})$

10. $\vec r'(t) = 2e^{2t}\,\vec i + 2\sqrt{2}\,e^t\,\vec j + 2\,\vec k$; $\|\vec r'(t)\| = \sqrt{(2e^{2t})^2 + (2\sqrt{2}\,e^t)^2 + 2^2}$

$= 2\sqrt{e^{4t} + 2e^{2t} + 1} = 2(e^{2t} + 1)$; $\vec T(t) = \frac{\vec r'(t)}{\|\vec r'(t)\|} = \frac{e^{2t}}{e^{2t} + 1}\vec i + \frac{\sqrt{2}\,e^t}{e^{2t} + 1}\vec j$

$+ \frac{1}{e^{2t} + 1}\vec k$; $\vec T'(t) = \frac{2e^{2t}(e^{2t} + 1) - e^{2t}(2e^{2t})}{(e^{2t} + 1)^2}\vec i$

$+ \frac{\sqrt{2}\,e^t(e^{2t} + 1) - \sqrt{2}\,e^t(2e^{2t})}{(e^{2t} + 1)^2}\vec j - \frac{2e^{2t}}{(e^{2t} + 1)^2}\vec k = \frac{2e^{2t}}{(e^{2t} + 1)^2}\vec i$

$+ \frac{\sqrt{2}\,(-e^{3t} + e^t)}{(e^{2t} + 1)^2}\vec j - \frac{2e^{2t}}{(e^{2t} + 1)^2}\vec k$; $\|\vec T'(t)\| = \frac{e^t}{(e^{2t} + 1)^2}\cdot$

$\cdot\sqrt{(2e^t)^2 + (\sqrt{2}\,(-e^{2t} + 1))^2 + (-2e^t)^2} = \frac{e^t}{(e^{2t} + 1)^2}\sqrt{2e^{4t} + 4e^{2t} + 2}$

$= \frac{\sqrt{2}\,e^t}{e^{2t} + 1}$; $\vec N(t) = \frac{\vec T'(t)}{\|\vec T'(t)\|} = \frac{\sqrt{2}\,e^t}{e^{2t} + 1}\vec i + \frac{(1 - e^{2t})}{e^{2t} + 1}\vec j - \frac{\sqrt{2}\,e^t}{e^{2t} + 1}\vec k$;

$\kappa(t) = \frac{\|\vec T'(t)\|}{\|\vec r'(t)\|} = \frac{\frac{\sqrt{2}\,e^t}{e^{2t} + 1}}{2(e^{2t} + 1)} = \frac{\sqrt{2}\,e^t}{2(e^{2t} + 1)^2}$

11. $\vec r = e^t\,\vec i + \ln(\sec e^t)\,\vec j$; $\vec v = e^t\,\vec i + \frac{(\sec e^t\tan e^t)\,e^t}{\sec e^t}\vec j = e^t\,\vec i$

$+ e^t\tan e^t\,\vec j$; $\|\vec v\| = e^t\sqrt{1 + \tan^2 e^t} = e^t\left|\sec e^t\right|$; at time 0,

$\|\vec v\| = e^0\left|\sec e^0\right| = \sec 1$.

12. $\vec r = \left[(\tfrac{3}{2}t)^{2/3} - 1\right]\vec i + \frac{2}{3}\left[(\tfrac{3}{2}t)^{2/3} - 1\right]^{3/2}\vec j$; $\vec v = \frac{2}{3}(\tfrac{3}{2}t)^{-1/3}(\tfrac{3}{2})\,\vec i$

$+ \left[(\tfrac{3}{2}t)^{2/3} - 1\right]^{1/2}(\tfrac{2}{3})(\tfrac{3}{2}t)^{-1/3}(\tfrac{3}{2})\,\vec j = (\tfrac{3}{2}t)^{-1/3}\,\vec i + \left[(\tfrac{3}{2}t)^{2/3} - 1\right]^{1/2}\cdot$

$\cdot(\tfrac{3}{2}t)^{-1/3}\,\vec j$; $\|\vec v\| = (\tfrac{3}{2}t)^{-1/3}\sqrt{1 + \left[(\tfrac{3}{2}t)^{2/3} - 1\right]} = (\tfrac{3}{2}t)^{-1/3}(\tfrac{3}{2}t)^{1/3} = 1$.

13. $\vec r(0) = 0\,\vec i + 0\,\vec j = \vec 0$, so that the Folium of Descartes passes through the origin. $\vec r'(t) = \frac{3(1 + t^3) - 3t(3t^2)}{(1 + t^3)^2}\vec i + \frac{6t(1 + t^3) - 3t^2(3t^2)}{(1 + t^3)^2}\vec j$

$= \frac{3(1 - 2t^3)}{(1 + t^3)^2}\vec i + \frac{3t(2 - t^3)}{(1 + t^3)^2}\vec j$; $\vec r'(0) = 3\,\vec i$; $\vec T(0) = \frac{\vec r'(0)}{\|\vec r'(0)\|} = \vec i$, so that $\vec T(0)$ is parallel to the x axis.

14. $\vec r'(t) = \cos t\,\vec i + \left[-\sin t + \frac{(\sec^2\frac{t}{2})\,\frac{1}{2}}{\tan\frac{t}{2}}\right]\vec j = \cos t\,\vec i + (-\sin t + \frac{1}{2\sin\frac{t}{2}\cos\frac{t}{2}})\,\vec j$

$= \cos t\,\vec i + (-\sin t + \frac{1}{\sin t})\,\vec j = \cos t\,\vec i + (\frac{-\sin^2 t + 1}{\sin t})\,\vec j = \cos t\,\vec i + \frac{\cos^2 t}{\sin t}\vec j$

$= \cos t\,\vec i + \cos t\cot t\,\vec j$. Thus if $0 < t < \pi$ and $t \neq \frac{\pi}{2}$, then an equation of the tangent line at $(\sin t, \cos t + \ln(\tan\frac{t}{2}))$ is $y - \cos t - \ln(\tan\frac{t}{2})$ $= \frac{\cos t\cot t}{\cos t}(x - \sin t) = (\cot t)(x - \sin t)$. This line intersects the y axis at the point $(0, y_0)$ for which $y_0 - \cos t - \ln(\tan\frac{t}{2})$ $= (\cot t)(0 - \sin t) = -\cos t$, so that $y_0 = \ln(\tan\frac{t}{2})$. Thus the distance from the point $(0, \ln(\tan\frac{t}{2}))$ of intersection with the y axis to the point $(\sin t, \cos t + \ln(\tan\frac{t}{2}))$ is

$$\sqrt{(\sin t - 0)^2 + (\cos t + \ln(\tan\frac{t}{2}) - \ln(\tan\frac{t}{2}))^2} = \sqrt{\sin^2 t + \cos^2 t} = 1.$$

15. $\vec{r}\,'(t) = (1 - \cos t)\vec{i} + \sin t\,\vec{j} + 2\cos\frac{t}{2}\vec{k}$; $\|\vec{r}\,'(t)\|$

$= \sqrt{(1 - \cos t)^2 + \sin^2 t + 4\cos^2\frac{t}{2}} = \sqrt{1 - 2\cos t + \cos^2 t + \sin^2 t + 4\cos^2\frac{t}{2}}$

$= \sqrt{2 - 2\cos t + 2 + 2\cos t} = 2$; $\vec{T}(t) = \frac{\vec{r}\,'(t)}{\|\vec{r}\,'(t)\|} = \frac{1}{2}(1 - \cos t)\vec{i}$

$+ \frac{1}{2}\sin t\,\vec{j} + \cos\frac{t}{2}\vec{k}$; $\vec{T}\,'(t) = \frac{1}{2}\sin t\,\vec{i} + \frac{1}{2}\cos t\,\vec{j} - \frac{1}{2}\sin\frac{t}{2}\vec{k}$; $\|\vec{T}\,'(t)\|$

$= \frac{1}{2}\sqrt{\sin^2 t + \cos^2 t + \sin^2\frac{t}{2}} = \frac{1}{2}\sqrt{1 + \sin^2\frac{t}{2}} = \frac{1}{2}\sqrt{\frac{3}{2} - \frac{1}{2}\cos t}$

$= \frac{\sqrt{2}}{4}\sqrt{3 - \cos t}$ $\quad \vec{N}(t) = \frac{\vec{T}\,'(t)}{\|\vec{T}\,'(t)\|} = \frac{\sqrt{2}\sin t}{\sqrt{3 - \cos t}}\vec{i} + \frac{\sqrt{2}\cos t}{\sqrt{3 - \cos t}}\vec{j}$

$- \frac{\sqrt{2}\sin\frac{t}{2}}{\sqrt{3 - \cos t}}\vec{k}$; $\kappa(t) = \frac{\|\vec{T}\,'(t)\|}{\|\vec{r}\,'(t)\|} = \frac{\sqrt{2}}{8}\sqrt{3 - \cos t}$

16. $\vec{v} = (3 - 3t^2)\vec{i} + 6t\,\vec{j} + (3 + 3t^2)\vec{k}$;

$\|\vec{v}\| = \sqrt{(3 - 3t^2)^2 + (6t)^2 + (3 + 3t^2)^2} = \sqrt{18 + 36t^2 + 18t^4}$

$= 3\sqrt{2}(1 + t^2)$; $\vec{a} = -6t\,\vec{i} + 6\,\vec{j} + 6t\,\vec{k}$;

$$\vec{v}\times\vec{a} = \begin{vmatrix} \vec{i} & \vec{j} & \vec{k} \\ 3-3t^2 & 6t & 3+3t^2 \\ -6t & 6 & 6t \end{vmatrix} = 18(t^2 - 1)\vec{i} - 36t\,\vec{j} + 18(t^2 + 1)\vec{k}$$

$\|\vec{v}\times\vec{a}\| = 18\sqrt{(t^2 - 1)^2 + (-2t)^2 + (t^2 + 1)^2} = 18\sqrt{2t^4 + 4t^2 + 2}$

$= 18\sqrt{2}(t^2 + 1)$; $\kappa = \frac{\|\vec{v}\times\vec{a}\|}{\|\vec{v}\|^3} = \frac{18\sqrt{2}(t^2 + 1)}{[3\sqrt{2}(1 + t^2)]^3} = \frac{1}{3(1 + t^2)^2}$

17. $\vec{v} = e^t(\cos t - \sin t)\vec{i} + e^t(\sin t + \cos t)\vec{j} + e^t\vec{k}$;

$\vec{a} = e^t(\cos t - \sin t - \sin t - \cos t)\vec{i} + e^t(\sin t + \cos t + \cos t - \sin t)\vec{j}$

$+ e^t\vec{k} = -2e^t\sin t\,\vec{i} + 2e^t\cos t\,\vec{j} + e^t\vec{k}$; $\|\vec{v}\|$

$= \sqrt{e^{2t}(\cos t - \sin t)^2 + e^{2t}(\sin t + \cos t)^2 + e^{2t}} = e^t\sqrt{3}$

$$\vec{v}\times\vec{a} = \begin{vmatrix} \vec{i} & \vec{j} & \vec{k} \\ e^t(\cos t - \sin t) & e^t(\sin t + \cos t) & e^t \\ -2e^t\sin t & 2e^t\cos t & e^t \end{vmatrix}$$

$= e^{2t}(\sin t - \cos t)\vec{i} - e^{2t}(\sin t + \cos t)\vec{j} + 2e^{2t}\vec{k}$;

$\|\vec{v}\times\vec{a}\| = e^{2t}\sqrt{(\sin t - \cos t)^2 + (\sin t + \cos t)^2 + 2^2} = e^{2t}\sqrt{6}$

$\kappa = \frac{\|\vec{v}\times\vec{a}\|}{\|\vec{v}\|^3} = \frac{e^{2t}\sqrt{6}}{(e^t\sqrt{3})^3} = \frac{\sqrt{2}}{3e^t}$; $\rho = \frac{1}{\kappa} = \frac{3\sqrt{2}e^t}{2}$

18. $\vec{v} = \vec{i} + \sinh t\,\vec{j}$; $\|\vec{v}\| = \sqrt{1 + \sinh^2 t} = \cosh t$; $\vec{a} = \cosh t\,\vec{j}$; $\vec{v}\times\vec{a}$

$= \cosh t\,\vec{k}$; $\|\vec{v}\times\vec{a}\| = \cosh t$; $\kappa = \frac{\|\vec{v}\times\vec{a}\|}{\|\vec{v}\|^3} = \frac{\cosh t}{\cosh^3 t} = \frac{1}{\cosh^2 t}$

19. a. $y = \frac{1}{x}$, $\frac{dy}{dx} = -\frac{1}{x^2}$, $\frac{d^2y}{dx^2} = \frac{2}{x^3}$; $\kappa = \frac{\left|\frac{d^2y}{dx^2}\right|}{\left[1 + \left(\frac{dy}{dx}\right)^2\right]^{3/2}} = \frac{\frac{2}{x^3}}{(1 + \frac{1}{x^4})^{3/2}}$

$= \frac{2x^3}{(x^4 + 1)^{3/2}}$

b. $\frac{d\kappa}{dx} = \frac{6x^2(x^4 + 1)^{3/2} - 2x^3\left(\frac{3}{2}\right)(x^4 + 1)^{1/2}(4x^3)}{(x^4 + 1)^3} = \frac{6x^2(1 - x^4)}{(x^4 + 1)^{5/2}}$

Since $\frac{d\kappa}{dx} > 0$ for $x < 1$ and $\frac{d\kappa}{dx} < 0$ for $x > 1$, it follows from Theorem 4.11 that κ is maximum for $x = 1$. Thus the maximum value of κ is $\kappa(1) = \frac{2}{2^{3/2}} = \frac{\sqrt{2}}{2}$.

c. Using the value of κ at $(1, 1)$ from part (b), we have $\rho(1) = \frac{1}{\kappa(1)}$ $= \sqrt{2}$. Thus the radius of curvature at $(1, 1)$ is $\sqrt{2}$.

20. Since $\|\vec{v}\| = 1$ and $\vec{a} = \frac{d\vec{v}}{dt}$, it follows from Corollary 12.11 that $\vec{v} \cdot \vec{a} = \vec{v} \cdot \frac{d\vec{v}}{dt} = 0$. Since $\|\vec{v}\| = \|\vec{a}\| = 1$, we conclude that $\vec{v}$ and $\vec{a}$ are perpendicular. Thus $\|\vec{v} \times \vec{a}\| = \|\vec{v}\|\,\|\vec{a}\| \sin\frac{\pi}{2} = 1$, so that

$$\kappa = \frac{\|\vec{v} \times \vec{a}\|}{\|\vec{v}\|^3} = 1.$$

13 PARTIAL DERIVATIVES

Section 13.1

1. all (x, y) such that $x \geq 0$ and $y \geq 0$
2. all (x, y) such that $x + y \geq 0$
3. all (x, y) such that $x \neq 0$ and $y \neq 0$
4. all (x, y) such that $xy \neq 0$
5. all (x, y) such that $x^2 + y^2 \geq 25$
6. all (x, y) such that $x^2 + y^2 \leq 25$
7. all (x, y) such that $x + y \neq 0$
8. all (u, v) such that $u^2 \neq v^2$
9. all (x, y, z) such that $x^2 + y^2 + z^2 \leq 1$
10. all (x, y, z) such that $xyz \neq 0$
11. all (x, y, z) such that $x \neq 0$, $y \neq 0$, and $z \neq 0$
12. all (x, y, z) such that $y \neq z$

13.

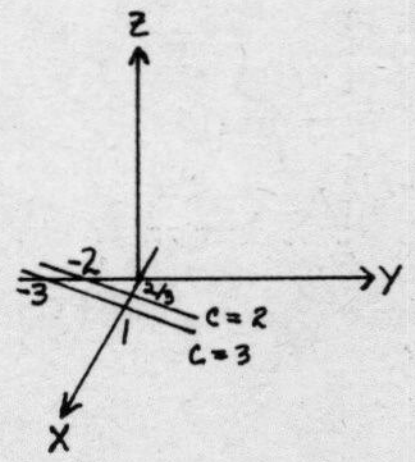

14.

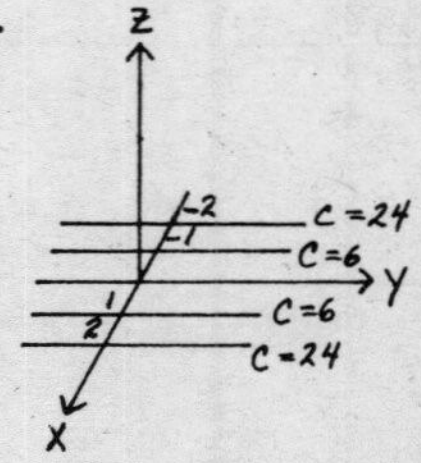

15.

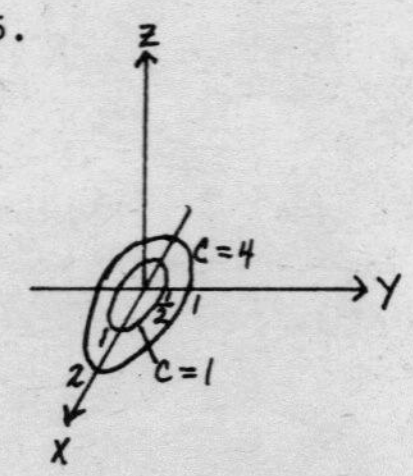

16.

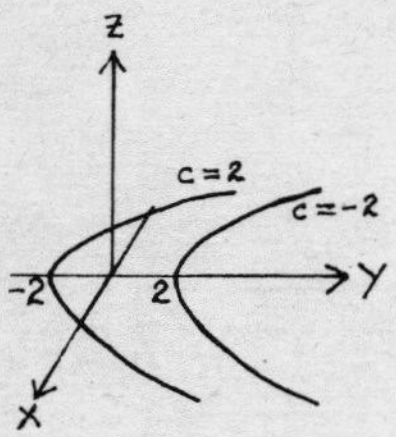

17.

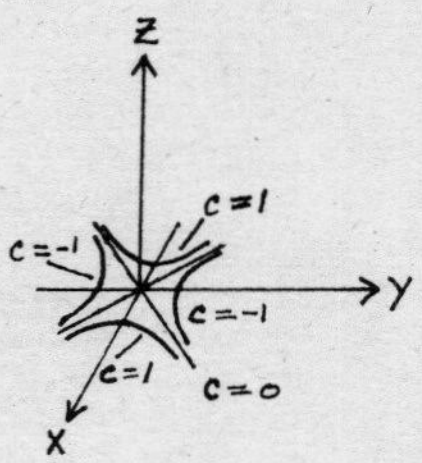

18.

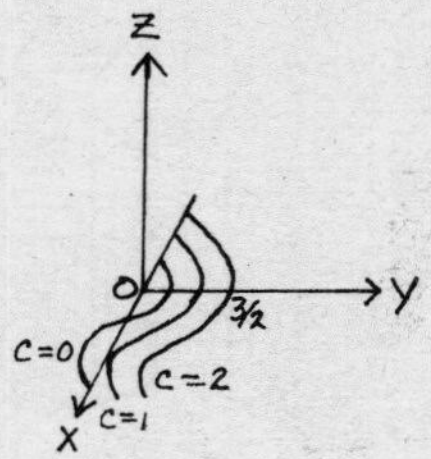

19.

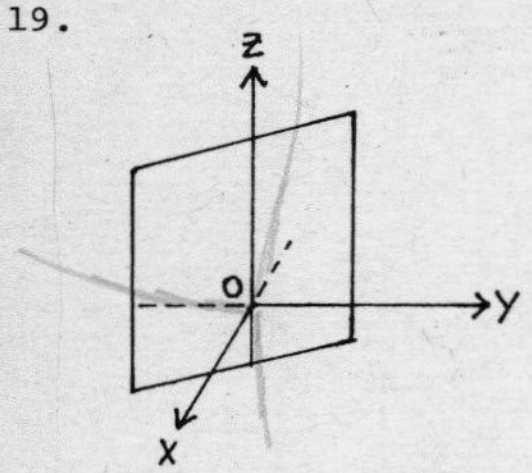

20.

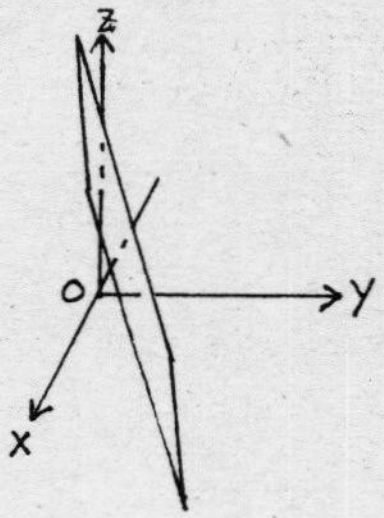

21.

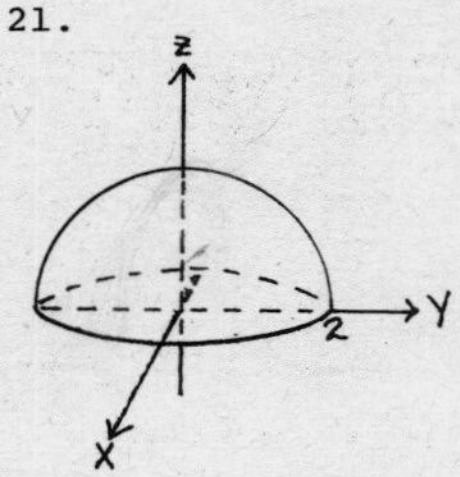

22.

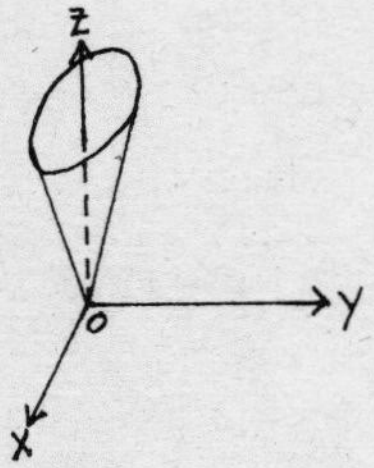

23.

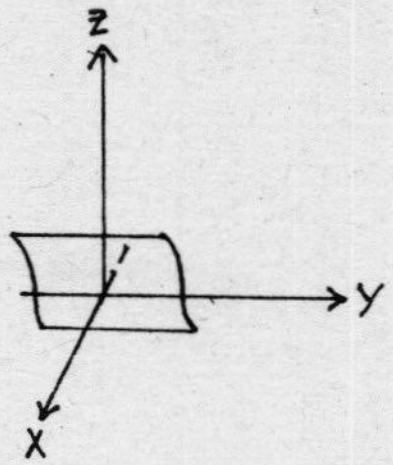

24.

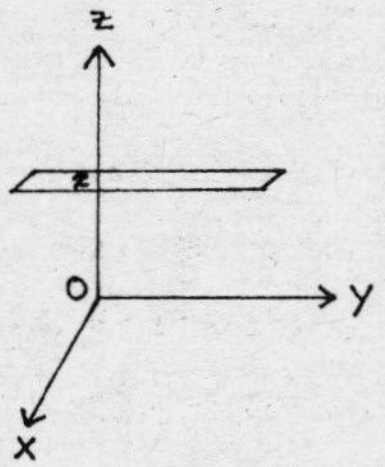

25.

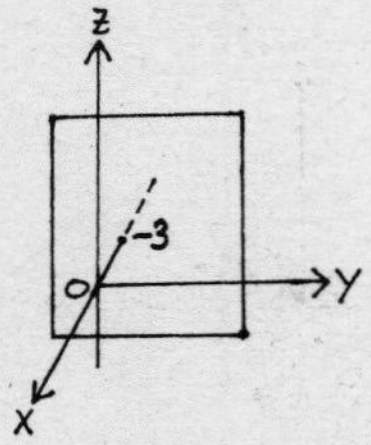

26.

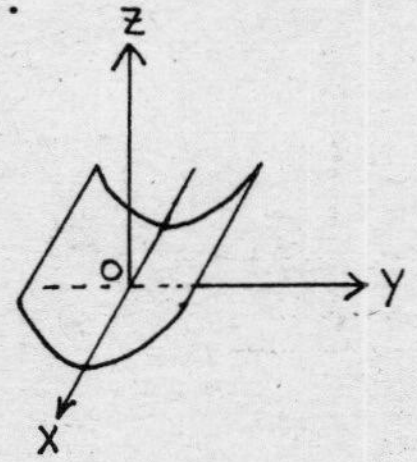

27.

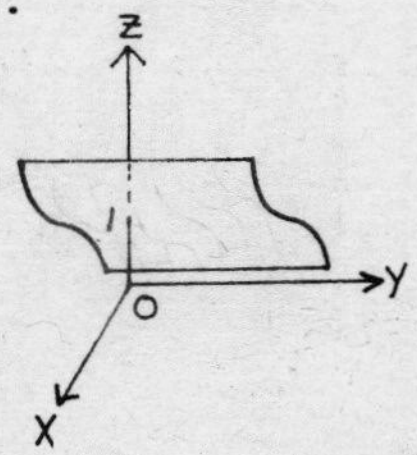

28.

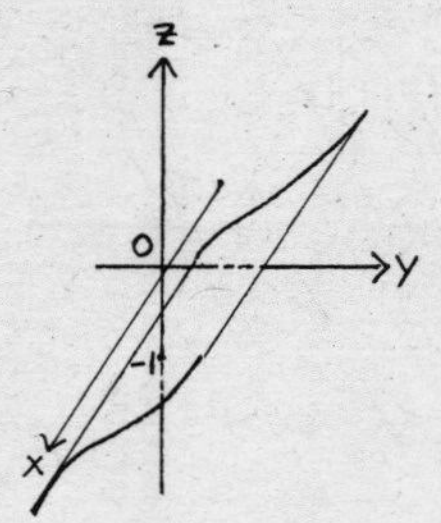

29.

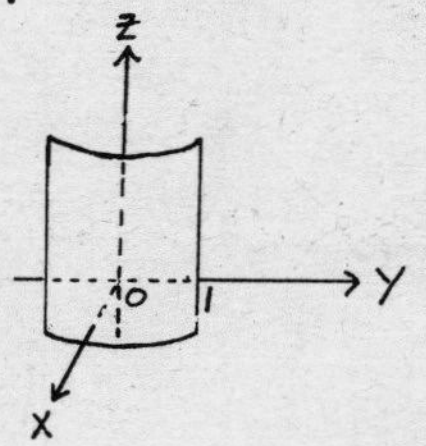

30.

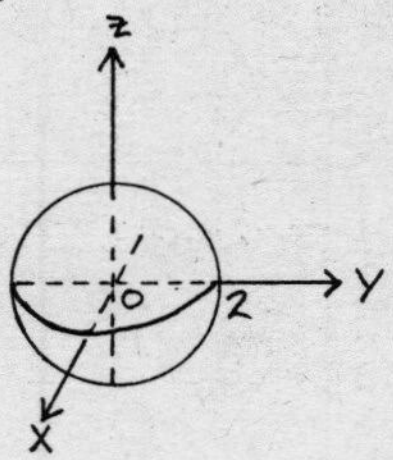

31.

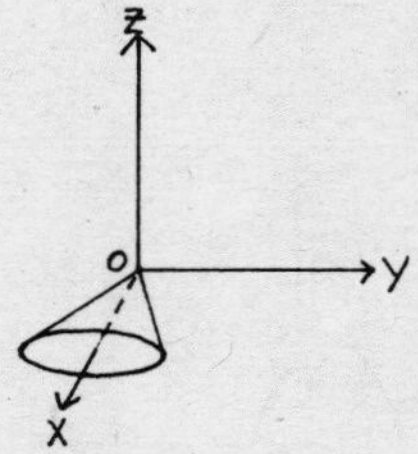

32.

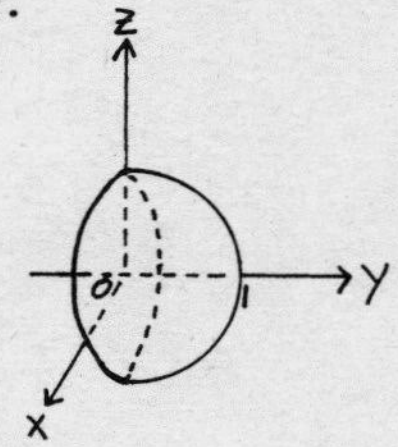

33.

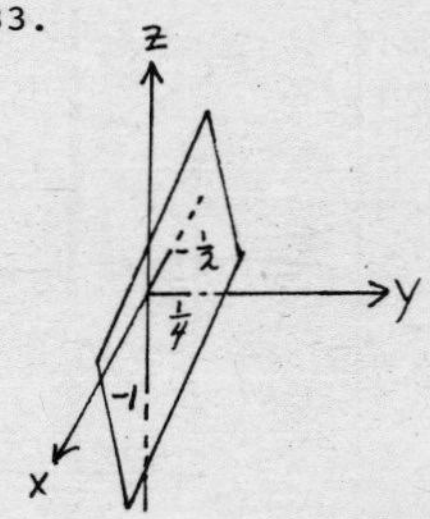

34.

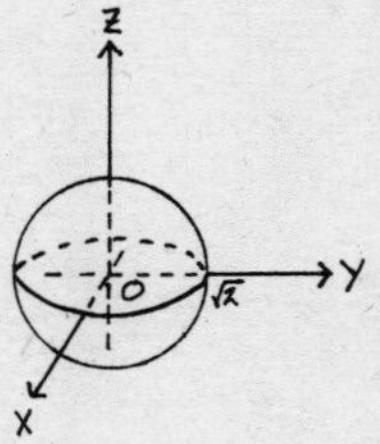

35.

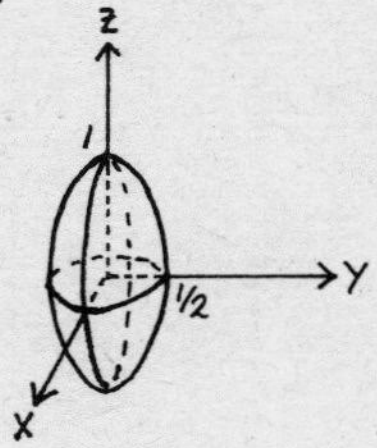

36.

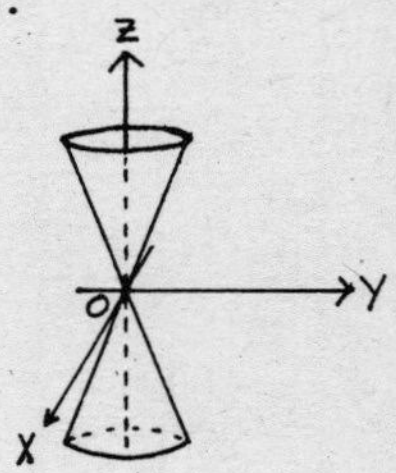

37.

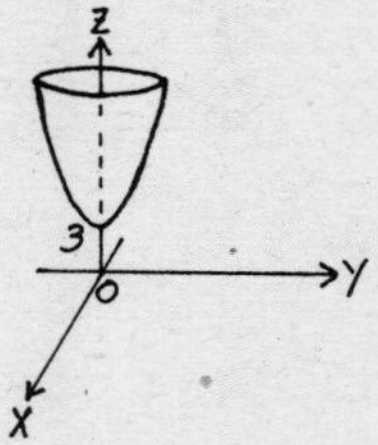

38.

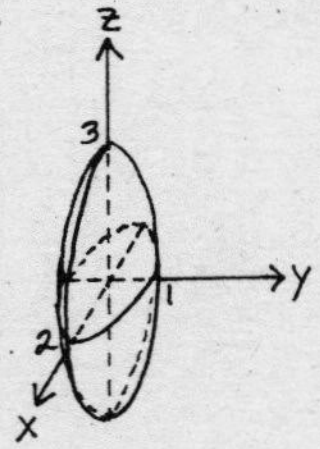

39.

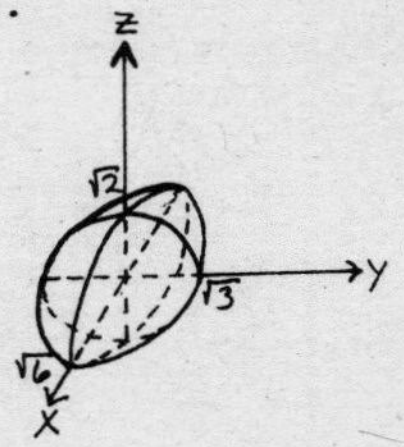

40.

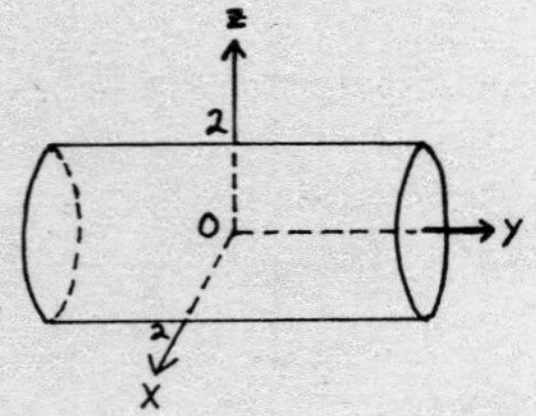

41.

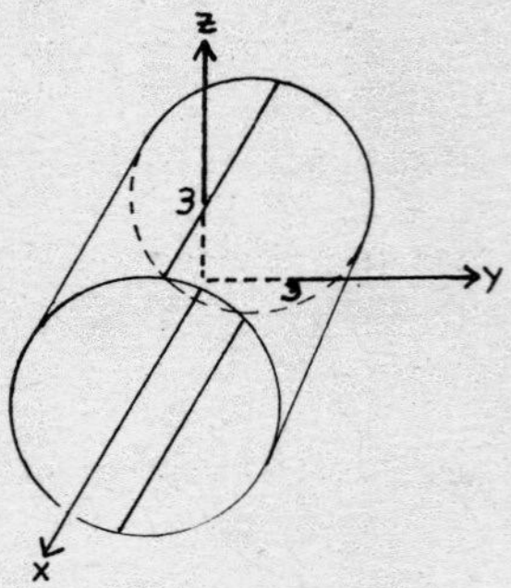

42.

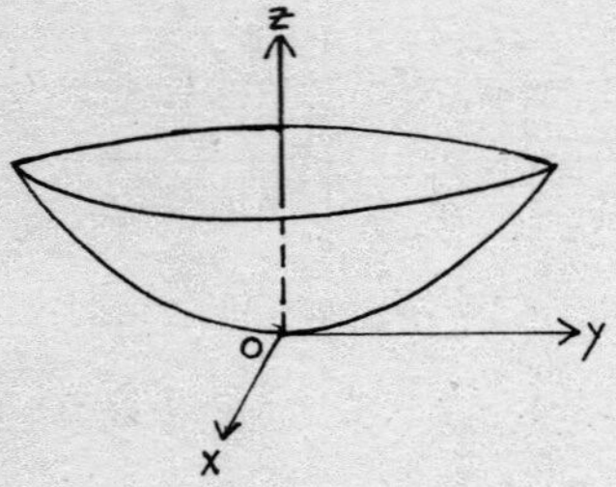

43.

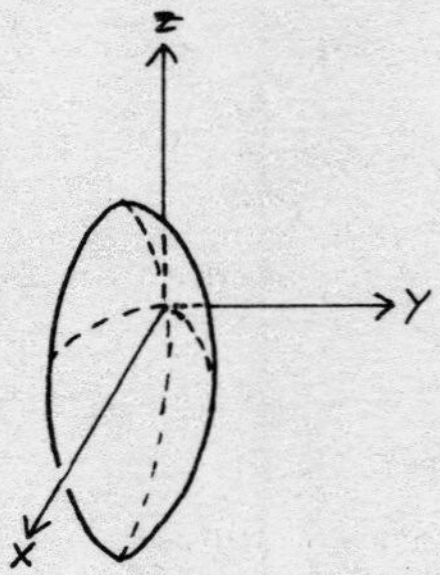

44.

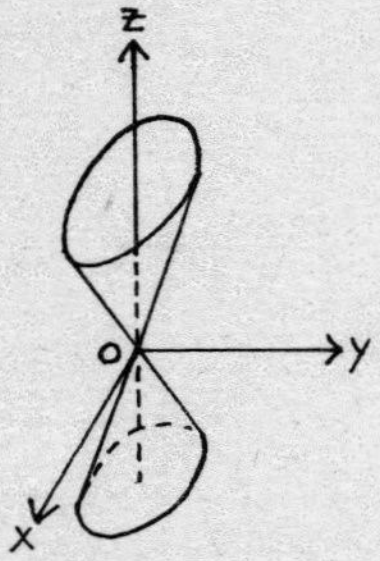

45.

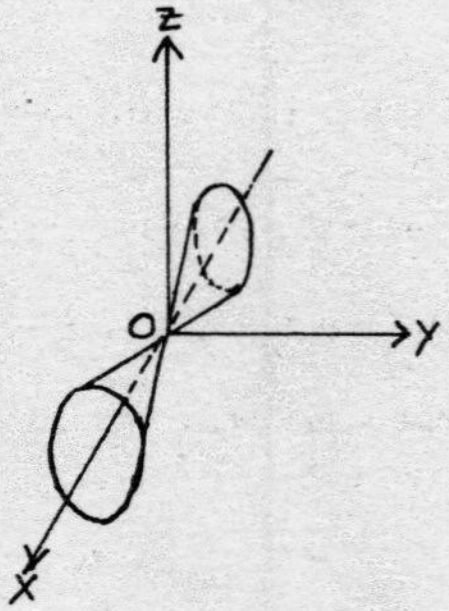

46.

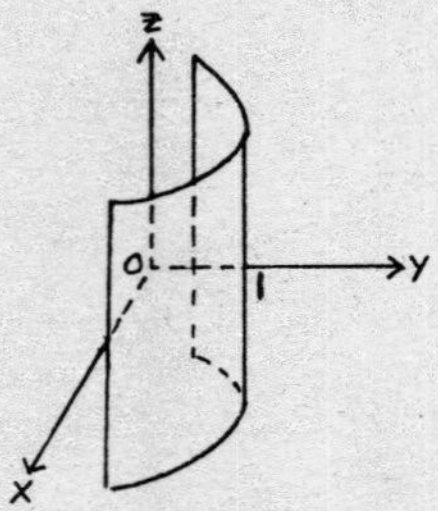

47.

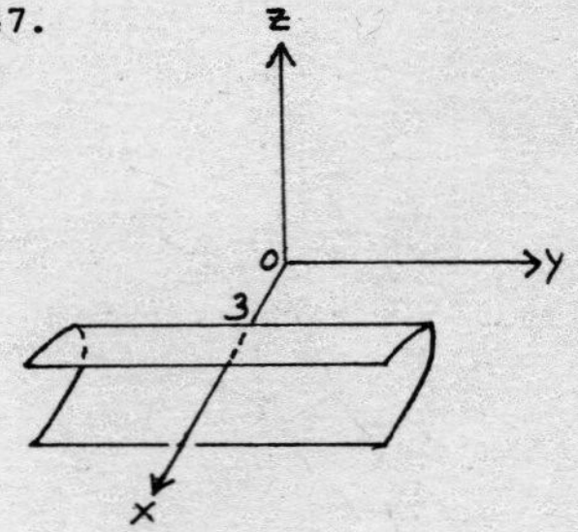

48.

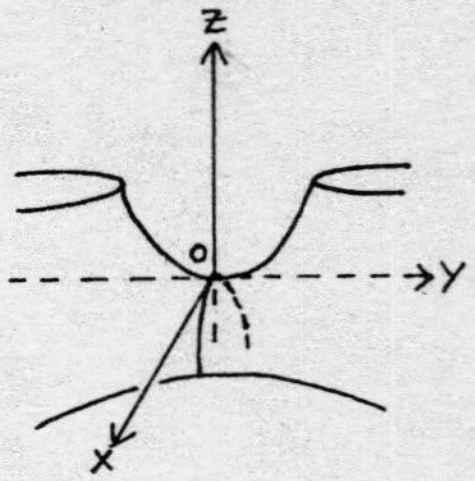

49.

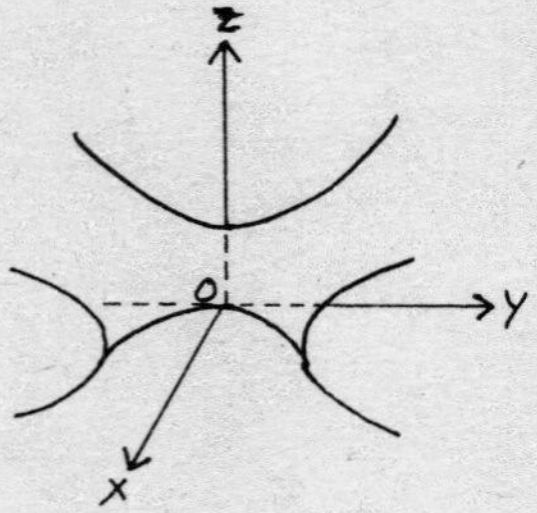

50.

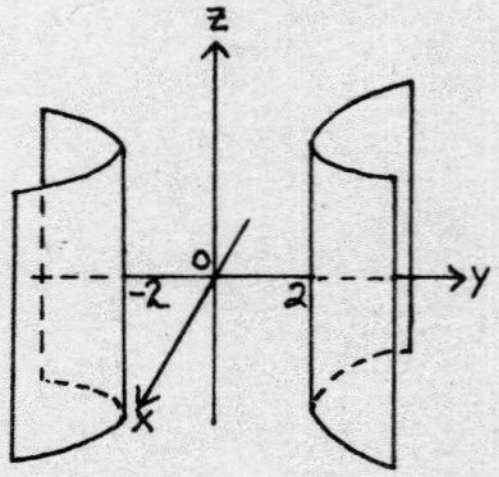

51.

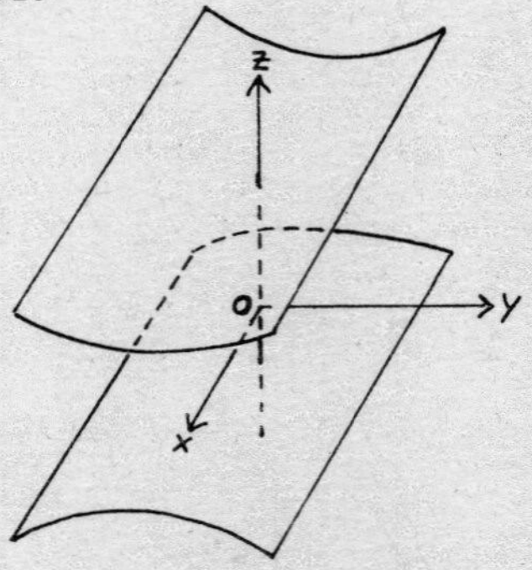

52.

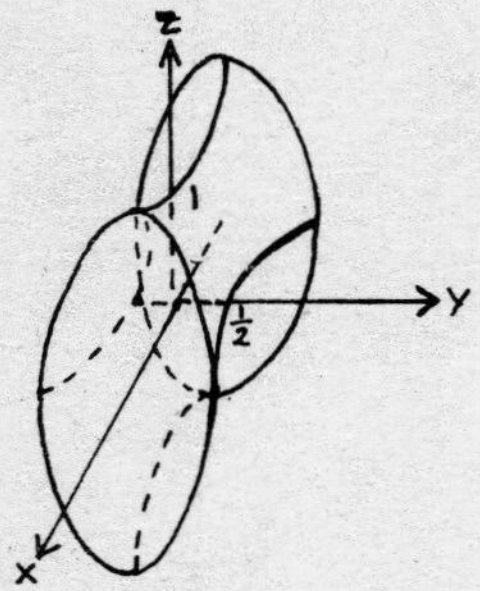

53.

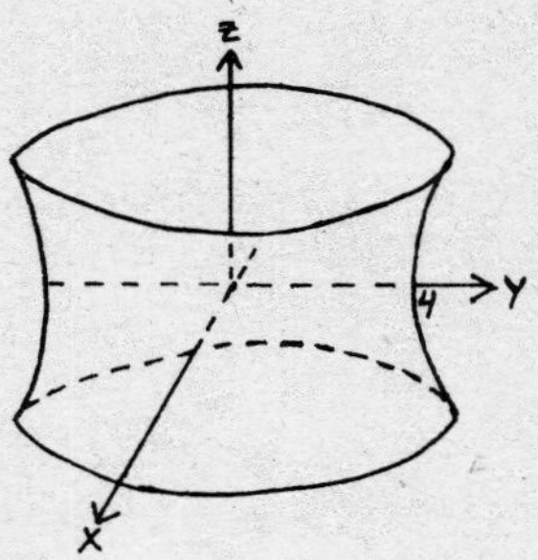

54.

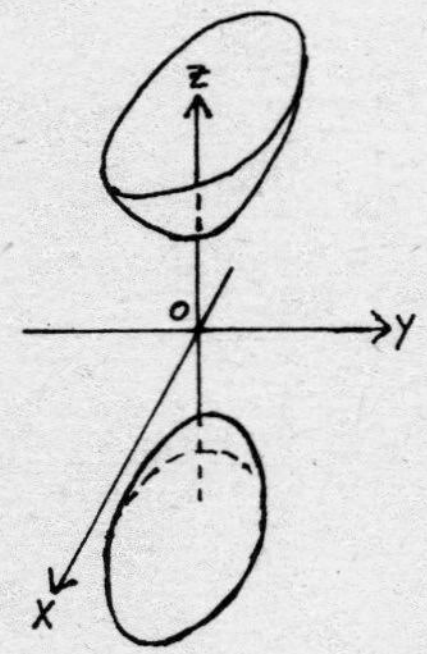

55.

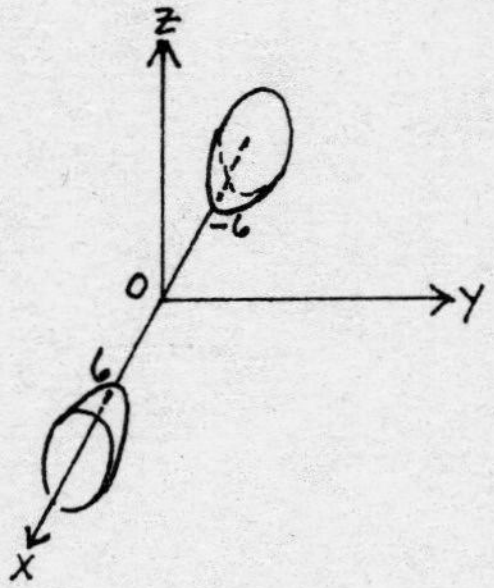

56. Let $f(x, y) = 4 - x^2 - y^2$ and $g(t) = \sqrt{t}$.

57. Let $f(x, y) = x^2 + 6y$ and $g(t) = \ln t$.

58. Let $f(x, y) = x\sqrt{y}$ and $g(t) = e^t$.

59. Let $f(x, y) = xy$ and $g(t) = t^2 + 5t + 10$.

60. Let $f(x, y) = \dfrac{x^2}{x^2 + y^2}$ and $g(t) = (\sin t)^{2/3} - 3$.

61. $h = \dfrac{V}{\pi r^2}$ for $r > 0$ and $V > 0$

62. $r = \sqrt{\dfrac{3V}{\pi h}}$ for $h > 0$ and $V > 0$

63. Let x and y denote the dimensions of the base and z the height. Then the surface area is given by $S = xy + 2xz + 2yz$ for $x > 0$, $y > 0$, and $z > 0$.

64. The amount of metal is given by $A = xy + 3xz + 7yz$ for $x > 0$, $y > 0$, and $z > 0$.

65. The cost in dollars is given by $C = \frac{1}{10}xy$ for $x > 0$ and $y > 0$.

66. The area to be painted is $xy - 1$ square meters; thus the cost in dollars is given by $C = \frac{1}{10}(xy - 1)$ for $xy > 1$.

67. For any positive constant b, the level surface $E(x, y, z) = b$ consists of all (x, y, z) such that $\dfrac{c}{\sqrt{x^2 + y^2}} = b$, or $x^2 + y^2 = \dfrac{c^2}{b^2}$. Thus the level surfaces are circular cylinders.

68. For any positive constant b, the level surface $F(x, y, z) = b$ consists of all (x, y, z) such that $\dfrac{c}{x^2 + y^2 + z^2} = b$, or $x^2 + y^2 + z^2 = \dfrac{c}{b}$. Thus the level surfaces are spheres.

69. For any constant b, the level curve $T(x, y) = b$ consists of all (x, y) such that $x \geq 0$, $y \geq 0$, and $xy = b$. Thus the level curves are either hyperbolas or two intersecting lines.

70. The level curve $f(x, y) = 3$ is given by $(x + 1)(y + 2) = 3$, or $y = \frac{3}{x + 1} - 2 = \frac{1 - 2x}{x + 1}$, for (x, y) such that $x \geq 0$ and $y \geq 0$. Since $y = \frac{1 - 2x}{x + 1} \geq 0$ if and only if $0 \leq x \leq \frac{1}{2}$, the level curve is given by $y = \frac{3}{x + 1} - 2 = \frac{1 - 2x}{x + 1}$ for $0 \leq x \leq \frac{1}{2}$. Analogously, the level curve $f(x, y) = 4$ is given by $(x + 1)(y + 2) = 4$, or $y = \frac{4}{x + 1} - 2 = \frac{2 - 2x}{x + 1}$, for $0 \leq x \leq 1$.

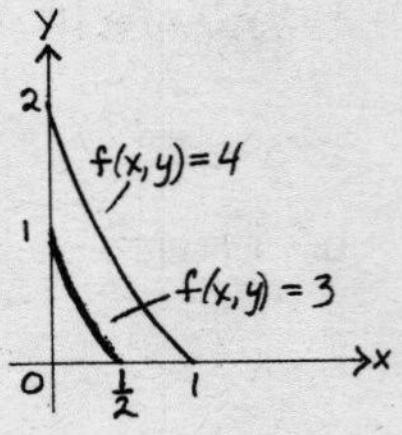

Section 13.2

1. $\lim_{(x, y)\to(2, 4)} (x + \frac{1}{2}) = 2 + \frac{1}{2} = \frac{5}{2}$

2. $\lim_{(x, y)\to(1, -2)} (2x^3 - 4xy + 5y^2) = 2(1)^3 - 4(1)(-2) + 5(-2)^2 = 30$

3. $\lim_{(x, y)\to(1, 0)} \frac{x^2 - xy + 1}{x^2 + y^2} = \frac{1^2 - (1)(0) + 1}{1^2 + 0^2} = 2$

4. $\lim_{(x, y, z)\to(-1, 2, 0)} (x^2 + 3y - 4z^2 + 2) = (-1)^2 + 3(2) - 4(0)^2 + 2 = 9$

5. $\lim_{(x, y, z)\to(2, 1, -1)} \frac{2x^2y - xz^2}{y^2 - xz} = \frac{2(2)^2(1) - (2)(-1)^2}{1^2 - (2)(-1)} = 2$

6. $\lim_{(x, y)\to(-1, 1)} \frac{x^2 + 2xy^2 + y^4}{1 + y^2} = \lim_{(x, y)\to(-1, 1)} \frac{(x + y^2)^2}{1 + y^2}$

$= \frac{(-1 + 1^2)^2}{1 + 1^2} = 0$

7. $\lim_{(x, y)\to(2, 1)} \frac{x^3 + 2x^2y - xy - 2y^2}{x + 2y} = \lim_{(x, y)\to(2, 1)} \frac{(x + 2y)(x^2 - y)}{x + 2y}$

$= \lim_{(x, y)\to(2, 1)} (x^2 - y) = 2^2 - 1 = 3$

8. Since $\lim_{(x, y)\to(\ln 2, 0)} (2x + y^2) = 2(\ln 2) + 0^2 = 2 \ln 2$ and the exponential function is continuous, it follows from the substitution formula that $\lim_{(x, y)\to(\ln 2, 0)} e^{2x + y^2} = e^{2 \ln 2} = (e^{\ln 2})^2 = 4$.

9. Since $\lim_{(x, y, z)\to(\pi/2, -\pi/2, 0)} (x + y + z) = \frac{\pi}{2} - \frac{\pi}{2} + 0 = 0$ and the cosine function is continuous, it follows from the substitution formula that

$\lim_{(x, y, z)\to(\pi/2, -\pi/2, 0)} \cos(x + y + z) = \cos 0 = 1.$

10. Since $\lim\limits_{(x,y)\to(0,1)} xy = (0)(1) = 0$ and $\lim\limits_{t\to 0} \sin t = 0$, it follows from the substitution formula that $\lim\limits_{(x,y)\to(0,1)} \sin xy = \lim\limits_{t\to 0} \sin t = 0$. Thus $\lim\limits_{(x,y)\to(0,1)} \dfrac{\sin xy}{y} = \dfrac{0}{1} = 0$.

11. Since $\lim\limits_{(x, y)\to(0, 0)} (x^2+y^2) = 0+0 = 0$ and $\lim\limits_{t\to 0} \dfrac{\sin t}{t} = 1$, it follows from the substitution formula that $\lim\limits_{(x, y)\to(0, 0)} \dfrac{\sin (x^2 + y^2)}{x^2 + y^2} = \lim\limits_{t\to 0} \dfrac{\sin t}{t} = 1$.

12. Since $\lim\limits_{(x, y)\to(1, 0)} \dfrac{-1}{|y|} = -\infty$ and $\lim\limits_{t\to -\infty} e^t = 0$, it follows from the substitution formula that $\lim\limits_{(x, y)\to(1, 0)} e^{-1/|y|} = \lim\limits_{t\to -\infty} e^t = 0$. Thus

$$\lim_{(x, y)\to(1, 0)} xe^{-1/|y|} = (1)(0) = 0.$$

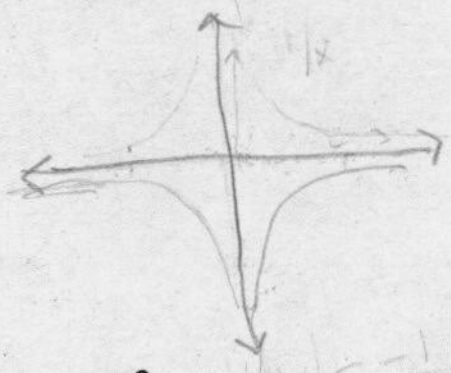

13. From Example 4 we have $\lim\limits_{(x, y)\to(0, 0)} \dfrac{x^3}{x^2 + y^2} = 0 = \lim\limits_{(x, y)\to(0, 0)} \dfrac{y^3}{x^2 + y^2}$.

Thus $\lim\limits_{(x, y)\to(0, 0)} xy \dfrac{x^2 - y^2}{x^2 + y^2} = \lim\limits_{(x, y)\to(0, 0)} \left[y \dfrac{x^3}{x^2 + y^2} - x \dfrac{y^3}{x^2 + y^2} \right]$

$= (0)(0) - (0)(0) = 0.$

14. For any $\varepsilon > 0$ let $\delta = \varepsilon$. If $0 < \sqrt{x^2 + y^2} < \delta$, then as in Example 4, $|x| < \delta = \varepsilon$, so that $\left| \dfrac{xy}{\sqrt{x^2 + y^2}} \right| = |x| \left| \dfrac{y}{\sqrt{x^2 + y^2}} \right| \le |x|\, 1 < \varepsilon$. Thus

$$\lim_{(x, y)\to(0, 0)} \frac{xy}{\sqrt{x^2 + y^2}} = 0.$$

15. For any $\varepsilon > 0$ let $\delta = \varepsilon$. If $0 < \sqrt{x^2 + y^2 + z^2} < \delta$, then $x = \sqrt{x^2} \le \sqrt{x^2 + y^2 + z^2} < \delta = \varepsilon$, so that $\left| \dfrac{x^3}{x^2 + y^2 + z^2} \right| = \left| x \dfrac{x^2}{x^2 + y^2 + z^2} \right| \le |x|\, 1 < \varepsilon$. Thus $\lim\limits_{(x, y, z)\to(0, 0, 0)} \dfrac{x^3}{x^2 + y^2 + z^2} = 0$. Similarly,

$$\lim_{(x, y, z)\to(0, 0, 0)} \frac{y^3}{x^2 + y^2 + z^2} = 0 = \lim_{(x, y, z)\to(0, 0, 0)} \frac{z^3}{x^2 + y^2 + z^2}.$$

It follows that $\lim\limits_{(x, y, z)\to(0, 0, 0)} \dfrac{x^3 + y^3 + z^3}{x^2 + y^2 + z^2}$

$= \lim\limits_{(x, y, z)\to(0, 0, 0)} \left[\dfrac{x^3}{x^2 + y^2 + z^2} + \dfrac{y^3}{x^2 + y^2 + z^2} + \dfrac{z^3}{x^2 + y^2 + z^2} \right]$

$= 0 + 0 + 0 = 0.$

16. Notice that if $y = 0$ and $x \ne 0$, then $\dfrac{y}{x} = 0$, whereas if $x = y \ne 0$, then $\dfrac{y}{x} = 1$. As in the solution of Example 3, it follows that $\lim\limits_{(x, y)\to(0, 0)} \dfrac{y}{x}$ does not exist.

17. Notice that if $y = 0$ and $x \ne 0$, then $\dfrac{x^2 - y^2}{x^2 + y^2} = 1$, whereas if $x = y \ne 0$, then $\dfrac{x^2 - y^2}{x^2 + y^2} = 0$. As in the solution of Example 3, it follows that $\lim\limits_{(x, y)\to(0, 0)} \dfrac{x^2 - y^2}{x^2 + y^2}$ does not exist.

18. Notice that if $y = 0$ and $x \ne 0$, then $|y|^x = 0$, whereas if $x = 0$ and $y \ne 0$, then $|y|^x = 1$. As in the solution of Example 3, it follows that $\lim\limits_{(x, y)\to(0, 0)} |y|^x$ does not exist.

19. Since $\lim\limits_{(x, y)\to(1, 1)} (x - y) = 1 - 1 = 0$ and the arcsine function is continuous, it follows from the substitution formula that $\lim\limits_{(x, y)\to(1, 1)} \arcsin (x - y) = \arcsin 0 = 0$. Since g is continuous, we conclude that $\lim\limits_{(x, y)\to(1, 1)} g(f (x, y)) = g (0) = -1$.

20. Since $\lim\limits_{(x, y)\to(-1, 1)} x^2y = (-1)^2(1) = 1$ and the exponential function is continuous, it follows from the substitution formula that $\lim\limits_{(x, y)\to(-1, 1)} e^{x^2y}$

$= e^1 = e$. Since g is continuous, $\lim_{(x, y)\to(-1, 1)} g(f(x, y)) = g(e) = 1$.

21. f is continuous because it is a polynomial.

22. f is continuous because it is a rational function.

23. f is continuous because it is a rational function.

24. Let $h(x, y, z) = xyz - 1$ and $g(t) = \sin t$. Then $f = g \circ h$. Since h and g are continuous, f is also continuous.

25. Let $h(x, y, z) = e^x + e^{yz}$ and $g(t) = \ln t$. Then $f = g \circ h$. Since h and g are continuous, f is also continuous.

26. Since the rational function $\frac{x^2y^2}{x^2 + y^2}$ is continuous, f is continuous at each $(x, y) \neq (0, 0)$. Since $0 \le \frac{x^2y^2}{x^2 + y^2} \le x^2$, it follows that

$$\lim_{(x, y)\to(0, 0)} \frac{x^2y^2}{x^2 + y^2} = 0 = f(0, 0),$$ which means that f is continuous at $(0, 0)$. Thus f is continuous.

27. a. Since $f(x, 0) = 0$ for all x and $f(0, y) = 0$ for all y, f is continuous in each variable separately at $(0, 0)$.

b. Notice that if $y = 0$, then $f(x, y) = 0$, whereas if $x = y \neq 0$, then $f(x, y) = \frac{1}{2}$. As in the solution of Example 3, it follows that $\lim_{(x, y)\to(0, 0)} f(x, y)$ does not exist. Thus f is not continuous at $(0, 0)$.

28. Notice that if $y = 0$, then $f(x, y) = 0$, whereas if $x = y \neq 0$, then $f(x, y) = \frac{\sin x^2}{2x^2}$. Since $\lim_{(x, y)\to(0, 0)} \frac{\sin x^2}{2x^2} = \frac{1}{2} \lim_{t\to0} \frac{\sin t}{t} = \frac{1}{2}$, it follows that in any disk about the origin there are points that are assigned 0 and points that are assigned values greater than $\frac{1}{4}$ by f. This means that $\lim_{(x, y)\to(0, 0)} f(x, y)$ does not exist. Thus f is not continuous at $(0, 0)$.

29. Notice that if $y = 0$ and $x \neq 0$, then $f(x, y) = 0$, whereas if $y = x^3 \neq 0$, then $f(x, y) = \frac{1}{2}$. As in the solution of Example 3, it follows that $\lim_{(x, y)\to(0, 0)} f(x, y)$ does not exist. Therefore f is not continuous at $(0, 0)$.

30. a. $(x + 3)^2 + (y - 2)^2 = 36$.

b. The boundary consists of the four line segments having the following formulas:

$y = 0$	and	$0 \le x \le 2$
$x = 2$	and	$-3 \le y \le 0$
$y = -3$	and	$0 \le x \le 2$
$x = 0$	and	$-3 \le y \le 0$

c. The boundary consists of the three line segments having the following formulas:

$y = 1$	and	$-1 \le x \le 1$
$y = -6x - 5$	and	$-1 \le x \le 0$
$y = 6x - 5$	and	$0 \le x \le 1$

d. $y = 0$

e. $y = 4x^2$

f. $x = 0 = y$

31. Notice that if $y = 0$ and $x \neq 0$, then $f(x, y) = 1$, whereas if $x = y \neq 0$, then $f(x, y) = \frac{1}{2}$. As in the solution of Example 3, it follows that $\lim_{(x, y)\to(0, 0)} f(x, y)$ does not exist.

32. From (1) in the solution of Example 4 we have $\lim_{(x, y)\to(0, 0)} \frac{x^3}{x^2 + y^2} = 0$.

33. If $|y| < |x^3|$, then $|f(x, y)| = \frac{|y|}{|x|} < \frac{|x^3|}{|x|} = x^2$. Thus for any $\varepsilon > 0$ we choose $\delta = \sqrt{\varepsilon}$. If (x, y) is in R and $0 < \sqrt{x^2 + y^2} < \delta$, we have $|f(x, y)| < x^2 < \varepsilon$. It follows that $\lim_{(x, y)\to(0, 0)} f(x, y) = 0$.

34. f is continuous on R since f is a rational function whose domain contains R.

35. Since $f(x, y) = 0$ for $x > 0$, the only possible value for $\lim_{(x, y)\to(0, 0)} f(x, y)$ is 0. But $f(0, 0) = 2$. Thus either $\lim_{(x, y)\to(0, 0)} f(x, y)$ does not exist or it is different from $f(0, 0)$. Either way f is not continuous at $(0, 0)$. Thus f is not continuous on R.

36. Since f is constant on R, f is continuous on R.

37. Since f is constant on R, f is continuous on R.

38. If (x_0, y_0) is any point on the circle $x^2 + y^2 = 9$, then any disk around (x_0, y_0) contains points at which f takes on the value 1 and points at which f takes on the value 0. Thus $\lim_{(x, y)\to(x_0, y_0)} f(x, y)$ does not exist, so that f is not continuous at (x_0, y_0). Since (x_0, y_0) is an interior point of R, f is not continuous on R.

39. a. A point P is called a boundary point of a set D if every ball centered at P contains points inside R and points outside R. The boundary of D is the collection of its boundary points.

b. A number L is the limit of a function f at a boundary point (x_0, y_0, z_0) of D if for every $\varepsilon > 0$ there is a number $\delta > 0$ such that

if (x, y, z) is in D and $0 < \sqrt{(x - x_0)^2 + (y - y_0)^2 + (z - z_0)^2} < \delta$

then $|f(x, y, z) - L| < \varepsilon$

c. A function f is continuous at a boundary point (x_0, y_0, z_0) of D if $\lim_{(x, y, z)\to(x_0, y_0, z_0)} f(x, y, z) = f(x_0, y_0, z_0)$.

40. If $x > 0$ and $y > 0$, then $0 < \frac{17{,}860xy}{(1.798)x + y} < 17{,}860x$. Thus $\lim_{(x, y)\to(0, 0)} Q(x, y) = 0$.

41. Notice that if $x = y > 0$, then $\frac{100ax}{ax + by} = \frac{100a}{a + b}$, whereas if $x = 2y > 0$, then $\frac{100ax}{ax + by} = \frac{200a}{2a + b} = \frac{100a}{a + b/2}$. As in the solution of Example 3, it follows that $\lim_{(x, y)\to(0, 0)} f(x, y)$ does not exist.

Section 13.3

1. $f_x(x, y) = x^{1/2}$, $f_y(x, y) = 0$

2. $f_x(x, y) = -2x$, $f_y(x, y) = -8y$

3. $f_x(x, y) = 2 + 6xy^4$, $f_y(x, y) = 12x^2y^3$

4. $g_x(x, y) = 3x^2e^{2y}$, $g_y(x, y) = 2x^3e^{2y}$

5. $g_u(u, v) = \dfrac{(u^2 + v^2)^3 u^2 - (u^3 + v^3)\, 2u}{(u^2 + v^2)^2} = \dfrac{u^4 + 3u^2v^2 - 2uv^3}{(u^2 + v^2)^2}$, $g_v(u, v)$

$= \dfrac{(u^2 + v^2)3v^2 - (u^3 + v^3)\, 2v}{(u^2 + v^2)^2} = \dfrac{v^4 + 3u^2v^2 - 2u^3v}{(u^2 + v^2)^2}$

6. $f_x(x, y) = \dfrac{x}{\sqrt{x^2 + y^2}}$, $f_y(x, y) = \dfrac{y}{\sqrt{x^2 + y^2}}$

7. $f_x(x, y) = \dfrac{-x}{\sqrt{4 - x^2 - 9y^2}}$, $f_y(x, y) = \dfrac{-9y}{\sqrt{4 - x^2 - 9y^2}}$

8. $\dfrac{\partial z}{\partial x} = \dfrac{x}{4\sqrt{\frac{1}{4}x^2 - y^2}}$, $\dfrac{\partial z}{\partial y} = \dfrac{-y}{\sqrt{\frac{1}{4}x^2 - y^2}}$

9. $\dfrac{\partial z}{\partial x} = \dfrac{1}{2\sqrt{(1 - x^{2/3})^3 - y^2}} \left[3(1 - x^{2/3})^2\right] (-\frac{2}{3}x^{-1/3})$

$= \dfrac{-(1 - x^{2/3})^2}{x^{1/3}\sqrt{(1 - x^{2/3})^3 - y^2}}$, $\dfrac{\partial z}{\partial y} = \dfrac{-y}{\sqrt{(1 - x^{2/3})^3 - y^2}}$

10. $\dfrac{\partial w}{\partial u} = \dfrac{-1}{v}\sin\dfrac{u}{v}$, $\dfrac{\partial w}{\partial v} = (-\sin\frac{u}{v})(\frac{-u}{v^2}) = \dfrac{u}{v^2}\sin\dfrac{u}{v}$

11. $\dfrac{\partial z}{\partial x} = 3(\sin x^2y)^2(\cos x^2y)(2xy) = 6xy\sin^2 x^2y\cos x^2y$, $\dfrac{\partial z}{\partial y}$

$= 3(\sin x^2y)^2(\cos x^2y)(x^2) = 3x^2\sin^2 x^2y\cos x^2y$

12. $z = x^y = e^{y\ln x}$; $\dfrac{\partial z}{\partial x} = e^{y\ln x}(\frac{y}{x}) = \frac{y}{x}(x^y) = yx^{y-1}$, $\dfrac{\partial z}{\partial y} = e^{y\ln x}(\ln x)$

$= x^y\ln x$

13. $f_x(x, y, z) = 2xy^5 + z^2$, $f_y(x, y, z) = 5x^2y^4$, $f_z(x, y, z) = 2xz$

14. $f_x(x, y, z) = (\cos y)\, e^z$, $f_y(x, y, z) = -x(\sin y)\, e^z$, $f_z(x, y, z)$

$= x(\cos y)\, e^z$

15. $f_x(x, y, z) = \dfrac{xy + yz + zx - (x + y + z)(y + z)}{(xy + yz + zx)^2} = \dfrac{-(y^2 + yz + z^2)}{(xy + yz + zx)^2}$,

$f_y(x, y, z) = \dfrac{xy + yz + zx - (x + y + z)(x + z)}{(xy + yz + zx)^2} = \dfrac{-(z^2 + zx + x^2)}{(xy + yz + zx)^2}$,

$f_z(x, y, z) = \dfrac{xy + yz + zx - (x + y + z)(y + x)}{(xy + yz + zx)^2} = \dfrac{-(x^2 + xy + y^2)}{(xy + yz + zx)^2}$

16. $f_u(u, v, w) = \dfrac{-u}{(u^2 + v^2 + w^2)^{3/2}}$, $f_v(u, v, w) = \dfrac{-v}{(u^2 + v^2 + w^2)^{3/2}}$,

$f_w(u, v, w) = \dfrac{-w}{(u^2 + v^2 + w^2)^{3/2}}$

17. $\dfrac{\partial w}{\partial x} = e^x(\cos y + \sin z)$, $\dfrac{\partial w}{\partial y} = e^x(-\sin y) = -e^x\sin y$, $\dfrac{\partial w}{\partial z} = e^x\cos z$

18. $w = e^{z\ln(x/y)} = e^{z(\ln x - \ln y)}$; $\dfrac{\partial w}{\partial x} = e^{z(\ln x - \ln y)}(\frac{z}{x}) = (\frac{z}{x})(\frac{x}{y})^z$,

$\dfrac{\partial w}{\partial y} = e^{z(\ln x - \ln y)}(\frac{-z}{y}) = (\frac{-z}{y})(\frac{x}{y})^z$, $\dfrac{\partial w}{\partial z}$

$= e^{z(\ln x - \ln y)}(\ln x - \ln y) = (\frac{x}{y})^z(\ln x - \ln y)$

19. $\dfrac{\partial w}{\partial x} = \dfrac{1}{\sqrt{1 - \frac{1}{(1 + xyz^2)^2}}}\left(\dfrac{-1}{(1 + xyz^2)^2}\right) yz^2 = \dfrac{-yz^2}{(1 + xyz^2)^2\sqrt{1 - (\frac{1}{1 + xyz^2})^2}}$,

$\dfrac{\partial w}{\partial y} = \dfrac{1}{\sqrt{1 - \frac{1}{(1 + xyz^2)^2}}}\left(\dfrac{-1}{(1 + xyz^2)^2}\right) xz^2 = \dfrac{-xz^2}{(1 + xyz^2)^2\sqrt{1 - (\frac{1}{1 + xyz^2})^2}}$,

$$\frac{\partial w}{\partial z} = \frac{1}{\sqrt{1 - \frac{1}{(1 + xyz^2)^2}}}\left(\frac{-1}{(1 + xyz^2)^2}\right) 2xyz = \frac{-2xyz}{(1 + xyz^2)^2\sqrt{1 - \left(\frac{1}{1 + xyz^2}\right)^2}}$$

20. $f_x(x, y) = 4x^3 - 12x - 3y^2$, $f_x(-1, 2) = 4(-1)^3 - 12(-1) - 3(2)^2 = -4$;

$f_y(x, y) = -6xy$, $f_y(-1, 2) = -6(-1)(2) = 12$

21. $f_x(x, y) = \frac{4x}{\sqrt{4x^2 + y^2}}$, $f_x(2, -3) = \frac{4(2)}{\sqrt{4(2)^2 + (-3)^2}} = \frac{8}{5}$; $f_y(x, y)$

$= \frac{y}{\sqrt{4x^2 + y^2}}$, $f_y(2, -3) = \frac{(-3)}{\sqrt{4(2)^2 + (-3)^2}} = \frac{-3}{5}$

22. $f_x(x, y, z) = y^2 \sin z$, $f_x(-1, 2, 0) = 2^2 \sin 0 = 0$;

$f_y(x, y, z) = 2xy \sin z$, $f_y(-1, 2, 0) = 2(-1)(2) \sin 0 = 0$;

$f_z(x, y, z) = xy^2 \cos z$, $f_z(-1, 2, 0) = (-1)(2)^2 \cos 0 = -4$

23. $f_x(x, y, z) = 2e^{2x - 4y - z}$, $f_x(0, -1, 1) = 2e^{2(0) - 4(-1) - 1} = 2e^3$;

$f_y(x, y, z) = -4e^{2x - 4y - z}$, $f_y(0, -1, 1) = -4e^{2(0) - 4(-1) - 1} = -4e^3$;

$f_z(x, y, z) = -e^{2x - 4y - z}$, $f_z(0, -1, 1) = -e^{2(0) - 4(-1) - 1} = -e^3$

24. $f_x(0, 0) = \lim_{h\to 0} \frac{f(h, 0) - f(0, 0)}{h - 0} = \lim_{h\to 0} \frac{h - 0}{h - 0} = \lim_{h\to 0} 1 = 1$,

$f_y(0, 0) = \lim_{h\to 0} \frac{f(0, h) - f(0, 0)}{h - 0} = \lim_{h\to 0} \frac{h - 0}{h - 0} = \lim_{h\to 0} 1 = 1$

25. $f_x(0, 0) = \lim_{h\to 0} \frac{f(h, 0) - f(0, 0)}{h - 0} = \lim_{h\to 0} \frac{0 - 0}{h - 0} = \lim_{h\to 0} 0 = 0$; $f_y(0, 0)$

$= \lim_{h\to 0} \frac{f(0, h) - f(0, 0)}{h - 0} = \lim_{h\to 0} \frac{0 - 0}{h - 0} = \lim_{h\to 0} 0 = 0$

26. $f_x(x, y) = \frac{\partial}{\partial x} \int_1^x P(t)dt + \frac{\partial}{\partial x} \int_1^y Q(t)dt = P(x) + 0 = P(x)$, $f_y(x, y)$

$= \frac{\partial}{\partial y} \int_1^x P(t)dt + \frac{\partial}{\partial y} \int_1^y Q(t)dt = 0 + Q(y) = Q(y)$

27. Let y be fixed, and let $g(x) = f(x, y)$, $h(u) = \int_\pi^u \sin t^2\, dt$, and $k(x)$ $= x^2 + y^2$. Then $g(x) = f(x, y) = \int_\pi^{x^2 + y^2} \sin t^2\, dt = h(k(x))$ and $h'(u)$ $= \sin u^2$, so that $f_x(x, y) = g'(x) = h'(k(x))k'(x) = [\sin (k(x))^2] 2x$ $= 2x \sin (x^2 + y^2)^2$. Interchanging the roles of x and y in the preceding discussion, we find that $f_y(x, y) = 2y \sin (x^2 + y^2)^2$.

28. $f_y(0, 1) = \lim_{h\to 0} \frac{f(0, 1 + h) - f(0, 1)}{h - 0} = \lim_{h\to 0} \frac{0 - 0}{h} = 0$

29. $f_x(x, y) = 6x - \sqrt{2}y^2$, $f_{xy}(x, y) = -2\sqrt{2}y$; $f_y(x, y) = -2\sqrt{2}xy + 5y^4$,

$f_{yx}(x, y) = -2\sqrt{2}y$

30. $f_x(x, y) = \frac{(x^2 + y^2)(2x) - (x^2 - y^2)(2x)}{(x^2 + y^2)^2} = \frac{4xy^2}{(x^2 + y^2)^2}$, $f_{xy}(x, y)$

$= \frac{(x^2 + y^2)^2(8xy) - (4xy^2)\, 2(x^2 + y^2)(2y)}{(x^2 + y^2)^4} = \frac{8x^3y - 8xy^3}{(x^2 + y^2)^3}$;

$f_y(x, y) = \frac{(x^2 + y^2)(-2y) - (x^2 - y^2)(2y)}{(x^2 + y^2)^2} = \frac{-4x^2y}{(x^2 + y^2)^2}$,

$f_{yx}(x, y) = \frac{(x^2 + y^2)^2(-8xy) - (-4x^2y)\, 2(x^2 + y^2)(2x)}{(x^2 + y^2)^4} = \frac{8x^3y - 8xy^3}{(x^2 + y^2)^3}$

31. $f_x(x, y) = \frac{x}{\sqrt{x^2 + y^2}}$, $f_{xy}(x, y) = \frac{-xy}{(x^2 + y^2)^{3/2}}$; $f_y(x, y) = \frac{y}{\sqrt{x^2 + y^2}}$,

$f_{yx}(x, y) = \frac{-xy}{(x^2 + y^2)^{3/2}}$

32. $f_x(x, y, z) = 4x^3 - 4xy\sqrt{z}$, $f_{xy}(x, y, z) = -4x\sqrt{z}$; $f_y(x, y, z) = -2x^2\sqrt{z}$ $+ 3z^4$, $f_{yx}(x, y, z) = -4x\sqrt{z}$

33. $f_x(x, y, z) = -yz \sin xy$, $f_{xy}(x, y, z) = -z \sin xy - xyz \cos xy$;

$f_y(x, y, z) = -xz \sin xy$, $f_{yx}(x, y, z) = -z \sin xy - xyz \cos xy$

34. $f_x(x, y) = \dfrac{-9x}{\sqrt{16 - 9x^2 - 4y^2}}$, $f_{xx}(x, y)$

$$= \frac{-9\sqrt{16 - 9x^2 - 4y^2} - (-9x)\dfrac{-9x}{\sqrt{16 - 9x^2 - 4y^2}}}{16 - 9x^2 - 4y^2} = \frac{-144 + 36y^2}{(16 - 9x^2 - 4y^2)^{3/2}};$$

$f_y(x, y) = \dfrac{-4y}{\sqrt{16 - 9x^2 - 4y^2}}$, $f_{yy}(x, y)$

$$= \frac{-4\sqrt{16 - 9x^2 - 4y^2} - (-4y)\dfrac{-4y}{\sqrt{16 - 9x^2 - 4y^2}}}{16 - 9x^2 - 4y^2} = \frac{-64 + 36x^2}{(16 - 9x^2 - 4y^2)^{3/2}}$$

35. $f_x(x, y) = e^{x - 2y}$, $f_{xx}(x, y) = e^{x - 2y}$; $f_y(x, y) = -2e^{x - 2y}$, $f_{yy}(x, y)$ $= 4e^{x - 2y}$

36. $f_x(x, y) = (\sin x^2)\int_0^y \cos t^2 dt$, $f_{xx}(x, y) = (2x \cos x^2)\int_0^y \cos t^2 dt$;

$f_y(x, y) = \left(\int_0^x \sin t^2 dt\right)(\cos y^2)$, $f_{yy}(x, y) = \left(\int_0^x \sin t^2 dt\right)(-2y \sin y^2)$

37. $f_x(x, y, z) = \dfrac{x}{\sqrt{x^2 + y^2 + z^2}}$, $f_{xx}(x, y, z)$

$$= \frac{\sqrt{x^2 + y^2 + z^2} - \dfrac{x^2}{\sqrt{x^2 + y^2 + z^2}}}{x^2 + y^2 + z^2} = \frac{y^2 + z^2}{(x^2 + y^2 + z^2)^{3/2}},$$

$f_y(x, y, z) = \dfrac{y}{\sqrt{x^2 + y^2 + z^2}}$, $f_{yy}(x, y, z)$

$$= \frac{\sqrt{x^2 + y^2 + z^2} - \dfrac{y^2}{\sqrt{x^2 + y^2 + z^2}}}{x^2 + y^2 + z^2} = \frac{x^2 + z^2}{(x^2 + y^2 + z^2)^{3/2}};\ f_z(x, y, z)$$

$= \dfrac{z}{\sqrt{x^2 + y^2 + z^2}}$, $f_{zz}(x, y, z)$

$$= \frac{\sqrt{x^2 + y^2 + z^2} - \dfrac{z^2}{\sqrt{x^2 + y^2 + z^2}}}{x^2 + y^2 + z^2} = \frac{x^2 + y^2}{(x^2 + y^2 + z^2)^{3/2}}$$

38. $f_x(x, y, z) = 2xe^{x^2} \sin yz + \dfrac{2x}{x^2 + y^2 + z^2}$, $f_{xx}(x, y, z) = 2e^{x^2} \sin yz$ $+ 4x^2e^{x^2} \sin yz + \dfrac{2(y^2 + z^2 - x^2)}{(x^2 + y^2 + z^2)^2}$; $f_y(x, y, z) = ze^{x^2} \cos yz + \dfrac{2y}{x^2 + y^2 + z^2}$,

$f_{yy}(x, y, z) = -z^2e^{x^2} \sin yz + \dfrac{2(x^2 + z^2 - y^2)}{(x^2 + y^2 + z^2)^2}$; $f_z(x, y, z) = ye^{x^2} \cos yz$ $+ \dfrac{2z}{x^2 + y^2 + z^2}$, $f_{zz}(x, y, z) = -y^2e^{x^2} \sin yz + \dfrac{2(x^2 + y^2 - z^2)}{(x^2 + y^2 + z^2)^2}$

39. Let $f(x, y) = x^2 + 16y^2$. Then $f_x(x, y) = 2x$, so that $f_x(-3, 1) = 2(-3)$ $= -6$, so the line in question has equations $y = 1$ and $z - 25 = -6(x + 3)$.

40. Let $f(x, y) = \sqrt{x^2 + y^2}$. Then $f_y(x, y) = \dfrac{y}{\sqrt{x^2 + y^2}}$, so that

$f_y(2, 2\sqrt{3}) = \dfrac{2\sqrt{3}}{\sqrt{4 + 12}} = \dfrac{\sqrt{3}}{2}$, so the line in question has equations

$x = 2$ and $z - 4 = \dfrac{\sqrt{3}}{2}(y - 2\sqrt{3})$

41. $f_x(x, y) = -1$ and $f_y(x, y) = 0$, so $\sqrt{f_x^2(x, y) + f_y^2(x, y) + 1}$ $= \sqrt{(-1)^2 + 0^2 + 1} = \sqrt{2}$

42. $f_x(x, y) = 0$ and $f_y(x, y) = -2y$, so $\sqrt{f_x^2(x, y) + f_y^2(x, y) + 1}$

$= \sqrt{0^2 + (-2y)^2 + 1} = \sqrt{4y^2 + 1}$.

43. $f_x(x, y) = \dfrac{x}{\sqrt{x^2 + y^2}}$ and $f_y(x, y) = \dfrac{y}{\sqrt{x^2 + y^2}}$, so

$\sqrt{f_x^2(x, y) + f_y^2(x, y) + 1} = \sqrt{\left(\dfrac{x}{\sqrt{x^2 + y^2}}\right)^2 + \left(\dfrac{y}{\sqrt{x^2 + y^2}}\right)^2 + 1} = \sqrt{2}$.

44. $f_x(x, y) = \dfrac{-x}{\sqrt{1 - x^2 - y^2}}$ and $f_y(x, y) = \dfrac{-y}{\sqrt{1 - x^2 - y^2}}$, so

$\sqrt{f_x^2(x, y) + f_y^2(x, y) + 1} = \sqrt{\left(\dfrac{-x}{\sqrt{1 - x^2 - y^2}}\right)^2 + \left(\dfrac{-y}{\sqrt{1 - x^2 - y^2}}\right)^2 + 1}$

$= \dfrac{1}{\sqrt{1 - x^2 - y^2}}$

45. $f_x(0, 0) = \lim_{h\to 0} \dfrac{f(h, 0) - f(0, 0)}{h - 0} = \lim_{h\to 0} \dfrac{0 - 0}{h} = \lim_{h\to 0} 0 = 0$, and $f_y(0, 0)$

$= \lim_{h\to 0} \dfrac{f(0, h) - f(0, 0)}{h - 0} = \lim_{h\to 0} \dfrac{0 - 0}{h} = \lim_{h\to 0} 0 = 0$. By Exercise 27 of Section 13.2, f is not continuous at $(0, 0)$.

46. a. $\dfrac{\partial x}{\partial r} = \cos\theta$ b. $\dfrac{\partial x}{\partial\theta} = -r\sin\theta$ c. $\dfrac{\partial y}{\partial r} = \sin\theta$

d. $\dfrac{\partial y}{\partial\theta} = r\cos\theta$ e. $\dfrac{\partial r}{\partial x} = \dfrac{x}{\sqrt{x^2 + y^2}}$ f. $\dfrac{\partial r}{\partial y} = \dfrac{y}{\sqrt{x^2 + y^2}}$

g. $\dfrac{\partial\theta}{\partial x} = \dfrac{1}{1 + \frac{y^2}{x^2}}\left(\dfrac{-y}{x^2}\right) = \dfrac{-y}{x^2 + y^2}$ h. $\dfrac{\partial\theta}{\partial y} = \dfrac{1}{1 + \frac{y^2}{x^2}}\left(\dfrac{1}{x}\right) = \dfrac{x}{x^2 + y^2}$

47. $\dfrac{\partial z}{\partial x} = -ae^{-ay}\sin ax$, $\dfrac{\partial^2 z}{\partial x^2} = -a^2e^{-ay}\cos ax$, $\dfrac{\partial z}{\partial y} = -ae^{-ay}\cos ax$; thus $\dfrac{\partial^2 z}{\partial x^2}$

$= -a^2e^{-ay}\cos ax = a\dfrac{\partial z}{\partial y}$

48. $\dfrac{\partial z}{\partial x} = cx^{c-1}e^{-y/x} + x^ce^{-y/x}\left(\dfrac{y}{x^2}\right) = x^{c-2}e^{-y/x}(cx + y)$; $\dfrac{\partial z}{\partial y}$

$= x^c e^{-y/x}\left(\dfrac{-1}{x}\right) = -x^{c-1}e^{-y/x}$, $\dfrac{\partial^2 z}{\partial y^2} = -x^{c-1}e^{-y/x}\left(\dfrac{-1}{x}\right) = x^{c-2}e^{-y/x}$;

thus $y\dfrac{\partial^2 z}{\partial y^2} + \dfrac{\partial z}{\partial y} = yx^{c-2}e^{-y/x} - x^{c-1}e^{-y/x} = x^{c-2}e^{-y/x}(y - x)$.

Consequently $\dfrac{\partial z}{\partial x} = y\dfrac{\partial^2 z}{\partial y^2} + \dfrac{\partial z}{\partial y}$ if $cx + y = y - x$, that is, if $c = -1$.

49. $u_x = 2x$, $v_y = 2x$, so $u_x = v_y$; $u_y = -2y$, $v_x = 2y$, so $u_y = -v_x$.

50. $u_x = 3x^2 - 3y^2$, $v_y = 3x^2 - 3y^2$, so $u_x = v_y$; $u_y = -6xy$, $v_x = 6xy$, so $u_y = -v_x$.

51. $u_x = e^x\cos y$, $v_y = e^x\cos y$, so $u_x = v_y$; $u_y = -e^x\sin y$, $v_x = e^x\sin y$, so $u_y = -v_x$.

52. $\dfrac{\partial z}{\partial x} = 4x^3 - 12xy^2$, $\dfrac{\partial^2 z}{\partial x^2} = 12x^2 - 12y^2$, $\dfrac{\partial z}{\partial y} = -12x^2y + 4y^3$, $\dfrac{\partial^2 z}{\partial y^2} = -12x^2 + 12y^2$,

so $\dfrac{\partial^2 z}{\partial x^2} + \dfrac{\partial^2 z}{\partial y^2} = (12x^2 - 12y^2) + (-12x^2 + 12y^2) = 0$.

53. $\dfrac{\partial z}{\partial x} = \dfrac{2x}{x^2 + y^2}$; $\dfrac{\partial^2 z}{\partial x^2} = \dfrac{2y^2 - 2x^2}{(x^2 + y^2)^2}$, $\dfrac{\partial z}{\partial y} = \dfrac{2y}{x^2 + y^2}$, $\dfrac{\partial^2 z}{\partial y^2} = \dfrac{2x^2 - 2y^2}{(x^2 + y^2)^2}$, so

$\dfrac{\partial^2 z}{\partial x^2} + \dfrac{\partial^2 z}{\partial y^2} = \dfrac{2y^2 - 2x^2}{(x^2 + y^2)^2} + \dfrac{2x^2 - 2y^2}{(x^2 + y^2)^2} = 0$.

54. Since the mixed partials of u and of v are continuous, Theorem 13.5 says that $u_{xy} = u_{yx}$ and $v_{xy} = v_{yx}$. Using these equations and the Cauchy-Riemann equations, we find that

$$u_{xx} + u_{yy} = (u_x)_x + (u_y)_y = (v_y)_x + (-v_x)_y = v_{yx} - v_{xy} = 0$$

and

$$v_{xx} + v_{yy} = (v_x)_x + (v_y)_y = (-u_y)_x + (u_x)_y = -u_{yx} + u_{xy} = 0.$$ Thus u and v each satisfy Laplace's equation.

55. By Example 3, $f_x(x, y) = \frac{x^4y + 4x^2y^3 - y^5}{(x^2 + y^2)^2}$, so $f_{xy}(x, 0)$

$= \lim_{h\to 0} \frac{f_x(x, h) - f_x(x, 0)}{h - 0} = \lim_{h\to 0} \frac{x^4h + 4x^2h^3 - h^5}{h(x^2 + h^2)^2} = \lim_{h\to 0} \frac{x^4 + 4x^2h^2 - h^4}{(x^2 + h^2)^2}$

$= 1$ if $x \neq 0$. Thus $\lim_{x\to 0} f_{xy}(x, 0) = 1$. Since $f_{xy}(0, 0) = -1$ by Example 7,

it follows that f_{xy} is not continuous at (0, 0).

56. a. The third-order partials are f_{xxx}, f_{xxy}, f_{xyx}, f_{xyy}, f_{yxx}, f_{yxy}, f_{yyx}, and f_{yyy}, eight in all. If they are continuous, then any two with the same number of x's as indices are equal, which means there are four distinct ones.

b. There are 2^2 second-order partials, and by part (a) there are 2^3 third-order partials. In general 2^n nth-order partials exist. If they are all continuous, then by the hint there are $n + 1$ distinct ones.

57. Let y be fixed in $[c, d]$, and let $f(x) = M(x, y)$. Then $f'(x)$

$= \frac{\partial M}{\partial x}(x, y)$ for $a \le x \le b$, so that by the Fundamental Theorem of Calculus,

$\int_a^b \frac{\partial M}{\partial x}(x, y)\, dx = \int_a^b f'(x)\, dx = f(x)\Big|_a^b = f(b) - f(a) = M(b, y) - M(a, y)$.

The other formula follows in a completely analogous fashion.

58. $\frac{\partial u}{\partial x} = a \cos ax \sin bt$, $\frac{\partial^2 u}{\partial x^2} = -a^2 \sin ax \sin bt$, $\frac{\partial u}{\partial t} = b \sin ax \cos bt$, and

$\frac{\partial^2 u}{\partial t^2} = -b^2 \sin ax \sin bt$, so that $\frac{a^2}{b^2}\frac{\partial^2 u}{\partial t^2} = -a^2 \sin ax \sin bt = \frac{\partial^2 u}{\partial x^2}$.

59. a. $\frac{\partial u}{\partial x} = ae^{ax + bt}$, $\frac{\partial^2 u}{\partial x^2} = a^2e^{ax + bt}$, and $\frac{\partial u}{\partial t} = be^{ax + bt}$, so that $\frac{b}{a^2}\frac{\partial^2 u}{\partial x^2}$

$= be^{ax + bt} = \frac{\partial u}{\partial t}$.

b. $\frac{\partial u}{\partial x} = \frac{1}{\sqrt{t}} e^{-x^2/at} \left(\frac{-2x}{at}\right) = \frac{-2x}{at^{3/2}} e^{-x^2/at}$, $\frac{\partial^2 u}{\partial x^2} = \frac{-2}{at^{3/2}} e^{-x^2/at}$

$- \frac{2x}{at^{3/2}} e^{-x^2/at} \left(\frac{-2x}{at}\right) = \left(\frac{4x^2}{a^2t^{5/2}} - \frac{2}{at^{3/2}}\right) e^{-x^2/at}$, and $\frac{\partial u}{\partial t}$

$= \frac{-1}{2t^{3/2}} e^{-x^2/at} + \frac{1}{t^{1/2}} e^{-x^2/at} \left(\frac{x^2}{at^2}\right) = \left(\frac{x^2}{at^{3/2}} - \frac{1}{2t^{3/2}}\right) e^{-x^2/at}$, so that

$\frac{\partial u}{\partial t} = \frac{a}{4}\frac{\partial^2 u}{\partial x^2}$.

60. a. By (6), $\frac{d}{dx}\int_1^{\sqrt{3}} \ln(x^2 + y^2)\, dy = \int_1^{\sqrt{3}} \frac{\partial}{\partial x} \ln(x^2 + y^2)\, dy$

$= \int_1^{\sqrt{3}} \frac{2x}{x^2 + y^2}\, dy = 2x\left(\frac{1}{x} \arctan \frac{y}{x}\right)\Big|_1^{\sqrt{3}} = 2\left(\arctan \frac{\sqrt{3}}{x} - \arctan \frac{1}{x}\right)$

b. By (6), $\frac{d}{dx}\int_1^2 \frac{1}{y} \arctan \frac{x}{y}\, dy = \int_1^2 \frac{\partial}{\partial x}\left(\frac{1}{y} \arctan \frac{x}{y}\right) dy$

$= \int_1^2 \frac{1}{x^2 + y^2}\, dy = \frac{1}{x} \arctan \frac{y}{x}\Big|_1^2 = \frac{1}{x}\left(\arctan \frac{2}{x} - \arctan \frac{1}{x}\right)$.

61. $\frac{\partial a}{\partial m_1} = \frac{(m_1 + m_2) - (m_1 - m_2)}{(m_1 + m_2)^2} g = \frac{2m_2}{(m_1 + m_2)^2} g$ and $\frac{\partial a}{\partial m_2}$

$= \frac{-(m_1 + m_2) - (m_1 - m_2)}{(m_1 + m_2)^2} g = \frac{-2m_1}{(m_1 + m_2)^2} g$, so that $m_1 \frac{\partial a}{\partial m_1} + m_2 \frac{\partial a}{\partial m_2}$

$= \frac{2m_1m_2}{(m_1 + m_2)^2} g - \frac{2m_1m_2}{(m_1 + m_2)^2} g = 0$.

62. $\frac{\partial R}{\partial R_1} = \frac{R_2(R_1 + R_2) - R_1R_2}{(R_1 + R_2)^2} = \frac{R_2^2}{(R_1 + R_2)^2}$ and $\frac{\partial^2 R}{\partial R_1^2} = \frac{-2R_2^2}{(R_1 + R_2)^3}$; $\frac{\partial R}{\partial R_2}$

$= \frac{R_1(R_1 + R_2) - R_1R_2}{(R_1 + R_2)^2} = \frac{R_1^2}{(R_1 + R_2)^2}$ and $\frac{\partial^2 R}{\partial R_2^2} = \frac{-2R_1^2}{(R_1 + R_2)^3}$. Thus $\frac{\partial^2 R}{\partial R_1^2}\frac{\partial^2 R}{\partial R_2^2}$

$= \frac{4R_1^2R_2^2}{(R_1 + R_2)^6} = \frac{4R^2}{(R_1 + R_2)^4}$

63. $\frac{\partial K}{\partial m} = \frac{1}{2} v^2$, $\frac{\partial K}{\partial v} = mv$, and $\frac{\partial^2 K}{\partial v^2} = m$, so that $\frac{\partial K}{\partial m}\frac{\partial^2 K}{\partial v^2} = \left(\frac{1}{2} v^2\right)(m) = \frac{1}{2} mv^2 = K$.

64. $\frac{\partial V}{\partial T} = \frac{nk}{p}$, $\frac{\partial T}{\partial p} = \frac{V}{nk}$, and $\frac{\partial p}{\partial V} = \frac{-nkT}{V^2}$, so that $\frac{\partial V}{\partial T}\frac{\partial T}{\partial p}\frac{\partial p}{\partial V} = (\frac{nk}{p})(\frac{V}{nk})(\frac{-nkT}{V^2})$

$= \frac{-nkT}{pV} = -1$.

65. If $\mu = 1.333$, then $i_\mu = \arcsin\sqrt{\frac{4-\mu^2}{3}} = \arcsin\sqrt{\frac{4-(1.333)^2}{3}}$

≈ 1.03691. By (3), $\theta(\mu, i_\mu) = 4\arcsin(\frac{\sin i_\mu}{\mu}) - 2i_\mu \approx .734402$, or

approximately 42.1°.

66. a. $\frac{\partial\theta}{\partial i} = 2 - 6\frac{1}{\sqrt{1-(\sin^2 i)/\mu^2}}\frac{\cos i}{\mu} = 2 - \frac{6\cos i}{\sqrt{\mu^2 - \sin^2 i}} = 0$ if

$\sqrt{\mu^2 - \sin^2 i} = 3\cos i$, that is, if $\mu^2 - \sin^2 i = 9\cos^2 i$

$= 9(1 - \sin^2 i)$, which yields $\sin i = \sqrt{\frac{9-\mu^2}{8}}$.

b. From (a), $i_{red} = \arcsin\sqrt{\frac{9-(1.330)^2}{8}} \approx \arcsin 0.950730$

≈ 1.25558, and $i_{violet} = \arcsin\sqrt{\frac{9-(1.342)^2}{8}}$

$\approx \arcsin 0.948620 \approx 1.24885$ (in radians). Thus by the

given formula, $\theta(\text{red}, i_{red}) \approx 230.1^\circ$ and $\theta(\text{violet}, i_{violet})$

$\approx 233.2^\circ$.

67. $R = c\frac{2\pi r(h+2r)}{\pi r^2(h+\frac{4}{3}r)} = \frac{6c(h+2r)}{3hr+4r^2}$; $\frac{\partial R}{\partial r} = \frac{12c(3hr+4r^2) - 6c(h+2r)(3h+8r)}{(3hr+4r^2)^2}$

$= \frac{-48chr - 18ch^2 - 48cr^2}{(3hr+4r^2)^2} < 0$; $\frac{\partial R}{\partial h} = \frac{6c(3hr+4r^2) - 6c(h+2r)3r}{(3hr+4r^2)^2}$

$= \frac{-12cr^2}{(3hr+4r^2)^2} < 0$.

68. Since the intensity of the beam decreases as the beam passes through the object, it follows that σ is positive.

a. $\left|\frac{\partial I}{\partial x}(1,\sigma)\right| = \left|-\sigma I_0 e^{-\sigma}\right| = \sigma I_0 e^{-\sigma}$. If $f(\sigma) = \sigma I_0 e^{-\sigma}$ for $\sigma > 0$,

then $f'(\sigma) = I_0 e^{-\sigma} - \sigma I_0 e^{-\sigma}$, and thus $f'(\sigma) = 0$ if $\sigma = 1$. Since

$f'(\sigma) > 0$ for $0 < \sigma < 1$ and $f'(\sigma) < 0$ for $\sigma > 1$, we conclude from

Theorem 4.11 that the maximum value of f, and hence $\left|\frac{\partial I}{\partial x}(1,\sigma)\right|$,

occurs for $\sigma = 1$.

b. $\left|\frac{\partial I}{\partial x}(x_0,\sigma)\right| = \left|-\sigma I_0 e^{-\sigma x_0}\right| = \sigma I_0 e^{-\sigma x_0}$. If $g(\sigma) = \sigma I_0 e^{-\sigma x_0}$ for

$\sigma > 0$, then $g'(\sigma) = I_0 e^{-\sigma x_0} - \sigma x_0 I_0 e^{-\sigma x_0}$, and thus $g'(\sigma) = 0$ if

$\sigma x_0 = 1$, or $\sigma = \frac{1}{x_0}$. Since $g'(\sigma) > 0$ for $0 < \sigma < \frac{1}{x_0}$ and

$g'(\sigma) < 0$ for $\sigma > \frac{1}{x_0}$, we conclude from Theorem 4.11 that the maximum

value of g, and hence $\left|\frac{\partial I}{\partial x}(x_0,\sigma)\right|$, occurs for $\sigma = \frac{1}{x_0}$.

69. a. $f(tx, ty) = (tx)^\alpha(ty)^\beta = t^{\alpha+\beta}x^\alpha y^\beta = t^{\alpha+\beta}f(x,y)$

b. $\frac{\partial z}{\partial x} = \alpha x^{\alpha-1}y^\beta$, so $\frac{1}{z}\frac{\partial z}{\partial x} = \frac{1}{x^\alpha y^\beta}(\alpha x^{\alpha-1}y^\beta) = \frac{\alpha}{x}$; $\frac{\partial z}{\partial y} = \beta x^\alpha y^{\beta-1}$, so $\frac{1}{z}\frac{\partial z}{\partial y}$

$= \frac{1}{x^\alpha y^\beta}(\beta x^\alpha y^{\beta-1}) = \frac{\beta}{y}$; $x\frac{\partial z}{\partial x} + y\frac{\partial z}{\partial y} = x(\alpha x^{\alpha-1}y^\beta) + y(\beta x^\alpha y^{\beta-1})$

$= (\alpha+\beta)x^\alpha y^\beta = (\alpha+\beta)z$

70. $\frac{\partial f}{\partial x} = 30x^{-1/2}y^{2/3}$ for $x > 0$ and $\frac{\partial f}{\partial y} = 40x^{1/2}y^{-1/3}$ for $y > 0$, so $\frac{\partial f}{\partial x}$

$= \frac{\partial f}{\partial y}$ if $30x^{-1/2}y^{2/3} = 40x^{1/2}y^{-1/3}$, or $y = \frac{4}{3}x$ for $x > 0$.

71. a. Since the tax on each unit is t, the total tax on x units is tx,

so the profit is given by $P(x,t) = P_0(x) - tx$.

b. By (a), $\frac{\partial P}{\partial x}(x,t) = P_0'(x) - t$ and thus $\frac{\partial^2 P}{\partial x^2}(x,t) = P_0''(x)$.

c. By (6), $0 = \frac{\partial P}{\partial x}(f(t),t)$ and by (b), $\frac{\partial P}{\partial x}(f(t),t) = P_0'(f(t)) - t$,

so $P_0'(f(t)) - t = 0$.

d. From (c), $P_0''(f(t))f'(t) - 1 = 0$, so with the help of (b) and (7) we

find that $f'(t) = \frac{1}{P_0''(f(t))} = \frac{1}{\frac{\partial^2 P}{\partial x^2}(f(t),t)} < 0$.

Section 13.4

1. $\frac{dz}{dt} = \frac{\partial z}{\partial x}\frac{dx}{dt} + \frac{\partial z}{\partial y}\frac{dy}{dt} = 4x\left(\frac{1}{2\sqrt{t}}\right) - 9y^2(2e^{2t}) = 4\sqrt{t}\left(\frac{1}{2\sqrt{t}}\right) - 9e^{4t}(2e^{2t})$

$= 2 - 18e^{6t}$

2. $\frac{dz}{dt} = \frac{\partial z}{\partial x}\frac{dx}{dt} + \frac{\partial z}{\partial y}\frac{dy}{dt} = \frac{6x}{3x^2 + y^3}(2e^{2t}) + \frac{3y^2}{3x^2 + y^3}\left(\frac{1}{3}t^{-2/3}\right) = \frac{6e^{2t}}{3e^{4t} + t}(2e^{2t})$

$+ \frac{3t^{2/3}}{3e^{4t} + t}\left(\frac{1}{3}t^{-2/3}\right) = \frac{12e^{4t} + 1}{3e^{4t} + 1}$

3. $\frac{dz}{dt} = \frac{\partial z}{\partial x}\frac{dx}{dt} + \frac{\partial z}{\partial y}\frac{dy}{dt} = (\cos x - y\sin xy)(2t) + (-x\sin xy)(0)$

$= 2t(\cos t^2 - \sin t^2)$

4. $\frac{dz}{dt} = \frac{\partial z}{\partial x}\frac{dx}{dt} + \frac{\partial z}{\partial y}\frac{dy}{dt} = \frac{-2x}{1 + (y^2 - x^2)^2}(\cos t) + \frac{2y}{1 + (y^2 - x^2)^2}(-\sin t)$

$= \frac{-2\sin t}{1 + (\cos^2 t - \sin^2 t)^2}(\cos t) + \frac{2\cos t}{1 + (\cos^2 t - \sin^2 t)^2}(-\sin t)$

$= \frac{-4\sin t\cos t}{1 + (\cos^2 t - \sin^2 t)^2} = \frac{-2\sin 2t}{1 + \cos^2 2t}$

5. $\frac{dz}{dt} = \frac{\partial z}{\partial x}\frac{dx}{dt} + \frac{\partial z}{\partial y}\frac{dy}{dt} = \frac{1}{\sqrt{2x - 4y}}\left(\frac{1}{t}\right) + \frac{-2}{\sqrt{2x - 4y}}(-9t^2)$

$+ \frac{\frac{1}{2}}{\sqrt{2x - 4y}}(-9t^2)$

$= \frac{1 + 18t^3}{t\sqrt{2\ln t - 4(1 - 3t^3)}}$

6. $\frac{\partial z}{\partial u} = \frac{\partial z}{\partial x}\frac{\partial x}{\partial u} + \frac{\partial z}{\partial y}\frac{\partial y}{\partial u} = \frac{1}{y^2}(1) - \frac{2x}{y^3}(1) = \frac{1}{(u - v - 1)^2} - \frac{2(u + v - 1)}{(u - v - 1)^3}$

$= \frac{1 - u - 3v}{(u - v - 1)^3}$; $\frac{\partial z}{\partial v} = \frac{\partial z}{\partial x}\frac{\partial x}{\partial v} + \frac{\partial z}{\partial y}\frac{\partial y}{\partial v} = \frac{1}{y^2}(1) - \frac{2x}{y^3}(-1) = \frac{1}{(u - v - 1)^2}$

$+ \frac{2(u + v - 1)}{(u - v - 1)^3} = \frac{3u + v - 3}{(u - v - 1)^3}$

7. $\frac{\partial z}{\partial u} = \frac{\partial z}{\partial x}\frac{\partial x}{\partial u} + \frac{\partial z}{\partial y}\frac{\partial y}{\partial u} = \left(\frac{-4}{x^2y} - \frac{1}{y}\right)(2u) + \left(\frac{-4}{xy^2} + \frac{x}{y^2}\right)(v) = \left(\frac{-4}{u^5v} - \frac{1}{uv}\right)(2u)$

$+ \left(\frac{-4}{u^4v^2} + \frac{1}{v^2}\right)(v) = \frac{-12 - u^4}{u^4v}$; $\frac{\partial z}{\partial v} = \frac{\partial z}{\partial x}\frac{\partial x}{\partial v} + \frac{\partial z}{\partial y}\frac{\partial y}{\partial v} = \left(\frac{-4}{x^2y} - \frac{1}{y}\right)(0)$

$+ \left(\frac{-4}{xy^2} + \frac{x}{y^2}\right)(u) = \left(\frac{-4}{u^4v^2} + \frac{1}{v^2}\right)(u) = \frac{-4 + u^4}{u^3v^2}$

8. $\frac{\partial z}{\partial u} = \frac{\partial z}{\partial x}\frac{\partial x}{\partial u} + \frac{\partial z}{\partial y}\frac{\partial y}{\partial u} = -8x(\sin v) - 2y(-v\sin u) = -8u\sin^2 v$

$+ 2v^2\cos u\sin u$

$\frac{\partial z}{\partial v} = \frac{\partial z}{\partial x}\frac{\partial x}{\partial v} + \frac{\partial z}{\partial y}\frac{\partial y}{\partial v} = -8x(u\cos v) - 2y(\cos u) = -8u^2\sin v\cos v$

$- 2v\cos^2 u$

9. $\frac{\partial z}{\partial u} = \frac{\partial z}{\partial x}\frac{\partial x}{\partial u} + \frac{\partial z}{\partial y}\frac{\partial y}{\partial u} = \frac{2x}{x^2 - y^2}(1) - \frac{2y}{x^2 - y^2}(2u) = \frac{2(u - v) - 4u(u^2 + v^2)}{(u - v)^2 - (u^2 + v^2)^2}$

$\frac{\partial z}{\partial v} = \frac{\partial z}{\partial x}\frac{\partial x}{\partial v} + \frac{\partial z}{\partial y}\frac{\partial y}{\partial v} = \frac{2x}{x^2 - y^2}(-1) - \frac{2y}{x^2 - y^2}(2v) = \frac{-2(u - v) - 4v(u^2 + v^2)}{(u - v)^2 - (u^2 + v^2)^2}$

10. $\frac{\partial z}{\partial u} = \frac{\partial z}{\partial x}\frac{\partial x}{\partial u} + \frac{\partial z}{\partial y}\frac{\partial y}{\partial u} = 4xye^{x^2y}\left(\frac{\sqrt{v}}{2\sqrt{u}}\right) + 2x^2e^{x^2y}\left(\frac{-1}{u^2}\right) = 2\frac{v}{u}e^v - 2\frac{v}{u}e^v = 0$

$\frac{\partial z}{\partial v} = \frac{\partial z}{\partial x}\frac{\partial x}{\partial v} + \frac{\partial z}{\partial y}\frac{\partial y}{\partial v} = 4xye^{x^2y}\left(\frac{\sqrt{u}}{2\sqrt{v}}\right) + 2x^2e^{x^2y}(0) = 2e^v$

11. $\frac{\partial z}{\partial r} = \frac{\partial z}{\partial u}\frac{\partial u}{\partial r} + \frac{\partial z}{\partial v}\frac{\partial v}{\partial r} = (2\cos 2u\cos 3v)(2(r + s))$

$+ (-3\sin 2u\sin 3v)(2(r - s)) = 4(r + s)\cos[2(r + s)^2]\cos[3(r - s)^2]$

$- 6(r - s)\sin[2(r + s)^2]\sin[3(r - s)^2]$

$\frac{\partial z}{\partial s} = \frac{\partial z}{\partial u}\frac{\partial u}{\partial s} + \frac{\partial z}{\partial v}\frac{\partial v}{\partial s} = (2\cos 2u\cos 3v)(2(r + s))$

$$+ (-3 \sin 2u \sin 3v)(-2(r - s)) = 4(r + s) \cos \left[2(r + s)^2\right] \cos \left[3(r - s)^2\right]$$

$$+ 6(r - s) \sin \left[2(r + s)^2\right] \sin \left[3(r - s)^2\right]$$

12. $$\frac{\partial z}{\partial r} = \frac{\partial z}{\partial u}\frac{\partial u}{\partial r} + \frac{\partial z}{\partial v}\frac{\partial v}{\partial r} = \frac{1}{u}(4^{rs}\ s \ln 4) + \frac{1}{v}\left(\frac{4^{r/s}}{s} \ln 4\right) = \left(s + \frac{1}{s}\right) \ln 4$$

$$\frac{\partial z}{\partial s} = \frac{\partial z}{\partial u}\frac{\partial u}{\partial s} + \frac{\partial z}{\partial v}\frac{\partial v}{\partial s} = \frac{1}{u}(4^{rs}\ r \ln 4) + \frac{1}{v}\left(-\frac{4^{r/s} r}{s^2} \ln 4\right) = r\left(1 - \frac{1}{s^2}\right) \ln 4$$

13. $$\frac{\partial z}{\partial r} = \frac{\partial z}{\partial u}\frac{\partial u}{\partial r} + \frac{\partial z}{\partial v}\frac{\partial v}{\partial r} = (e^v - ve^{-u})\left(\frac{1}{r}\right) + (ue^v + e^{-u})\left(\frac{s}{r}\right) = \frac{1}{r}\left(r^s - \frac{s}{r} \ln r\right)$$

$$+ \frac{s}{r}\left(r^s \ln r + \frac{1}{r}\right)$$

$$\frac{\partial z}{\partial s} = \frac{\partial z}{\partial u}\frac{\partial u}{\partial s} + \frac{\partial z}{\partial v}\frac{\partial v}{\partial s} = (e^v - ve^{-u})(0) + (ue^v + e^{-u})(\ln r)$$

$$= \left(r^s \ln r + \frac{1}{r}\right) \ln r$$

14. $$\frac{\partial z}{\partial r} = \frac{\partial z}{\partial u}\frac{\partial u}{\partial r} + \frac{\partial z}{\partial v}\frac{\partial v}{\partial r} = (2^{u - v} \ln 2)(\cos s) + (-2^{u - v} \ln 2)(\sin s)$$

$$= 2^{r(\cos s - \sin s)} (\ln 2)(\cos s - \sin s)$$

$$\frac{\partial z}{\partial s} = \frac{\partial z}{\partial u}\frac{\partial u}{\partial s} + \frac{\partial z}{\partial v}\frac{\partial v}{\partial s} = (2^{u - v} \ln 2)(-r \sin s) + (-2^{u - v} \ln 2)(r \cos s)$$

$$= 2^{r(\cos s - \sin s)} (\ln 2)(-r \sin s - r \cos s)$$

15. $$\frac{dw}{dt} = \frac{\partial w}{\partial x}\frac{dx}{dt} + \frac{\partial w}{\partial y}\frac{dy}{dt} + \frac{\partial w}{\partial z}\frac{dz}{dt} = \left(\frac{1}{y} + \frac{z}{x^2}\right)(\cos t) - \frac{x}{y^2}(-\sin t) - \frac{1}{x}(\sec^2 t)$$

$$= 1 + \csc t + \tan^2 t - \csc t \sec^2 t$$

16. $$\frac{dw}{dt} = \frac{\partial w}{\partial x}\frac{dx}{dt} + \frac{\partial w}{\partial y}\frac{dy}{dt} + \frac{\partial w}{\partial z}\frac{dz}{dt} = \frac{-z}{x^2y^2}\left(\frac{-2}{t^3}\right) - \frac{2z}{xy^3}(-5) + \frac{1}{xy^2}\left(\frac{1}{2\sqrt{t}}\right) = \frac{1}{50\sqrt{t}}$$

17. $$\frac{dw}{dt} = \frac{\partial w}{\partial x}\frac{dx}{dt} + \frac{\partial w}{\partial y}\frac{dy}{dt} + \frac{\partial w}{\partial z}\frac{dz}{dt} = \frac{x}{\sqrt{x^2 + y^2 + z^2}}(e^t) + \frac{y}{\sqrt{x^2 + y^2 + z^2}}(-e^{-t})$$

$$+ \frac{z}{\sqrt{x^2 + y^2 + z^2}}(2) = \frac{e^{2t} - e^{-2t} + 4t}{\sqrt{e^{2t} + e^{-2t} + 4t^2}}$$

18. $$\frac{dw}{dt} = \frac{\partial w}{\partial x}\frac{dx}{dt} + \frac{\partial w}{\partial y}\frac{dy}{dt} + \frac{\partial w}{\partial z}\frac{dz}{dt} = \frac{2x}{x^2 + y^2 + z^2}(\cos t) + \frac{2y}{x^2 + y^2 + z^2}(-\sin t)$$

$$+ \frac{2z}{x^2 + y^2 + z^2}(-2te^{-t^2}) = \frac{-4te^{-2t^2}}{1 + e^{-2t^2}}$$

19. $$\frac{dw}{dt} = \frac{\partial w}{\partial x}\frac{dx}{dt} + \frac{\partial w}{\partial y}\frac{dy}{dt} + \frac{\partial w}{\partial z}\frac{dz}{dt} = (y^2z^3 \cos xy^2z^3)(3)$$

$$+ (2xyz^3 \cos xy^2z^3)\left(\tfrac{1}{2}t^{-1/2}\right) + (3xy^2z^2 \cos xy^2z^3)\left(\tfrac{1}{3}t^{-2/3}\right) = 9t^2 \cos 3t^3$$

20. $$\frac{dw}{dt} = \frac{\partial w}{\partial x}\frac{dx}{dt} + \frac{\partial w}{\partial y}\frac{dy}{dt} + \frac{\partial w}{\partial z}\frac{dz}{dt} = \frac{x}{\sqrt{x^2 + y^2}}(2t)$$

$$+ \left(\frac{y}{\sqrt{x^2 + y^2}} - \frac{3y^2}{2\sqrt{y^3 - z^3}}\right)(3t^2) + \frac{3z^2}{2\sqrt{y^3 - z^3}}(-3t^2) = \frac{t(2 + 3t^2)}{\sqrt{1 + t^2}} - \frac{9}{\sqrt{2}} t^{7/2}$$

21. $$\frac{\partial w}{\partial u} = \frac{\partial w}{\partial x}\frac{\partial x}{\partial u} + \frac{\partial w}{\partial y}\frac{\partial y}{\partial u} + \frac{\partial w}{\partial z}\frac{\partial z}{\partial u} = \frac{-yz(2x+y)}{x^2(x+y)^2}(2u) + \frac{\partial w}{\partial y}(0) + \frac{y}{x(x+y)}(2u)$$

$$= \frac{-v^2(u^2-v^2)(2u^2+v^2)2u + v^2(2u)\left[u^2(u^2+v^2)\right]}{u^4(u^2+v^2)^2} = \frac{2v^2(-u^4+2u^2v^2+v^4)}{u^3(u^2+v^2)^2}$$

$$\frac{\partial w}{\partial v} = \frac{\partial w}{\partial x}\frac{\partial x}{\partial v} + \frac{\partial w}{\partial y}\frac{\partial y}{\partial v} + \frac{\partial w}{\partial z}\frac{\partial z}{\partial v} = \frac{\partial w}{\partial x}(0) + \frac{(x^2+xy)z - yzx}{x^2(x+y)^2}(2v) + \frac{y}{x(x+y)}(-2v)$$

$$= \frac{u^4(u^2-v^2)(2v) - v^2(2v)\left[u^2(u^2+v^2)\right]}{u^4(u^2+v^2)^2} = \frac{2v(u^2-2u^2v^2-v^4)}{u^2(u^2+v^2)^2}$$

22. $$\frac{\partial w}{\partial u} = \frac{\partial w}{\partial x}\frac{\partial x}{\partial u} + \frac{\partial w}{\partial y}\frac{\partial y}{\partial u} + \frac{\partial w}{\partial z}\frac{\partial z}{\partial u} = 2x(v \sin(\pi - u)) - 2(\sin(\pi - v)) - 7(v)$$

$$= 2v^2 \cos(\pi - u) \sin(\pi - u) - 2\sin(\pi - v) - 7v$$

$$\frac{\partial w}{\partial v} = \frac{\partial w}{\partial x}\frac{\partial x}{\partial v} + \frac{\partial w}{\partial y}\frac{\partial y}{\partial v} + \frac{\partial w}{\partial z}\frac{\partial z}{\partial v} = 2x(\cos(\pi - u)) - 2(-u\cos(\pi - v)) - 7(u)$$

$= 2v\cos^2(\pi - u) + 2u\cos(\pi - v) - 7u$

23. $\frac{\partial w}{\partial u} = \frac{\partial w}{\partial x}\frac{\partial x}{\partial u} + \frac{\partial w}{\partial y}\frac{\partial y}{\partial u} + \frac{\partial w}{\partial z}\frac{\partial z}{\partial u} = \frac{y}{x}(ve^u) + (\ln xz)(2uv^4) + \frac{y}{z}e^v = \frac{u^2v^4}{ve^u}(ve^u)$

$+ 2uv^4\ln(ve^u ue^v) + \frac{u^2v^4}{ue^v}e^v = uv^4\left[1 + u + 2\ln(uve^u e^v)\right]$

$\frac{\partial w}{\partial v} = \frac{\partial w}{\partial x}\frac{\partial x}{\partial v} + \frac{\partial w}{\partial y}\frac{\partial y}{\partial v} + \frac{\partial w}{\partial z}\frac{\partial z}{\partial v} = \frac{y}{x}(e^u) + (\ln xz)(4u^2v^3) + \frac{y}{z}(ue^v)$

$= \frac{u^2v^4}{ve^u}(e^u) + 4u^2v^3\ln(ve^u ue^v) + \frac{u^2v^4}{ue^v}(ue^v) = u^2v^3\left[1+v+4\ln(uve^u e^v)\right]$

24. $\frac{\partial w}{\partial u} = \frac{\partial w}{\partial x}\frac{\partial x}{\partial u} + \frac{\partial w}{\partial y}\frac{\partial y}{\partial u} + \frac{\partial w}{\partial z}\frac{\partial z}{\partial u} = \left(\frac{e^{x/y}}{y} - \frac{ze^{z/x}}{x^2}\right)\left(\frac{1}{uv}\right) - \frac{xe^{x/y}}{y^2}\left(\frac{1}{u}\right)$

$+ \frac{e^{z/x}}{x}\left(\frac{1 - \ln u}{u^2 v}\right) = \frac{-e^{1/u}}{u^2}$

$\frac{\partial w}{\partial v} = \frac{\partial w}{\partial x}\frac{\partial x}{\partial v} + \frac{\partial w}{\partial y}\frac{\partial y}{\partial v} + \frac{\partial w}{\partial z}\frac{\partial z}{\partial v} = \left(\frac{e^{x/y}}{y} - \frac{ze^{z/x}}{x^2}\right)\left(\frac{-\ln u}{v^2}\right) - \frac{xe^{x/y}}{y^2}(0)$

$+ \frac{e^{z/x}}{x}\left(\frac{-\ln u}{uv^2}\right) = \frac{-e^{1/v}}{v^2}$

25. Let $z = x^3 + 4x^2y - 3xy^2 + 2y^3 + 5$. Then $\frac{dy}{dx} = \frac{-\partial z/\partial x}{\partial z/\partial y} = \frac{-3x^2 - 8xy + 3y^2}{4x^2 - 6xy + 6y^2}$

26. Let $z = x^{2/3} + y^{2/3} - 2$. Then $\frac{dy}{dx} = \frac{-\partial z/\partial x}{\partial z/\partial y} = \frac{-\frac{2}{3}x^{-1/3}}{\frac{2}{3}y^{-1/3}} = \frac{-y^{1/3}}{x^{1/3}}$

27. Let $z = x^2 + y^2 + \sin xy^2$. Then $\frac{dy}{dx} = \frac{-\partial z/\partial x}{\partial z/\partial y} = \frac{-2x - y^2\cos xy^2}{2y + 2xy\cos xy^2}$

28. Let $z = e^{x/y} + \ln\frac{y}{x} + 15$. Then $\frac{dy}{dx} = \frac{-\partial z/\partial x}{\partial z/\partial y} = \frac{\frac{-e^{x/y}}{y} + \frac{1}{x}}{\frac{-xe^{x/y}}{y^2} + \frac{1}{y}} = \frac{-xye^{x/y} + y^2}{-x^2e^{x/y} + xy}$

29. Let $z = x^2 - \frac{y^2}{y^2 - 1}$. Then $\frac{dy}{dx} = \frac{-\partial z/\partial x}{\partial z/\partial y} = \frac{-2x}{\frac{2y}{(y^2 - 1)^2}} = \frac{-x(y^2 - 1)^2}{y}$.

30. Let $w = x^2z^2 - 2xyz + z^3y^2 - 3$. Then $\frac{\partial z}{\partial x} = \frac{-\partial w/\partial x}{\partial w/\partial z}$

$= \frac{-2xz^2 + 2yz}{2x^2z - 2xy + 3z^2y^2}$ and $\frac{\partial z}{\partial y} = \frac{-\partial w/\partial y}{\partial w/\partial z} = \frac{2xz - 2z^3y}{2x^2z - 2xy + 3z^2y^2}$

31. Let $w = x - yz + \cos xyz - 2$. Then $\frac{\partial z}{\partial x} = \frac{-\partial w/\partial x}{\partial w/\partial z} = \frac{-1 + yz\sin xyz}{-y - xy\sin xyz}$ and

$\frac{\partial z}{\partial y} = \frac{-\partial w/\partial y}{\partial w/\partial z} = \frac{z + xz\sin xyz}{-y - xy\sin xyz}$

32. Let $w = \frac{1}{z} + \frac{1}{y + z} + \frac{1}{x + y + z} - \frac{1}{2}$. Then $\frac{\partial z}{\partial x} = \frac{-\partial w/\partial x}{\partial w/\partial z}$

$= \frac{\frac{1}{(x + y + z)^2}}{\frac{-1}{z^2} - \frac{1}{(y + z)^2} - \frac{1}{(x + y + z)^2}}$ and $\frac{\partial z}{\partial y} = \frac{-\partial w/\partial y}{\partial w/\partial z}$

$= \frac{\frac{1}{(y + z)^2} + \frac{1}{(x + y + z)^2}}{\frac{-1}{z^2} - \frac{1}{(y + z)^2} - \frac{1}{(x + y + z)^2}}$

33. If we let $u = x - y$, then $z = f(u)$, so that $\frac{\partial z}{\partial x} = \frac{dz}{du}\frac{\partial u}{\partial x} = \frac{dz}{du}$ and $\frac{\partial z}{\partial y} =$

$\frac{dz}{du}\frac{\partial u}{\partial y} = -\frac{dz}{du}$. Thus $\frac{\partial z}{\partial x} = -\frac{\partial z}{\partial y}$.

34. If we let $r = x - y$, $s = y - z$, and $t = z - x$, then $w = f(r, s, t)$, so

that $\frac{\partial w}{\partial x} = \frac{\partial w}{\partial r}\frac{\partial r}{\partial x} + \frac{\partial w}{\partial s}\frac{\partial s}{\partial x} + \frac{\partial w}{\partial t}\frac{\partial t}{\partial x} = \frac{\partial w}{\partial r} - \frac{\partial w}{\partial t}$, $\frac{\partial w}{\partial y} = \frac{\partial w}{\partial r}\frac{\partial r}{\partial y} + \frac{\partial w}{\partial s}\frac{\partial s}{\partial y} + \frac{\partial w}{\partial t}\frac{\partial t}{\partial y}$

$= -\frac{\partial w}{\partial r} + \frac{\partial w}{\partial s}$, and $\frac{\partial w}{\partial z} = \frac{\partial w}{\partial r}\frac{\partial r}{\partial z} + \frac{\partial w}{\partial s}\frac{\partial s}{\partial z} + \frac{\partial w}{\partial t}\frac{\partial t}{\partial z} = -\frac{\partial w}{\partial s} + \frac{\partial w}{\partial t}$. Thus $\frac{\partial w}{\partial x} + \frac{\partial w}{\partial y}$

$+ \frac{\partial w}{\partial z} = \left(\frac{\partial w}{\partial r} - \frac{\partial w}{\partial t}\right) + \left(-\frac{\partial w}{\partial r} + \frac{\partial w}{\partial s}\right) + \left(-\frac{\partial w}{\partial s} + \frac{\partial w}{\partial t}\right) = 0.$

35. If $u = y + ax$ and $v = y - ax$, then $z = f(u) + g(v)$, so that $\frac{\partial z}{\partial x}$

$= \frac{\partial z}{\partial u}\frac{\partial u}{\partial x} + \frac{\partial z}{\partial v}\frac{\partial v}{\partial x} = a\frac{df}{du} - a\frac{dg}{dv}$ and $\frac{\partial z}{\partial y} = \frac{\partial z}{\partial u}\frac{\partial u}{\partial y} + \frac{\partial z}{\partial v}\frac{\partial v}{\partial y} = \frac{df}{du} + \frac{dg}{dv}$. It follows

that $\frac{\partial^2 z}{\partial x^2} = \frac{\partial}{\partial x}(\frac{\partial z}{\partial x}) = \frac{\partial}{\partial x}(a\frac{df}{du} - a\frac{dg}{dv}) = \left[\frac{\partial}{\partial u}(a\frac{df}{du} - a\frac{dg}{dv})\right]\frac{\partial u}{\partial x}$

$+ \left[\frac{\partial}{\partial v}(a\frac{df}{du} - a\frac{dg}{dv})\right]\frac{\partial v}{\partial x} = (a\frac{d^2f}{du^2} - 0)(a) + (0 - a\frac{d^2g}{dv^2})(-a) = a^2(\frac{d^2f}{du^2} + \frac{d^2g}{dv^2})$.

Similarly, $\frac{\partial^2 z}{\partial y^2} = \frac{\partial}{\partial y}(\frac{\partial z}{\partial y}) = \frac{\partial}{\partial y}(\frac{df}{du} + \frac{dg}{dv}) = \frac{\partial}{\partial u}(\frac{df}{du} + \frac{dg}{dv})\frac{\partial u}{\partial y} + \frac{\partial}{\partial v}(\frac{df}{du} + \frac{dg}{dv})\frac{\partial v}{\partial y}$

$= (\frac{d^2f}{du^2} + 0)(1) + (0 + \frac{d^2g}{dv^2})(1) = \frac{d^2f}{du^2} + \frac{d^2g}{dv^2}$. Thus $\frac{\partial^2 z}{\partial x^2} = a^2\frac{\partial^2 z}{\partial y^2}$.

36. a. $\frac{\partial z}{\partial r} = \frac{\partial z}{\partial x}\frac{\partial x}{\partial r} + \frac{\partial z}{\partial y}\frac{\partial y}{\partial r} = \frac{\partial z}{\partial x}\cos\theta + \frac{\partial z}{\partial y}\sin\theta$ and $\frac{\partial z}{\partial \theta} = \frac{\partial z}{\partial x}\frac{\partial x}{\partial \theta} + \frac{\partial z}{\partial y}\frac{\partial y}{\partial \theta}$

$= -\frac{\partial z}{\partial x} r\sin\theta + \frac{\partial z}{\partial y} r\cos\theta$. Thus $\frac{\partial z}{\partial r}\cos\theta - \frac{\partial z}{\partial \theta}\frac{\sin\theta}{r}$

$= (\frac{\partial z}{\partial x}\cos\theta + \frac{\partial z}{\partial y}\sin\theta)\cos\theta - (-\frac{\partial z}{\partial x} r\sin\theta + \frac{\partial z}{\partial y} r\cos\theta)\frac{\sin\theta}{r} = \frac{\partial z}{\partial x}$

and $\frac{\partial z}{\partial r}\sin\theta + \frac{\partial z}{\partial \theta}\frac{\cos\theta}{r} = (\frac{\partial z}{\partial x}\cos\theta + \frac{\partial z}{\partial y}\sin\theta)\sin\theta$

$+ (-\frac{\partial z}{\partial x} r\sin\theta + \frac{\partial z}{\partial y} r\cos\theta)\frac{\cos\theta}{r} = \frac{\partial z}{\partial y}$.

b. From part (a) we find that $(\frac{\partial z}{\partial x})^2 + (\frac{\partial z}{\partial y})^2 = (\frac{\partial z}{\partial r}\cos\theta - \frac{\partial z}{\partial \theta}\frac{\sin\theta}{r})^2$

$+ (\frac{\partial z}{\partial r}\sin\theta + \frac{\partial z}{\partial \theta}\frac{\cos\theta}{r})^2 = (\frac{\partial z}{\partial r})^2 + \frac{1}{r^2}(\frac{\partial z}{\partial \theta})^2$.

37. We have $\frac{\partial w}{\partial s} = \frac{\partial w}{\partial x}\frac{\partial x}{\partial s} + \frac{\partial w}{\partial y}\frac{\partial y}{\partial s} = \frac{\partial w}{\partial x}e^s\cos t + \frac{\partial w}{\partial y}e^s\sin t$ and $\frac{\partial w}{\partial t} = \frac{\partial w}{\partial x}\frac{\partial x}{\partial t}$

$+ \frac{\partial w}{\partial y}\frac{\partial y}{\partial t} = -\frac{\partial w}{\partial x}e^s\sin t + \frac{\partial w}{\partial y}e^s\cos t$. Thus $\frac{\partial^2 w}{\partial s^2} = \frac{\partial}{\partial s}(\frac{\partial w}{\partial s})$

$= \frac{\partial}{\partial s}(\frac{\partial w}{\partial x}e^s\cos t + \frac{\partial w}{\partial y}e^s\sin t) = \left[\frac{\partial}{\partial s}(\frac{\partial w}{\partial x})\right]e^s\cos t + \frac{\partial w}{\partial x}e^s\cos t$

$+ \left[\frac{\partial}{\partial s}(\frac{\partial w}{\partial y})\right]e^s\sin t + \frac{\partial w}{\partial y}e^s\sin t$ and $\frac{\partial^2 w}{\partial t^2} = \frac{\partial}{\partial t}(\frac{\partial w}{\partial t})$

$= \frac{\partial}{\partial t}(-\frac{\partial w}{\partial x}e^s\sin t + \frac{\partial w}{\partial y}e^s\cos t) = -\left[\frac{\partial}{\partial t}(\frac{\partial w}{\partial x})\right]e^s\sin t - \frac{\partial w}{\partial x}e^s\cos t$

$+ \left[\frac{\partial}{\partial t}(\frac{\partial w}{\partial y})\right]e^s\cos t - \frac{\partial w}{\partial y}e^s\sin t$. But $\frac{\partial}{\partial s}(\frac{\partial w}{\partial x}) = \left[\frac{\partial}{\partial x}(\frac{\partial w}{\partial x})\right]\frac{\partial x}{\partial s}$

$+ \left[\frac{\partial}{\partial y}(\frac{\partial w}{\partial x})\right]\frac{\partial y}{\partial s} = \frac{\partial^2 w}{\partial x^2}e^s\cos t + \frac{\partial^2 w}{\partial y\partial x}e^s\sin t$, $\frac{\partial}{\partial s}(\frac{\partial w}{\partial y}) = \left[\frac{\partial}{\partial x}(\frac{\partial w}{\partial y})\right]\frac{\partial x}{\partial s}$

$+ \left[\frac{\partial}{\partial y}(\frac{\partial w}{\partial y})\right]\frac{\partial y}{\partial s} = \frac{\partial^2 w}{\partial x\partial y}e^s\cos t + \frac{\partial^2 w}{\partial y^2}e^s\sin t$, $\frac{\partial}{\partial t}(\frac{\partial w}{\partial x}) = \left[\frac{\partial}{\partial x}(\frac{\partial w}{\partial x})\right]\frac{\partial x}{\partial t}$

$+ \left[\frac{\partial}{\partial y}(\frac{\partial w}{\partial x})\right]\frac{\partial y}{\partial t} = -\frac{\partial^2 w}{\partial x^2}e^s\sin t + \frac{\partial^2 w}{\partial y\partial x}e^s\cos t$, and $\frac{\partial}{\partial t}(\frac{\partial w}{\partial y})$

$= \left[\frac{\partial}{\partial x}(\frac{\partial w}{\partial y})\right]\frac{\partial x}{\partial t} + \left[\frac{\partial}{\partial y}(\frac{\partial w}{\partial y})\right]\frac{\partial y}{\partial t} = -\frac{\partial^2 w}{\partial x\partial y}e^s\sin t + \frac{\partial^2 w}{\partial y^2}e^s\cos t$. Thus $\frac{\partial^2 w}{\partial s^2}$

$+ \frac{\partial^2 w}{\partial t^2} = \Big[(\frac{\partial^2 w}{\partial x^2}e^s\cos t + \frac{\partial^2 w}{\partial y\partial x}e^s\sin t)e^s\cos t + \frac{\partial w}{\partial x}e^s\cos t$

$+ (\frac{\partial^2 w}{\partial x\partial y}e^s\cos t + \frac{\partial^2 w}{\partial y^2}e^s\sin t)e^s\sin t + \frac{\partial w}{\partial y}e^s\sin t\Big]$

$$+\left[-\left(-\frac{\partial^2 w}{\partial x^2}e^s \sin t+\frac{\partial^2 w}{\partial y\partial x}e^s\cos t\right)e^s\sin t-\frac{\partial w}{\partial x}e^s\cos t\right.$$

$$\left.+\left(-\frac{\partial^2 w}{\partial x\partial y}e^s\sin t+\frac{\partial^2 w}{\partial y^2}e^s\cos t\right)e^s\cos t-\frac{\partial w}{\partial y}e^s\sin t\right]$$

$= e^{2s}\left(\frac{\partial^2 w}{\partial x^2}+\frac{\partial^2 w}{\partial y^2}\right)$. Thus $\frac{\partial^2 w}{\partial x^2}+\frac{\partial^2 w}{\partial y^2}=e^{-2s}\left(\frac{\partial^2 w}{\partial s^2}+\frac{\partial^2 w}{\partial t^2}\right)$.

38. For any given x and y, let $u = tx$, $v = ty$, and $z = f(tx, ty)$. Then $z = f(u, v)$, so that $\frac{dz}{dt}=\frac{\partial z}{\partial u}\frac{du}{dt}+\frac{\partial z}{\partial v}\frac{dv}{dt}=\frac{\partial z}{\partial u}x+\frac{\partial z}{\partial v}y = xf_u(tx, ty)$ $+ yf_v(tx, ty)$. Since $z = t^n f(x, y)$, we also have $\frac{dz}{dt}=nt^{n-1}f(x, y)$. Thus $xf_u(tx, ty) + yf_v(tx, ty) = nt^{n-1}f(x, y)$. Setting $t = 1$, we obtain $xf_x(x, y) + yf_y(x, y) = nf(x, y)$.

39. Since $f(tx, ty) = \tan\frac{(tx)^2+(ty)^2}{txty} = f(x, y) = t^0 f(x, y)$, we find from Exercise 38 with $n = 0$ that $xf_x(x, y) + yf_y(x, y) = 0$.

40. Assume that f is differentiable at (x_0, y_0). From (8) we find that

$$\lim_{(x,y)\to(x_0,y_0)}[f(x, y) - f(x_0, y_0)] = \lim_{(x,y)\to(x_0,y_0)}[f_x(x_0, y_0)(x - x_0)$$

$$+ f_y(x_0, y_0)(y - y_0) + \varepsilon_1(x, y)(x - x_0) + \varepsilon_2(x, y)(y - y_0)] = f_x(x_0, y_0)\cdot 0$$

$+ f_y(x_0, y_0)\cdot 0 + 0\cdot 0 + 0\cdot 0 = 0$. Thus $\lim_{(x,y)\to(x_0,y_0)} f(x, y) = f(x_0, y_0)$, which means that f is continuous at (x_0, y_0).

41. By Example 3 in Section 13.2, f is not continuous at $(0, 0)$. From Exercise 40, it follows that f is not differentiable at $(0, 0)$.

42. The volume V of wood in the trunk is given by $V = \frac{1}{4}\pi D^2 h$, where D is the diameter of the trunk and h is the height of the trunk. Then $\frac{dV}{dt}$ $= \frac{\partial V}{\partial D}\frac{dD}{dt}+\frac{\partial V}{\partial h}\frac{dh}{dt} = (\frac{1}{2}\pi Dh)(1) + (\frac{1}{4}\pi D^2)(6)$. Thus, when $D = 5$ and $h = 100$, we have $\frac{dV}{dt} = 250\pi + \frac{75}{2}\pi = \frac{575}{2}\pi$ (cubic inches per year).

43. $\frac{dQ}{dt}=\frac{\partial Q}{\partial r}\frac{dr}{dt}+\frac{\partial Q}{\partial p}\frac{dp}{dt} = \left(\frac{4\pi pr^3}{8l\eta}\right)\left(\frac{1}{10}\right) + \left(\frac{\pi r^4}{8l\eta}\right)\left(\frac{-1}{5}\right) = \frac{\pi r^3}{40l\eta}(2p - r)$

44. Let x be the distance from the car to the intersection, and y the distance from the train to the intersection. Then the distance D between the car and the train is given by $D = \sqrt{x^2+y^2}$, so that $\frac{dD}{dt}=\frac{\partial D}{\partial x}\frac{dx}{dt}$ $+\frac{\partial D}{\partial y}\frac{dy}{dt} = \left(\frac{x}{\sqrt{x^2+y^2}}\right)(-20) + \left(\frac{y}{\sqrt{x^2+y^2}}\right)(-100)$. When $x = .5$ and $y = 1.2$, we have $\frac{dD}{dt} = \left(\frac{.5}{1.3}\right)(-20) + \left(\frac{1.2}{1.3}\right)(-100) = -100$. Thus the distance between the car and the train is decreasing at the rate of 100 miles per hour.

45. $\frac{dF}{dt}=\frac{\partial F}{\partial m}\frac{dm}{dt}+\frac{\partial F}{\partial r}\frac{dr}{dt}=\frac{GM}{r^2}\frac{dm}{dt}-\frac{2GMm}{r^3}\frac{dr}{dt}$. Thus if $\frac{dm}{dt} = -40$, $r = 6400$, and $\frac{dr}{dt} = 100$, we have $\frac{dF}{dt} = \frac{GM}{(6400)^2}(-40) - \frac{2GMm}{(6400)^3}(100) = \frac{-GM}{(6400)^2}\left(40 + \frac{m}{32}\right)$.

Section 13.5

1. $f_x(x, y) = 4x - 3y$, $f_y(x, y) = -3x + 2y$, and $\|\vec{a}\| = 1$; $D_{\vec{a}}f(1, 1)$

$= f_x(1, 1)(\frac{1}{\sqrt{2}}) + f_y(1, 1)(\frac{1}{\sqrt{2}}) = \frac{1}{\sqrt{2}} - \frac{1}{\sqrt{2}} = 0.$

2. $f_x(x, y) = 2x$, $f_y(x, y) = 2y$, and $\|\vec{a}\| = 1$; $D_{\vec{a}}f(1, 2) = f_x(1, 2)(\frac{1}{\sqrt{3}})$

$+ f_y(1, 2)(\frac{-\sqrt{2}}{\sqrt{3}}) = \frac{2}{\sqrt{3}} - \frac{4\sqrt{2}}{\sqrt{3}} = \frac{2}{\sqrt{3}}(1 - 2\sqrt{2}).$

3. $f_x(x, y) = \frac{2x(x^2 + y^2) - (x^2 - y^2)2x}{(x^2 + y^2)^2} = \frac{4xy^2}{(x^2 + y^2)^2}$, $f_y(x, y)$

$= \frac{-2y(x^2 + y^2) - (x^2 - y^2)\,2y}{(x^2 + y^2)^2} = \frac{-4x^2y}{(x^2 + y^2)^2}$, and $\|\vec{a}\| = 1$; $D_{\vec{a}}f(3, 4)$

$= f_x(3, 4)(\frac{1}{2}) + f_y(3, 4)(\frac{-\sqrt{3}}{2}) = \frac{96 + 72\sqrt{3}}{625}$

4. $f_x(x, y) = 1$, $f_y(x, y) = -2y$, and $\|\vec{a}\| = \sqrt{5}$, so that $\vec{u} = \frac{\vec{a}}{\|\vec{a}\|}$

$= \frac{1}{\sqrt{5}}\vec{i} + \frac{2}{\sqrt{5}}\vec{j}$; $D_{\vec{u}}f(2, -3) = f_x(2, -3)(\frac{1}{\sqrt{5}}) + f_y(2, -3)(\frac{2}{\sqrt{5}}) = \frac{1}{\sqrt{5}}$

$+ \frac{12}{\sqrt{5}} = \frac{13}{5}\sqrt{5}$

5. $f_x(x, y) = 0$, $f_y(x, y) = 4e^{4y}$, and $\|\vec{a}\| = 4$, so that $\vec{u} = \frac{\vec{a}}{\|\vec{a}\|} = \vec{i}$;

$D_{\vec{u}}f(\frac{1}{2}, \frac{1}{4}) = f_x(\frac{1}{2}, \frac{1}{4})(1) + f_y(\frac{1}{2}, \frac{1}{4})(0) = 0$

6. $f_x(x, y) = y^2 \cos xy^2$, $f_y(x, y) = 2xy \cos xy^2$, and $\|\vec{a}\| = \sqrt{10}$, so that

$\vec{u} = \frac{\vec{a}}{\|\vec{a}\|} = \frac{1}{\sqrt{10}}\vec{i} - \frac{3}{\sqrt{10}}\vec{j}$; $D_{\vec{u}}f(\frac{1}{\pi}, \pi) = f_x(\frac{1}{\pi}, \pi)(\frac{1}{\sqrt{10}}) + f_y(\frac{1}{\pi}, \pi)(\frac{-3}{\sqrt{10}})$

$= \frac{-\pi^2}{\sqrt{10}} + \frac{6}{\sqrt{10}} = \frac{1}{\sqrt{10}}(6 - \pi^2).$

7. $f_x(x, y) = \sec^2(x + 2y)$, $f_y(x, y) = 2\sec^2(x + 2y)$, and $\|\vec{a}\| = \sqrt{41}$,

so that $\vec{u} = \frac{\vec{a}}{\|\vec{a}\|} = \frac{-4}{\sqrt{41}}\vec{i} + \frac{5}{\sqrt{41}}\vec{j}$; $D_{\vec{u}}f(0, \frac{\pi}{6}) = f_x(0, \frac{\pi}{6})(\frac{-4}{\sqrt{41}})$

$+ f_y(0, \frac{\pi}{6})(\frac{5}{\sqrt{41}}) = \frac{-16}{\sqrt{41}} + \frac{40}{\sqrt{41}} = \frac{24}{41}\sqrt{41}.$

8. $f_x(x, y, z) = 3$, $f_y(x, y, z) = -2$, $f_z(x, y, z) = 4$, $\|\vec{a}\| = \sqrt{3}$, so that

$\vec{u} = \frac{\vec{a}}{\|\vec{a}\|} = \frac{1}{\sqrt{3}}\vec{i} + \frac{1}{\sqrt{3}}\vec{j} + \frac{1}{\sqrt{3}}\vec{k}$; $D_{\vec{u}}f(1, -1, 2) = f_x(1, -1, 2)(\frac{1}{\sqrt{3}})$

$+ f_y(1, -1, 2)(\frac{1}{\sqrt{3}}) + f_z(1, -1, 2)(\frac{1}{\sqrt{3}}) = \frac{3}{\sqrt{3}} - \frac{2}{\sqrt{3}} + \frac{4}{\sqrt{3}} = \frac{5}{3}\sqrt{3}$

9. $f_x(x, y, z) = 3x^2y^2z$, $f_y(x, y, z) = 2x^3yz$, $f_z(x, y, z) = x^3y^2$, and $\|\vec{a}\|$

$= 3$, so that $\vec{u} = \frac{\vec{a}}{\|\vec{a}\|} = \frac{2}{3}\vec{i} - \frac{1}{3}\vec{j} - \frac{2}{3}\vec{k}$; $D_{\vec{u}}f(2, -1, 2) = f_x(2, -1, 2)(\frac{2}{3})$

$+ f_y(2, -1, 2)(\frac{-1}{3}) + f_z(2, -1, 2)(\frac{-2}{3}) = 16 + \frac{32}{3} - \frac{16}{3} = \frac{64}{3}$

10. $f_x(x, y, z) = y + 3z$, $f_y(x, y, z) = x - z$, $f_z(x, y, z) = -y + 3x$, and $\|\vec{a}\|$

$= \sqrt{14}$, so that $\vec{u} = \frac{\vec{a}}{\|\vec{a}\|} = -\frac{1}{\sqrt{14}}\vec{i} + \frac{3}{\sqrt{14}}\vec{j} + \frac{2}{\sqrt{14}}\vec{k}$; $D_{\vec{u}}f(1, -1, 3)$

$= f_x(1, -1, 3)(\frac{-1}{\sqrt{14}}) + f_y(1, -1, 3)(\frac{3}{\sqrt{14}}) + f_z(1, -1, 3)(\frac{2}{\sqrt{14}}) = \frac{-8}{\sqrt{14}}$

$- \frac{6}{\sqrt{14}} + \frac{8}{\sqrt{14}} = \frac{-3}{7}\sqrt{14}$

11. $f_x(x, y, z) = \frac{(x + y + z) - (x - y - z)}{(x + y + z)^2} = \frac{2y + 2z}{(x + y + z)^2}$, $f_y(x, y, z)$

$= \frac{-(x + y + z) - (x - y - z)}{(x + y + z)^2} = \frac{-2x}{(x + y + z)^2}$, $f_z(x, y, z)$

$= \frac{-(x + y + z) - (x - y - z)}{(x + y + z)^2} = \frac{-2x}{(x + y + z)^2}$, and $\|\vec{a}\| = \sqrt{6}$, so that

$\vec{u} = \frac{\vec{a}}{\|\vec{a}\|} = \frac{-2}{\sqrt{6}}\vec{i} - \frac{1}{\sqrt{6}}\vec{j} - \frac{1}{\sqrt{6}}\vec{k}$; $D_{\vec{u}}f(2, 1, -1) = f_x(2, 1, -1)(\frac{-2}{\sqrt{6}})$

$+ f_y(2, 1, -1)(\frac{-1}{\sqrt{6}}) + f_z(2, 1, -1)(\frac{-1}{\sqrt{6}}) = 0 + \frac{1}{\sqrt{6}} + \frac{1}{\sqrt{6}} = \frac{\sqrt{6}}{3}$.

12. $f_x(x, y, z) = 2xe^{x^2 + y^2 + z^2}$, $f_y(x, y, z) = 2ye^{x^2 + y^2 + z^2}$, $f_z(x, y, z) = 2ze^{x^2 + y^2 + z^2}$, $\|\vec{a}\| = \sqrt{3}$, so that $\vec{u} = \frac{\vec{a}}{\|\vec{a}\|} = \frac{-1}{\sqrt{3}}\vec{i} + \frac{1}{\sqrt{3}}\vec{j} - \frac{1}{\sqrt{3}}\vec{k}$; $D_{\vec{u}}f(0, 0, 0) = f_x(0, 0, 0)(\frac{-1}{\sqrt{3}}) + f_y(0, 0, 0)(\frac{1}{\sqrt{3}}) + f_z(0, 0, 0)(\frac{-1}{\sqrt{3}}) = 0 + 0 + 0 = 0$

13. $f(x, y, z) = yz2^x = yze^{x \ln 2}$; $f_x(x, y, z) = (\ln 2)\, yze^{x \ln 2} = yz2^x \ln 2$, $f_y(x, y, z) = z2^x$, $f_z(x, y, z) = y2^x$, $\|\vec{a}\| = \sqrt{5}$, so that $\vec{u} = \frac{\vec{a}}{\|\vec{a}\|} = \frac{2}{\sqrt{5}}\vec{j} - \frac{1}{\sqrt{5}}\vec{k}$; $D_{\vec{u}}f(1, -1, 1) = f_x(1, -1, 1)(0) + f_y(1, -1, 1)(\frac{2}{\sqrt{5}}) + f_z(1, -1, 1)(\frac{-1}{\sqrt{5}}) = 0 + \frac{4}{\sqrt{5}} + \frac{2}{\sqrt{5}} = \frac{6}{5}\sqrt{5}$.

14. $f_x(x, y, z) = \frac{yz}{\sqrt{1 - x^2z^2}}$, $f_y(x, y, z) = \arcsin xz$, $f_z(x, y, z) = \frac{xy}{\sqrt{1 - x^2z^2}}$, $\|\vec{a}\| = 2\sqrt{3}$, so that $\vec{u} = \frac{\vec{a}}{\|\vec{a}\|} = \frac{-1}{\sqrt{3}}\vec{i} - \frac{1}{\sqrt{3}}\vec{j} - \frac{1}{\sqrt{3}}\vec{k}$; $D_{\vec{u}}f(\frac{1}{\sqrt{2}}, 0, \frac{1}{\sqrt{2}}) = f_x(\frac{1}{\sqrt{2}}, 0, \frac{1}{\sqrt{2}})(\frac{-1}{\sqrt{3}}) + f_y(\frac{1}{\sqrt{2}}, 0, \frac{1}{\sqrt{2}})(\frac{-1}{\sqrt{3}}) + f_z(\frac{1}{\sqrt{2}}, 0, \frac{1}{\sqrt{2}})(\frac{-1}{\sqrt{3}}) = 0 + (\arcsin \frac{1}{2})(\frac{-1}{\sqrt{3}}) + 0 = \frac{-\pi\sqrt{3}}{18}$.

15. Let $r = f_x(1, 2)$ and $s = f_y(1, 2)$. Since $\|\vec{a}\| = \sqrt{2}$ and $\|\vec{b}\| = 3\sqrt{2}$, let $\vec{u}_{\vec{a}} = \frac{\vec{a}}{\|\vec{a}\|} = \frac{1}{\sqrt{2}}\vec{i} - \frac{1}{\sqrt{2}}\vec{j}$ and $\vec{u}_{\vec{b}} = \frac{\vec{b}}{\|\vec{b}\|} = \frac{1}{\sqrt{2}}\vec{i} + \frac{1}{\sqrt{2}}\vec{j}$. Then

$$6\sqrt{2} = D_{\vec{u}_{\vec{a}}}f(1, 2) = f_x(1, 2)(\frac{1}{\sqrt{2}}) + f_y(1, 2)(\frac{-1}{\sqrt{2}}) = \frac{r}{\sqrt{2}} - \frac{s}{\sqrt{2}}$$

and

$$-2\sqrt{2} = D_{\vec{u}_{\vec{b}}}f(1, 2) = f_x(1, 2)(\frac{1}{\sqrt{2}}) + f_y(1, 2)(\frac{1}{\sqrt{2}}) = \frac{r}{\sqrt{2}} + \frac{s}{\sqrt{2}}.$$

Adding, we obtain $4\sqrt{2} = \frac{2r}{\sqrt{2}}$ so that $r = 4$, and thus $s = -8$. Consequently $f_x(1, 2) = 4$ and $f_y(1, 2) = -8$.

16. Let $r = f_x(x_0, y_0, z_0)$, $s = f_y(x_0, y_0, z_0)$, and $t = f_z(x_0, y_0, z_0)$. Since $\|\vec{a}\| = \sqrt{3}$, $\|\vec{b}\| = \sqrt{10}$, and $\|\vec{c}\| = \sqrt{5}$, let $\vec{u}_{\vec{a}} = \frac{1}{\sqrt{3}}\vec{i} - \frac{1}{\sqrt{3}}\vec{j} + \frac{1}{\sqrt{3}}\vec{k}$, $\vec{u}_{\vec{b}} = \frac{1}{\sqrt{10}}\vec{j} - \frac{3}{\sqrt{10}}\vec{k}$, and $\vec{u}_{\vec{c}} = \frac{2}{\sqrt{5}}\vec{i} - \frac{1}{\sqrt{5}}\vec{j}$. Then

$$2\sqrt{3} = D_{\vec{u}_{\vec{a}}}f(x_0, y_0, z_0) = \frac{r}{\sqrt{3}} - \frac{s}{\sqrt{3}} + \frac{t}{\sqrt{3}}$$

$$-\sqrt{10} = D_{\vec{u}_{\vec{b}}}f(x_0, y_0, z_0) = \frac{s}{\sqrt{10}} - \frac{3t}{\sqrt{10}}$$

$$\sqrt{5} = D_{\vec{u}_{\vec{c}}}f(x_0, y_0, z_0) = \frac{2r}{\sqrt{5}} - \frac{s}{\sqrt{5}}$$

Thus $r - s + t = 6$, $s - 3t = -10$, and $2r - s = 5$, so that from the first two equations, $r - 2t = -4$, and from the last two equations, $2r - 3t = -5$. Therefore $t = 3$, $r = 2$, and $s = -1$. Consequently $f_x(x_0, y_0, z_0) = 2$, $f_y(x_0, y_0, z_0) = -1$, and $f_z(x_0, y_0, z_0) = 3$.

Section 13.6

1. grad $f(x, y) = 3\vec{i} - 5\vec{j}$

2. grad $f(x, y) = (\sin x^2y + 2x^2y \cos x^2y)\vec{i} + (2y + x^3 \cos x^2y)\vec{j}$

3. grad $g(x, y) = -2e^{-2x} \ln (y - 4)\vec{i} + \frac{e^{-2x}}{y - 4}\vec{j}$

4. grad $f(x, y) = \frac{y(x^2 + y^2) - (xy - 1)(2x)}{(x^2 + y^2)^2}\vec{i} + \frac{x(x^2 + y^2) - (xy - 1)(2y)}{(x^2 + y^2)^2}\vec{j}$

$= \frac{-x^2y + y^3 + 2x}{(x^2 + y^2)^2}\vec{i} + \frac{x^3 - xy^2 + 2y}{(x^2 + y^2)^2}\vec{j}$

5. grad $f(x, y, z) = 4x\vec{i} - 2y\vec{j} - 8z\vec{k}$

6. grad $f(x, y, z) = 5(2x + y^2 + z^3)^{3/2}\vec{i} + 5y(2x + y^2 + z^3)^{3/2}\vec{j}$

$+ \frac{15}{2} z^2(2x + y^2 + z^3)^{3/2}\vec{k}$

7. grad $g(x, y, z) = \frac{-(-x + z) - (-x + y)(-1)}{(-x + z)^2}\vec{i} + \frac{1}{-x + z}\vec{j} - \frac{-x + y}{(-x + z)^2}\vec{k}$

$= \frac{y - z}{(-x + z)^2}\vec{i} + \frac{1}{-x + z}\vec{j} + \frac{x - y}{(-x + z)^2}\vec{k}$

8. grad $g(x, y, z) = -2xy^3e^{(z^2)}\vec{i} - 3x^2y^2e^{(z^2)}\vec{j} - 2x^2y^3ze^{(z^2)}\vec{k}$

9. grad $f(x, y) = \frac{5x + 2y - (x + 3y)(5)}{(5x + 2y)^2}\vec{i} + \frac{3(5x + 2y) - (x + 3y)(2)}{(5x + 2y)^2}\vec{j}$

$= \frac{-13y}{(5x + 2y)^2}\vec{i} + \frac{13x}{(5x + 2y)^2}\vec{j}$

grad $f(-1, \frac{3}{2}) = -\frac{39}{8}\vec{i} - \frac{13}{4}\vec{j}$

10. grad $f(x, y) = (\cos xy - xy \sin xy)\vec{i} - x^2 \sin xy\,\vec{j}$

grad $f(1, -\pi) = -\vec{i}$

11. grad $g(x, y) = \left[\ln (x + y) + \frac{x}{x + y}\right]\vec{i} + \frac{x}{x + y}\vec{j}$

grad $g(-2, 3) = -2\vec{i} - 2\vec{j}$

12. grad $f(x, y, z) = \frac{-x}{\sqrt{x^2 + y^2}}\vec{i} - \frac{y}{\sqrt{x^2 + y^2}}\vec{j} + \vec{k}$

grad $f(3, -4, 7) = -\frac{3}{5}\vec{i} + \frac{4}{5}\vec{j} + \vec{k}$

13. grad $f(x, y, z) = -ze^{-x} \tan y\,\vec{i} + ze^{-x} \sec^2 y\,\vec{j} + e^{-x} \tan y\,\vec{k}$

grad $f(0, \pi, -2) = -2\vec{j}$

14. grad $g(x, y, z) = e^x(\sin y + \sin z)\vec{i} + e^x \cos y\,\vec{j} + e^x \cos z\,\vec{k}$

grad $g(1, \frac{\pi}{2}, \frac{\pi}{2}) = 2e\,\vec{i}$

15. grad $f(x, y) = e^x (\cos y + \sin y)\vec{i} + e^x (-\sin y + \cos y)\vec{j}$, so grad $f(0, 0)$ $= \vec{i} + \vec{j}$. Consequently the direction in which f increases most rapidly at $(0, 0)$ is $\frac{1}{\|\vec{i} + \vec{j}\|}(\vec{i} + \vec{j}) = \frac{1}{\sqrt{2}}(\vec{i} + \vec{j})$.

16. grad $f(x, y) = 2e^{2x} (\cos y - \sin y)\vec{i} + e^{2x} (-\sin y - \cos y)\vec{j}$, so that grad $f(\frac{1}{6}, \frac{-\pi}{2}) = 2e^{1/3}\vec{i} + e^{1/3}\vec{j}$. Thus the direction in which f increases most rapidly at $(\frac{1}{6}, \frac{-\pi}{2})$ is $\frac{1}{\|2e^{1/3}\vec{i} + e^{1/3}\vec{j}\|}(2e^{1/3}\vec{i} + e^{1/3}\vec{j})$

$= \frac{2}{\sqrt{5}}\vec{i} + \frac{1}{\sqrt{5}}\vec{j}$.

17. grad $f(x, y) = 6x\vec{i} + 8y\vec{j}$, so that grad $f(-1, 1) = -6\vec{i} + 8\vec{j}$. Thus the direction in which f increases most rapidly at $(-1, 1)$ is

$\frac{1}{\|-6\vec{i} + 8\vec{j}\|}(-6\vec{i} + 8\vec{j}) = -\frac{3}{5}\vec{i} + \frac{4}{5}\vec{j}$.

18. grad $f(x, y, z) = \frac{2x}{x^2 + y^2 + z^2}\vec{i} + \frac{2y}{x^2 + y^2 + z^2}\vec{j} + \frac{2z}{x^2 + y^2 + z^2}\vec{k}$, so that grad $f(2, 0, 1) = \frac{4}{5}\vec{i} + \frac{2}{5}\vec{k}$. Thus the direction in which f increases most rapidly at $(2, 0, 1)$ is $\frac{1}{\|\frac{4}{5}\vec{i} + \frac{2}{5}\vec{k}\|}(\frac{4}{5}\vec{i} + \frac{2}{5}\vec{k}) = \frac{2}{\sqrt{5}}\vec{i} + \frac{1}{\sqrt{5}}\vec{k}$.

19. grad $f(x, y, z) = e^x\vec{i} + e^y\vec{j} + 2e^{2z}\vec{k}$, so that grad $f(1, 1, -1) = e\vec{i} + e\vec{j} + 2e^{-2}\vec{k}$. Thus the direction in which f increases most rapidly at $(1, 1, -1)$ is $\frac{1}{\|e\vec{i} + e\vec{j} + 2e^{-2}\vec{k}\|}(e\vec{i} + e\vec{j} + 2e^{-2}\vec{k})$

$= \frac{1}{\sqrt{2e^2 + 4e^{-4}}}(e\vec{i} + e\vec{j} + 2e^{-2}\vec{k})$

20. grad $f(x, y, z) = -yz \sin xyz\,\vec{i} - xz \sin xyz\,\vec{j} - xy \sin xyz\,\vec{k}$, so that grad $f(\frac{1}{3}, \frac{1}{2}, \pi) = \frac{-\pi}{4}\vec{i} - \frac{\pi}{6}\vec{j} - \frac{1}{12}\vec{k}$. Thus the direction in which f increases most rapidly at $(\frac{1}{3}, \frac{1}{2}, \pi)$ is $\frac{1}{\|\frac{-\pi}{4}\vec{i} - \frac{\pi}{6}\vec{j} - \frac{1}{12}\vec{k}\|}\cdot$

$(-\frac{\pi}{4}\vec{i} - \frac{\pi}{6}\vec{j} - \frac{1}{12}\vec{k}) = \frac{-1}{\sqrt{13\pi^2 + 1}}(3\pi\vec{i} + 2\pi\vec{j} + \vec{k})$.

21. grad $f(x, y) = \pi y \cos \pi xy\,\vec{i} + \pi x \cos \pi xy\,\vec{j}$, so that grad $f(\frac{1}{2}, \frac{2}{3}) = \frac{\pi}{3}\vec{i} + \frac{\pi}{4}\vec{j}$. Thus the direction in which f decreases most rapidly at $(\frac{1}{2}, \frac{2}{3})$ is

$\frac{-1}{\|\frac{\pi}{3}\vec{i} + \frac{\pi}{4}\vec{j}\|}(\frac{\pi}{3}\vec{i} + \frac{\pi}{4}\vec{j}) = -\frac{4}{5}\vec{i} - \frac{3}{5}\vec{j}$.

22. grad $f(x, y) = \frac{1}{1 + (x - y)^2}\vec{i} - \frac{1}{1 + (x - y)^2}\vec{j}$, so that grad $f(2, -2) = \frac{1}{17}\vec{i} - \frac{1}{17}\vec{j}$. Thus the direction in which f decreases most rapidly at $(2, -2)$ is $\frac{-1}{\|\frac{1}{17}\vec{i} - \frac{1}{17}\vec{j}\|}(\frac{1}{17}\vec{i} - \frac{1}{17}\vec{j}) = -\frac{1}{\sqrt{2}}\vec{i} + \frac{1}{\sqrt{2}}\vec{j}$.

23. grad $f(x, y, z) = \frac{1}{y + z}\vec{i} - \frac{x - z}{(y + z)^2}\vec{j} + \frac{-(y + z) - (x - z)}{(y + z)^2}\vec{k} = \frac{1}{y + z}\vec{i}$ $+ \frac{z - x}{(y + z)^2}\vec{j} - \frac{y + x}{(y + z)^2}\vec{k}$, so that grad $f(-1, 1, 3) = \frac{1}{4}\vec{i} + \frac{1}{4}\vec{j}$. Thus the direction in which f decreases most rapidly at $(-1, 1, 3)$ is

$\frac{-1}{\|\frac{1}{4}\vec{i} + \frac{1}{4}\vec{j}\|}(\frac{1}{4}\vec{i} + \frac{1}{4}\vec{j}) = -\frac{1}{\sqrt{2}}(\vec{i} + \vec{j})$.

24. Let $f(x, y) = x^3 - 3x^2y + y^2$. Since the graph of the given equation is a level curve of f, Theorem 13.16 implies that grad $f(1, -1)$ is normal to the graph at $(1, -1)$. Since grad $f(x, y) = (3x^2 - 6xy)\vec{i} + (-3x^2 + 2y)\vec{j}$, so that grad $f(1, -1) = 9\vec{i} - 5\vec{j}$, we find that $9\vec{i} - 5\vec{j}$ is normal to the graph at $(1, -1)$.

25. Let $f(x, y) = \sin \pi xy$. Since the graph of the given equation is a level curve of f, Theorem 13.16 implies that grad $f(\frac{1}{6}, 2)$ is normal to the graph at $(\frac{1}{6}, 2)$. Since grad $f(x, y) = \pi y \cos \pi xy\,\vec{i} + \pi x \cos \pi xy\,\vec{j}$, so that grad $f(\frac{1}{6}, 2) = \pi\vec{i} + \frac{\pi}{12}\vec{j}$, we find that $\pi\vec{i} + \frac{\pi}{12}\vec{j}$ is normal to the graph at $(\frac{1}{6}, 2)$.

26. Let $f(x, y) = e^{x^2y}$. Since the graph of the given equation is a level curve of f, Theorem 13.16 implies that grad $f(1, \ln 2)$ is normal to the graph at $(1, \ln 2)$. Since grad $f(x, y) = 2xye^{x^2y}\vec{i} + x^2e^{x^2y}\vec{j}$, so that grad $f(1, \ln 2) = 4 \ln 2\,\vec{i} + 2\vec{j}$, we find that $4 \ln 2\,\vec{i} + 2\vec{j}$ is normal to the graph at $(1, \ln 2)$.

27. By (2), $f_x(-2, 1)\vec{i} + f_y(-2, 1)\vec{j} - \vec{k}$ is normal to the graph of f at $(-2, 1, 16)$. Since $f_x(x, y) = 6x$ and $f_y(x, y) = 8y$, so $f_x(-2, 1) = -12$ and $f_y(-2, 1) = 8$, it follows that $-12\vec{i} + 8\vec{j} - \vec{k}$ is normal to the graph at $(-2, 1, 16)$.

28. By (2), $f_x(-1, 1)\vec{i} + f_y(-1, 1)\vec{j} - \vec{k}$ is normal to the graph of f at $(-1, 1, \sqrt{2})$. Since $f_x(x, y) = \dfrac{-x}{\sqrt{4 - x^2 - y^2}}$ and $f_y(x, y) = \dfrac{-y}{\sqrt{4 - x^2 - y^2}}$, so $f_x(-1, 1) = \dfrac{1}{\sqrt{2}}$ and $f_y(-1, 1) = \dfrac{-1}{\sqrt{2}}$, it follows that $\dfrac{1}{\sqrt{2}}\vec{i} - \dfrac{1}{\sqrt{2}}\vec{j} - \vec{k}$ is normal to the graph at $(-1, 1, \sqrt{2})$.

29. By (2), $f_x(0, 2)\vec{i} + f_y(0, 2)\vec{j} - \vec{k}$ is normal to the graph of f at $(0, 2, 1)$. Since $f_x(x, y) = -2x$ and $f_y(x, y) = 0$, so $f_x(0, 2) = 0 = f_y(0, 2)$, it follows that $-\vec{k}$ is normal to the graph at $(0, 2, 1)$.

30. By (2), $f_x(0, -3)\vec{i} + f_y(0, -3)\vec{j} - \vec{k}$ is normal to the graph of f at $(0, -3, 9)$. Since $f_x(x, y) = y^2e^x$ and $f_y(x, y) = 2ye^x$, so $f_x(0, -3) = 9$ and $f_y(0, -3) = -6$, it follows that $9\vec{i} - 6\vec{j} - \vec{k}$ is normal to the graph at $(0, -3, 9)$.

31. Since $f_x(x, y) = y - 1$ and $f_y(x, y) = x + 1$, so $f_x(0, 2) = 1$ and $f_y(0, 2) = 1$, it follows from (3) that an equation of the plane tangent at $(0, 2, 7)$ is $(x - 0) + (y - 2) - (z - 7) = 0$, or $x + y - z = -5$.

32. Since $f_x(x, y) = \dfrac{1}{y + 1}$ and $f_y(x, y) = \dfrac{-(x + 2)}{(y + 1)^2}$, so $f_x(2, 3) = \frac{1}{4}$ and $f_y(2, 3) = -\frac{1}{4}$, it follows from (3) that an equation of the plane tangent at $(2, 3, 1)$ is $\frac{1}{4}(x - 2) - \frac{1}{4}(y - 3) - (z - 1) = 0$, or $\frac{1}{4}x - \frac{1}{4}y - z = -\frac{5}{4}$.

33. Since $g_x(x, y) = \pi y \cos \pi xy$ and $g_y(x, y) = \pi x \cos \pi xy$, so $g_x(-\sqrt{2}, \sqrt{2}) = \pi\sqrt{2}$, $g_y(-\sqrt{2}, \sqrt{2}) = -\pi\sqrt{2}$, $g_x(-\frac{1}{2}, \frac{1}{3}) = \dfrac{\pi\sqrt{3}}{6}$, and $g_y(-\frac{1}{2}, \frac{1}{3}) = \dfrac{-\pi\sqrt{3}}{4}$, it follows from (3) that an equation of the plane tangent at $(-\sqrt{2}, \sqrt{2}, 0)$ is $\pi\sqrt{2}(x + \sqrt{2}) - \pi\sqrt{2}(y - \sqrt{2}) - (z - 0) = 0$, or $\pi\sqrt{2}x - \pi\sqrt{2}y - z = -4\pi$, and that an equation of the plane tangent at $(-\frac{1}{2}, \frac{1}{3}, \frac{-1}{2})$ is $\dfrac{\pi\sqrt{3}}{6}(x + \frac{1}{2}) - \dfrac{\pi\sqrt{3}}{4}(y - \frac{1}{3}) - (z + \frac{1}{2}) = 0$, or $\dfrac{\pi\sqrt{3}}{6}x - \dfrac{\pi\sqrt{3}}{4}y - z = \dfrac{-\pi\sqrt{3}}{6} + \dfrac{1}{2}$.

34. Since $f_x(x, y) = e^{x + y^2}$ and $f_y(x, y) = 2ye^{x + y^2}$, so $f_x(-1, 0) = e^{-1}$, $f_y(-1, 0) = 0$, $f_x(0, 1) = e$, and $f_y(0, 1) = 2e$, it follows from (3) that an equation of the plane tangent at $(-1, 0, e^{-1})$ is $e^{-1}(x + 1) + 0(y - 0) - (z - e^{-1}) = 0$, or $e^{-1}x - z = -2e^{-1}$, and that an equation of the plane tangent at $(0, 1, e)$ is $e(x - 0) + 2e(y - 1) - (z - e) = 0$, or $ex + 2ey - z = e$.

35. Since $f_x(x, y) = 2(2 + x - y)$ and $f_y(x, y) = -2(2 + x - y)$, so $f_x(3, -1) = 12$ and $f_y(3, -1) = -12$, it follows from (3) that an equation

of the plane tangent at $(3, -1, 36)$ is $12(x - 3) - 12(y + 1) - (z - 36) = 0$, or $12x - 12y - z = 12$.

36. Since $g_x(x, y) = 8x$ and $g_y(x, y) = 2y$, so $g_x(2, 1) = 16$ and $g_y(2, 1) = 2$, it follows from (3) that an equation of the plane tangent at $(2, 1, 16)$ is $16(x - 2) + 2(y - 1) - (z - 16) = 0$, or $16x + 2y - z = 18$.

37. Since $f_x(x, y) = \frac{2x}{x^2 + y^2}$ and $f_y(x, y) = \frac{2y}{x^2 + y^2}$, so $f_x(-1, 0) = -2$, $f_y(-1, 0) = 0$, $f_x(-1, 1) = -1$, and $f_y(-1, 1) = 1$, it follows from (3) that an equation of the plane tangent at $(-1, 0, 0)$ is $-2(x + 1) + 0(y - 0) - (z - 0) = 0$, or $2x + z = -2$, and that an equation of the plane tangent at $(-1, 1, \ln 2)$ is $-(x + 1) + (y - 1) - (z - \ln 2) = 0$, or $x - y + z = \ln 2 - 2$.

38. $f_x(0, 0) = \lim_{h \to 0} \frac{f(0 + h, 0) - f(0, 0)}{h} = \lim_{h \to 0} \frac{h - 0}{h} = 1$; $f_y(0, 0) = \lim_{h \to 0} \frac{f(0, 0 + h) - f(0, 0)}{h} = \lim_{h \to 0} \frac{-h - 0}{h} = -1$. By (3), an equation of the plane tangent at $(0, 0, 0)$ is $(x - 0) - (y - 0) - (z - 0) = 0$, or $x - y - z = 0$.

39. If $f(x, y, z) = x^2 + y^2 + z^2$, then $x^2 + y^2 + z^2 = 1$ is a level surface of f. Since $f_x(x, y, z) = 2x$, $f_y(x, y, z) = 2y$, and $f_z(x, y, z) = 2z$, so $f_x(\frac{1}{2}, -\frac{1}{2}, -\frac{1}{\sqrt{2}}) = 1$, $f_y(\frac{1}{2}, -\frac{1}{2}, -\frac{1}{\sqrt{2}}) = -1$, and $f_z(\frac{1}{2}, -\frac{1}{2}, -\frac{1}{\sqrt{2}}) = -\sqrt{2}$, it follows that an equation of the plane tangent at $(\frac{1}{2}, -\frac{1}{2}, -\frac{1}{\sqrt{2}})$ is $(x - \frac{1}{2}) - (y + \frac{1}{2}) - \sqrt{2}\,(z + \frac{1}{\sqrt{2}}) = 0$, or $x - y - \sqrt{2}\, z = 2$.

40. If $f(x, y, z) = \frac{x^2}{4} + \frac{y^2}{9} + \frac{z^2}{16}$, then the given level surface is a level surface of f. Since $f_x(x, y, z) = \frac{x}{2}$, $f_y(x, y, z) = \frac{2y}{9}$, and $f_z(x, y, z) = \frac{z}{8}$, so $f_x(0, 0, -4) = 0$, $f_y(0, 0, -4) = 0$ and $f_z(0, 0, -4) = -\frac{1}{2}$, it follows that an equation of the plane tangent at $(0, 0, -4)$ is $0(x - 0) + 0(y - 0) - \frac{1}{2}(z + 4) = 0$, or $z = -4$.

41. If $f(x, y, z) = xyz$, then the given level surface is a level surface of f. Since $f_x(x, y, z) = yz$, $f_y(x, y, z) = xz$, and $f_z(x, y, z) = xy$, so $f_x(\frac{1}{2}, -2, -1) = 2$, $f_y(\frac{1}{2}, -2, -1) = -\frac{1}{2}$, and $f_z(\frac{1}{2}, -2, 1) = -1$, it follows that an equation of the plane tangent at $(\frac{1}{2}, -2, -1)$ is $2(x - \frac{1}{2}) - \frac{1}{2}(y + 2) - (z + 1) = 0$, or $2x - \frac{1}{2}y - z = 3$.

42. If $f(x, y, z) = z^2 + \sin xy$, then the given level surface is a level surface of f. Since $f_x(x, y, z) = y \cos xy$, $f_y(x, y, z) = x \cos xy$, and $f_z(x, y, z) = 2z$, so $f_x(\pi, \frac{1}{2}, -1) = 0$, $f_y(\pi, \frac{1}{2}, -1) = 0$, and $f_z(\pi, \frac{1}{2}, -1) = -2$, it follows that an equation of the plane tangent at $(\pi, \frac{1}{2}, -1)$ is $0(x - \pi) + 0(y - \frac{1}{2}) - 2(z + 1) = 0$, or $z = -1$.

43. If $f(x, y, z) = ye^{xy} + z^2$, then the given level surface is a level surface of f. Since $f_x(x, y, z) = y^2e^{xy}$, $f_y(x, y, z) = e^{xy} + xye^{xy}$, and $f_z(x, y, z) = 2z$, so $f_x(0, -1, 1) = 1$, $f_y(0, -1, 1) = 1$, and $f_z(0, -1, 1)$

$= 2$, it follows that an equation of the plane tangent at $(0, -1, 1)$ is $(x - 0) + (y + 1) + 2(z - 1) = 0$, or $x + y + 2z = 1$.

44. If $f(x, y, z) = \dfrac{x^2 - y^2}{x^2 + y^2}$, then the given level surface is a level surface of f. Since $f_x(x, y, z) = \dfrac{2x(x^2 + y^2) - (x^2 - y^2)(2x)}{(x^2 + y^2)^2} = \dfrac{4xy^2}{(x^2 + y^2)^2}$, $f_y(x, y, z) = \dfrac{-2y(x^2 + y^2) - (x^2 - y^2)(2y)}{(x^2 + y^2)^2} = \dfrac{-4x^2y}{(x^2 + y^2)^2}$, and $f_z(x, y, z) = 0$, so $f_x(-1, -1, -1) = -1$, $f_y(-1, -1, -1) = 1$, and $f_z(-1, -1, -1) = 0$, it follows that an equation of the plane tangent at $(-1, -1, -1)$ is $-(x + 1) + (y + 1) + 0(z + 1) = 0$, or $-x + y = 0$.

45. If $f(x, y, z) = \ln \sqrt{x^2 + y^2 + z^2} = \frac{1}{2} \ln (x^2 + y^2 + z^2)$, then the given level surface is a level surface of f. Since $f_x(x, y, z) = \dfrac{x}{x^2 + y^2 + z^2}$, $f_y(x, y, z) = \dfrac{y}{x^2 + y^2 + z^2}$, and $f_z(x, y, z) = \dfrac{z}{x^2 + y^2 + z^2}$, so $f_x(0, -1, 0) = 0$, $f_y(0, -1, 0) = -1$ and $f_z(0, -1, 0) = 0$, it follows that an equation of the plane tangent at $(0, -1, 0)$ is $0(x - 0) - (y + 1) + 0(z - 0) = 0$, or $y = -1$.

46. Let $f(x, y) = x^2 - 3y^2$. Then $f_x(x, y) = 2x$ and $f_y(x, y) = -6y$. By (2), a vector normal to the tangent plane at any point (x_0, y_0, z_0) on the graph of f is $2x_0 \vec{i} - 6y_0 \vec{j} - \vec{k}$. If the tangent plane is parallel to the plane $8x + 3y - z = 4$, whose normal is $8\vec{i} + 3\vec{j} - \vec{k}$, then $2x_0 \vec{i} - 6y_0 \vec{j} - \vec{k} = c\,(8\vec{i} + 3\vec{j} - \vec{k})$ for some constant c. It follows that $c = 1$, so that $x_0 = 4$ and $y_0 = -\frac{1}{2}$. The corresponding point on the hyperbolic paraboloid is $(4, -\frac{1}{2}, \frac{61}{4})$.

47. Let $f(x, y) = 9 - 4x^2 - y^2$. Then $f_x(x, y) = -8x$ and $f_y(x, y) = -2y$. By (2), a vector normal to the tangent plane at any point (x_0, y_0, z_0) on the graph of f is $-8x_0 \vec{i} - 2y_0 \vec{j} - \vec{k}$. If the tangent plane is parallel to the plane $z = 4y$, whose normal is $-4\vec{j} + \vec{k}$, then $-8x_0 \vec{i} - 2y_0 \vec{j} - \vec{k} = c\,(-4\vec{j} + \vec{k})$ for some constant c. It follows that $c = -1$, so that $x_0 = 0$ and $y_0 = -2$. The corresponding point on the paraboloid is $(0, -2, 5)$.

48. Let $f(x, y) = \sqrt{x^2 + y^2}$ and $g(x, y) = \frac{1}{10}(25 + x^2 + y^2)$. Then $f_x(x, y) = \dfrac{x}{\sqrt{x^2 + y^2}}$, $f_y(x, y) = \dfrac{y}{\sqrt{x^2 + y^2}}$, $g_x(x, y) = \frac{1}{5}x$, and $g_y(x, y) = \frac{1}{5}y$. Since $f_x(3, 4)\vec{i} + f_y(3, 4)\vec{j} - \vec{k} = \frac{3}{5}\vec{i} + \frac{4}{5}\vec{j} - \vec{k} = g_x(3, 4)\vec{i} + g_y(3, 4)\vec{j} - \vec{k}$, and since both surfaces pass through $(3, 4, 5)$, it follows from (2) that the graphs of f and g have the same tangent plane at $(3, 4, 5)$.

49. Let $f(x, y) = xy - 2$. Then $f_x(x, y) = y$ and $f_y(x, y) = x$. By (2), a vector normal to the plane tangent to the graph of f at $(1, 1, -1)$ is $\vec{i} + \vec{j} - \vec{k}$. Let $g(x, y, z) = x^2 + y^2 + z^2$. Then grad $g(x, y, z) = 2x\vec{i} + 2y\vec{j} + 2z\vec{k}$. By Definition 13.17, a vector normal to the plane tangent to the level surface $g(x, y, z) = 3$ at $(1, 1, -1)$ is $2\vec{i} + 2\vec{j} - 2\vec{k}$. Since the vectors normal to the two tangent planes are parallel, and since

both surfaces pass through (1, 1, -1), the two tangent planes at (1, 1, -1) are identical.

50. Let $f(x, y, z) = x^2 + y^2 + z^2$. Then grad $f(x, y, z) = 2x\,\vec{i} + 2y\,\vec{j} + 2z\,\vec{k}$, so that by Definition 13.17 a vector normal to the level surface $f(x, y, z) = 16$ at $(2, 2, 2\sqrt{2})$ is $4\,\vec{i} + 4\,\vec{j} + 4\sqrt{2}\,\vec{k}$. Let $g(x, y, z) = z^2 - x^2 - y^2$. Then grad $g(x, y, z) = -2x\,\vec{i} - 2y\,\vec{j} + 2z\,\vec{k}$, so that by Definition 13.17 a vector normal to the level surface $g(x, y, z) = 0$ at $(2, 2, 2\sqrt{2})$ is $-4\,\vec{i} - 4\,\vec{j} + 4\sqrt{2}\,\vec{k}$. Since $(4\,\vec{i} + 4\,\vec{j} + 4\sqrt{2}\,\vec{k}) \cdot (-4\,\vec{i} - 4\,\vec{j} + 4\sqrt{2}\,\vec{k}) = -16 - 16 + 32 = 0$, the two normal vectors and hence the two planes tangent at $(2, 2, 2\sqrt{2})$ are perpendicular. Thus the two surfaces are normal at $(2, 2, 2\sqrt{2})$.

51. Let $f(x, y) = x^2 + 4y^2 - 12$. Then $f_x(x, y) = 2x$ and $f_y(x, y) = 8y$, so that by (2) a vector normal to the plane tangent to the graph of f at $(-3, -1, 1)$ is $-6\,\vec{i} - 8\,\vec{j} - \vec{k}$. Let $g(x, y) = \frac{1}{8}(4x + y^2 + 19)$. Then $g_x(x, y) = \frac{1}{2}$ and $g_y(x, y) = \frac{1}{4}y$, so that a vector normal to the plane tangent to the graph of g at $(-3, -1, 1)$ is $\frac{1}{2}\vec{i} - \frac{1}{4}\vec{j} - \vec{k}$. Since $(-6\,\vec{i} - 8\,\vec{j} - \vec{k}) \cdot (\frac{1}{2}\vec{i} - \frac{1}{4}\vec{j} - \vec{k}) = -3 + 2 + 1 = 0$, the two normal vectors and hence the two planes tangent at $(-3, -1, 1)$ are perpendicular. Thus the two surfaces are normal at $(-3, -1, 1)$.

52. Let $f(x, y, z) = z^2(x^2 + y^2)$. Then $f_x(x, y, z) = 2xz^2$, $f_y(x, y, z) = 2yz^2$, and $f_z(x, y, z) = 2z(x^2 + y^2)$, so that $f_x(2\cos\theta, 2\sin\theta, 1) = 4\cos\theta$, $f_y(2\cos\theta, 2\sin\theta, 1) = 4\sin\theta$, and $f_z(2\cos\theta, 2\sin\theta, 1) = 8$. Thus an equation of the plane tangent to the level surface $f(x, y, z) = 4$ at the point $(2\cos\theta, 2\sin\theta, 1)$ is $(4\cos\theta)(x - 2\cos\theta) + (4\sin\theta)(y - 2\sin\theta) + 8(z - 1) = 0$, or $(\cos\theta)x + (\sin\theta)y + 2z = 4$. The intersection of this plane with the plane $z = 0$ is the line with equation $(\cos\theta)x + (\sin\theta)y = 4$. Now let $g(x, y) = x^2 + y^2$. Then $g_x(x, y) = 2x$ and $g_y(x, y) = 2y$, so that $g_x(4\cos\theta, 4\sin\theta) = 8\cos\theta$ and $g_y(4\cos\theta, 4\sin\theta) = 8\sin\theta$. Thus an equation of the line tangent to the level curve $g(x, y) = 16$ at the point $(4\cos\theta, 4\sin\theta)$ is $(8\cos\theta)(x - 4\cos\theta) + (8\sin\theta)(y - 4\sin\theta) = 0$, or $(\cos\theta)x + (\sin\theta)y = 4$. Since the two lines have the same equation, they are identical.

53. Let $f(x, y, z) = \frac{x^2}{a^2} + \frac{y^2}{b^2} + \frac{z^2}{c^2}$. Then $f_x(x, y, z) = \frac{2x}{a^2}$, $f_y(x, y, z) = \frac{2y}{b^2}$, and $f_z(x, y, z) = \frac{2z}{c^2}$, so that by Definition 13.17 an equation of the plane tangent to the level surface $f(x, y, z) = 1$ at (x_0, y_0, z_0) is $\frac{2x_0}{a^2}(x - x_0) + \frac{2y_0}{b^2}(y - y_0) + \frac{2z_0}{c^2}(z - z_0) = 0$, or $\frac{xx_0}{a^2} + \frac{yy_0}{b^2} + \frac{zz_0}{c^2} = \frac{x_0^2}{a^2} + \frac{y_0^2}{b^2} + \frac{z_0^2}{c^2} = 1$.

54. Since $c \neq 0$, we may let $f(x, y) = \frac{1}{c}\left(\frac{x^2}{a^2} + \frac{y^2}{b^2}\right)$. Then $f_x(x, y) = \frac{2x}{ca^2}$ and $f_y(x, y) = \frac{2y}{cb^2}$, so that by (3) an equation of the plane tangent to the the graph of f at (x_0, y_0, z_0) is $\frac{2x_0}{ca^2}(x - x_0) + \frac{2y_0}{cb^2}(y - y_0)$

$- (z - z_0) = 0,$ or $\frac{2xx_0}{a^2} + \frac{2yy_0}{b^2} = c(z - z_0) + \frac{2x_0^2}{a^2} + \frac{2y_0^2}{b^2} = c(z - z_0) + 2cz_0$ $= c(z + z_0)$.

55. Since $f_x(x, y) = g(\frac{y}{x}) - \frac{y}{x} g'(\frac{y}{x})$ and $f_y(x, y) = g'(\frac{y}{x})$, it follows from (3) that an equation of the plane tangent to the graph of f at $(x_0, y_0, x_0 g(\frac{y_0}{x_0}))$ is $\left[g(\frac{y_0}{x_0}) - \frac{y_0}{x_0} g'(\frac{y_0}{x_0})\right](x - x_0) + g'(\frac{y_0}{x_0})(y - y_0)$ $- (z - x_0 g(\frac{y_0}{x_0})) = 0$, or $\left[g(\frac{y_0}{x_0}) - \frac{y_0}{x_0} g'(\frac{y_0}{x_0})\right] x + g'(\frac{y_0}{x_0})y - z = x_0 g(\frac{y_0}{x_0})$ $- y_0 g'(\frac{y_0}{x_0}) + y_0 g'(\frac{y_0}{x_0}) - x_0 g(\frac{y_0}{x_0}) = 0$. Thus the origin lies on the tangent plane.

56. Let $f(x, y, z) = x^2 + y^2 + z^2$. Then grad $f(x, y, z) = 2x\,\vec{i} + 2y\,\vec{j} + 2z\,\vec{k}$. By Definition 13.17 the vector $2x_0\,\vec{i} + 2y_0\,\vec{j} + 2z_0\,\vec{k}$ is normal to the plane tangent to the level surface $f(x, y, z) = 1$ at any point (x_0, y_0, z_0) on the level surface. Thus if x_0, y_0, and z_0 are nonzero, then equations of the normal line are $\frac{x - x_0}{2x_0} = \frac{y - y_0}{2y_0} = \frac{z - z_0}{2z_0}$, from which it follows that the normal line passes through the origin. If $x_0 = 0$ and y_0 and z_0 are nonzero, then equations of the normal line are $x = 0$ and $\frac{y - y_0}{2y_0} = \frac{z - z_0}{2z_0}$, from which it again follows that the normal line passes through the origin. All other cases are handled analogously.

57. Let $f(x, y, z) = z^2 - x^2 - y^2$. Then grad $f(x, y, z) = -2x\,\vec{i} - 2y\,\vec{j}$ $+ 2z\,\vec{k}$. By Definition 13.17 the vector $-2x_0\,\vec{i} - 2y_0\,\vec{j} + 2z_0\,\vec{k}$ is normal to the plane tangent to the level surface $f(x, y, z) = 0$ at any point (x_0, y_0, z_0) on the level surface. Thus if x_0, y_0, and z_0 are nonzero, then equations of the normal line are $\frac{x - x_0}{-2x_0} = \frac{y - y_0}{-2y_0} = \frac{z - z_0}{2z_0}$, from which it follows that $(0, 0, 2z_0)$ lies on the normal line and hence that the normal line intersects the z axis. If $x_0 = 0$, and y_0 and z_0 are nonzero, then equations of the normal line are $x_0 = 0$ and $\frac{y - y_0}{-2y_0}$ $= \frac{z - z_0}{2z_0}$, from which it again follows that the normal line intersects the z axis at $(0, 0, 2z_0)$. All other cases are handled analogously.

58. Let $f(x, y) = x^2 + y^2$. Then $f_x(x, y) = 2x$ and $f_y(x, y) = 2y$. Thus for any (x_0, y_0) it follows from (2) that the vector $2x_0\,\vec{i} + 2y_0\,\vec{j} - \vec{k}$ is normal to the plane tangent to the graph of f at $(x_0, y_0, f(x_0, y_0))$. If $\mathcal{P}$ is any nonvertical plane, then $\mathcal{P}$ has a normal vector of the form $a\,\vec{i} + b\,\vec{j} - \vec{k}$. Since $2x_0\,\vec{i} + 2y_0\,\vec{j} - \vec{k}$ is parallel to the $a\,\vec{i} + b\,\vec{j} - \vec{k}$ if and only if $x_0 = \frac{a}{2}$ and $y_0 = \frac{b}{2}$, we conclude that there is exactly one plane tangent to the paraboloid and parallel to $\mathcal{P}$.

59. $2x - 2z\frac{\partial z}{\partial x} = 0$, so that $\frac{\partial z}{\partial x} = \frac{x}{z}$; $-2y - 2z\frac{\partial z}{\partial y} = 0$, so that $\frac{\partial z}{\partial y} = -\frac{y}{z}$. Thus $\left.\frac{\partial z}{\partial x}\right|_{(\sqrt{2}, 0, 1)} = \sqrt{2}$, and $\left.\frac{\partial z}{\partial y}\right|_{(\sqrt{2}, 0, 1)} = 0$, so that an equation of the plane tangent to the given level surface at $(\sqrt{2}, 0, 1)$ is $\sqrt{2}(x - \sqrt{2}) + 0(y - 0) - (z - 1) = 0$, or $\sqrt{2}x - z = 1$.

60. $yz + xy\frac{\partial z}{\partial x} = 0$, so that $\frac{\partial z}{\partial x} = -\frac{z}{x}$; $xz + xy\frac{\partial z}{\partial y} = 0$, so that $\frac{\partial z}{\partial y} = -\frac{z}{y}$. Thus $\left.\frac{\partial z}{\partial x}\right|_{(2, -3, \frac{-1}{6})} = \frac{1}{12}$ and $\left.\frac{\partial z}{\partial y}\right|_{(2, -3, \frac{-1}{6})} = -\frac{1}{18}$, so that an

equation of the plane tangent to the given level surface at $(2, -3, \frac{-1}{6})$ is $\frac{1}{12}(x - 2) - \frac{1}{18}(y + 3) - (z + \frac{1}{6}) = 0$, or $3x - 2y - 36z = 18$.

61. $\frac{1}{x} + \frac{1}{z}\frac{\partial z}{\partial x} = 0$, so that $\frac{\partial z}{\partial x} = -\frac{z}{x}$; $\frac{1}{y} + \frac{1}{z}\frac{\partial z}{\partial y} = 0$, so that $\frac{\partial z}{\partial y} = -\frac{z}{y}$. Thus $\left.\frac{\partial z}{\partial x}\right|_{(1, 1, e)} = -e$ and $\left.\frac{\partial z}{\partial y}\right|_{(1, 1, e)} = -e$, so that an equation of the plane tangent to the given level surface at $(1, 1, e)$ is $-e(x - 1) - e(y - 1) - (z - e) = 0$, or $ex + ey + z = 3e$.

62. Let $f(x, y) = 5 - x^2 - 2y^2$. Then grad $f(x, y) = -2x\,\vec{i} - 4y\,\vec{j}$, so that grad $f(\frac{1}{2}, -\frac{1}{2}) = -\vec{i} + 2\,\vec{j}$. Thus f is decreasing most rapidly in the direction of $\frac{-1}{\|-\vec{i} + 2\,\vec{j}\|}(-\vec{i} + 2\,\vec{j}) = \frac{1}{\sqrt{5}}\vec{i} - \frac{2}{\sqrt{5}}\vec{j}$. This is the direction in which the climber should descend.

63. The temperature $T(x, y)$ at any point (x, y) on the plate is given by $T(x, y) = \frac{c}{\sqrt{x^2 + y^2}}$, where c is a positive constant. Then grad $T(x, y)$ $= \frac{-cx}{(x^2 + y^2)^{3/2}}\vec{i} - \frac{cy}{(x^2 + y^2)^{3/2}}\vec{j}$, so that grad $T(3, 2)$ $= \frac{-3c}{(13)^{3/2}}\vec{i} - \frac{2c}{(13)^{3/2}}\vec{j}$. Thus T is decreasing most rapidly in the direction of $\frac{-1}{\left\|\frac{-3c}{(13)^{3/2}}\vec{i} - \frac{2c}{(13)^{3/2}}\vec{j}\right\|}\left(\frac{-3c}{(13)^{3/2}}\vec{i} - \frac{2c}{(13)^{3/2}}\vec{j}\right) = \frac{3}{\sqrt{13}}\vec{i}$ $+ \frac{2}{\sqrt{13}}\vec{j}$. This is the direction in which the ant should crawl.

64. Let $V(x, y, z) = x^2 - y^2 - z$. Then the electric force on a positive unit charge at the origin is parallel to grad $V(0, 0, 0)$. But grad $V(x, y, z)$ $= 2x\,\vec{i} - 2y\,\vec{j} - \vec{k}$, so that grad $V(0, 0, 0) = -\vec{k}$. Thus the electric force is parallel to $-\vec{k}$ and hence is perpendicular to the xy plane.

Section 13.7

1. Let $x_0 = 3$, $y_0 = 4$, $h = .01$, and $k = .03$. Since $f_x(x, y) = \dfrac{x}{\sqrt{x^2 + y^2}}$ and $f_y(x, y) = \dfrac{y}{\sqrt{x^2 + y^2}}$, we have $f_x(3, 4) = \frac{3}{5}$ and $f_y(3, 4) = \frac{4}{5}$. Also $f(3, 4) = 5$. By (6), $f(3.01, 4.03) \approx 5 + \frac{3}{5}(.01) + \frac{4}{5}(.03) = 5.03$

2. Let $x_0 = 3$, $y_0 = -5$, $h = .02$, and $k = .02$. Since $f_x(x, y) = \dfrac{x}{\sqrt{x^2 + y}}$ and $f_y(x, y) = \dfrac{1}{2\sqrt{x^2 + y}}$, we have $f_x(3, -5) = \frac{3}{2}$ and $f_y(3, -5) = \frac{1}{4}$

   Also $f(3, -5) = 2$. By (6),

   $$f(3.02, -4.98) \approx 2 + \frac{3}{2}(.02) + \frac{1}{4}(.02) = 2.035$$

3. Let $x_0 = 0$, $y_0 = 1$, $h = -.03$, and $k = -.02$. Since $f_x(x, y) = \dfrac{2x}{x^2 + y^2}$ and $f_y(x, y) = \dfrac{2y}{x^2 + y^2}$, we have $f_x(0, 1) = 0$ and $f_y(0, 1) = 2$. Also $f(0, 1) = 0$. By (6),

   $$f(-.03, .98) \approx 0 + 0(-.03) + 2(-.02) = -.04$$

4. Let $x_0 = -2$, $y_0 = 2$, $h = .03$, and $k = .005$. Since $f_x(x, y) = \pi y \cos \pi xy$ and $f_y(x, y) = \pi x \cos \pi xy$, we have $f_x(-2, 2) = 2\pi$ and $f_y(-2, 2) = -2\pi$. Also $f(-2, 2) = 0$. By (6),

   $$f(-1.97, 2.005) \approx 0 + 2\pi(.03) - 2\pi(.005) = .05\pi \approx .157080$$

5. Let $x_0 = \pi$, $y_0 = .25$, $h = -.01\pi$, and $k = -.01$. Since $f_x(x, y) = y \sec^2 xy$ and $f_y(x, y) = x \sec^2 xy$, we have $f_x(\pi, .25) = \frac{1}{4}\sec^2 \frac{\pi}{4} = \frac{1}{2}$ and $f_y(\pi, .25) = 2\pi$. Also $f(\pi, .25) = \tan \frac{\pi}{4} = 1$. By (6),

   $$f(.99\pi, .24) \approx 1 + \frac{1}{2}(-.01\pi) + 2\pi(-.01) = 1 - .025\pi \approx .921460$$

6. Let $x_0 = 1$, $y_0 = 1$, $h = -.013$, and $k = .013$. Since $f_x(x, y) = \dfrac{-x}{\sqrt{6 - x^2 - y^2}}$ and $f_y(x, y) = \dfrac{-y}{\sqrt{6 - x^2 - y^2}}$, we have $f_x(1, 1) = \frac{-1}{2}$ and $f_y(1, 1) = \frac{-1}{2}$. Also $f(1, 1) = 2$. By (6),

   $$f(.987, 1.013) \approx 2 - \frac{1}{2}(-.013) - \frac{1}{2}(.013) = 2$$

7. Let $x_0 = 3$, $y_0 = 4$, $z_0 = 12$, $h = .01$, $k = .02$, and $\ell = -.02$. Since $f_x(x, y, z) = \dfrac{x}{\sqrt{x^2 + y^2 + z^2}}$, $f_y(x, y, z) = \dfrac{y}{\sqrt{x^2 + y^2 + z^2}}$, and $f_z(x, y, z) = \dfrac{z}{\sqrt{x^2 + y^2 + z^2}}$, we have $f_x(3, 4, 12) = \frac{3}{13}$, $f_y(3, 4, 12) = \frac{4}{13}$, and $f_z(3, 4, 12) = \frac{12}{13}$. Also $f(3, 4, 12) = 13$. By (7),

   $$f(3.01, 4.02, 11.98) \approx 13 + \frac{3}{13}(.01) + \frac{4}{13}(.02) + \frac{12}{13}(-.02) = 12.99.$$

8. Let $x_0 = -2$, $y_0 = 1$, $z_0 = 1$, $h = -.1$, $k = .01$, and $\ell = -.011$. Since $f_x(x, y, z) = yz^2$, $f_y(x, y, z) = xz^2$, and $f_z(x, y, z) = 2xyz$, we have $f_x(-2, 1, 1) = 1$, $f_y(-2, 1, 1) = -2$, and $f_z(-2, 1, 1) = -4$. Also $f(-2, 1, 1) = -2$. By (7),

   $$f(-2.1, 1.01, .989) \approx -2 + 1(-.1) - 2(.01) - 4(-.011) = -2.076.$$

9. Let $f(x, y) = \sqrt[4]{x^3 + y^3}$, $x_0 = 2$, $y_0 = 2$, $h = -.1$, and $k = .1$. Since $f_x(x, y) = \dfrac{3x^2}{4(x^3 + y^3)^{3/4}}$ and $f_y(x, y) = \dfrac{3y^2}{4(x^3 + y^3)^{3/4}}$, we have

$f_x(2, 2) = \frac{3}{8}$ and $f_y(2, 2) = \frac{3}{8}$. Also $f(2, 2) = 2$. By (6),

$$\sqrt[4]{(1.9)^3 + (2.1)^3} = f(1.9, 2.1) \approx 2 + \frac{3}{8}(-.1) + \frac{3}{8}(.1) = 2.$$

10. Let $f(x, y) = x^{1/4}y^{2/3}$, $x_0 = 16$, $y_0 = 8$, $h = .05$, and $k = -.05$. Since $f_x(x, y) = \frac{1}{4}x^{-3/4}y^{2/3}$ and $f_y(x, y) = \frac{2}{3}x^{1/4}y^{-1/3}$, we have $f_x(16, 8) = \frac{1}{8}$ and $f_y(16, 8) = \frac{2}{3}$. Also $f(16, 8) = 8$. By (6),

$$(16.05)^{1/4}(7.95)^{2/3} = f(16.05, 7.95) \approx 8 + \frac{1}{8}(.05) + \frac{2}{3}(-.05) \approx 7.97292.$$

11. Let $f(x, y) = e^x \ln y$, $x_0 = 0$, $y_0 = 1$, $h = .1$, and $k = -.1$. Since $f_x(x, y) = e^x \ln y$ and $f_y(x, y) = \frac{e^x}{y}$, we have $f_x(0, 1) = 0$ and $f_y(0, 1) = 1$. Also $f(0, 1) = 0$. By (6),

$$e^{.1} \ln .9 = f(.1, .9) \approx 0 + 0(.1) + 1(-.1) = -.1.$$

12. Let $f(x, y) = \sin x \cos y$, $x_0 = \frac{\pi}{2}$, $y_0 = \frac{\pi}{3}$, $h = \frac{-\pi}{20}$, and $k = \frac{-\pi}{30}$. Since $f_x(x, y) = \cos x \cos y$ and $f_y(x, y) = -\sin x \sin y$, we have $f_x(\frac{\pi}{2}, \frac{\pi}{3}) = 0$ and $f_y(\frac{\pi}{2}, \frac{\pi}{3}) = \frac{-\sqrt{3}}{2}$. Also $f(\frac{\pi}{2}, \frac{\pi}{3}) = \frac{1}{2}$. By (6),

$$\sin\frac{9\pi}{20}\cos\frac{9\pi}{30} = f\left(\frac{9\pi}{20}, \frac{9\pi}{30}\right) \approx \frac{1}{2} + 0\left(\frac{-\pi}{20}\right) - \frac{\sqrt{3}}{2}\left(\frac{-\pi}{30}\right) \approx .590690$$

13. Since $\frac{\partial f}{\partial x} = 9x^2 - 2xy$ and $\frac{\partial f}{\partial y} = -x^2 + 1$, we have $df = (9x^2 - 2xy)\,dx + (-x^2 + 1)\,dy$.

14. Since $\frac{\partial f}{\partial x} = y\frac{1 - x}{1 + x}\left(\frac{1 - x - (1 + x)(-1)}{(1 - x)^2}\right) = \frac{2y}{1 - x^2}$ and $\frac{\partial f}{\partial y} = \ln\frac{1 + x}{1 - x}$, we have $df = \frac{2y}{1 - x^2}\,dx + \ln\frac{1 + x}{1 - x}\,dy$.

15. Since $\frac{\partial f}{\partial x} = 2x$ and $\frac{\partial f}{\partial y} = 2y$, we have $df = 2x\,dx + 2y\,dy$.

16. Since $\frac{\partial f}{\partial x} = -\sin(x + y) - \sin(x - y)$ and $\frac{\partial f}{\partial y} = -\sin(x + y) + \sin(x - y)$, we have $df = [-\sin(x + y) - \sin(x - y)]\,dx + [-\sin(x + y) + \sin(x - y)]\,dy$.

17. Since $\frac{\partial f}{\partial x} = \tan y - y\csc^2 x$ and $\frac{\partial f}{\partial y} = x\sec^2 y + \cot x$, we have $df = (\tan y - y\csc^2 x)\,dx + (x\sec^2 y + \cot x)\,dy$.

18. Since $\frac{\partial f}{\partial x} = 2x$, $\frac{\partial f}{\partial y} = 2y$, and $\frac{\partial f}{\partial z} = 2z$, we have $df = 2x\,dx + 2y\,dy + 2z\,dz$.

19. Since $\frac{\partial f}{\partial x} = \frac{xz^2}{\sqrt{1 + x^2 + y^2}}$, $\frac{\partial f}{\partial y} = \frac{yz^2}{\sqrt{1 + x^2 + y^2}}$, and $\frac{\partial f}{\partial z} = 2z\sqrt{1 + x^2 + y^2}$, we have $df = \frac{xz^2}{\sqrt{1 + x^2 + y^2}}\,dx + \frac{yz^2}{\sqrt{1 + x^2 + y^2}}\,dy + 2z\sqrt{1 + x^2 + y^2}\,dz$.

20. Since $f(x, y, z) = \ln\sqrt{x^2 + y^2 + z^2} = \frac{1}{2}\ln(x^2 + y^2 + z^2)$, we have $\frac{\partial f}{\partial x} = \frac{x}{x^2 + y^2 + z^2}$, $\frac{\partial f}{\partial y} = \frac{y}{x^2 + y^2 + z^2}$, and $\frac{\partial f}{\partial z} = \frac{z}{x^2 + y^2 + z^2}$, so that

$$df = \frac{x}{x^2 + y^2 + z^2}\,dx + \frac{y}{x^2 + y^2 + z^2}\,dy + \frac{z}{x^2 + y^2 + z^2}\,dz.$$

21. Since $\frac{\partial f}{\partial x} = e^{y^2 - z^2}$, $\frac{\partial f}{\partial y} = 2yxe^{y^2 - z^2}$, and $\frac{\partial f}{\partial z} = -2zxe^{y^2 - z^2}$, we have

$$df = e^{y^2 - z^2}\,dx + 2yxe^{y^2 - z^2}\,dy - 2zxe^{y^2 - z^2}\,dz.$$

22. Since $\frac{\partial f}{\partial x} = \frac{(x^2 + y^2 + z^2) - 2x^2}{(x^2 + y^2 + z^2)^2} = \frac{y^2 + z^2 - x^2}{(x^2 + y^2 + z^2)^2}$, $\frac{\partial f}{\partial y} = \frac{-2yx}{(x^2 + y^2 + z^2)^2}$, and $\frac{\partial f}{\partial z} = \frac{-2zx}{(x^2 + y^2 + z^2)^2}$, we have $df = \frac{y^2 + z^2 - x^2}{(x^2 + y^2 + z^2)^2}\,dx - \frac{2yx}{(x^2 + y^2 + z^2)^2}\,dy - \frac{2zx}{(x^2 + y^2 + z^2)^2}\,dz$.

23. Since $\frac{\partial R}{\partial R_1} = \frac{R_2(R_1 + R_2) - R_1R_2}{(R_1 + R_2)^2} = \frac{R_2^{\,2}}{(R_1 + R_2)^2}$ and $\frac{\partial R}{\partial R_2} = \frac{R_1(R_1 + R_2) - R_1R_2}{(R_1 + R_2)^2}$ $= \frac{R_1^{\,2}}{(R_1 + R_2)^2}$, we have $\frac{\partial R}{\partial R_1}(2, 6) = \frac{9}{16}$ and $\frac{\partial R}{\partial R_2}(2, 6) = \frac{1}{16}$. Since $R(2, 6) = \frac{3}{2}$, if we let $h = .013$ and $k = -.028$, then by (6),

$$R(2.013, 5.972) \approx \frac{3}{2} + \frac{9}{16}(.013) + \frac{1}{16}(-.028) = \frac{3}{2} + \frac{.089}{16} \approx 1.50556 \text{ (ohms)}$$

24. Let x and y denote the lengths of the two legs, $f(x, y)$ the length of the corresponding hypotenuse and $g(x, y)$ the area of the corresponding right triangle. We let $x_0 = 5$, $y_0 = 12$, $h = .011$, and $k = -.123$. By the Pythagorean Theorem, $f(x, y) = \sqrt{x^2 + y^2}$, so that $f_x(x, y) = \frac{x}{\sqrt{x^2 + y^2}}$ and $f_y(x, y) = \frac{y}{\sqrt{x^2 + y^2}}$, and hence $f_x(5, 12) = \frac{5}{13}$ and $f_y(5, 12) = \frac{12}{13}$. Since $f(5, 12) = 13$, we conclude from (6) that

$$f(5.011, 11.877) \approx 13 + \frac{5}{13}(.011) + \frac{12}{13}(-.123) = 13 - \frac{1.421}{13} \approx 12.8907$$

The area is given by $g(x, y) = \frac{1}{2}xy$, so that $g_x(x, y) = \frac{1}{2}y$ and $g_y(x, y) = \frac{1}{2}x$, and hence $g_x(5, 12) = 6$ and $g_y(5, 12) = 2.5$. Since $g(5, 12) = 30$, we conclude from (6) that

$$g(5.011, 11.877) \approx 30 + 6(.011) + 2.5(-.123) = 29.7585$$

25. Let the dimensions of the box be x, y, and z, respectively, and let the surface area be $f(x, y, z)$. Furthermore, let $x_0 = 3$, $y_0 = 4$, $z_0 = 12$, $h = .019$, $k = -.021$, and $\ell = -.027$. Because the box has a top, $f(x, y, z) = 2xy + 2xz + 2yz$, so that $f_x(x, y, z) = 2y + 2z$, $f_y(x, y, z) = 2x + 2z$, and $f_z(x, y, z) = 2x + 2y$, and hence $f_x(3, 4, 12) = 32$, $f_y(3, 4, 12) = 30$, and $f_z(3, 4, 12) = 14$. Since $f(3, 4, 12) = 192$, we find from (7) that

$$f(3.019, 3.979, 11.973) \approx 192 + 32(.019) + 30(-.021) + 14(-.027) = 191.6$$

26. Let the width and length of the sheet be x and y, respectively, and let $C(x, y)$ be the cost of the corresponding sheet, so that $C(x, y) = 3xy$. Let $x_0 = 3$, $y_0 = 6$, $h = .012$, and $k = -.018$. Since $C_x(x, y) = 3y$ and $C_y(x, y) = 3x$, we have $C_x(3, 6) = 18$ and $C_y(3, 6) = 9$. Also $C(3, 6) = 54$. By (6) we find that $C(3.012, 5.982) \approx 54 + 18(.012) + 9(-.018) = 54.054$. Thus the cost would be approximately \$54.06, rounded upward.

Section 13.8

1. $f_x(x, y) = 2x - 6$ and $f_y(x, y) = 4y + 8$, so $f_x(x, y) = 0 = f_y(x, y)$ if $x = 3$ and $y = -2$. Thus $(3, -2)$ is a critical point. Next, $f_{xx}(x, y) = 2$, $f_{yy}(x, y) = 4$, and $f_{xy}(x, y) = 0$. Thus $D(3, -2) = f_{xx}(3, -2)\, f_{yy}(3, -2) - [f_{xy}(3, -2)]^2 = (2)(4) - 0^2 = 8$. Since $D(3, -2) > 0$ and $f_{xx}(3, -2) > 0$, f has a relative minimum value at $(3, -2)$.

2. $f_x(x, y) = 2x - 6$ and $f_y(x, y) = -4y + 8$, so $f_x(x, y) = 0 = f_y(x, y)$ if $x = 3$ and $y = 2$. Thus $(3, 2)$ is a critical point. Next, $f_{xx}(x, y) = 2$, $f_{yy}(x, y) = -4$, and $f_{xy}(x, y) = 0$. Thus $D(3, 2) = f_{xx}(3, 2)\, f_{yy}(3, 2) - [f_{xy}(3, 2)]^2 = (2)(-4) - 0^2 = -8$. Since $D(3, 2) < 0$, f has a saddle point at $(3, 2)$.

3. $f_x(x, y) = 2x + 6y - 6$ and $f_y(x, y) = 6x + 4y + 10$, so $f_x(x, y) = 0 = f_y(x, y)$ if $2x + 6y - 6 = 0$ and $6x + 4y + 10 = 0$. Solving for x in the first equation and substituting for it in the second equation yields $6(3 - 3y) + 4y + 10 = 0$, or $y = 2$. Then $x = -3$, so $(-3, 2)$ is a critical point. Next, $f_{xx}(x, y) = 2$, $f_{yy}(x, y) = 4$, and $f_{xy}(x, y) = 6$. Thus $D(-3, 2) = f_{xx}(-3, 2)\, f_{yy}(-3, 2) - [f_{xy}(-3, 2)]^2 = (2)(4) - 6^2 = -28$. Since $D(-3, 2) < 0$, f has a saddle point at $(-3, 2)$.

4. $g_x(x, y) = 2x - y + 7$ and $g_y(x, y) = -x - 4y - 8$, so $g_x(x, y) = 0 = g_y(x, y)$ if $2x - y + 7 = 0$ and $-x - 4y - 8 = 0$. Solving for y in the first equation and substituting for it in the second equation yields $-x - 4(2x + 7) - 8 = 0$, or $x = -4$. Then $y = -1$, so $(-4, -1)$ is a critical point. Next, $g_{xx}(x, y) = 2$, $g_{yy}(x, y) = -4$, and $g_{xy}(x, y) = -1$. Thus $D(-4, -1) = g_{xx}(-4, -1)\, g_{yy}(-4, -1) - [g_{xy}(-4, -1)]^2 = (2)(-4) - (-1)^2 = -9$. Since $D(-4, -1) < 0$, g has a saddle point at $(-4, -1)$.

5. $k_x(x, y) = 2x + 2y - 6$ and $k_y(x, y) = 2x + 4y + 10$, so $k_x(x, y) = 0 = k_y(x, y)$ if $2x + 2y - 6 = 0$ and $2x + 4y + 10 = 0$. Solving for y in the first equation and substituting for it in the second equation yields $2x + 4(3 - x) + 10 = 0$, or $x = 11$. Then $y = -8$, so $(11, -8)$ is a critical point. Next, $k_{xx}(x, y) = 2$, $k_{yy}(x, y) = 4$, and $k_{xy}(x, y) = 2$. Thus $D(11, -8) = k_{xx}(11, -8)\, k_{yy}(11, -8) - [k_{xy}(11, -8)]^2 = (2)(4) - 2^2 = 4$. $-2^2 = 4$. Since $D(11, -8) > 0$ and $k_{xx}(11, -8) > 0$, k has a relative minimum value at $(11, -8)$.

6. $f_x(x, y) = -2x + 4y - 2$ and $f_y(x, y) = 4x + 2y$, so $f_x(x, y) = 0 = f_y(x, y)$ if $-2x + 4y - 2 = 0$ and $4x + 2y = 0$. Solving for y in the second equation and substituting for it in the first equation yields $-2x + 4(-2x) - 2 = 0$, or $x = -\frac{1}{5}$. Then $y = \frac{2}{5}$, so $(-\frac{1}{5}, \frac{2}{5})$ is a critical point. Next, $f_{xx}(x, y) = -2$, $f_{yy}(x, y) = 2$, and $f_{xy}(x, y) = 4$. Thus $D(-\frac{1}{5}, \frac{2}{5}) = f_{xx}(-\frac{1}{5}, \frac{2}{5})\, f_{yy}(-\frac{1}{5}, \frac{2}{5}) - [f_{xy}(-\frac{1}{5}, \frac{2}{5})]^2 = (-2)(2) - 4^2 = -20$.

Since $D(-\frac{1}{5}, \frac{2}{5}) < 0$, f has a saddle point at $(-\frac{1}{5}, \frac{2}{5})$.

7. $f_x(x, y) = 2xy - 2y = 2y(x - 1)$ and $f_y(x, y) = x^2 - 2x + 4y - 15$, so $f_x(x, y) = 0 = f_y(x, y)$ if $2y(x - 1) = 0$ and $x^2 - 2x + 4y - 15 = 0$. From the first equation we see that $y = 0$ or $x = 1$. If $y = 0$, it follows from the second equation that $x^2 - 2x - 15 = 0$, so that $x = -3$ or $x = 5$. Thus $(-3, 0)$ and $(5, 0)$ are critical points. If $x = 1$, it follows from the second equation that $1 - 2 + 4y - 15 = 0$, or $y = 4$. Thus $(1, 4)$ is also a critical point. Next, $f_{xx}(x, y) = 2y$, $f_{yy}(x, y) = 4$, and $f_{xy}(x, y) = 2x - 2$. Thus $D(-3, 0) = f_{xx}(-3, 0)\, f_{yy}(-3, 0) - [f_{xy}(-3, 0)]^2 = (0)(4) - (-8)^2 = -64$, $D(5, 0) = f_{xx}(5, 0)\, f_{yy}(5, 0) - [f_{xy}(5, 0)]^2 = (0)(4) - 8^2 = -64$, and $D(1, 4) = f_{xx}(1, 4)\, f_{yy}(1, 4) - [f_{xy}(1, 4)]^2 = (8)(4) - 0^2 = 32$. Since $D(1, 4) > 0$ and $f_{xx}(1, 4) > 0$, f has a relative minimum value at $(1, 4)$. Since $D(-3, 0) < 0$ and $D(5, 0) < 0$, f has saddle points at $(-3, 0)$ and at $(5, 0)$.

8. $f_x(x, y) = 3x^2 - 12x = 3x(x - 4)$ and $f_y(x, y) = -6y$, so $f_x(x, y) = 0 = f_y(x, y)$ if $3x(x - 4) = 0$ and $y = 0$. Thus $(0, 0)$ and $(4, 0)$ are critical points. Next, $f_{xx}(x, y) = 6x - 12$, $f_{yy}(x, y) = -6$, and $f_{xy}(x, y) = 0$. Thus $D(0, 0) = f_{xx}(0, 0)\, f_{yy}(0, 0) - [f_{xy}(0, 0)]^2 = (-12)(-6) - 0^2 = 72$ and $D(4, 0) = f_{xx}(4, 0)\, f_{yy}(4, 0) - [f_{xy}(4, 0)]^2 = (12)(-6) - 0^2 = -72$. Since $D(0, 0) > 0$ and $f_{xx}(0, 0) < 0$, f has a relative maximum value at $(0, 0)$. Since $D(4, 0) < 0$, f has a saddle point at $(4, 0)$.

9. $f_x(x, y) = 6x - 3y^2$ and $f_y(x, y) = -6xy + 3y^2 + 6y = 3y(-2x + y + 2)$, so $f_x(x, y) = 0 = f_y(x, y)$ if $6x - 3y^2 = 0$ and $3y(-2x + y + 2) = 0$. From the first equation we see that $x = \frac{1}{2}y^2$, so from the second equation, $y = 0$ or $0 = -2x + y + 2 = -y^2 + y + 2$, so that $y = 0$, $y = -1$, or $y = 2$. The corresponding values of x are $0, \frac{1}{2}$, and 2. Thus $(0, 0)$, $(\frac{1}{2}, -1)$, and $(2, 2)$ are critical points. Next, $f_{xx}(x, y) = 6$, $f_{yy}(x, y) = -6x + 6y + 6$, and $f_{xy}(x, y) = -6y$. Thus $D(0, 0) = f_{xx}(0, 0)\, f_{yy}(0, 0) - [f_{xy}(0, 0)]^2 = (6)(6) - 0^2 = 36$, $D(\frac{1}{2}, -1) = f_{xx}(\frac{1}{2}, -1)\, f_{yy}(\frac{1}{2}, -1) - [f_{xy}(\frac{1}{2}, -1)]^2 = (6)(-3) - 6^2 = -54$, and $D(2, 2) = f_{xx}(2, 2)\, f_{yy}(2, 2) - [f_{xy}(2, 2)]^2 = (6)(6) - (-12)^2 = -108$. Since $D(0, 0) > 0$ and $f_{xx}(0, 0) > 0$, f has a relative minimum value at $(0, 0)$. Since $D(\frac{1}{2}, -1) < 0$ and $D(2, 2) < 0$, f has saddle points at $(\frac{1}{2}, -1)$ and $(2, 2)$.

10. $f_u(u, v) = 3u^2 - 6v$ and $f_v(u, v) = 3v^2 - 6u$, so $f_u(u, v) = 0 = f_v(u, v)$ if $3u^2 - 6v = 0$ and $3v^2 - 6u = 0$. From the first equation we see that $v = \frac{1}{2}u^2$, so from the second equation, $0 = 3v^2 - 6u = \frac{3}{4}u^4 - 6u = \frac{3}{4}u(u^3 - 8)$. Thus $u = 0$ or $u = 2$. The corresponding values of v are 0 and 2. Thus $(0, 0)$ and $(2, 2)$ are critical points. Next, $f_{uu}(u, v) = 6u$, $f_{vv}(u, v) = 6v$, and $f_{uv}(u, v) = -6$. Thus $D(0, 0) = f_{uu}(0, 0)\, f_{vv}(0, 0) - [f_{uv}(0, 0)]^2 = (0)(0) - (-6)^2 = -36$ and $D(2, 2) = f_{uu}(2, 2)\, f_{vv}(2, 2) - [f_{uv}(2, 2)]^2 = (12)(12) - (-6)^2 = 108$. Since

$D(2, 2) > 0$ and $f_{uu}(2, 2) > 0$, f has a relative minimum value at $(2, 2)$.

Since $D(0, 0) < 0$, f has a saddle point at $(0, 0)$.

11. $f_x(x, y) = 4y + 4xy - y^2 = y(4 + 4x - y)$ and $f_y(x, y) = 4x + 2x^2 - 2xy = 2x(2 + x - y)$, so $f_x(x, y) = 0 = f_y(x, y)$ if $y(4 + 4x - y) = 0$ and $2x(2 + x - y) = 0$. From the first equation we see that either $y = 0$ or $y = 4 + 4x$. If $y = 0$, the second equation implies that $x = 0$ or $x = -2$. Thus $(0, 0)$ and $(-2, 0)$ are critical points. If $y = 4 + 4x$, the second equation implies that either $x = 0$ or $0 = 2 + x - y = 2 + x - (4 + 4x)$, so that $x = 0$ or $x = -\frac{2}{3}$. The corresponding values of y are 4 and $\frac{4}{3}$. Thus $(0, 4)$ and $(-\frac{2}{3}, \frac{4}{3})$ are critical points. Next, $f_{xx}(x, y) = 4y$, $f_{yy}(x, y) = -2x$, and $f_{xy}(x, y) = 4 + 4x - 2y$. Thus $D(0, 0) = f_{xx}(0, 0)\, f_{yy}(0, 0) - [f_{xy}(0, 0)]^2 = (0)(0) - 4^2 = -16$, $D(-2, 0) = f_{xx}(-2, 0)\, f_{yy}(-2, 0) - [f_{xy}(-2, 0)]^2 = (0)(4) - (-4)^2 = -16$, $D(0, 4) = f_{xx}(0, 4)\, f_{yy}(0, 4) - [f_{xy}(0, 4)]^2 = (16)(0) - (-4)^2 = -16$, and $D(-\frac{2}{3}, \frac{4}{3}) = f_{xx}(-\frac{2}{3}, \frac{4}{3})\, f_{yy}(-\frac{2}{3}, \frac{4}{3}) - [f_{xy}(-\frac{2}{3}, \frac{4}{3})]^2 = (\frac{16}{3})(\frac{4}{3}) - (\frac{-4}{3})^2 = \frac{16}{3}$.

Since $D(-\frac{2}{3}, \frac{4}{3}) > 0$ and $f_{xx}(-\frac{2}{3}, \frac{4}{3}) > 0$, f has a relative minimum value at $(-\frac{2}{3}, \frac{4}{3})$. Since $D(0, 0) < 0$, $D(0, 4) < 0$, and $D(-2, 0) < 0$, f has saddle points at $(0, 0)$, $(0, 4)$, and $(-2, 0)$.

12. $f_x(x, y) = -\frac{1}{x^2} + y$ and $f_y(x, y) = -\frac{1}{y^2} + x$, so $f_x(x, y) = 0 = f_y(x, y)$ if $-\frac{1}{x^2} + y = 0$ and $-\frac{1}{y^2} + x = 0$. From the first equation we see that $y = \frac{1}{x^2}$, so from the second equation $0 = -\frac{1}{y^2} + x = -x^4 + x = -x(x^3 - 1)$. Since $x \neq 0$, it follows that $x = 1$. The corresponding value of y is 1. Thus $(1, 1)$ is a critical point. Next, $f_{xx}(x, y) = \frac{2}{x^3}$, $f_{yy}(x, y) = \frac{2}{y^3}$, and $f_{xy}(x, y) = 1$. Thus $D(1, 1) = f_{xx}(1, 1)\, f_{yy}(1, 1) - [f_{xy}(1, 1)]^2 = (2)(2) - 1^2 = 3$. Since $D(1, 1) > 0$ and $f_{xx}(1, 1) > 0$, f has a relative minimum value at $(1, 1)$.

13. $f_x(x,y) = 2x$ and $f_y(x,y) = -2ye^{y^2}$, so $f_x(x,y) = 0 = f_y(x,y)$ if $x = 0$ and $y = 0$. Thus $(0,0)$ is a critical point. Next, $f_{xx}(x,y) = 2$, $f_{yy}(x,y) = -2e^{y^2} - 4y^2e^{y^2}$, and $f_{xy}(x,y) = 0$. Thus $D(0,0) = f_{xx}(0,0)f_{yy}(0,0) - [f_{xy}(0,0)]^2 = (2)(-2) - (0)^2 = -4$. Since $D(0,0) < 0$, it follows that f has a saddle point at $(0,0)$.

14. $f_x(x, y) = (y - 2)\frac{1}{x}$ and $f_y(x, y) = \ln xy + (y - 2)\frac{1}{y}$, so $f_x(x, y) = 0 = f_y(x, y)$ if $(y - 2)\frac{1}{x} = 0$ and $\ln xy + (y - 2)\frac{1}{y} = 0$. The first equation implies that $y = 2$, so that the second equation implies that $\log xy = 0$. Therefore $xy = 1$, so that $x = \frac{1}{y} = \frac{1}{2}$. Thus $(\frac{1}{2}, 2)$ is a critical point. Next, $f_{xx}(x, y) = \frac{-(y - 2)}{x^2}$, $f_{yy}(x, y) = \frac{1}{y} + \frac{2}{y^2}$, and $f_{xy}(x, y) = \frac{1}{x}$. Thus $D(\frac{1}{2}, 2) = f_{xx}(\frac{1}{2}, 2)\, f_{yy}(\frac{1}{2}, 2) - [f_{xy}(\frac{1}{2}, 2)]^2 = (0)(1) - 2^2 = -4$. Since $D(\frac{1}{2}, 2) < 0$, f has a saddle point at $(\frac{1}{2}, 2)$.

15. $k_x(x, y) = e^x \sin y$ and $k_y(x, y) = e^x \cos y$, so $k_x(x, y) = 0 = k_y(x, y)$

if $e^x \sin y = 0$ and $e^x \cos y = 0$, or $\sin y = 0$ and $\cos y = 0$, which is impossible. Thus k has no critical points.

16. $f_x(x, y) = e^x(\sin y - 1)$ and $f_y(x, y) = e^x \cos y$, so $f_x(x, y) = 0 = f_y(x, y)$ if $e^x(\sin y - 1) = 0$ and $e^x \cos y = 0$, or $\sin y = 1$ and $\cos y = 0$. This implies that $y = \frac{\pi}{2} + 2n\pi$ for some integer n. Thus any point of the form $(x, \frac{\pi}{2} + 2n\pi)$ is a critical point. Next, $f_{xx}(x, y) = e^x(\sin y - 1)$, $f_{yy}(x, y) = -e^x \sin y$, and $f_{xy}(x, y) = e^x \cos y$. Since $D(x, \frac{\pi}{2} + 2n\pi) = f_{xx}(x, \frac{\pi}{2} + 2n\pi)\, f_{yy}(x, \frac{\pi}{2} + 2n\pi) - \left[f_{xy}(x, \frac{\pi}{2} + 2n\pi)\right]^2 = (0)(-e^x) - 0^2 = 0$, the Second Partials Test yields no conclusion. However, since $f(x, \frac{\pi}{2} + 2n\pi) = 0$ and $f(x, y) \leq 0$ for all x and y, it follows that f has a (relative) maximum value at every point of the form $(x, \frac{\pi}{2} + 2n\pi)$, where n is an integer.

17. $f_u(u, v) = 1$ if $u > 0$, $f_u(u, v) = -1$ if $u < 0$, and $f_u(u, v)$ does not exist if $u = 0$. Similarly, $f_v(u, v) = 1$ if $v > 0$, $f_v(u, v) = -1$ if $v < 0$, and $f_v(u, v)$ does not exist if $v = 0$. Thus any point of the form $(0, v)$ or $(u, 0)$ is a critical point of f. Since either f_{uu} or f_{vv} does not exist at each such point, the Second Partials Test does not apply. Notice that $f(0, 0) = 0$ and $f(u, v) \geq 0$ for all u and v, so that f has a (relative) minimum value at $(0, 0)$. However, at any other critical point (u, v), either $f_u(u, v) \neq 0$ or $f_v(u, v) \neq 0$, so that f does not have a relative extreme value or a saddle point at any critical point except $(0, 0)$.

18. As in the solution of Exercise 17, we see that g has a critical point at any point of the form $(2, v)$ or $(u, -1)$. Since $g(2, -1) = 3$, $g(u, -1) < 3$ for $u \neq 2$, and $g(2, v) > 3$ for $v \neq -1$, it follows that g has a saddle point at $(2, -1)$. At any other critical point (u, v) either $g_u(u, v) \neq 0$ or $g_v(u, v) \neq 0$, so that g does not have a relative extreme value or a saddle point at any critical point other than $(2, -1)$.

19. $f_x(x, y) = ye^{xy}$ and $f_y(x, y) = xe^{xy}$, so $f_x(x, y) = 0 = f_y(x, y)$ if $x = 0$ and $y = 0$. Thus $(0, 0)$ is a critical point. Next, $f_{xx}(x, y) = y^2e^x$, $f_{yy}(x, y) = x^2e^{xy}$, and $f_{xy}(x, y) = e^{xy} + xye^{xy}$. Thus $D(0, 0) = f_{xx}(0, 0)\, f_{yy}(0, 0) - \left[f_{xy}(0, 0)\right]^2 = (0)(0) - 1^2 = -1$. Since $D(0, 0) < 0$, f has a saddle point at $(0, 0)$.

20. $f_x(x, y) = \cos x$ and $f_y(x, y) = \cos y$ for $0 < x < \frac{\pi}{2}$ and $0 < y < \frac{\pi}{2}$. Since $\cos x \neq 0$ for $0 < x < \frac{\pi}{2}$ and $\cos y \neq 0$ for $0 < y < \frac{\pi}{2}$, f has no critical points.

21. $f_x(x, y) = \cos x$ and $f_y(x, y) = \cos y$, so $f_x(x, y) = 0 = f_y(x, y)$ if $\cos x = 0$ and $\cos y = 0$. Thus f has a critical point at any point of the form $(\frac{\pi}{2} + m\pi, \frac{\pi}{2} + n\pi)$, where m and n are integers. Next, $f_{xx}(x, y) = -\sin x$, $f_{yy}(x, y) = -\sin y$, and $f_{xy}(x, y) = 0$. Thus $D(\frac{\pi}{2} + m\pi, \frac{\pi}{2} + n\pi) = f_{xx}(\frac{\pi}{2} + m\pi, \frac{\pi}{2} + n\pi)\, f_{yy}(\frac{\pi}{2} + m\pi, \frac{\pi}{2} + n\pi) - \left[f_{xy}(\frac{\pi}{2} + m\pi, \frac{\pi}{2} + n\pi)\right]^2 = (-\sin(\frac{\pi}{2} + m\pi))(-\sin(\frac{\pi}{2} + n\pi)) - 0^2 = \sin(\frac{\pi}{2} + m\pi)\sin(\frac{\pi}{2} + n\pi)$. Since $D(\frac{\pi}{2} + m\pi, \frac{\pi}{2} + n\pi) = 1 > 0$ and

$f_{xx}(\frac{\pi}{2} + m\pi, \frac{\pi}{2} + n\pi) = -1 < 0$ if m and n are both even, f has a relative maximum value at the corresponding point $(\frac{\pi}{2} + m\pi, \frac{\pi}{2} + n\pi)$. Since $D(\frac{\pi}{2} + m\pi, \frac{\pi}{2} + n\pi) = 1$ and $f_{xx}(\frac{\pi}{2} + m\pi, \frac{\pi}{2} + n\pi) = 1 > 0$ if m and n are both odd, f has a relative minimum value at the corresponding point $(\frac{\pi}{2} + m\pi, \frac{\pi}{2} + n\pi)$. Since $D(\frac{\pi}{2} + m\pi, \frac{\pi}{2} + n\pi) = -1 < 0$ if either m or n is odd and the other is even, f has a saddle point at the corresponding point $(\frac{\pi}{2} + m\pi, \frac{\pi}{2} + n\pi)$.

22. $k_u(u, v) = 2(u + v) = k_v(u, v)$, so $k_u(u, v) = 0 = k_v(u, v)$ if $u + v = 0$, or $v = -u$. Thus any point of the form $(u, -u)$ is a critical point. Next, $k_{uu}(u, v) = 2$, $k_{vv}(u, v) = 2$, and $k_{uv}(u, v) = 2$. Thus $D(u, -u) = k_{uu}(u, -u)\, k_{vv}(u, -u) - [k_{uv}(u, -u)]^2 = (2)(2) - 2^2 = 0$, so the Second Partials Test yields no conclusion. However, since $k(u, -u) = 0$ and $k(u, v) \geqslant 0$ for all u and v, it follows that k has a (relative) minimum value at any point of the form $(u, -u)$.

23. $f_x(x, y) = 2a(y + ax + b)$ and $f_y(x, y) = 2(y + ax + b)$, so $f_x(x, y) = 0 = f_y(x, y)$ if $y + ax + b = 0$, or $y = -(ax + b)$. Thus any point of the form $(x, -(ax + b))$ is a critical point. Next, $f_{xx}(x, y) = 2a^2$, $f_{yy}(x, y) = 2$, and $f_{xy}(x, y) = 2a$. Thus $D(x, -(ax + b)) = f_{xx}(x, -(ax + b))\, f_{yy}(x, -(ax + b)) - [f_{xy}(x, -(ax + b))]^2 = (2a^2)(2) - (2a)^2 = 0$, so the Second Partials Test yields no conclusion. However, $f(x, -(ax + b)) = 0$ and $f(x, y) \geqslant 0$ for all x and y. Thus f has a (relative) minimum value at any point of the form $(x, -(ax + b))$, that is, at any point on the line $y = -(ax + b) = -ax - b$.

24. $f_x(x, y) = ae^{-x^2-y^2} - 2x(ax + by)e^{-x^2-y^2}$ and $f_y(x, y) = be^{-x^2-y^2} - 2y(ax + by)e^{-x^2-y^2}$, so $f_x(x, y) = 0 = f_y(x, y)$ if $a - 2x(ax + by) = 0$ and $b - 2y(ax + by) = 0$. Since $a \neq 0$, the first equation implies that $x \neq 0$. Since $b \neq 0$, the second equation implies that $y \neq 0$. Thus $\frac{a}{2x} = ax + by = \frac{b}{2y}$, so that $2ay = 2bx$, or $y = \frac{b}{a}x$. Thus all critical points lie on the line $y = \frac{b}{a}x$.

25. $f_x(x,y) = 2x$ and $f_y(x,y) = -2y$, so $f_x(x,y) = 0 = f_y(x,y)$ if $x = 0$ and $y = 0$. Thus $(0,0)$ is a critical point in R. On the boundary $x^2 + y^2 = 1$ of R we have $y^2 = 1 - x^2$, so that $f(x, y) = x^2 - (1 - x^2) = 2x^2 - 1$ for $-1 \leq x \leq 1$. The maximum value of $2x^2 - 1$ on $[-1, 1]$ is 1 and occurs for $x = 1$ and $x = -1$, and the minimum value is -1 and occurs for $x = 0$. Since $f(0,0) = 0$, it follows that the maximum value of f on R is $f(1,0) = f(-1,0) = 1$, and the minimum value is $f(0,1) = f(0,-1) = -1$.

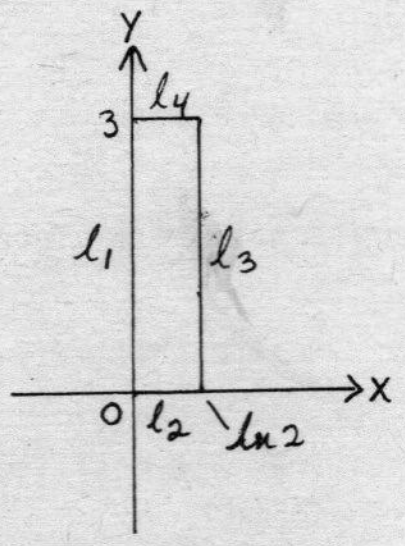

26. $f_x(x,y) = -ye^{-x}$ and $f_y(x,y) = e^{-x}$, so since $f_y(x,y) \neq 0$ for all (x,y), we know there is no extreme value of f interior to R. From the figure we see that on ℓ_1, we have $x = 0$ and $f(0,y) = ye^{-0} = y$; the maximum value on ℓ_1 is $f(0,3) = 3$ and the minimum value on ℓ_1 is $f(0,0) = 0$. On ℓ_2, we have $y = 0$ and $f(x,0) = 0$, so the maximum and minimum values on ℓ_2

are both 0. On ℓ_3, we have $x = \ln 2$ and $f(\ln 2, y) = ye^{-\ln 2} = y/2$; the maximum value on ℓ_3 is $f(\ln 2, 3) = \frac{3}{2}$ and the minimum value on ℓ_3 is 0. On ℓ_4, we have $y = 3$ and $f(x,3) = 3e^{-x}$; the maximum value on ℓ_4 is $f(0,3) = 3e^{-0} = 3$ and the minimum value on ℓ_4 is $f(\ln 2, 3) = 3e^{-\ln 2} = \frac{3}{2}$. Thus the maximum value of f on R is $f(0,3) = 3$ and the minimum value is $f(x,0) = 0$, occurring for $0 \le x \le \ln 2$.

27. $f_x(x,y) = 2\cos x$ and $f_y(x,y) = -3\sin y$, so $f_x(x,y) = 0 = f_y(x,y)$ for (x,y) in R if $x = \pi/2$ and $y = 0$. Thus $(\pi/2, 0)$ is a critical point of f in R. From the figure we observe that for (x,y) on ℓ_1 we have $y = -\pi/2$ and $\cos(-\pi/2) = 0$, so that $f(x,y) = 2\sin x$. Thus on ℓ_1 the maximum value of f is $f(\pi/2, -\pi/2) = 2\sin \pi/2 = 2$ and the minimum value is $f(0,-\pi/2) = 2\sin 0 = 0$. The same extreme values are obtained for ℓ_3. For (x,y) on ℓ_2 we have $x = \pi$, so that $f(x,y) = 3\cos y$. Thus on ℓ_2 the maximum value of f is $f(\pi, 0) = 3\cos 0 = 3$ and the minimum value is $f(\pi, -\pi/2) = 3\cos(-\pi/2) = 0$. The same extreme values are obtained for ℓ_4. Since $f(\pi/2, 0) = 2\sin \pi/2 + 3\cos 0 = 2 + 3 = 5$, the maximum value of f on R is $f(\pi/2, 0) = 5$ and the minimum value is $f(\pi, -\pi/2) = 0$.

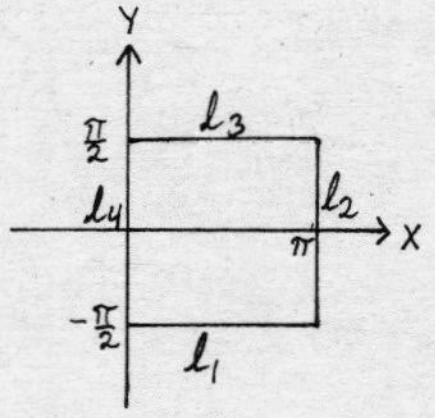

28. $f_x(x,y) = 2xe^{x^2-y^2}$ and $f_y(x,y) = -2ye^{x^2-y^2}$, so $f_x(x,y) = 0 = f_y(x,y)$ if $x = 0$ and $y = 0$. But $(0,0)$ is not in R, so f has no critical points and hence no extreme values interior to R. On the circle $x^2 + y^2 = \frac{1}{2}$ we have $y^2 = \frac{1}{2} - x^2$, so $f(x,y) = e^{x^2-(1/2 - x^2)} = e^{2x^2-1/2}$ and $-1/\sqrt{2} \le x \le 1/\sqrt{2}$. Thus on the circle the maximum value of f is $f(1/\sqrt{2}, 0) = e^{2(1/2) - 1/2} = e^{1/2}$ and the minimum value is $f(0, 1/\sqrt{2}) = e^{-1/2}$. On the circle $x^2 + y^2 = 2$ we have $y^2 = 2 - x^2$, so $f(x,y) = e^{x^2-(2-x^2)} = e^{2x^2-2}$ and $-\sqrt{2} \le x \le \sqrt{2}$. Thus on this circle the maximum value of f is $f(\sqrt{2}, 0) = e^{2(2)-2} = e^2$ and the minimum value is $f(0, \sqrt{2}) = e^{0-2} = e^{-2}$. Consequently the maximum value of f on R is $f(\sqrt{2}, 0) = e^2$ and the minimum value is $f(0, \sqrt{2}) = e^{-2}$.

29. Let $P = xyz$ for any nonnegative numbers x, y, and z satisfying $x + y + z = 48$. Then $z = 48 - x - y$, so $P = xy(48 - x - y)$. We seek the maximum value of P on the triangular region R consisting of all (x, y) for which $x \ge 0$, $y \ge 0$, and $x + y \le 48$. Such a maximum value exists by the Maximum-Minimum Theorem. Since $P = 0$ if $x = 0$, $y = 0$, or $x + y = 48$, the maximum value of P on R does not occur on the boundary of R and hence must occur at a critical point in the interior of R.

$\frac{\partial P}{\partial x} = y(48 - x - y) - xy = y(48 - 2x - y)$ and

$\frac{\partial P}{\partial y} = x(48 - x - y) - xy = x(48 - x - 2y)$, so $\frac{\partial P}{\partial x} = 0 = \frac{\partial P}{\partial y}$ if

$y(48 - 2x - y) = 0$ and $x(48 - x - 2y) = 0$. From the first equation we see that $y = 0$ or $48 - 2x - y = 0$, and from the second equation we see that $x = 0$ or $48 - x - 2y = 0$. Since $x \ne 0$ and $y \ne 0$ at each interior point of R, it follows that a point (x, y) in the interior of R is a critical point of P only if $48 - 2x - y = 0$ and $48 - x - 2y = 0$. Solving for y in the first of these equations, we obtain $y = 48 - 2x$. Substituting for y in the second equation gives us $48 - x - 2(48 - 2x) = 0$, so that $x = 16$. Then $y = 16$, so $(16, 16)$ is the only critical point of P in R, and the corresponding value of z is 16 also. The maximum product must occur at a critical point, so it is $P(16, 16) = 4096$.

30. Let $S = x + y + z$ for any positive numbers x, y, and z satisfying $xyz = 48$. Then $z = \frac{48}{xy}$, so that $S = x + y + \frac{48}{xy}$. We seek the minimum value of S on the set R of points (x, y) satisfying $x > 0$ and $y > 0$. Although the Maximum-Minimum Theorem does not apply, S has a minimum value on R. Since R has no boundary point, the minimum value must occur at a critical point in R. $\frac{\partial S}{\partial x} = 1 - \frac{48}{x^2y}$ and $\frac{\partial S}{\partial y} = 1 - \frac{48}{xy^2}$, so that $\frac{\partial S}{\partial x} = 0 = \frac{\partial S}{\partial y}$ if $1 - \frac{48}{x^2y} = 0$ and $1 - \frac{48}{xy^2} = 0$. Thus $x^2y = 48 = xy^2$, and since $x \neq 0$ and $y \neq 0$, it follows that $x = y = \sqrt[3]{48}$, so the only critical point in R is $(\sqrt[3]{48}, \sqrt[3]{48})$, and the corresponding value of z is $\sqrt[3]{48}$ also. Thus the minimum sum is $\sqrt[3]{48} + \sqrt[3]{48} + \sqrt[3]{48} = 3\sqrt[3]{48}$.

31. Set up a coordinate system with the origin at the center of the sphere and with the coordinate planes parallel to the sides of the box. If r is the radius of the sphere, then an equation of the sphere is $x^2 + y^2 + z^2 = r^2$. If (x, y, z) is the vertex of the box with $x \geq 0$, $y \geq 0$, and $z \geq 0$, then $z = \sqrt{r^2 - x^2 - y^2}$, and the volume V of the box is given by $V = xyz = xy\sqrt{r^2 - x^2 - y^2}$. We seek the maximum value of V on the set R of points (x, y) satisfying $x \geq 0$, $y \geq 0$, and $x^2 + y^2 \leq r^2$. Such a maximum value exists by the Maximum-Minimum Theorem. Since $V = 0$ if $x = 0$, $y = 0$, or $x^2 + y^2 = r^2$, V does not have its maximum value on R at any boundary point of R. Thus the maximum value of V on R occurs at a critical point in the interior of R. $\frac{\partial V}{\partial x} = y\sqrt{r^2 - x^2 - y^2} - \frac{x^2y}{\sqrt{r^2 - x^2 - y^2}}$ and $\frac{\partial V}{\partial y} = x\sqrt{r^2 - x^2 - y^2} - \frac{xy^2}{\sqrt{r^2 - x^2 - y^2}}$, so $\frac{\partial V}{\partial x} = 0 = \frac{\partial V}{\partial y}$ if $y\sqrt{r^2 - x^2 - y^2} - \frac{x^2y}{\sqrt{r^2 - x^2 - y^2}} = 0$ and $x\sqrt{r^2 - x^2 - y^2} - \frac{xy^2}{\sqrt{r^2 - x^2 - y^2}} = 0$. Since $x \neq 0$ and $y \neq 0$ at any interior point of R, we conclude from these equations that $0 = \sqrt{r^2 - x^2 - y^2} - \frac{x^2}{\sqrt{r^2 - x^2 - y^2}} = \frac{r^2 - x^2 - y^2 - x^2}{\sqrt{r^2 - x^2 - y^2}}$ and $0 = \sqrt{r^2 - x^2 - y^2} - \frac{y^2}{\sqrt{r^2 - x^2 - y^2}} = \frac{r^2 - x^2 - y^2 - y^2}{\sqrt{r^2 - x^2 - y^2}}$. Thus $r^2 - x^2 - y^2 - x^2 = 0 = r^2 - x^2 - y^2 - y^2$, or $x^2 = y^2$, or $x = y$. Therefore $0 = r^2 - x^2 - y^2$

$-x^2 = r^2 - 3x^2$, so that $x = \frac{r}{\sqrt{3}}$. Then $y = \frac{r}{\sqrt{3}}$, so the only critical point of S in R is $(\frac{r}{\sqrt{3}}, \frac{r}{\sqrt{3}})$. The maximum value must occur at a critical point, so it occurs for $x = \frac{r}{\sqrt{3}} = y$. This means that $z = \sqrt{r^2 - x^2 - y^2} = \frac{r}{\sqrt{3}}$ and thus the box is a cube.

32. If the dimensions of such a box are x, y, and z, as shown in the figure, then $xyz = 32$ and the surface area S is given by $S = xy + 2xz + 2yz = xy + 2x(\frac{32}{xy}) + 2y(\frac{32}{xy}) = xy + \frac{64}{y} + \frac{64}{x}$. We seek the minimum value of S on the set R of all points (x, y) with $x > 0$ and $y > 0$. Although the Maximum-Minimum Theorem does not apply, S has a minimum value on R. The minimum value must occur at a critical point in R since R has no boundary points.

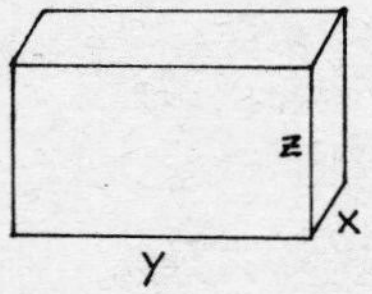

$\frac{\partial S}{\partial x} = y - \frac{64}{x^2}$ and $\frac{\partial S}{\partial y} = x - \frac{64}{y^2}$. Thus $\frac{\partial S}{\partial x} = 0$ and $\frac{\partial S}{\partial y} = 0$ if $x^2y = 64$ and $xy^2 = 64$. Since $x \neq 0$ and $y \neq 0$ at any critical point of R and since $x^2y = xy^2$, we conclude that $x = y$. Thus $64 = x^2y = x^3$, so that $x = 4$. Then $y = 4$, so the only critical point of S in R is $(4, 4)$. The smallest surface area must occur at a critical point, so it occurs if the length and the width are 4 meters, and the height is 2 meters.

33. The distance from a point to the origin will be minimum if and only if the square of the distance from the point to the origin is minimum. To simplify the calculations, we will minimize the square of the distance. Thus for points (x, y, z) satisfying $x + y + z = 48$, we seek the minimum value of $x^2 + y^2 + z^2 = x^2 + y^2 + (48 - x - y)^2$. Let $f(x, y) = x^2 + y^2 + (48 - x - y)^2$. Since $f(0, 0) = (48)^2$ and $f(x, y) > (48)^2$ if $x^2 + y^2 > (48)^2$, and since the Maximum-Minimum Theorem implies that f has a minimum value on the disk $x^2 + y^2 \leq (48)^2$, it follows that f has a minimum value. Since the domain of f is the entire xy plane, the minimum value of f occurs at a critical point. $f_x(x, y) = 2x - 2(48 - x - y)$ and $f_y(x, y) = 2y - 2(48 - x - y)$. Thus $f_x(x, y) = 0 = f_y(x, y)$ if $2x - 2(48 - x - y) = 0$ and $2y - 2(48 - x - y) = 0$, so $x = y$. Then $0 = 2x - 2(48 - x - y) = 2x - 2(48 - 2x)$, so that $x = 16$. Then $y = 16$ so the only critical point of f is $(16, 16)$. The minimum value of f must occur at a critical point, so it occurs at $(16, 16)$. Since $z = 16$ if $x = 16 = y$, $(16, 16, 16)$ is the point the sum of whose coordinates is 48 and whose distance to the origin is minimum.

34. It suffices to consider only vectors whose $\vec{k}$ components are nonnegative. If $x\vec{i} + y\vec{j} + z\vec{k}$ is such a vector with length 16, then $x^2 + y^2 + z^2 = (16)^2 = 256$ and $z \geq 0$, so the sum of the components is $x + y + z = x + y + \sqrt{256 - x^2 - y^2}$. Let $f(x, y) = x + y + \sqrt{256 - x^2 - y^2}$. The domain of f is the disk $x^2 + y^2 \leq 256$, so the Maximum-Minimum Theorem implies that f has a maximum value. For (x, y) in the interior of the

disk $x^2 + y^2 \leq 256$, $f_x(x, y) = 1 - \frac{x}{\sqrt{256 - x^2 - y^2}}$ and $f_y(x, y) = 1 - \frac{y}{\sqrt{256 - x^2 - y^2}}$. Thus if $f_x(x, y) = 0 = f_y(x, y)$, then

$$1 - \frac{x}{\sqrt{256 - x^2 - y^2}} = 0 = 1 - \frac{y}{\sqrt{256 - x^2 - y^2}},$$ so that $x = y$. Then

$$0 = 1 - \frac{x}{\sqrt{256 - x^2 - y^2}} = 1 - \frac{x}{\sqrt{256 - 2x^2}},$$ so that $x = \sqrt{256 - 2x^2}$, or

$3x^2 = 256$, or $x = \sqrt{\frac{256}{3}}$. Then $y = \sqrt{\frac{256}{3}}$. Thus the only critical point

is $\left(\sqrt{\frac{256}{3}}, \sqrt{\frac{256}{3}}\right)$ and $f\left(\sqrt{\frac{256}{3}}, \sqrt{\frac{256}{3}}\right) = \sqrt{\frac{256}{3}} + \sqrt{\frac{256}{3}}$

$+ \sqrt{256 - \frac{256}{3} - \frac{256}{3}} = \sqrt{768}$. For (x, y) on the boundary $x^2 + y^2 = 256$

of the disk $x^2 + y^2 \leq 256$ we have $f(x, y) = x + y + \sqrt{256 - x^2 - y^2}$, so

the maximum value of f on the boundary will occur at a point with non-negative coordinates. If $x^2 + y^2 = 256$ and $x \geq 0$ and $y \geq 0$, let

$g(x) = f(x, y) = f(x, \sqrt{256 - x^2}) = x + \sqrt{256 - x^2} + \sqrt{256 - x^2 - (256 - x^2)}$

$= x + \sqrt{256 - x^2}$. Since $g'(x) = 1 - \frac{x}{\sqrt{256 - x^2}}$, it follows that the maximum

value of g occurs for $1 - \frac{x}{\sqrt{256 - x^2}} = 0$, or $x = \sqrt{128}$. Thus the maximum

value of g is $\sqrt{128} + \sqrt{256 - 128} = 2\sqrt{128} = \sqrt{512}$, so that the maximum

value of f on the entire disk $x^2 + y^2 \leq 256$ is $\sqrt{768}$. Thus the vector

$\frac{16}{\sqrt{3}}\vec{i} + \frac{16}{\sqrt{3}}\vec{j} + \frac{16}{\sqrt{3}}\vec{k}$ is the vector of length 16 whose components

have the largest sum.

35. If $f_{xx}(x_0, y_0) > 0$ and $f_{yy}(x_0, y_0) < 0$, then $D(x_0, y_0) =$

$= f_{xx}(x_0, y_0)\, f_{yy}(x_0, y_0) - [f_{xy}(x_0, y_0)]^2 < 0$. Since $D(x_0, y_0) < 0$,

the Second Partials Test implies that f has a saddle point at (x_0, y_0).

36. $f(m, b) = [1 - (m + b)]^2 + [3 - (2m + b)]^2 + [4 - (3m + b)]^2$

$= 1 - 2(m + b) + (m + b)^2 + 9 - 6(2m + b) + (2m + b)^2 + 16 - 8(3m + b)$

$+ (3m + b)^2 = 26 - 38m - 16b + 14m^2 + 12mb + 3b^2$. $f_m(m, b) = -38 + 28m$

$+ 12b$ and $f_b(m, b) = -16 + 12m + 6b$. Thus $f_m(m, b) = 0 = f_b(m, b)$ if

$-38 + 28m + 12b = 0$ and $-16 + 12m + 6b = 0$. Solving for $6b$ in the

second equation and substituting for it in the first equation, we obtain

$0 = -38 + 28m + 12b = -38 + 28m + 2(16 - 12m)$, so that $m = \frac{3}{2}$. Then

$b = -\frac{1}{3}$. Thus an equation of the line of best fit is $y = \frac{3}{2}x - \frac{1}{3}$.

37. $f(m, b) = [0 - (0 + b)]^2 + [-1 - (m + b)]^2 + [1 - (-2m + b)]^2$

$= b^2 + 1 + 2(m + b) + (m + b)^2 + 1 - 2(-2m + b) + (-2m + b)^2 = 2 + 6m$

$+ 5m^2 - 2mb + 3b^2$. $f_m(m, b) = 6 + 10m - 2b$ and $f_b(m, b) = -2m + 6b$.

Thus $f_m(m, b) = 0 = f_b(m, b)$ if $6 + 10m - 2b = 0$ and $-2m + 6b = 0$.

Solving for m in the second equation and substituting in the first

equation, we obtain $0 = 6 + 10m - 2b = 6 + 10(3b) - 2b$, so that $b = -\frac{3}{14}$.

Then $m = -\frac{9}{14}$. Thus an equation of the line of best fit is

$y = -\frac{9}{14}x - \frac{3}{14}$.

38. If the dimensions of such a box are x, y, and z, then $4x + 4y + 4z = \ell$, so that $z = \frac{1}{4}\ell - x - y$, and the volume V of the box is given by $V = xyz = xy\left(\frac{1}{4}\ell - x - y\right)$. We seek the maximum value of V on the triangular region R consisting of all (x, y) such that $x \geq 0$, $y \geq 0$, and $x + y \leq \frac{1}{4}\ell$. Such a maximum value exists by the Maximum-Minimum Theorem. If $x = 0$, $y = 0$, or $x + y = \frac{1}{4}\ell$, then $V = 0$. Thus V assumes its maximum value at a critical point in the interior of R. $\frac{\partial V}{\partial x} = y\left(\frac{1}{4}\ell - x - y\right) - xy = y\left(\frac{1}{4}\ell - 2x - y\right)$ and $\frac{\partial V}{\partial y} = x\left(\frac{1}{4}\ell - x - y\right) - xy = x\left(\frac{1}{4}\ell - x - 2y\right)$. Thus $\frac{\partial V}{\partial x} = 0 = \frac{\partial V}{\partial y}$ if $y\left(\frac{1}{4}\ell - 2x - y\right) = 0$ and $x\left(\frac{1}{4}\ell - x - 2y\right) = 0$. Since $x \neq 0$ and $y \neq 0$ at any interior point of R, it follows that $\frac{1}{4}\ell - 2x - y = 0 = \frac{1}{4}\ell - x - 2y$, so that $x = y$. Then $0 = \frac{1}{4}\ell - 2x - y = \frac{1}{4}\ell - 3x$, so that $x = \frac{1}{12}\ell$. Then $y = \frac{1}{12}\ell$, so the only critical point of V in R is $\left(\frac{1}{12}\ell, \frac{1}{12}\ell\right)$. The corresponding value of V is given by $V = xy\left(\frac{1}{4}\ell - x - y\right) = \left(\frac{1}{12}\ell\right)\left(\frac{1}{12}\ell\right)\left(\frac{1}{4}\ell - \frac{1}{12}\ell - \frac{1}{12}\ell\right) = \frac{\ell^3}{1728}$. Thus the maximum volume is $\frac{\ell^3}{1728}$.

39. Let x be the length in feet of the front and back walls, y the length of the side walls, and z the height of the gymnasium. Then $xyz = 960{,}000$, so that $z = \frac{960{,}000}{xy}$. If a is the cost per square foot of the side and back walls and the floor, then the total cost C is given by $C = a(2xz + xz + 2yz + xy + \frac{3}{2}xy) = a(3xz + 2yz + \frac{5}{2}xy) = a\left(\frac{2{,}880{,}000}{y} + \frac{1{,}920{,}000}{x} + \frac{5}{2}xy\right)$. Although the Maximum-Minimum Theorem does not apply, C has a minimum value, which occurs at a critical point. Now $\frac{\partial C}{\partial x} = a\left(\frac{-1{,}920{,}000}{x^2} + \frac{5}{2}y\right)$ and $\frac{\partial C}{\partial y} = a\left(\frac{-2{,}880{,}000}{y^2} + \frac{5}{2}x\right)$. Thus $\frac{\partial C}{\partial x} = 0 = \frac{\partial C}{\partial y}(x, y)$ if $\frac{-1{,}920{,}000}{x^2} + \frac{5}{2}y = 0$ and $\frac{-2{,}880{,}000}{y^2} + \frac{5}{2}x = 0$, so that $y = \frac{768{,}000}{x^2}$ and $x = \frac{1{,}152{,}000}{y^2}$. Thus $x = \frac{1{,}152{,}000}{y^2} = \frac{(1{,}152{,}000)x^4}{(768{,}000)^2} = \frac{x^4}{512{,}000}$. Since $x \neq 0$, we have $x^3 = 512{,}000$, or $x = 80$. Then $y = \frac{768{,}000}{(80)^2} = 120$, so the only critical point of C is $(80, 120)$. Thus the maximum value of C occurs for $x = 80$ and $y = 120$. The corresponding value of z is given by $z = \frac{960{,}000}{(80)(120)} = 100$. Consequently the front and back walls should be 80 feet long, the side walls should be 120 feet wide, and the gymnasium should be 100 feet tall.

40. The distance the ranger travels in the thicket is $\sqrt{1 + x^2}$, the distance in the marshland is $\sqrt{\frac{9}{4} + y^2}$, and the distance along the road is $10 - x - y$. Thus the time T of the walk is given by $T = \frac{\sqrt{1 + x^2}}{3} + \frac{\sqrt{\frac{9}{4} + y^2}}{4} + \frac{10 - x - y}{5}$. We seek the minimum value of T on the triangular region R consisting of all (x, y) satisfying $x \geq 0$, $y \geq 0$, and $x + y \leq 10$. Such a minimum exists by the Maximum-Minimum Theorem.

First we find the critical points of T in the interior of R. Now

$$\frac{\partial T}{\partial x} = \frac{x}{3\sqrt{1+x^2}} - \frac{1}{5} \quad \text{and} \quad \frac{\partial T}{\partial y} = \frac{y}{4\sqrt{\frac{9}{4}+y^2}} - \frac{1}{5}. \quad \text{Thus}$$

$$\frac{\partial T}{\partial x} = 0 = \frac{\partial T}{\partial y} \quad \text{if} \quad \frac{x}{3\sqrt{1+x^2}} - \frac{1}{5} = 0 \quad \text{and} \quad \frac{y}{4\sqrt{\frac{9}{4}+y^2}} - \frac{1}{5} = 0,$$

so that $x^2 = \frac{9}{25}(1 + x^2)$ and $y^2 = \frac{16}{25}(\frac{9}{4} + y^2)$, or $x = \frac{3}{4}$ and $y = 2$.

Thus the only critical point is $(\frac{3}{4}, 2)$, and $T(\frac{3}{4}, 2) = \frac{\sqrt{1+\frac{9}{16}}}{3}$

$+ \frac{\sqrt{\frac{9}{4}+4}}{4} + \frac{10 - \frac{3}{4} - 2}{5} = \frac{5}{12} + \frac{5}{8} + \frac{29}{20} = \frac{299}{120} < 2.5$. Now we find the minimum value of T on the boundary of R, which is composed of three line segments ℓ_1, ℓ_2, and ℓ_3 (see the figure). On ℓ_1, $x = 0$

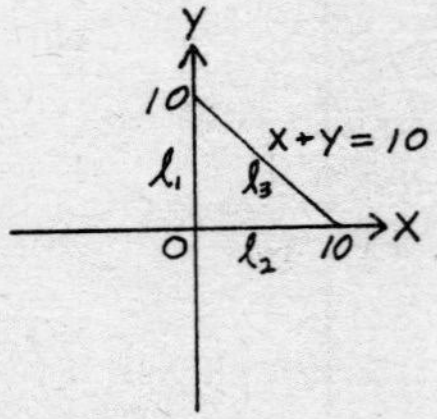

and $0 \le y \le 10$. Let $f(y) = T(0, y) = \frac{1}{3} + \frac{\sqrt{\frac{9}{4}+y^2}}{4} + 2 - \frac{1}{5}y$ for $0 \le y \le 10$. Then $f'(y) = \frac{y}{4\sqrt{\frac{9}{4}+y^2}} - \frac{1}{5}$,

and $f'(y) = 0$ if $\frac{y}{4\sqrt{\frac{9}{4}+y^2}} = \frac{1}{5}$, which means that $25y^2 = 16(\frac{9}{4} + y^2)$,

so that $y = 2$. Thus the minimum value of f on $[0, 10]$ is $f(0)$, $f(2)$, or $f(10)$. Since $f(0) = \frac{65}{24}$, $f(2) = \frac{307}{120}$, and $f(10) = \frac{1}{3} + \frac{\sqrt{409}}{8}$, it follows that $T(0, y) = f(y) \geq 2.5$ for $0 \le y \le 10$. On ℓ_2, $y = 0$ and $0 \le x \le 10$. Let $g(x) = T(x, 0) = \frac{\sqrt{1+x^2}}{3} + \frac{3}{8} + 2 - \frac{1}{5}x$ for $0 \le x \le 10$.

Then $g'(x) = \frac{x}{3\sqrt{1+x^2}} - \frac{1}{5}$, and $g'(x) = 0$ if $\frac{x}{3\sqrt{1+x^2}} = \frac{1}{5}$, which means that $25x^2 = 9(1 + x^2)$, so that $x = \frac{3}{4}$. Thus the minimum value of g on $[0, 10]$ is $g(0)$, $g(\frac{3}{4})$, or $g(10)$. Since $g(0) = \frac{65}{24}$, $g(\frac{3}{4}) = \frac{317}{120}$, and $g(10) = \frac{\sqrt{101}}{3} + \frac{3}{8}$, it follows that $T(x, 0) = g(x) \geq 2.5$ for $0 \le x \le 10$. On ℓ_3, $x + y = 10$, and the ranger does not walk along the road. In that case the total time $T(x, 10 - x)$ of walk is greater than it would be if the ranger walked at 4 kilometers an hour in a straight line to the ranger station, and that time is $\frac{\sqrt{(2.5)^2 + 100}}{4} > 2.5$. Thus $T(x, 10 - x) > 2.5$ for $0 \le x \le 10$. Consequently $T(x, y) > 2.5$ for (x, y) in ℓ_1, ℓ_2, or ℓ_3, and therefore the minimum time is attained if $x = \frac{3}{4}$ (kilometers) and $y = 2$ (kilometers).

41. Since the cross section is a trapezoid, its area is given by $A = \frac{1}{2}[(\ell - 2x) + (\ell - 2x + 2x\cos\theta)]\,(x\sin\theta) = \ell x\sin\theta - 2x^2\sin\theta + x^2\sin\theta\cos\theta$. We seek the maximum value of A on the rectangular region R consisting of all (x, θ) for which $0 \le x \le \frac{\ell}{2}$ and $0 \le \theta \le \frac{\pi}{2}$. Such a maximum value exists by the Maximum-Minimum Theorem. First we find the critical points in the interior of R. Now $\frac{\partial A}{\partial x} = \ell\sin\theta - 4x\sin\theta + 2x\sin\theta\cos\theta$ and $\frac{\partial A}{\partial \theta} = \ell x\cos\theta - 2x^2\cos\theta + x^2(\cos^2\theta - \sin^2\theta)$. Thus $\frac{\partial A}{\partial x} = 0 = \frac{\partial A}{\partial \theta}$ if $\ell\sin\theta - 4x\sin\theta + 2x\sin\theta\cos\theta = 0$ and $\ell x\cos\theta - 2x^2\cos\theta + x^2(\cos^2\theta - \sin^2\theta) = 0$. Since $\sin\theta \neq 0$ if (x, θ) is in

the interior of R, we can cancel $\sin\theta$ in the first equation and solve for ℓ, which means that $\ell = 4x - 2x\cos\theta$. Substituting for ℓ in the second equation, we obtain $(4x - 2x\cos\theta)x\cos\theta - 2x^2\cos\theta + x^2(\cos^2\theta - \sin^2\theta) = 0$, or $2x^2\cos\theta - x^2\cos^2\theta - x^2\sin^2\theta = 0$, or $2x^2\cos\theta - x^2 = 0$. Since $x \neq 0$ if (x, θ) is in the interior of R, we may cancel x^2 in the last equation and obtain $2\cos\theta - 1 = 0$, or $\cos\theta = \frac{1}{2}$, or $\theta = \frac{\pi}{3}$. Then $\ell = 4x - 2x\cos\frac{\pi}{3} = 3x$, so $x = \frac{\ell}{3}$. Thus the only critical point in the interior of R is $(\frac{\ell}{3}, \frac{\pi}{3})$. The corresponding area is given by $A(\frac{\ell}{3}, \frac{\pi}{3}) = (\ell)(\frac{\ell}{3})(\frac{\sqrt{3}}{2}) - 2(\frac{\ell}{3})^2(\frac{\sqrt{3}}{2}) + (\frac{\ell}{3})^2(\frac{\sqrt{3}}{2})(\frac{1}{2})$

$= \dfrac{\ell^2\sqrt{3}}{12}$. The boundary of R consists of the four line segments ℓ_1, ℓ_2, ℓ_3, and ℓ_4 shown in the figure.

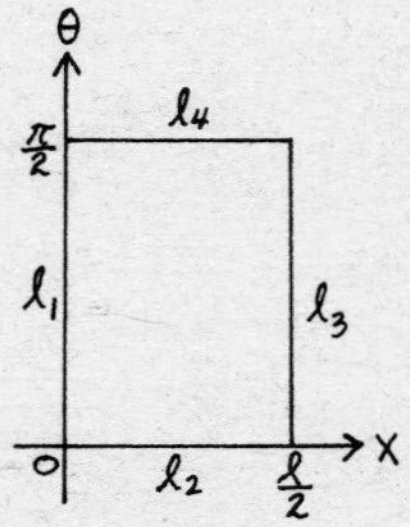

On ℓ_1, $x = 0$, so $A = 0$. On ℓ_2, $\theta = 0$, so $A = 0$. On ℓ_3, $x = \frac{\ell}{2}$, so $A = \frac{\ell^2}{4}\sin\theta\cos\theta = \frac{\ell^2}{8}\sin 2\theta$ for $0 \le \theta \le \frac{\pi}{2}$. Since $\frac{dA}{d\theta} = \frac{1}{4}\ell^2\cos 2\theta$, we find that $\frac{dA}{d\theta} = 0$ for $\theta = \frac{\pi}{4}$. It follows that the maximum value of A on ℓ_3 is $A(\frac{\ell}{2}, 0) = 0$, $A(\frac{\ell}{2}, \frac{\pi}{4}) = \frac{\ell^2}{8}$, or $A(\frac{\ell}{2}, \frac{\pi}{2}) = 0$. Thus the maximum value of A on ℓ_3 is $\frac{\ell^2}{8}$. On ℓ_4, $\theta = \frac{\pi}{2}$, so $A = \ell x - 2x^2$ for $0 \le x \le \frac{\ell}{2}$. Since $\frac{dA}{dx} = \ell - 4x$, we find that $\frac{dA}{dx} = 0$ if $x = \frac{\ell}{4}$. It follows that the maximum value of A on ℓ_4 is $A(0, \frac{\pi}{2}) = 0$, $A(\frac{\ell}{4}, \frac{\pi}{2}) = \frac{\ell^2}{8}$, or $A(\frac{\ell}{2}, \frac{\pi}{2}) = 0$. Comparing the value of A at the critical point $(\frac{\ell}{3}, \frac{\pi}{3})$ with the maximum values of A on ℓ_1, ℓ_2, ℓ_3, and ℓ_4, and noting that $\frac{\sqrt{3}}{12} > \frac{1}{8}$, we conclude that the maximum value of A is obtained if $x = \frac{\ell}{3}$ and $\theta = \frac{\pi}{3}$.

Section 13.9

1. Let $g(x, y) = x^2 + y^2$, so the constraint is $g(x, y) = x^2 + y^2 = 4$. Next, $\text{grad } f(x, y) = \vec{i} + 2y\,\vec{j}$ and $\text{grad } g(x, y) = 2x\,\vec{i} + 2y\,\vec{j}$, so that $\text{grad } f(x, y) = \lambda \text{ grad } g(x, y)$ if

$$1 = 2x\lambda \quad \text{and} \quad 2y = 2y\lambda$$

By the second equation, $y = 0$ or $\lambda = 1$. By the constraint,

if $y = 0$, then $x^2 + 0^2 = 4$, so $x = \pm 2$.
if $\lambda = 1$, then $1 = 2x$, so $x = \frac{1}{2}$ and $y = \pm\sqrt{4 - \frac{1}{4}} = \pm \frac{\sqrt{15}}{2}$.

The possible extreme values of f are $f(2, 0) = 2$, $f(-2, 0) = -2$, $f(\frac{1}{2}, \frac{\sqrt{15}}{2}) = \frac{17}{4}$, and $f(\frac{1}{2}, \frac{-\sqrt{15}}{2}) = \frac{17}{4}$. The maximum value is $\frac{17}{4}$ and the minimum value is -2.

2. Let $g(x, y) = (x + 1)^2 + y^2$, so the constraint is $g(x, y) = (x + 1)^2 + y^2 = 1$. Next, $\text{grad } f(x, y) = y\,\vec{i} + x\,\vec{j}$ and $\text{grad } g(x, y) = 2(x + 1)\,\vec{i} + 2y\,\vec{j}$, so that $\text{grad } f(x, y) = \lambda \text{ grad } g(x, y)$ if

$$y = 2(x + 1)\lambda \quad \text{and} \quad x = 2y\lambda$$

Either $y = 0$, so that $x = 0$, which does not contradict the constraint, or $y \neq 0$, so that $\lambda = \frac{x}{2y}$ by the second equation, and consequently $y = 2(x + 1)\frac{x}{2y}$, or $y^2 = x^2 + x$ by the first equation. The constraint becomes $(x + 1)^2 + x^2 + x = 1$, or simplified, $x(2x + 3) = 0$, so that $x = 0$ or $x = -\frac{3}{2}$. By the constraint, if $x = 0$, then $y = 0$, and if $x = \frac{-3}{2}$, then $y^2 = 1 - \frac{1}{4} = \frac{3}{4}$, so $y = \frac{\pm\sqrt{3}}{2}$. The possible extreme values of f are $f(0, 0) = 0$, $f(\frac{-3}{2}, \frac{\sqrt{3}}{2}) = \frac{-3\sqrt{3}}{4}$, and $f(\frac{-3}{2}, \frac{-\sqrt{3}}{2}) = \frac{3\sqrt{3}}{4}$. The maximum value is $\frac{3\sqrt{3}}{4}$ and the minimum value is $\frac{-3\sqrt{3}}{2}$.

3. Let $g(x, y) = x^2 + y^2$, so the constraint is $g(x, y) = x^2 + y^2 = 1$. Next, $\text{grad } f(x, y) = 3x^2\,\vec{i} + 6y^2\,\vec{j}$ and $\text{grad } g(x, y) = 2x\,\vec{i} + 2y\,\vec{j}$, so that $\text{grad } f(x, y) = \lambda \text{grad } g(x, y)$ if

$$3x^2 = 2x\lambda \quad \text{and} \quad 6y^2 = 2y\lambda$$

By the first equation, either $x = 0$ or $x = \frac{2}{3}\lambda$, and by the second equation, either $y = 0$ or $y = \frac{1}{3}\lambda$. Now if $x = 0$, then by the constraint, $y = \pm 1$, and if $y = 0$, then by the constraint, $x = \pm 1$. Otherwise $x = \frac{2}{3}\lambda$ and $y = \frac{1}{3}\lambda$, so the constraint becomes $(\frac{2}{3}\lambda)^2 + (\frac{1}{3}\lambda)^2 = 1$. Then $\lambda = \pm\frac{3}{\sqrt{5}}$, so that $x = \pm\frac{2}{\sqrt{5}}$ and $y = \pm\frac{1}{\sqrt{5}}$. The possible extreme values are $f(0, 1) = 2$, $f(0, -1) = -2$, $f(1, 0) = 1$, $f(-1, 0) = -1$, $f(\frac{2}{\sqrt{5}}, \frac{1}{\sqrt{5}}) = \frac{2}{\sqrt{5}}$, $f(\frac{-2}{\sqrt{5}}, \frac{-1}{\sqrt{5}}) = \frac{-2}{\sqrt{5}}$, $f(\frac{2}{\sqrt{5}}, \frac{-1}{\sqrt{5}}) = \frac{6}{5\sqrt{5}}$, and $f(\frac{-2}{\sqrt{5}}, \frac{1}{\sqrt{5}}) = \frac{-6}{5\sqrt{5}}$. The maximum value is 2 and the minimum value is -2.

4. Let $g(x, y, z) = x^2 + y^2 + z^2$, so the constraint is $g(x, y, z) = x^2 + y^2 + z^2 = 1$. Next, $\text{grad } f(x, y, z) = z^2\,\vec{i} + 3y^2\,\vec{j} + 2xz\,\vec{k}$ and $\text{grad } g(x, y, z) = 2x\,\vec{i} + 2y\,\vec{j} + 2z\,\vec{k}$, so that $\text{grad } f(x, y, z) = \lambda \text{ grad } g(x, y, z)$ if

$$z^2 = 2x\lambda, \quad 3y^2 = 2y\lambda, \quad \text{and} \quad 2xz = 2z\lambda$$

If $\lambda = 0$, then $y = z = 0$, so by the constraint, $x = \pm 1$. Now assume that $\lambda \neq 0$. From $2xz = 2z\lambda$ we obtain $z = 0$ or $x = \lambda$. If $z = 0$, then $x = 0$, so from the constraint, $y = \pm 1$. If $z \neq 0$, then $x = \lambda$, and the first equation becomes $z^2 = 2x^2$. Next, from $3y^2 = 2y\lambda$ we obtain $y = 0$ or $y = \frac{2}{3}\lambda$. If $y = 0$, then from the constraint, $x^2 + 0^2 + 2x^2 = 1$, so $x = \frac{\pm 1}{\sqrt{3}}$ and $z = \frac{\pm\sqrt{2}}{\sqrt{3}}$. If $y \neq 0$, then $3y^2 = 2y\lambda = 2yx$, so $y = \frac{2}{3}x$, and the constraint becomes $x^2 + \frac{4}{9}x^2 + 2x^2 = 1$, so $x = \frac{\pm 3}{\sqrt{31}}$, $y = \frac{\pm 2}{\sqrt{31}}$, and $z = \frac{\pm 3\sqrt{2}}{\sqrt{31}}$. A check of the values of f at $(\pm 1, 0, 0)$, $(0, \pm 1, 0)$, $\left(\frac{\pm 1}{\sqrt{3}}, 0, \frac{\pm\sqrt{2}}{\sqrt{3}}\right)$, and $\left(\frac{\pm 3}{\sqrt{31}}, \frac{\pm 2}{\sqrt{31}}, \frac{\pm 3\sqrt{2}}{\sqrt{31}}\right)$ shows that the maximum value of f is 1 and the minimum value is -1.

5. Let $g(x, y, z) = x^2 + y^2 + 4z^2$, so the constraint is $g(x, y, z) = x^2 + y^2 + 4z^2 = 6$. Next, grad $f(x, y, z) = yz\,\vec{i} + xz\,\vec{j} + xy\,\vec{k}$ and grad $g(x, y, z) = 2x\,\vec{i} + 2y\,\vec{j} + 8z\,\vec{k}$, so that grad $f(x, y, z) = \lambda$ grad $g(x, y, z)$ if

$$yz = 2x\lambda, \quad xz = 2y\lambda, \quad \text{and} \quad xy = 8z\lambda$$

If $x = 0$ or $y = 0$ or $z = 0$ or $\lambda = 0$, then $f(x, y, z) = 0$. Assume henceforth that $x, y, z,$ and λ are nonzero. Then

$$\lambda = \frac{yz}{2x} = \frac{xz}{2y} = \frac{xy}{8z}$$

so that $x^2 = y^2$ and $y^2 = 4z^2$. By the constraint, $y^2 + y^2 + y^2 = 6$, so $y = \pm\sqrt{2}$. Thus $x = \pm\sqrt{2}$ and $z = \frac{\pm\sqrt{2}}{2}$. Since $f\left(\pm\sqrt{2}, \pm\sqrt{2}, \frac{\pm\sqrt{2}}{2}\right) = \pm\sqrt{2}$, the maximum value of f is $\sqrt{2}$ and the minimum value of f is $-\sqrt{2}$.

6. Let $g(x, y, z) = x^2 + y^2 + z^2$, so the constraint is $g(x, y, z) = x^2 + y^2 + z^2 = 8$. Next, grad $f(x, y, z) = y\,\vec{i} + (x + z)\,\vec{j} + y\,\vec{k}$ and grad $g(x, y, z) = 2x\,\vec{i} + 2y\,\vec{j} + 2z\,\vec{k}$, so that grad $f(x, y, z) = \lambda$ grad $g(x, y, z)$ if

$$y = 2x\lambda, \quad x + z = 2y\lambda, \quad \text{and} \quad y = 2z\lambda$$

If $y = 0$, then $x + z = 0$ from the second equation, so by the constraint, $x^2 + 0^2 + (-x)^2 = 8$, so $x = \pm 2$, and $z = \mp 2$. If $y \neq 0$, then $x \neq 0$, $z \neq 0$, and $\lambda \neq 0$, so $\frac{y}{2x} = \lambda = \frac{y}{2z}$, and thus $x = z$. Therefore the equation $x + z = 2y\lambda$ becomes $x = y\lambda$. Since $y = 2x\lambda$ from the first equation, we obtain $\lambda = \frac{\pm 1}{\sqrt{2}}$, so that $y = \pm\sqrt{2}x$. The constraint becomes $x^2 + 2x^2 + x^2 = 8$, or $x = \pm\sqrt{2}$. Then $y = \pm 2$ and $z = \pm\sqrt{2}$. The possible extreme values of f are $f(\pm 2, 0, \mp 2) = 0$, $f(\sqrt{2}, 2, \sqrt{2}) = 4\sqrt{2}$, $f(\sqrt{2}, -2, \sqrt{2}) = -4\sqrt{2}$, $f(-\sqrt{2}, 2, -\sqrt{2}) = -4\sqrt{2}$, and $f(-\sqrt{2}, -2, -\sqrt{2}) = 4\sqrt{2}$. The maximum value is $4\sqrt{2}$ and the minimum value is $-4\sqrt{2}$.

misprint - answer book did different problem

7. Let $g(x, y) = 2x^2 - \frac{3}{2}y^2$, so the constraint is $g(x, y) = 2x^2 - \frac{3}{2}y^2 = 1$. Next, grad $f(x, y) = 8x\,\vec{i} + (3y^2 + 3)\,\vec{j}$ and grad $g(x, y) = 4x\,\vec{i} - 3y\,\vec{j}$, so that grad $f(x, y) = \lambda$grad $g(x, y)$ if

$$8x = 4x\lambda \quad \text{and} \quad 3y^2 + 3 = -3y\lambda$$

Notice that because of the constraint, $x \neq 0$, so the first equation becomes $8 = 4\lambda$, or $\lambda = 2$. Then the second equation becomes $3y^2 + 3$

$= -6y$, so $y = -1$. Then the constraint tells us that $2x^2 - \frac{3}{2} = 1$, so that $x = \frac{\pm\sqrt{5}}{2}$. Thus the possible minimum values of f are

$f(\frac{\pm\sqrt{5}}{2}, -1) = 3$; 3 is the minimum value.

8. Let $g(x, y, z) = x + y + z$, so the constraint is $g(x, y, z) = x + y + z = 4$. Next, grad $f(x, y, z) = 2x\vec{i} + 4y\vec{j} + 2z\vec{k}$ and grad $g(x, y, z) = \vec{i} + \vec{j} + \vec{k}$, so that grad $f(x, y, z) = \lambda$ grad $g(x, y, z)$ if

$$2x = \lambda, \quad 4y = \lambda, \quad \text{and} \quad 2z = \lambda$$

Then $x = \frac{\lambda}{2}$, $y = \frac{\lambda}{4}$, and $z = \frac{\lambda}{2}$, so that the constraint becomes $\frac{\lambda}{2} + \frac{\lambda}{4} + \frac{\lambda}{2} = 4$, and thus $\lambda = \frac{16}{5}$. Therefore $x = \frac{8}{5}$, $y = \frac{4}{5}$, and $z = \frac{8}{5}$, so that $f(\frac{8}{5}, \frac{4}{5}, \frac{8}{5}) = \frac{32}{5}$ is the minimum value of f.

9. Let $g(x, y, z) = x + y + z$, so the constraint becomes $g(x, y, z) = x + y + z = \frac{11}{12}$. Next, grad $f(x, y, z) = 4x^3\vec{i} + 32y^3\vec{j} + 108z^3\vec{k}$ and grad $g(x, y, z) = \vec{i} + \vec{j} + \vec{k}$, so that grad $f(x, y, z) = \lambda$ grad $g(x, y, z)$ if

$$4x^3 = \lambda, \quad 32y^3 = \lambda, \quad \text{and} \quad 108z^3 = \lambda$$

Thus $4x^3 = 32y^3$, so that $y = \frac{1}{2}x$, and $4x^3 = 108z^3$, so that $z = \frac{1}{3}x$. The constraint becomes $x + \frac{1}{2}x + \frac{1}{3}x = \frac{11}{12}$, which means that $x = \frac{1}{2}$, and thus $y = \frac{1}{4}$ and $z = \frac{1}{6}$. Then $f(\frac{1}{2}, \frac{1}{4}, \frac{1}{6}) = (\frac{1}{2})^4 + 8(\frac{1}{4})^4 + 27(\frac{1}{6})^4 = \frac{11}{96}$ is the minimum value of f.

10. Let $g(x, y, z) = x^2 + 4y^2 - z$, so the constraint becomes $g(x, y, z) = x^2 + 4y^2 - z = 0$. Next, grad $f(x, y, z) = -\vec{i} - 2\vec{j} + 3\vec{k}$ and grad $g(x, y, z) = 2x\vec{i} + 8y\vec{j} - \vec{k}$, so that grad $f(x, y, z) = \lambda$ grad $g(x, y, z)$ if

$$-1 = 2x\lambda, \quad -2 = 8y\lambda, \quad \text{and} \quad 3 = -\lambda$$

Then $\lambda = -3$, so that $x = \frac{1}{6}$ and $y = \frac{1}{12}$. From the constraint, $z = \frac{1}{36} + \frac{1}{36} = \frac{1}{18}$. Therefore $f(\frac{1}{6}, \frac{1}{12}, \frac{1}{18}) = \frac{1}{6} - \frac{1}{6} - \frac{1}{6} = -\frac{1}{6}$ is the minimum value of f.

11. First we use Lagrange multipliers to find the possible extreme values of f on the circle $x^2 + y^2 = 4$. Let $g(x, y) = x^2 + y^2$, so the constraint becomes $g(x, y) = x^2 + y^2 = 4$. Since grad $f(x, y) = 4x\vec{i} + (2y + 2)\vec{j}$ and grad $g(x, y) = 2x\vec{i} + 2y\vec{j}$, it follows that grad $f(x, y) = \lambda$ grad $g(x, y)$ if

$$4x = 2x\lambda \quad \text{and} \quad 2y + 2 = 2y\lambda$$

From the first equation, $x = 0$ or $\lambda = 2$. If $x = 0$, then from the constraint, $0^2 + y^2 = 4$, so that $y = \pm 2$. If $\lambda = 2$, then from the second equation, $2y + 2 = 4y$, so that $y = 1$, and then the constraint implies that $x^2 + 1 = 4$, or $x = \pm\sqrt{3}$. The possible extreme values of f on the circle $x^2 + y^2 = 4$ are $f(0, 2) = 5$, $f(0, -2) = -3$, and $f(\pm\sqrt{3}, 1) = 6$. For the interior $x^2 + y^2 < 4$ of the disk, we find that

$$f_x(x, y) = 4x \quad \text{and} \quad f_y(x, y) = 2y + 2$$

so that $f_x(x, y) = 0 = f_y(x, y)$ only if $x = 0$ and $y = -1$. But $f(0, -1) = -4$. Consequently the maximum value and minimum value of f on the disk $x^2 + y^2 \leq 4$ are 6 and -4, respectively.

12. First we use Lagrange multipliers to find the possible extreme values of f on the circle $x^2 + y^2 = 36$. Let $g(x, y) = x^2 + y^2$, so the constraint is

$g(x, y) = x^2 + y^2 = 36$. Since grad $f(x, y) = (3x^2 + 2x)\vec{i} + \frac{2}{3}y\vec{j}$ and grad $g(x, y) = 2x\vec{i} + 2y\vec{j}$, it follows that grad $f(x, y) = \lambda$grad $g(x, y)$ if

$$3x^2 + 2x = 2x\lambda \quad \text{and} \quad \frac{2}{3}y = 2y\lambda$$

From the second equation, $y = 0$ or $\lambda = \frac{1}{3}$. If $y = 0$, then from the constraint, $x = \pm 6$. If $\lambda = \frac{1}{3}$, then the first equation becomes $3x^2 + 2x = \frac{2}{3}x$, so that either $x = 0$ or else $3x + 2 = \frac{2}{3}$, which means that $x = -\frac{4}{9}$.

If $x = 0$, then by the constraint, $0^2 + y^2 = 36$, so that $y = \pm 6$. If $x = \frac{-4}{9}$, then the constraint becomes $\frac{16}{81} + y^2 = 36$, so that $y = \pm\frac{10}{9}\sqrt{29}$. The possible extreme values of f on the circle $x^2 + y^2 = 36$ are $f(6, 0) = 252$, $f(-6, 0) = -180$, $f(0, \pm 6) = 12$, and $f(\frac{-4}{9}, \pm\frac{10}{9}\sqrt{29}) = \frac{-64}{729} + \frac{16}{81} + \frac{2900}{243}$. For the interior $x^2 + y^2 < 36$ of the disk, we find that

$$f_x(x, y) = 3x^2 + 2x \quad \text{and} \quad f_y(x, y) = \frac{2}{3}y$$

so that $f_x(x, y) = 0 = f_y(x, y)$ only if $y = 0$ and $3x^2 + 2x = 0$, which means that $x = 0$ or $x = \frac{-2}{3}$. But $f(0, 0) = 0$ and $f(\frac{-2}{3}, 0) = \frac{4}{27}$. Consequently the maximum and minimum values of f on the disk $x^2 + y^2 \le 36$ are 252 and -180, respectively.

13. First we use Lagrange multipliers to find the possible extreme values of f on the ellipse $2x^2 + y^2 = 4$. Let $g(x, y) = 2x^2 + y^2$, so the constraint is $g(x, y) = 2x^2 + y^2 = 4$. Since grad $f(x, y) = y\vec{i} + x\vec{j}$ and grad $g(x, y) = 4x\vec{i} + 2y\vec{j}$, it follows that grad $f(x, y) = \lambda$grad $g(x, y)$ if

$$y = 4x\lambda \quad \text{and} \quad x = 2y\lambda$$

Because of the constraint, $y \ne 0$, since if $y = 0$ then the second equation would then imply that $x = 0$ also. Thus $\lambda = \frac{x}{2y}$, so that the first equation becomes $y = 4x(\frac{x}{2y})$, and therefore $y^2 = 2x^2$. The constraint then becomes $2x^2 + 2x^2 = 4$, so $x = \pm 1$ and hence $y = \pm\sqrt{2}$. The possible extreme values of f on the ellipse are $f(1, \sqrt{2}) = \sqrt{2}$, $f(1, -\sqrt{2}) = -\sqrt{2}$, $f(-1, \sqrt{2}) = -\sqrt{2}$, and $f(-1, -\sqrt{2}) = \sqrt{2}$. For the interior $2x^2 + y^2 < 4$ of the ellipse, we find that

$$f_x(x, y) = y \quad \text{and} \quad f_y(x, y) = x$$

so that $f_x(x, y) = 0 = f_y(x, y)$ only if $x = 0$ and $y = 0$. But $f(0, 0) = 0$. Consequently the maximum and minimum values of f on $2x^2 + y^2 \le 4$ are $\sqrt{2}$ and $-\sqrt{2}$, respectively.

14. First we use Lagrange multipliers to find the possible extreme values of f on the curve $x^4 + 2y^4 = 1$. Let $g(x,y) = x^4 + 2y^4$, so the constraint is $g(x,y) = x^4 + 2y^4 = 1$. Since grad $f(x,y) = -2x\vec{i} - 8y\vec{j}$ and grad $g(x,y) = 4x^3\vec{i} + 8y^3\vec{j}$, it follows that grad $f(x,y) = \lambda$ grad $g(x,y)$ if

$$-2x = 4x^3\lambda \quad \text{and} \quad -8y = 8y^3\lambda$$

From the constraint, if $x = 0$ then $y = 1/2^{1/4}$ or $y = -1/2^{1/4}$, and if $y = 0$ then $x = 1$ or $x = -1$. If $x \ne 0$ and $y \ne 0$, then $2x^2\lambda = -1 = y^2\lambda$ and thus $\lambda \ne 0$, so $y^2 = 2x^2$. By the constraint, $x^4 + 2(2x^2)^2 = 1$, so $x = 1/\sqrt{3}$ or $x = -1/\sqrt{3}$. Thus $y = \sqrt{2/3}$ or $y = -\sqrt{2/3}$. The possible extreme values of f on the curve are $f(0, \pm 1/2^{1/4}) = 16 - 0 - 4/\sqrt{2} = 16 - 4/\sqrt{2} \approx 13.1716$, $f(\pm 1, 0) = 16 - 1 = 15$, $f(\pm 1/\sqrt{3}, \pm\sqrt{2/3}) = 16 - \frac{1}{3} - 4(\frac{2}{3}) = 13$. Next, $f_x(x,y) = -2x$ and $f_y(x,y) = -8y$, so

$f_x(x,y) = 0 = f_y(x,y)$ inside the curve only at $(0,0)$. Since $f(0,0) = 16$, we conclude that the maximum value of f on the region is $f(0,0) = 16$ and the minimum value is $f(\pm 1/\sqrt{3}, \pm\sqrt{2/3}) = 13$.

15. The distance from (x, y, z) to the origin is minimum if and only if the square of the distance is minimum, so let $f(x, y, z) = x^2 + y^2 + z^2$. Also let $g(x, y, z) = x^2 - yz$, so the constraint becomes $g(x, y, z) = x^2 - yz = 1$. Since grad $f(x, y, z) = 2x\vec{i} + 2y\vec{j} + 2z\vec{k}$ and grad $g(x, y, z) = 2x\vec{i} - z\vec{j} - y\vec{k}$, it follows that grad $f(x, y, z) = \lambda$ grad $g(x, y, z)$ if

$$2x = 2x\lambda, \quad 2y = -z\lambda, \quad \text{and} \quad 2z = -y\lambda$$

From the first equation, $x = 0$ or $\lambda = 1$. If $x = 0$, the constraint becomes $-yz = 1$, or $z = \frac{-1}{y}$. Then the second equation becomes $2y = \frac{\lambda}{y}$, so $\lambda = 2y^2$. This means that the third equation becomes $2(\frac{-1}{y}) = -y(2y^2)$, so $1 = y^4$, and thus $y = \pm 1$, and hence $z = \mp 1$. If $x \neq 0$, then $\lambda = 1$, so the third equation becomes $2z = -y$, and the second equation then becomes $2(-2z) = -z$, which means that $z = 0$, and thus $y = 0$ and $x = \pm 1$. The possible minimum values of f are $f(0, 1, -1) = 2$, $f(0, -1, 1) = 2$, $f(1, 0, 0) = 1$, and $f(-1, 0, 0) = 1$. Consequently the points on $x^2 - yz = 1$ closest to the origin are $(1, 0, 0)$ and $(-1, 0, 0)$.

16. The distance from (x, y, z) to $(4, 2, 1)$ is extreme if and only if the square of the distance is extreme, so let $f(x, y, z) = (x - 4)^2 + (y - 2)^2 + (z - 1)^2$. Also let $g(x, y, z) = x^2 + y^2 + z^2$, so the constraint becomes $g(x, y, z) = x^2 + y^2 + z^2 = 1$. Since grad $f(x, y, z) = 2(x - 4)\vec{i} + 2(y - 2)\vec{j} + 2(z - 1)\vec{k}$ and grad $g(x, y, z) = 2x\vec{i} + 2y\vec{j} + 2z\vec{k}$, it follows that grad $f(x, y, z) = \lambda$ grad $g(x, y, z)$ if

$$2(x - 4) = 2x\lambda, \quad 2(y - 2) = 2y\lambda, \quad \text{and} \quad 2(z - 1) = 2z\lambda$$

By these equations, $\lambda \neq 1$. Solving for x, y, z in the three equations yields

$$x = \frac{4}{1-\lambda}, \quad y = \frac{2}{1-\lambda}, \quad \text{and} \quad z = \frac{1}{1-\lambda}$$

Then the constraint becomes $\frac{16}{(1-\lambda)^2} + \frac{4}{(1-\lambda)^2} + \frac{1}{(1-\lambda)^2} = 1$, which means that $1 - \lambda = \pm\sqrt{21}$. Then $x = \frac{\pm 4}{\sqrt{21}}$, $y = \frac{\pm 2}{\sqrt{21}}$, and $z = \frac{\pm 1}{\sqrt{21}}$. Of the eight values of f that arise, $f(\frac{-4}{\sqrt{21}}, \frac{-2}{\sqrt{21}}, \frac{-1}{\sqrt{21}})$ is the maximum, and $f(\frac{4}{\sqrt{21}}, \frac{2}{\sqrt{21}}, \frac{1}{\sqrt{21}})$ is the minimum. Thus $(\frac{4}{\sqrt{21}}, \frac{2}{\sqrt{21}}, \frac{1}{\sqrt{21}})$ is closest to $(4, 2, 1)$, and $(\frac{-4}{\sqrt{21}}, \frac{-2}{\sqrt{21}}, \frac{-1}{\sqrt{21}})$ is farthest.

17. Let x and y be the acute angles, so that $x + y = \frac{\pi}{2}$. Let $f(x, y) = \sin x \sin y$ and $g(x, y) = x + y$, so the constraint is $g(x, y) = x + y = \frac{\pi}{2}$. Since grad $f(x, y) = \cos x \sin y\,\vec{i} + \sin x \cos y\,\vec{j}$ and grad $g(x, y) = \vec{i} + \vec{j}$, it follows that grad $f(x, y) = \lambda$ grad $g(x, y)$ if

$$\cos x \sin y = \lambda \quad \text{and} \quad \sin x \cos y = \lambda$$

Then $\sin x \cos y - \cos x \sin y = 0$, so $\sin(x - y) = 0$, or $x = y$. Then the constraint becomes $x + x = \frac{\pi}{2}$, or $x = \frac{\pi}{4}$ and $y = \frac{\pi}{4}$. The maximum value of f is $f(\frac{\pi}{4}, \frac{\pi}{4}) = \frac{1}{2}$.

18. Let x, y, and z be the angles, so that $x + y + z = \pi$ and $0 \le x, y, z \le \pi$. Let $f(x, y, z) = \sin x \sin y \sin z$ and $g(x, y, z) = x + y + z$, so the constraint is $g(x, y, z) = x + y + z = \pi$. Since $\text{grad } f(x, y, z) = \cos x \sin y \sin z \vec{i} + \sin x \cos y \sin z \vec{j} + \sin x \sin y \cos z \vec{k}$ and $\text{grad } g(x, y, z) = \vec{i} + \vec{j} + \vec{k}$, it follows that $\text{grad } f(x, y, z) = \lambda \text{ grad } g(x, y, z)$ if

$$\cos x \sin y \sin z = \lambda, \quad \sin x \cos y \sin z = \lambda, \quad \text{and} \quad \sin x \sin y \cos z = \lambda$$

The maximum value of f is not 0, so it occurs for (x, y, z) such that $\sin x \ne 0$, $\sin y \ne 0$, and $\sin z \ne 0$. Then the first two equations yield $\sin x \cos y - \cos x \sin y = 0$, so that $\sin (x - y) = 0$, so $x = y$. Likewise the first and third equations yield $\sin (x - z) = 0$, so $x = z$. The constraint becomes $x + x + x = \pi$, so that $x = y = z = \frac{\pi}{3}$. The maximum value of f is $f(\frac{\pi}{3}, \frac{\pi}{3}, \frac{\pi}{3}) = \frac{\sqrt{3}}{2} \frac{\sqrt{3}}{2} \frac{\sqrt{3}}{2} = \frac{3\sqrt{3}}{8}$.

19. Let (x, y, z) be on the sphere in the first octant, and let $f(x, y, z) = \frac{1}{6xyz}$ denote the volume of the corresponding tetrahedron with vertex at (x, y, z). Let $g(x, y, z) = x^2 + y^2 + z^2$, so that the constraint is $g(x, y, z) = x^2 + y^2 + z^2 = 1$. Since $\text{grad } f(x, y, z) = \frac{-1}{6x^2yz}\vec{i} - \frac{1}{6xy^2z}\vec{j} - \frac{1}{6xyz^2}\vec{k}$ and $\text{grad } g(x, y, z) = 2x \vec{i} + 2y \vec{j} + 2z \vec{k}$, it follows that $\text{grad } f(x, y, z) = \lambda \text{ grad } g(x, y, z)$ if

$$\frac{-1}{6x^2yz} = 2x\lambda, \quad \frac{-1}{6xy^2z} = 2y\lambda, \quad \text{and} \quad \frac{-1}{6xyz^2} = 2z\lambda$$

Then $\lambda \ne 0$, and the three equations in turn yield $\frac{-1}{6xyz\lambda} = x^2 = y^2 = z^2$. Since $x > 0$, $y > 0$, and $z > 0$, this means that $x = y = z$. From the constraint, $x^2 + x^2 + x^2 = 1$, so that $x = \frac{1}{\sqrt{3}}$, and thus $y = \frac{1}{\sqrt{3}}$ and $z = \frac{1}{\sqrt{3}}$. The minimum volume is given by $f(\frac{1}{\sqrt{3}}, \frac{1}{\sqrt{3}}, \frac{1}{\sqrt{3}}) = \frac{1}{2}\sqrt{3}$.

20. Let (x, y, z) be on the plane $2x + y + 4z = 12$, and let $f(x, y, z) = xyz$ denote the volume of the corresponding parallelepiped with vertex at (x, y, z). Let $g(x, y, z) = 2x + y + 4z$, so that the constraint is $g(x, y, z) = 2x + y + 4z = 12$. Since $\text{grad } f(x, y, z) = yz \vec{i} + xz \vec{j} + xy \vec{k}$ and $\text{grad } g(x, y, z) = 2\vec{i} + \vec{j} + 4\vec{k}$, it follows that $\text{grad } f(x, y, z) = \lambda \text{ grad } g(x, y, z)$ if

$$yz = 2\lambda, \quad xz = \lambda, \quad \text{and} \quad xy = 4\lambda$$

The volume cannot be a maximum if x, y, or z is 0, so they are all positive. The first and second equations imply that $yz = 2xz$, so that $y = 2x$. The first and third equations imply that $2yz = xy$, so that $z = \frac{1}{2}x$. This means that the constraint becomes $2x + 2x + 4(\frac{1}{2}x) = 12$, so that $x = 2$, and hence $y = 4$ and $z = 1$. The maximum volume is given by $f(2, 4, 1) = 8$.

21. Let x, y, and z be as in the figure, with $x > 0$, $y > 0$, and $z > 0$. Then the surface area is given by $S(x, y, z) = 3xz + 7yz + xy$. Let V denote the volume, so that $V(x, y, z) = xyz$. The constraint becomes $V(x, y, z) = xyz = 12$. Since grad $S(x, y, z) = (3z + y)\vec{i} + (7z + x)\vec{j} + (3x + 7y)\vec{k}$ and grad $V(x, y, z) = yz\vec{i} + xz\vec{j} + xy\vec{k}$, it follows that grad $S(x, y, z) = \lambda$grad $V(x, y, z)$ if

$$3z + y = yz\lambda, \quad 7z + x = xz\lambda, \quad \text{and} \quad 3x + 7y = xy\lambda$$

Solving for λ in the three equations, and noting that $x > 0$, $y > 0$, and $z > 0$, we obtain

$$\lambda = \frac{3z + y}{yz} = \frac{3}{y} + \frac{1}{z}, \quad \lambda = \frac{7z + x}{xz} = \frac{7}{x} + \frac{1}{z}, \quad \text{and } \lambda = \frac{3x + 7y}{xy} = \frac{3}{y} + \frac{7}{x}$$

so that $\quad \frac{3}{y} + \frac{1}{z} = \frac{7}{x} + \frac{1}{z}$ and $\frac{7}{x} + \frac{1}{z} = \frac{3}{y} + \frac{7}{x}$

Thus $x = \frac{7}{3}y$ and $z = \frac{1}{3}y$, so the constraint becomes $(\frac{7}{3}y)(y)(\frac{1}{3}y) = 12$, so that $y = (\frac{108}{7})^{1/3}$, and hence $x = \frac{7}{3}(\frac{108}{7})^{1/3} = (196)^{1/3}$, and $z = \frac{1}{3}(\frac{108}{7})^{1/3} = (\frac{4}{7})^{1/3}$. These dimensions yield the minimum surface area.

22. Let x, y, and z denote the dimensions of the box, with z denoting the height. Then the volume is given by $V(x, y, z) = xyz$, and the constraint is $V(x, y, z) = xyz = 1728$. Let a be the cost per unit surface area of the material for the sides.

a. The cost is given by $C(x, y, z) = a(2xz + 2yz + 16\,xy)$. Since

grad $C(x, y, z) = a(2z + 16y)\vec{i} + a(2z + 16x)\vec{j} + a(2x + 2y)\vec{k}$ and grad $V(x, y, z) = yz\vec{i} + xz\vec{j} + xy\vec{k}$, it follows that grad $C(x, y, z) = \lambda$grad $V(x, y, z)$ if

$$a(2z + 16y) = yz\lambda, \quad a(2z + 16x) = xz\lambda, \quad \text{and} \quad a(2x + 2y) = xy\lambda$$

Solving for λ in the three equations, and noting that $x > 0$, $y > 0$, and $z > 0$, we obtain

$$\lambda = \frac{a(2z + 16y)}{yz} = \frac{2a}{y} + \frac{16a}{z}, \quad \lambda = \frac{a(2z + 16x)}{xz} = \frac{2a}{x} + \frac{16a}{z}, \quad \text{and}$$

$$\lambda = \frac{a(2x + 2y)}{xy} = \frac{2a}{y} + \frac{2a}{x}$$

Thus

$$\frac{2a}{y} + \frac{16a}{z} = \frac{2a}{x} + \frac{16a}{z} \quad \text{and} \quad \frac{2a}{x} + \frac{16a}{z} = \frac{2a}{y} + \frac{2a}{x}$$

so that $x = y$ and $z = 8y$. Therefore the constraint becomes $(y)(y)(8y) = 1728$, so $y = 6$, and thus $x = 6$ and $z = 48$. The dimensions minimizing the cost are 6 inches a side on the bottom, and 48 inches for the height.

b. The cost is given by $C(x, y, z) = a(2xz + 2yz + 2xy)$. Since

grad $C(x, y, z) = a(2z + 2y)\vec{i} + a(2z + 2x)\vec{j} + a(2x + 2y)\vec{k}$ and grad $V(x, y, z) = yz\vec{i} + xz\vec{j} + xy\vec{k}$, it follows that grad $C(x, y, z) = \lambda$grad $V(x, y, z)$ if

$$a(2z + 2y) = yz\lambda, \quad a(2z + 2x) = xz\lambda, \quad \text{and} \quad a(2x + 2y) = xy\lambda$$

Again $x > 0$, $y > 0$, and $z > 0$, so that by solving for λ we obtain

$$\lambda = \frac{a(2z + 2y)}{yz} = \frac{2a}{y} + \frac{2a}{z}, \quad \lambda = \frac{a(2z + 2x)}{xz} = \frac{2a}{x} + \frac{2a}{z}, \quad \text{and}$$

$$\lambda = \frac{a(2x + 2y)}{xy} = \frac{2a}{y} + \frac{2a}{x}$$

Thus

$$\frac{2a}{y} + \frac{2a}{z} = \frac{2a}{x} + \frac{2a}{z} \quad \text{and} \quad \frac{2a}{x} + \frac{2a}{z} = \frac{2a}{y} + \frac{2a}{x}$$

so that $x = y$ and $y = z$. Therefore the constraint becomes $y^3 = 1728$, so $x = y = z = 12$. The dimensions minimizing the cost are 12 inches on a side, which makes the box a cube.

23. The volume of the pipe is given by $V(r, \ell) = \pi r^2 \ell$, with $r > 0$ and $\ell > 0$. Since $2r + \frac{1}{2}\ell = 3 \sec \frac{\pi}{4} = 3\sqrt{2}$, let $g(r, \ell) = 2r + \frac{1}{2}\ell$, so that the constraint becomes $g(r, \ell) = 2r + \frac{1}{2}\ell = 3\sqrt{2}$. Since grad $V(r, \ell) = 2\pi r \ell \vec{i} + \pi r^2 \vec{j}$ and grad $g(r, \ell) = 2\vec{i} + \frac{1}{2}\vec{j}$, it follows that grad $V(r, \ell) = \lambda$ grad $g(r, \ell)$ if

$$2\pi r \ell = 2\lambda \quad \text{and} \quad \pi r^2 = \frac{1}{2}\lambda$$

Solving for λ in the two equations, we obtain $\pi r \ell = \lambda = 2\pi r^2$. Since $r \neq 0$, this means that $\ell = 2r$. From the constraint, $2r + \frac{1}{2}(2r) = 3\sqrt{2}$, so that $r = \sqrt{2}$, and thus $\ell = 2\sqrt{2}$. The pipe has maximum volume if it has a radius of $\sqrt{2}$ meters and is $2\sqrt{2}$ meters long.

24. Let $g(x, y, z) = x^2 + y^2 + z^2 = 225$, so the constraint becomes $g(x, y, z) = x^2 + y^2 + z^2 = 225$. Since grad $f(x, y, z) = 2\vec{i} + \vec{j} + 2\vec{k}$ and grad $g(x, y, z) = 2x\vec{i} + 2y\vec{j} + 2z\vec{k}$, it follows that grad $f(x, y, z) = \lambda$ grad $g(x, y, z)$ if

$$2 = 2x\lambda, \quad 1 = 2y\lambda, \quad \text{and} \quad 2 = 2z\lambda$$

Then x, y, and z are nonzero, and solving for λ, we obtain

$$\lambda = \frac{1}{x} = \frac{1}{2y} = \frac{1}{z}$$

Thus $x = z$ and $y = \frac{1}{2}x$, so the constraint becomes $x^2 + \frac{1}{4}x^2 + x^2 = 225$. Thus $x = 10$, and hence $y = 5$ and $z = 10$. You should spend 10 days each in San Francisco and New York, and 5 days in your home town.

25. The volume of the box is given by $V(x, y, z) = xyz$, and the constraint is $V(x, y, z) = xyz = V$ for a constant V. Since grad $E(x, y, z) = \frac{-h^2}{4mx^3}\vec{i} - \frac{h^2}{4my^3}\vec{j} - \frac{h^2}{4mz^3}\vec{k}$ and grad $V(x, y, z) = yz\vec{i} + xz\vec{j} + xy\vec{k}$, it follows that grad $E(x, y, z) = \lambda$ grad $V(x, y, z)$ if

$$\frac{-h^2}{4mx^3} = yz\lambda, \quad \frac{-h^2}{4my^3} = xz\lambda, \quad \text{and} \quad \frac{-h^2}{4mz^3} = xy\lambda$$

Thus $\frac{-h^2}{4mxyz\lambda} = x^2 = y^2 = z^2$, so since x, y, and z are positive, $x = y = z$. The constraint becomes $x^3 = V$, so $x = y = z = V^{1/3}$, and the box is a cube whose sides are $V^{1/3}$ units long.

26. Let $D(p, q) = p + q$, and let $g(p, q) = \frac{1}{p} + \frac{1}{q}$, so the constraint becomes $g(p, q) = \frac{1}{p} + \frac{1}{q} = \frac{1}{f}$. Since grad $D(p, q) = \vec{i} + \vec{j}$ and grad $g(p, q) = -\frac{1}{p^2}\vec{i} - \frac{1}{q^2}\vec{j}$, it follows that grad $D(p, q) = \lambda$ grad $g(p, q)$ if

$$1 = -\frac{1}{p^2}\lambda \quad \text{and} \quad 1 = -\frac{1}{q^2}\lambda$$

Then $\lambda = -p^2 = -q^2$. Since p and q are positive, we find that $p = q$.

The constraint becomes $\frac{1}{p} + \frac{1}{p} = \frac{1}{f}$, so that $p = 2f$ and hence $q = 2f$. The minimum distance is $D(2f, 2f) = 2f + 2f = 4f$.

27. Let A be a units from the horizontal line and let B be b units from the horizontal line. Then the distance light travels in the medium containing A is $\sqrt{x^2 + a^2}$ and the distance light travels in the medium containing B is $\sqrt{y^2 + b^2}$. Thus the total time $t(x, y)$ required for light to travel from A to B is given by $t(x, y) = \frac{\sqrt{x^2 + a^2}}{v} + \frac{\sqrt{y^2 + b^2}}{u}$, and we wish to minimize t. If $D(x, y) = x + y$, than the constraint is $D(x, y) = x + y = \ell$. Since grad $t(x, y) = \frac{x}{v\sqrt{x^2 + a^2}}\vec{i} + \frac{y}{u\sqrt{y^2 + b^2}}\vec{j}$ and grad $D(x, y) = \vec{i} + \vec{j}$, it follows that grad $t(x, y) = \lambda$ grad $D(x, y)$ if

$$\frac{x}{v\sqrt{x^2 + a^2}} = \lambda \quad \text{and} \quad \frac{y}{u\sqrt{y^2 + b^2}} = \lambda$$

which implies that

$$\frac{x}{v\sqrt{x^2 + a^2}} = \frac{y}{u\sqrt{y^2 + b^2}}$$

Since $\frac{x}{\sqrt{x^2 + a^2}} = \sin\theta$ and $\frac{y}{\sqrt{y^2 + b^2}} = \sin\varphi$, it follows that

$$\frac{\sin\theta}{v} = \frac{\sin\varphi}{u}$$

28. The surface area of the cylindrical capsule is given by $S(r, h) = 2\pi rh + 4\pi r^2$, and the volume is given by $V(r, h) = \pi r^2 h + \frac{4}{3}\pi r^3$. The constraint is $V(r, h) = \pi r^2 h + \frac{4}{3}\pi r^3 = V$. Since grad $S(r, h) = (2\pi h + 8\pi r)\vec{i} + 2\pi r\vec{j}$ and grad $V(r, h) = (2\pi rh + 4\pi r^2)\vec{i} + \pi r^2\vec{j}$, it follows that grad $S(r, h) = \lambda$ grad $V(r, h)$ if

$$2\pi h + 8\pi r = (2\pi rh + 4\pi r^2)\lambda \quad \text{and} \quad 2\pi r = \pi r^2\lambda$$

For the volume to be nonzero, $r \neq 0$, so that the second equation reduces to $\lambda = \frac{2}{r}$. Then the first equation becomes $2\pi h + 8\pi r = 4\pi h + 8\pi r$, or $2\pi h = 4\pi h$, so that $h = 0$. Thus the minimum surface area occurs when $h = 0$, which means that the capsule is spherical. The sphere-promoting executive should get the next promotion.

29. Let (x, y, z) be on the paraboloid and the plane. The distance from (x, y, z) to the origin is minimum if and only if the square of the distance is minimum, so let $f(x, y, z) = x^2 + y^2 + z^2$. Let $g_1(x, y, z) = x^2 + y^2 + z$ and $g_2(x, y, z) = x + 2y$. The constraints are $g_1(x, y, z) = x^2 + y^2 + z = \frac{3}{2}$ and $g_2(x, y, z) = x + 2y = 1$. Since grad $f(x, y, z) = 2x\vec{i} + 2y\vec{j} + 2z\vec{k}$, grad $g_1(x, y, z) = 2x\vec{i} + 2y\vec{j} + \vec{k}$, and grad $g_2(x, y, z) = \vec{i} + 2\vec{j}$, it follows that grad $f(x, y, z) = \lambda$grad $g_1(x, y, z) + \mu$grad $g_2(x, y, z)$ if

$$2x = 2x\lambda + \mu, \quad 2y = 2y\lambda + 2\mu, \quad \text{and} \quad 2z = \lambda \qquad (*)$$

Solving the first two equations in (*) for μ, we obtain $2x - 2x\lambda = \mu = y - y\lambda$, and thus $2x(1 - \lambda) = y(1 - \lambda)$. If

$\lambda = 1$ then the third equation in (*) yields $z = \frac{1}{2}$. With $z = \frac{1}{2}$ and the fact that $x = 1 - 2y$ by the second constraint, the first constraint becomes $(1 - 2y)^2 + y^2 + \frac{1}{2} = \frac{3}{2}$, or $1 - 4y + 5y^2 = 1$. Thus $5y^2 = 4y$, so $y = 0$ or $y = \frac{4}{5}$. If $y = 0$ then $x = 1 - 2(0) = 1$, and if $y = \frac{4}{5}$ then $x = 1 - 2(\frac{4}{5}) = -\frac{3}{5}$. For $(1,0,\frac{1}{2})$ the distance is $\sqrt{f(1,0,\frac{1}{2})} = \sqrt{1^2 + (\frac{1}{2})^2} = \frac{1}{2}\sqrt{5}$. For $(-\frac{3}{5},\frac{4}{5},\frac{1}{2})$ the distance is $\sqrt{f(-\frac{3}{5},\frac{4}{5},\frac{1}{2})} = \sqrt{(-\frac{3}{5})^2 + (\frac{4}{5})^2 + (\frac{1}{2})^2} = \sqrt{\frac{9}{25} + \frac{16}{25} + \frac{1}{4}} = \sqrt{\frac{125}{10}} = \frac{1}{2}\sqrt{5}$.

Next, if $\lambda \neq 1$, then the equation $2x(1 - \lambda) = y(1 - \lambda)$ becomes $2x = y$, so since $x + 2y = 1$ by the second constraint, we obtain $x + 2(2x) = 1$; thus $x = \frac{1}{5}$, so $y = \frac{2}{5}$, and by the first constraint, $z = \frac{3}{2} - (\frac{1}{5})^2 - (\frac{2}{5})^2 = \frac{13}{10}$. For $(\frac{1}{5},\frac{2}{5},\frac{13}{10})$ the distance is $\sqrt{f(\frac{1}{5},\frac{2}{5},\frac{13}{10})} = \sqrt{(\frac{1}{5})^2 + (\frac{2}{5})^2 + (\frac{13}{10})^2} = \sqrt{\frac{189}{100}} = \frac{1}{10}\sqrt{189}$. Since $\frac{1}{2}\sqrt{5} < \frac{1}{10}\sqrt{189}$, the minimum distance is $\frac{1}{2}\sqrt{5}$.

30. Let (x, y, z) be on the two planes. Notice that the distance from $(2, -2, 3)$ to (x, y, z) is minimum if and only if the square of the distance is minimum, so let $f(x, y, z) = (x - 2)^2 + (y + 2)^2 + (z - 3)^2$. Also let $g_1(x, y, z) = 2x - y + 3z$ and $g_2(x, y, z) = -x + 3y + z$. The constraints are $g_1(x, y, z) = 2x - y + 3z = 1$ and $g_2(x, y, z) = -x + 3y + z = -3$. Since grad $f(x, y, z) = 2(x - 2)\vec{i} + 2(y + 2)\vec{j} + 2(z - 3)\vec{k}$, grad $g_1(x, y, z) = 2\vec{i} - \vec{j} + 3\vec{k}$, and grad $g_2(x, y, z) = -\vec{i} + 3\vec{j} + \vec{k}$, it follows that grad $f(x, y, z) = \lambda$ grad $g_1(x, y, z) + \mu$ grad $g_2(x, y, z)$ if

$$2(x - 2) = 2\lambda - \mu, \quad 2(y + 2) = -\lambda + 3\mu, \quad \text{and} \quad 2(z - 3) = 3\lambda + \mu$$

Solving for x, y, z in turn, these equations become

$$x = 2 + \lambda - \frac{\mu}{2}, \quad y = -2 - \frac{\lambda}{2} + \frac{3}{2}\mu, \quad \text{and} \quad z = 3 + \frac{3}{2}\lambda + \frac{\mu}{2} \qquad (*)$$

Substituting for x, y, z in the two constraints, we find that

$$2(2 + \lambda - \frac{\mu}{2}) - (-2 - \frac{\lambda}{2} + \frac{3}{2}\mu) + 3(3 + \frac{3}{2}\lambda + \frac{\mu}{2}) = 1, \quad \text{or } \mu = 7\lambda + 14$$

and

$$-(2 + \lambda - \frac{\mu}{2}) + 3(-2 - \frac{\lambda}{2} + \frac{3}{2}\mu) + (3 + \frac{3}{2}\lambda + \frac{\mu}{2}) = -3, \quad \text{or } \mu = \frac{2}{13}(\lambda + 2)$$

Substituting for μ in terms of λ, we have $7\lambda + 14 = \frac{2}{13}(\lambda + 2)$, so that $\lambda = -2$, and hence $\mu = 0$. With our values of λ and μ, (*) yields $x = 0$, $y = -1$, and $z = 0$. The minimum distance is $\sqrt{f(0, -1, 0)} = \sqrt{(-2)^2 + 1^2 + (-3)^2} = \sqrt{14}$.

31. a. Let $g(x, y) = ax + by$, so the constraint is $g(x, y) = ax + by = c$. Since grad $f(x_0, y_0) = f_x(x_0, y_0)\vec{i} + f_y(x_0, y_0)\vec{j}$ and grad $g(x_0, y_0) = a\vec{i} + b\vec{j}$, it follows that grad $f(x_0, y_0) = \lambda$ grad $g(x_0, y_0)$ if

$$f_x(x_0, y_0) = a\lambda \quad \text{and} \quad f_y(x_0, y_0) = b\lambda$$

If a and b are nonzero, then

$$\frac{f_x(x_0, y_0)}{a} = \frac{f_y(x_0, y_0)}{b} = \lambda$$

b. If $f(x, y) = x^\alpha y^\beta$, then $f_x(x_0, y_0) = \alpha x_0^{\alpha - 1} y_0^\beta$ and $f_y(x_0, y_0) = \beta x_0^\alpha y_0^{\beta - 1}$. By part (a) we have

$$\frac{\alpha x_0^{\alpha-1} y_0^\beta}{a} = \frac{\beta x_0 \, y_0^{\beta-1}}{b} = \lambda$$

Canceling terms, we conclude that $\frac{y_0}{x_0} = \frac{\beta a}{\alpha b}$.

Chapter 13 - Review

1. all (x, y) such that $\frac{1}{4}x^2 + \frac{1}{25}y^2 \le 1$

2. all (u, v) such that $-1 \le u - v \le 1$

3. all (x, y, z) such that $x - y + z > 0$

4. If $y - x + 4 = -1$, then $y = x - 5$, and if $y - x + 4 = 6$, then $y = x + 2$.

   Thus the level curves are the lines $y = x - 5$ and $y = x + 2$, respectively.

5. The level curves are the hyperbolas $xy = 1$ and $xy = -1$, respectively.

6. If $\dfrac{x^2 - y^2}{x^2 + y^2} = \dfrac{1}{2}$, then $3y^2 = x^2$, so that $y = \pm \dfrac{1}{\sqrt{3}}x$. The level curve

   is composed of the lines $y = \dfrac{1}{\sqrt{3}}x$ and $y = -\dfrac{1}{\sqrt{3}}x$.

7.

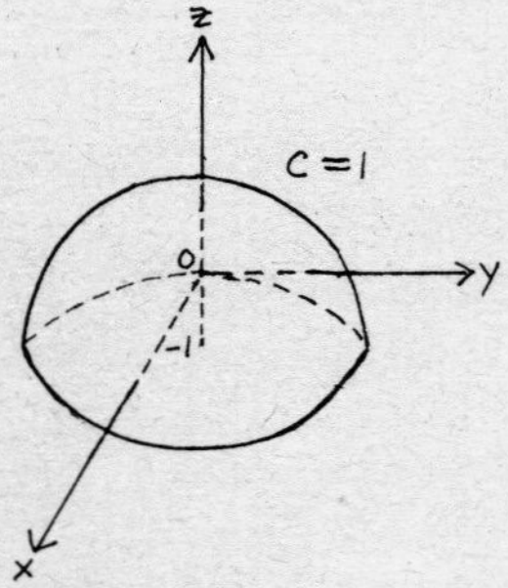

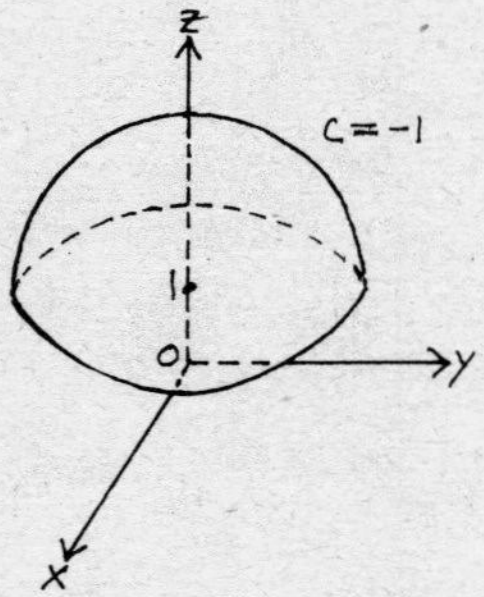

8.

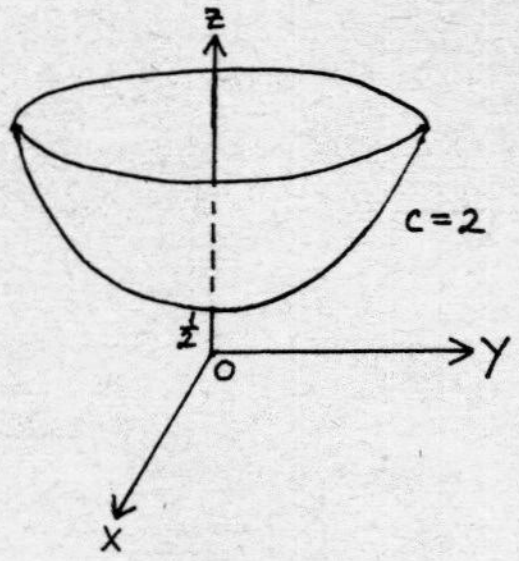

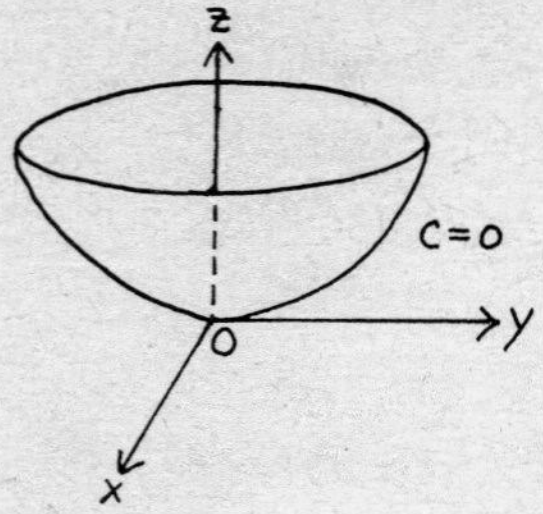

9.

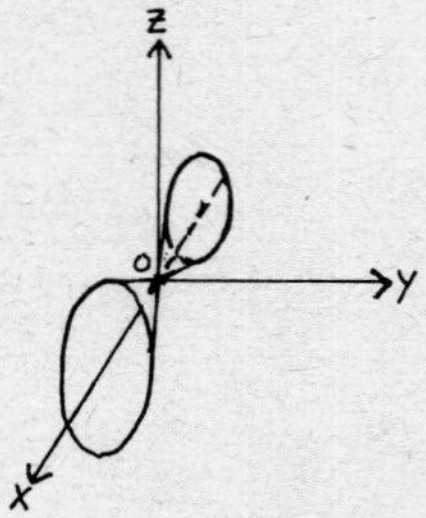

10.

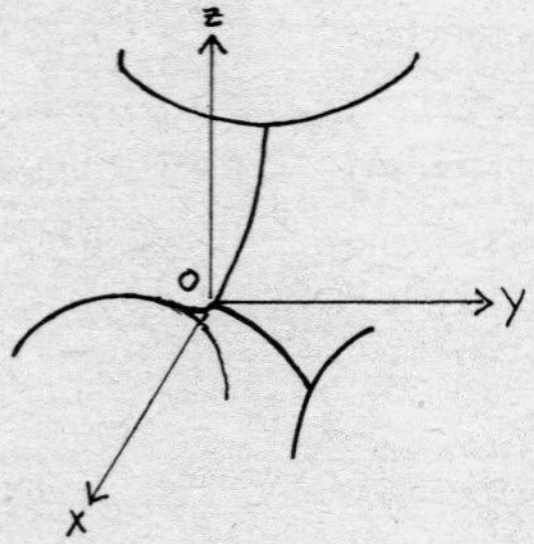

11.

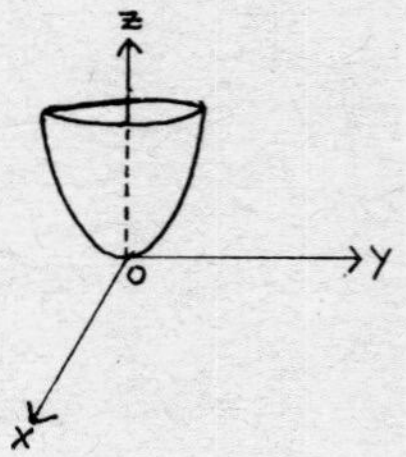

12.

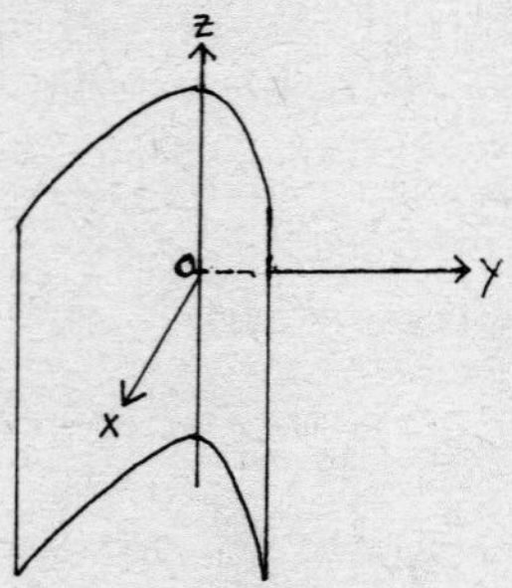

13.

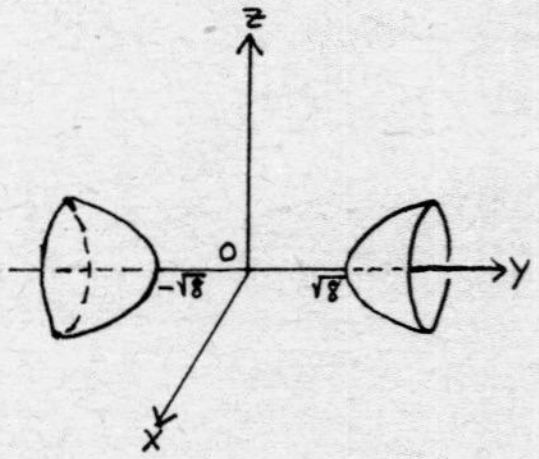

14. For any $\varepsilon > 0$ let $\delta = \varepsilon$. If $0 < \sqrt{x^2 + y^2} < \delta$, then $|y| < \delta = \varepsilon$, so that $\left|\frac{y^2}{\sqrt{x^2 + y^2}}\right| = |y| \left|\frac{y}{\sqrt{x^2 + y^2}}\right| \le |y| < \varepsilon$. Thus

$$\lim_{(x, y)\to(0, 0)} \frac{y^2}{\sqrt{x^2 + y^2}} = 0.$$

15. $$\lim_{(x, y)\to(-2, \sqrt{2})} \frac{x^4 + x^2y^2 - 6y^4}{x^2 - 2y^2} = \lim_{(x, y)\to(-2, \sqrt{2})} \frac{(x^2 + 3y^2)(x^2 - 2y^2)}{x^2 - 2y^2}$$

$$= \lim_{(x, y)\to(-2, \sqrt{2})} (x^2 + 3y^2) = 10.$$

16. $$\lim_{(x, y, z)\to(-1, 1, 2)} \frac{2x^2 + 4xy - 6x^3z^2}{xyz^2} = \frac{2(-1)^2 + 4(-1)(1) - 6(-1)^3(2)^2}{(-1)(1)(2)^2} = \frac{-11}{2}$$

17. $f_x(x, y) = 12x^2$, $f_y(x, y) = -6y$

18. $g_x(x, y) = \frac{(x^2 + 2y^2) - (x - y)\,2x}{(x^2 + 2y^2)^2} = \frac{2y^2 + 2xy - x^2}{(x^2 + 2y^2)^2}$, $g_y(x, y)$

$$= \frac{-(x^2 + 2y^2) - (x - y)\,4y}{(x^2 + 2y^2)^2} = \frac{2y^2 - 4xy - x^2}{(x^2 + 2y^2)^2}$$

19. $f_x(x, y, z) = 2xe^{x^2} \ln (y^2 - 3z)$, $f_y(x, y, z) = \frac{2ye^{x^2}}{y^2 - 3z}$, $f_z(x, y, z)$

$$= \frac{-3e^{x^2}}{y^2 - 3z}$$

20. $f_x(x, y, z) = \frac{-\cos z^4}{x^2y^2}$, $f_y(x, y, z) = \frac{-2 \cos z^4}{xy^3}$, $f_z(x, y, z) = \frac{-4z^3 \sin z^4}{xy^2}$

21. $k_x(x, y, z) = \frac{5}{2}\left[\sqrt{z} \tan (x^2 + y)\right]^{3/2} (2x\sqrt{z} \sec^2(x^2 + y))$

$$= 5xz^{5/4} \left[\tan^{3/2}(x^2 + y)\right] \sec^2(x^2 + y),\ k_y(x, y, z)$$

$$= \frac{5}{2} z^{5/4} \left[\tan^{3/2} (x^2 + y)\right] \sec^2 (x^2 + y),\ k_z(x, y, z)$$

$$= \frac{5}{2}\left[\sqrt{z} \tan (x^2 + y)\right]^{3/2}\left[\frac{1}{2} \frac{1}{\sqrt{z}} \tan (x^2 + y)\right] = \frac{5}{4} \sqrt[4]{z} \tan^{5/2} (x^2 + y)$$

22. $f_y(x, y) = \sin y$ and $g_x(x, y) = \sin y$, so $f_y = g_x$.

23. $f_y(x, y) = 1 + 2xe^y$ and $g_x(x, y) = 1 + 2xe^y$, so $f_y = g_x$.

24. $f_x(x, y) = \frac{2x}{\sqrt{1 - (x^2 - y^2)^2}}$, $f_{xx}(x, y)$

$$= \frac{2\sqrt{1 - (x^2 - y^2)^2} - \frac{2x}{2\sqrt{1 - (x^2 - y^2)^2}}\left[-2(x^2 - y^2)\, 2x\right]}{1 - (x^2 - y^2)^2}$$

$$= \frac{2 + 2x^4 - 2y^4}{\left[1 - (x^2 - y^2)^2\right]^{3/2}},\ f_{xy}(x, y) = \frac{-x\left[-2(x^2 - y^2)(-2y)\right]}{\left[(1 - (x^2 - y^2)^2\right]^{3/2}}$$

$$= \frac{4xy^3 - 4x^3y}{\left[1 - (x^2 - y^2)^2\right]^{3/2}};\ f_y(x, y) = \frac{-2y}{\sqrt{1 - (x^2 - y^2)^2}},\ f_{yy}(x, y)$$

$$= \frac{-2\sqrt{1 - (x^2 - y^2)^2} - \frac{-2y}{2\sqrt{1 - (x^2 - y^2)^2}}\left[-2(x^2 - y^2)(-2y)\right]}{1 - (x^2 - y^2)^2}$$

$$= \frac{-2 + 2x^4 - 2y^4}{\left[1 - (x^2 - y^2)^2\right]^{3/2}},\ f_{yx}(x, y) = \frac{y\left[-2(x^2 - y^2)(2x)\right]}{\left[1 - (x^2 - y^2)^2\right]^{3/2}} = \frac{4xy^3 - 4x^3y}{\left[1 - (x^2 - y^2)^2\right]^{3/2}}$$

25. $g(u, v) = \ln \frac{u^2}{e^v} = \ln u^2 - \ln e^v = 2 \ln u - v$; $g_u(u, v) = \frac{2}{u}$, $g_{uu}(u, v)$

$= \frac{-2}{u^2}$, $g_{uv}(u, v) = 0$; $g_v(u, v) = -1$, $g_{vv}(u, v) = g_{vu}(u, v) = 0$.

26. $f_x(x, y, z) = \sin yz^2$, $f_{xx}(x, y, z) = 0$, $f_{xy}(x, y, z) = z^2 \cos yz^2$,

$f_{xz}(x, y, z) = 2yz \cos yz^2$; $f_y(x, y, z) = xz^2 \cos yz^2$, $f_{yy}(x, y, z)$

$= -xz^4 \sin yz^2$, $f_{yx}(x, y, z) = z^2 \cos yz^2$, $f_{yz}(x, y, z) = 2xz \cos yz^2$

$- 2xyz^3 \sin yz^2$; $f_z(x, y, z) = 2xyz \cos yz^2$, $f_{zz}(x, y, z) = 2xy \cos yz^2$

$- 4xy^2z^2 \sin yz^2$, $f_{zx}(x, y, z) = 2yz \cos yz^2$, $f_{zy}(x, y, z) = 2xz \cos yz^2$

$- 2xyz^3 \sin yz^2$

27. $\frac{\partial z}{\partial x} = -be^{-ay} \sin bx$, $\frac{\partial^2 z}{\partial x^2} = -b^2e^{-ay} \cos bx$, $\frac{\partial z}{\partial y} = -ae^{-ay} \cos bx$, $\frac{\partial^2 z}{\partial y^2}$

$= a^2e^{-ay} \cos bx$; thus $a^2 \frac{\partial^2 z}{\partial x^2} + b^2 \frac{\partial^2 z}{\partial y^2} = - a^2b^2e^{-ay} \cos bx + a^2b^2e^{-ay} \cos bx$

$= 0$.

28. $\frac{\partial z}{\partial x} = \frac{x}{\sqrt{x^2 + y^2}}$, $\frac{\partial^2 z}{\partial x^2} = \frac{\sqrt{x^2 + y^2} - \frac{x^2}{\sqrt{x^2 + y^2}}}{x^2 + y^2} = \frac{y^2}{(x^2 + y^2)^{3/2}}$;

$\frac{\partial z}{\partial y} = \frac{y}{\sqrt{x^2 + y^2}}$, $\frac{\partial^2 z}{\partial y^2} = \frac{\sqrt{x^2 + y^2} - \frac{y^2}{\sqrt{x^2 + y^2}}}{x^2 + y^2} = \frac{x^2}{(x^2 + y^2)^{3/2}}$;

$\frac{\partial^2 z}{\partial x \partial y} = \frac{-xy}{(x^2 + y^2)^{3/2}}$; thus $\frac{\partial^2 z}{\partial x^2} \frac{\partial^2 z}{\partial y^2} = \frac{x^2y^2}{(x^2 + y^2)^3} = (\frac{\partial^2 z}{\partial x \partial y})^2$.

29. $\frac{dz}{dt} = \frac{\partial z}{\partial x} \frac{dx}{dt} + \frac{\partial z}{\partial y} \frac{dy}{dt} = (2xe^{x^2})(2t) + (- \frac{1}{2}e^{y/2})(3t^2 - 1) = 4t^3e^{t^4}$

$- \frac{1}{2}(3t^2 - 1)e^{(t^3 - t)/2}$

30. $\frac{\partial z}{\partial u} = \frac{\partial z}{\partial x} \frac{\partial x}{\partial u} + \frac{\partial z}{\partial y} \frac{\partial y}{\partial u} = (y \cos xy + y^2 \sin x)(2uv) + (x \cos xy - 2y \cos x)(0)$

$= 2u(\cos u^2 + \frac{1}{v} \sin u^2v)$; $\frac{\partial z}{\partial v} = \frac{\partial z}{\partial x} \frac{\partial x}{\partial v} + \frac{\partial z}{\partial y} \frac{\partial y}{\partial v} = (y \cos xy + y^2 \sin x)(u^2)$

$+ (x \cos xy - 2y \cos x)(\frac{-1}{v^2}) = \frac{1}{v^2}(u^2 \sin u^2v + \frac{2}{v} \cos u^2v)$

31. $\frac{dw}{dt} = \frac{\partial w}{\partial x} \frac{dx}{dt} + \frac{\partial w}{\partial y} \frac{dy}{dt} + \frac{\partial w}{\partial z} \frac{dz}{dt} = \frac{x}{\sqrt{x^2 + y^2z^4}}(2) + \frac{yz^4}{\sqrt{x^2 + y^2z^4}}(3t^2)$

$+ \frac{2y^2z^3}{\sqrt{x^2 + y^2z^4}} (\frac{-1}{t^2}) = \frac{\sqrt{5}t}{|t|}$

32. $\frac{\partial w}{\partial u} = \frac{\partial w}{\partial x} \frac{\partial x}{\partial u} + \frac{\partial w}{\partial y} \frac{\partial y}{\partial u} + \frac{\partial w}{\partial z} \frac{\partial z}{\partial u} = (2x)(2u) + (\sin yz + yz \cos yz)(v)$

$+ (y^2 \cos yz)(2u) = 4u(u^2 + v^2) + v \sin [uv(u^2 - v^2)]$

$+ uv^2(3u^2 - v^2) \cos [uv(u^2 - v^2)]$; $\frac{\partial w}{\partial v} = \frac{\partial w}{\partial x} \frac{\partial x}{\partial v} + \frac{\partial w}{\partial y} \frac{\partial y}{\partial v} + \frac{\partial w}{\partial z} \frac{\partial z}{\partial v} = (2x)(2v)$

$+ (\sin yz + yz \cos yz)(u) + (y^2 \cos yz)(-2v) = 4v(u^2 + v^2)$

$+ u \sin [uv(u^2 - v^2)] + u^2v(u^2 - 3v^2) \cos [uv(u^2 - v^2)]$

33. $\frac{\partial z}{\partial x} = 2x f'(x^2 + y^2)$ and $\frac{\partial z}{\partial y} = 2y f'(x^2 + y^2)$. Thus $y \frac{\partial z}{\partial x} - x \frac{\partial z}{\partial y}$

$= 2xy f'(x^2 + y^2) - 2xy f'(x^2 + y^2) = 0$.

34. Differentiating implicitly with respect to x, we find that

$\frac{1}{1 + x^2y^2}(y + x \frac{dy}{dx}) + \frac{1}{\sqrt{1 - x^2y^2}} (y + x \frac{dy}{dx}) = 0$. Solving for $\frac{dy}{dx}$, we

obtain $\frac{dy}{dx} = - \frac{y}{x}$.

35. Treating z as a function of x and y and taking partial derivatives with respect to x, we find that $yz + xy \frac{\partial z}{\partial x} - \frac{1}{x^2yz} - \frac{1}{xyz^2} \frac{\partial z}{\partial x} = 3z^2 \frac{\partial z}{\partial x}$. Solving

for $\frac{\partial z}{\partial x}$, we obtain $\frac{\partial z}{\partial x} = \dfrac{yz - \frac{1}{x^2yz}}{3z^2 + \frac{1}{xyz^2} - xy} = \dfrac{z(x^2y^2z^2 - 1)}{x(3xyz^4 + 1 - x^2y^2z^2)}$.

Interchanging the roles of x and y, we obtain $\frac{\partial z}{\partial y} = \dfrac{z(x^2y^2z^2 - 1)}{y(3xyz^4 + 1 - x^2y^2z^2)}$

36. $f_x(x, y) = -2x$, $f_y(x, y) = 6y + 1$, and $\|\vec{a}\| = 1$; $D_{\vec{a}}f(-1, 0)$

$= f_x(-1, 0)(\frac{-1}{\sqrt{2}}) + f_y(-1, 0)(\frac{1}{\sqrt{2}}) = \frac{-2}{\sqrt{2}} + \frac{1}{\sqrt{2}} = \frac{-\sqrt{2}}{2}$

37. $f_x(x, y, z) = \dfrac{-2x}{(x^2 + y^2 + z^2)^2}$, $f_y(x, y, z) = \dfrac{-2y}{(x^2 + y^2 + z^2)^2}$, $f_z(x, y, z)$

$= \dfrac{-2z}{(x^2 + y^2 + z^2)^2}$, and $\|\vec{a}\| = \sqrt{3}$, so that $\vec{u} = \frac{1}{\sqrt{3}}\vec{i} - \frac{1}{\sqrt{3}}\vec{j} - \frac{1}{\sqrt{3}}\vec{k}$;

$D_{\vec{u}}f(-1, 0, 2) = f_x(-1, 0, 2)(\frac{1}{\sqrt{3}}) + f_y(-1, 0, 2)(\frac{-1}{\sqrt{3}}) + f_z(-1, 0, 2)(\frac{-1}{\sqrt{3}})$

$= \dfrac{2}{25\sqrt{3}} + 0 + \dfrac{4}{25\sqrt{3}} = \frac{2}{25}\sqrt{3}$

38. $f_x(x, y, z) = -\csc(yz + x)\cot(yz + x)$, $f_y(x, y, z)$

$= -z\csc(yz + x)\cot(yz + x)$, $f_z(x, y, z) = -y\csc(yz + x)\cot(yz + x)$,

and $\|\vec{a}\| = \sqrt{14}$, so $\vec{u} = \frac{-3}{\sqrt{14}}\vec{i} - \frac{1}{\sqrt{14}}\vec{j} - \frac{2}{\sqrt{14}}\vec{k}$; $D_{\vec{u}}f(\pi, \frac{-\pi}{4}, 1)$

$= f_x(\pi, \frac{-\pi}{4}, 1)(\frac{-3}{\sqrt{14}}) + f_y(\pi, \frac{-\pi}{4}, 1)(\frac{-1}{\sqrt{14}}) + f_z(\pi, \frac{-\pi}{4}, 1)(\frac{-2}{\sqrt{14}})$

$= \dfrac{-3\sqrt{2}}{\sqrt{14}} - \dfrac{\sqrt{2}}{\sqrt{14}} + \dfrac{\pi\sqrt{2}}{2\sqrt{14}} = \dfrac{(\pi - 8)\sqrt{7}}{14}$.

39. grad $f(x, y) = 2e^{2x}\ln y\,\vec{i} + e^{2x}\frac{1}{y}\vec{j}$, so that grad $f(0, 1) = \vec{j}$.

40. grad $f(x, y, z) = 2x\cos y\sin(\frac{\pi}{2}\sin z)\vec{i} - x^2\sin y\sin(\frac{\pi}{2}\sin z)\vec{j}$

$+ x^2\cos y\left[\cos(\frac{\pi}{2}\sin z)\right](\frac{\pi}{2}\cos z)\vec{k}$, so that grad $f(1, \frac{-\pi}{6}, \frac{\pi}{3})$

$= \sqrt{3}\sin\frac{\pi\sqrt{3}}{4}\vec{i} + \frac{1}{2}\sin\frac{\pi\sqrt{3}}{4}\vec{j} + \frac{\pi\sqrt{3}}{8}\cos\frac{\pi\sqrt{3}}{4}\vec{k}$

41. grad $f(x, y) = -y\sin xy\,\vec{i} - x\sin xy\,\vec{j}$, so that grad $f(\frac{1}{2}, \pi) = -\pi\vec{i}$

$- \frac{1}{2}\vec{j}$. Thus the direction in which f increases most rapidly at $(\frac{1}{2}, \pi)$ is

$\dfrac{1}{\|-\pi\vec{i} - \frac{1}{2}\vec{j}\|}(-\pi\vec{i} - \frac{1}{2}\vec{j}) = \dfrac{-1}{\sqrt{4\pi^2 + 1}}(2\pi\vec{i} + \vec{j})$.

42. grad $f(x, y, z) = ye^z\vec{i} + xe^z\vec{j} + xye^z\vec{k}$, so that grad $f(2, 3, 0) = 3\vec{i}$

$+ 2\vec{j} + 6\vec{k}$. Thus the direction in which f increases most rapidly at

$(2, 3, 0)$ is $\dfrac{1}{\|3\vec{i} + 2\vec{j} + 6\vec{k}\|}(3\vec{i} + 2\vec{j} + 6\vec{k}) = \frac{3}{7}\vec{i} + \frac{2}{7}\vec{j} + \frac{6}{7}\vec{k}$.

43. Let $f(x, y) = \arctan(x^2 + y)$. Since the graph of the given equation is a level curve of f, Theorem 13.15 implies that grad $f(\frac{1}{2}, \frac{3}{4})$ is normal to the graph at $(\frac{1}{2}, \frac{3}{4})$. Since grad $f(x, y) = \dfrac{2x}{1 + (x^2 + y)^2}\vec{i}$

$+ \dfrac{1}{1 + (x^2 + y)^2}\vec{j}$, so that grad $f(\frac{1}{2}, \frac{3}{4}) = \frac{1}{2}\vec{i} + \frac{1}{2}\vec{j}$, we find that $\frac{1}{2}\vec{i}$

$+ \frac{1}{2}\vec{j}$ is normal to the graph at $(\frac{1}{2}, \frac{3}{4})$.

44. Let $f(x, y) = x^4 - 3x^2y + 2y^3$. Since the graph of the given equation is a level curve of f, Theorem 13.16 implies that grad $f(-1, 2)$ is normal to the graph at $(-1, 2)$. Since grad $f(x, y) = (4x^3 - 6xy)\vec{i} + (-3x^2 + 6y^2)\vec{j}$,

so that grad $f(-1, 2) = 8\vec{i} + 21\vec{j}$, we find that $8\vec{i} + 21\vec{j}$ is normal to the graph at $(-1, 2)$.

45. Since $f_x(x, y) = \frac{-1}{x^2}$ and $f_y(x, y) = \frac{1}{y^2}$, so that $f_x(-\frac{1}{2}, \frac{1}{3}) = -4$ and $f_y(-\frac{1}{2}, \frac{1}{3}) = 9$, the vector $-4\vec{i} + 9\vec{j} - \vec{k}$ is normal to the graph of f at $(-\frac{1}{2}, \frac{1}{3}, -5)$, and an equation of the plane tangent at $(-\frac{1}{2}, \frac{1}{3}, -5)$ is $-4(x + \frac{1}{2}) + 9(y - \frac{1}{3}) - (z + 5) = 0$, or $-4x + 9y - z = 10$.

46. Since $f_x(x, y) = ye^x$ and $f_y(x, y) = e^x$, so that $f_x(0, 1) = 1$ and $f_y(0, 1) = 1$, the vector $\vec{i} + \vec{j} - \vec{k}$ is normal to the graph of f at $(0, 1, 1)$, and an equation of the plane tangent at $(0, 1, 1)$ is $(x - 0) + (y - 1) - (z - 1) = 0$, or $x + y - z = 0$.

47. Since $f_x(x, y) = \frac{3x}{\sqrt{3x^2 + 2y^2 + 2}}$ and $f_y(x, y) = \frac{2y}{\sqrt{3x^2 + 2y^2 + 2}}$, so that $f_x(4, -5) = \frac{6}{5}$ and $f_y(4, -5) = -1$, the vector $\frac{6}{5}\vec{i} - \vec{j} - \vec{k}$ is normal to the graph of f at $(4, -5, 10)$, and an equation of the plane tangent at $(4, -5, 10)$ is $\frac{6}{5}(x - 4) - (y + 5) - (z - 10) = 0$, or $6x - 5y - 5z = -1$.

48. If $f(x, y, z) = x^2 - y^2 - z^2$, then $x^2 - y^2 - z^2 = 1$ is a level surface of f. Since $f_x(x, y, z) = 2x$, $f_y(x, y, z) = -2y$, and $f_z(x, y, z) = -2z$, so $f_x(3, -2, 2) = 6$, $f_y(3, -2, 2) = 4$, and $f_z(3, -2, 2) = -4$, it follows that an equation of the plane tangent at $(3, -2, 2)$ is $6(x - 3) + 4(y + 2) - 4(z - 2) = 0$, or $3x + 2y - 2z = 1$.

49. If $f(x, y, z) = xe^{yz} - 2y$, then $xe^{yz} - 2y = -1$ is a level surface of f. Since $f_x(x, y, z) = e^{yz}$, $f_y(x, y, z) = xze^{yz} - 2$, and $f_z(x, y, z) = xye^{yz}$, so $f_x(1, 1, 0) = 1$, $f_y(1, 1, 0) = -2$, and $f_z(1, 1, 0) = 1$, it follows that an equation of the plane tangent at $(1, 1, 0)$ is $(x - 1) - 2(y - 1) + (z - 0) = 0$, or $x - 2y + z = -1$.

50. If $f(x, y, z) = \sin xy + \cos yz$, then $\sin xy + \cos yz = 0$ is a level surface of f. Since $f_x(x, y, z) = y\cos xy$, $f_y(x, y, z) = x\cos xy - z\sin yz$, and $f_z(x, y, z) = -y\sin yz$, so $f_x(0, \frac{\pi}{2}, 1) = \frac{\pi}{2}$, $f_y(0, \frac{\pi}{2}, 1) = -1$, and $f_z(0, \frac{\pi}{2}, 1) = -\frac{\pi}{2}$, it follows that an equation of the plane tangent at $(0, \frac{\pi}{2}, 1)$ is $\frac{\pi}{2}(x - 0) - (y - \frac{\pi}{2}) - \frac{\pi}{2}(z - 1) = 0$, or $\pi x - 2y - \pi z = -2\pi$.

51. Let $f(x, y, z) = 2x^3 + y - z^2$. Then $f_x(x, y, z) = 6x^2$, $f_y(x, y, z) = 1$, and $f_z(x, y, z) = -2z$, so a vector normal to the plane tangent at any point (x_0, y_0, z_0) on the level surface $2x^3 + y - z^2 = 5$ is $6x_0^2\vec{i} + \vec{j} - 2z_0\vec{k}$. If the tangent plane is parallel to the plane $24x + y - 6z = 3$, whose normal is $24\vec{i} + \vec{j} - 6\vec{k}$, then $6x_0^2\vec{i} + \vec{j} - 2z_0\vec{k} = c(24\vec{i} + \vec{j} - 6\vec{k})$ for some c. It follows that $c = 1$, so that $x_0 = \pm 2$ and $z_0 = 3$. Because (x_0, y_0, z_0) is on the level surface $2x^3 + y - z^2 = 5$ we find that if $x_0 = 2$ and $z_0 = 3$, then $y_0 = -2$, and if $x_0 = -2$ and $z_0 = 3$, then $y_0 = 30$. The required points on the level surface are

$(2, -2, 3)$ and $(-2, 30, 3)$.

52. Let $f(x, y, z) = x^2 + y^2 + z^2$. Then $f_x(x, y, z) = 2x$, $f_y(x, y, z) = 2y$, and $f_z(x, y, z) = 2z$, so a vector normal to the plane tangent at any point (x_0, y_0, z_0) on the sphere $x^2 + y^2 + z^2 = 1$ is $2x_0 \vec{i} + 2y_0 \vec{j} + 2z_0 \vec{k}$. If $\mathcal{P}$ is any given plane, then $\mathcal{P}$ has a normal vector of the form $a \vec{i} + b \vec{j} + c \vec{k}$. Now $2x_0 \vec{i} + 2y_0 \vec{j} + 2z_0 \vec{k}$ and $a \vec{i} + b \vec{j} + c \vec{k}$ are parallel if and only if there is a number d such that

$$2x_0 = da, \quad 2y_0 = db, \quad \text{and} \quad 2z_0 = dc \qquad (*)$$

This means that $d^2a^2 + d^2b^2 + d^2c^2 = 4x_0^2 + 4y_0^2 + 4z_0^2 = 4$, so that

$$d = \pm \frac{2}{\sqrt{a^2 + b^2 + c^2}}.$$ Along with $(*)$, this means that

$$x_0 = \pm \frac{a}{\sqrt{a^2 + b^2 + c^2}}, \quad y_0 = \pm \frac{b}{\sqrt{a^2 + b^2 + c^2}}, \quad \text{and} \quad z_0 = \pm \frac{c}{\sqrt{a^2 + b^2 + c^2}}$$

It follows that the planes tangent to the sphere $x^2 + y^2 + z^2 = 1$ are given by

$$a\left(x - \frac{a}{\sqrt{a^2 + b^2 + c^2}}\right) + b\left(y - \frac{b}{\sqrt{a^2 + b^2 + c^2}}\right) + c\left(z - \frac{c}{\sqrt{a^2 + b^2 + c^2}}\right) = 0$$ and $$a\left(x + \frac{a}{\sqrt{a^2 + b^2 + c^2}}\right) + b\left(y + \frac{b}{\sqrt{a^2 + b^2 + c^2}}\right) + c\left(z + \frac{c}{\sqrt{a^2 + b^2 + c^2}}\right) = 0.$$

53. Let $f(x, y) = x^2 + 4y^2$. Then $f_x(x, y) = 2x$ and $f_y(x, y) = 8y$, so that $f_x(2, 0) = 4$ and $f_y(2, 0) = 0$. Thus a vector normal to the plane tangent to the graph of f at $(2, 0, 4)$ is $4\vec{i} - \vec{k}$. Next, let $g(x, y) = 4x + y^2 - 4$. Then $g_x(x, y) = 4$ and $g_y(x, y) = 2y$, so that $g_x(2, 0) = 4$ and $g_y(2, 0) = 0$. Thus a vector normal to the plane tangent to the graph of g at $(2, 0, 4)$ is $4\vec{i} - \vec{k}$. Since the normals are identical and the planes both pass through $(2, 0, 4)$, the two planes are identical.

54. Let $f(x, y, z) = \frac{x^2}{a^2} - \frac{y^2}{b^2} + \frac{z^2}{c^2}$. Then $f_x(x, y, z) = \frac{2x}{a^2}$, $f_y(x, y, z) = \frac{-2y}{b^2}$, and $f_z(x, y, z) = \frac{2z}{c^2}$, so that an equation of the plane tangent to the level surface $f(x, y, z) = 1$ at (x_0, y_0, z_0) is $\frac{2x_0}{a^2}(x - x_0) - \frac{2y_0}{b^2}(y - y_0) + \frac{2z_0}{c^2}(z - z_0) = 0$, or $\frac{xx_0}{a^2} - \frac{yy_0}{b^2} + \frac{zz_0}{c^2} = \frac{x_0^2}{a^2} - \frac{y_0^2}{b^2} + \frac{z_0^2}{c^2} = 1$.

55. Let $x_0 = 1$, $y_0 = 0$, $h = -.03$, and $k = .05$. Since $f_x(x, y)$

$$= \frac{1}{1 + \left(\frac{x}{1+y}\right)^2}\left(\frac{1}{1+y}\right) = \frac{1+y}{(1+y)^2 + x^2}$$ and $f_y(x, y)$

$$= \frac{1}{1 + \left(\frac{x}{1+y}\right)^2}\left(\frac{-x}{(1+y)^2}\right) = \frac{-x}{(1+y)^2 + x^2},$$ we have $f_x(1, 0) = \frac{1}{2}$ and $f_y(1, 0) = \frac{-1}{2}$. Also $f(1, 0) = \frac{\pi}{4}$. Thus

$$f(.97, .05) \approx \frac{\pi}{4} + \frac{1}{2}(-.03) - \frac{1}{2}(.05) = \frac{\pi}{4} - .04 \approx .745398$$

56. Let $x_0 = 3$, $y_0 = 2$, $z_0 = 1$, $h = -.1$, $k = .1$, and $\ell = -.1$. Since

$$f_x(x, y, z) = \frac{3x}{\sqrt{3x^2 + y^2 + 5z^2}}, \quad f_y(x, y, z) = \frac{y}{\sqrt{3x^2 + y^2 + 5z^2}},$$ and

$f_z(x, y, z) = \dfrac{5z}{\sqrt{3x^2 + y^2 + 5z^2}}$, we have $f_x(3, 2, 1) = \frac{3}{2}$, $f_y(3, 2, 1) = \frac{1}{3}$, and $f_z(3, 2, 1) = \frac{5}{6}$. Also $f(3, 2, 1) = 6$. Thus

$$f(2.9, 2.1, .9) \approx 6 + \tfrac{3}{2}(-.1) + \tfrac{1}{3}(.1) + \tfrac{5}{6}(-.1) = 5.8$$

57. Since $f(x, y) = \ln \frac{x}{y} = \ln x - \ln y$, we have $\frac{\partial f}{\partial x} = \frac{1}{x}$ and $\frac{\partial f}{\partial y} = \frac{-1}{y}$, so that $df = \frac{1}{x}\,dx - \frac{1}{y}\,dy$.

58. Since $\frac{\partial f}{\partial x} = 2xy$, $\frac{\partial f}{\partial y} = x^2 + ze^{(z^2)} \sin yz$, and $\frac{\partial f}{\partial z} = -2ze^{(z^2)} \cos yz + ye^{(z^2)} \sin yz$, we have $df = 2xy\,dx + (x^2 + ze^{(z^2)} \sin yz)\,dy + (-2ze^{(z^2)} \cos yz + ye^{(z^2)} \sin yz)\,dz$.

59. $f_x(x, y) = 2x - 2$ and $f_y(x, y) = 2y - 4$, so $f_x(x, y) = 0 = f_y(x, y)$ if $x = 1$ and $y = 2$. Thus $(1, 2)$ is a critical point. Next, $f_{xx}(x, y) = 2$, $f_{yy}(x, y) = 2$, and $f_{xy}(x, y) = 0$. Thus $D(1, 2) = f_{xx}(1, 2)f_{yy}(1, 2) - [f_{xy}(1, 2)]^2 = (2)(2) - 0^2 = 4$. Since $D(1, 2) > 0$ and $f_{xx}(1, 2) > 0$, f has a relative minimum value at $(1, 2)$.

60. $f_x(x, y) = 2x$ and $f_y(x, y) = 1 + \frac{1}{y^3}$, so $f_x(x, y) = 0 = f_y(x, y)$ if $x = 0$ and $1 + \frac{1}{y^3} = 0$, so $y = -1$. Thus $(0, -1)$ is a critical point. Next, $f_{xx}(x, y) = 2$, $f_{yy}(x, y) = \frac{-3}{y^4}$, and $f_{xy}(x, y) = 0$. Thus $D(0, -1) = f_{xx}(0, -1)f_{yy}(0, -1) - [f_{xy}(0, -1)]^2 = (2)(-3) - 0^2 = -6$. Since $D(0, -1) < 0$, f has a saddle point at $(0, -1)$.

61. $f_x(x, y) = y - \frac{16}{x^3}$ and $f_y(x, y) = x - \frac{16}{y^3}$, so $f_x(x, y) = 0 = f_y(x, y)$ if $y - \frac{16}{x^3} = 0$ and $x - \frac{16}{y^3} = 0$. Solving for y in the first equation and substituting for it in the second equation yields $x - 16(\frac{x^3}{16})^3 = 0$, so that $x^8 = 256$, and thus $x = \pm 2$. Then $y = \pm 2$, so that $(2, 2)$ and $(-2, -2)$ are critical points. Next, $f_{xx}(x, y) = \frac{48}{x^4}$, $f_{yy}(x, y) = \frac{48}{y^4}$, and $f_{xy}(x, y) = 1$. Thus $D(2, 2) = f_{xx}(2, 2)f_{yy}(2, 2) - [f_{xy}(2, 2)]^2 = (3)(3) - 1^2 = 8$. Since $D(2, 2) > 0$ and $f_{xx}(2, 2) > 0$, f has a relative minimum value at $(2, 2)$. Finally, $D(-2, -2) = f_{xx}(-2, -2)f_{yy}(-2, -2) - [f_{xy}(-2, -2)]^2 = (3)(3) - 1^2 = 8$, and since $D(-2, -2) > 0$ and $f_{xx}(-2, -2) > 0$, f has a relative minimum value at $(-2, -2)$.

62. $f_x(x, y) = -4x + y - 4$ and $f_y(x, y) = x + 2y + 3$, so $f_x(x, y) = 0 = f_y(x, y)$ if $-4x + y - 4 = 0$ and $x + 2y + 3 = 0$. Solving for y in the first equation and substituting for it in the second equation yields $x + 2(4x + 4) + 3 = 0$, so $x = \frac{-11}{9}$. Then $y = \frac{-8}{9}$, so that $(\frac{-11}{9}, \frac{-8}{9})$ is a critical point. Next, $f_{xx}(x, y) = -4$, $f_{yy}(x, y) = 2$, and $f_{xy}(x, y) = 1$. Since $D(\frac{-11}{9}, \frac{-8}{9}) = f_{xx}(\frac{-11}{9}, \frac{-8}{9})f_{yy}(\frac{-11}{9}, \frac{-8}{9}) - [f_{xy}(\frac{-11}{9}, \frac{-8}{9})]^2 = (-4)(2) - 1^2 = -9$, f has a saddle point at $(\frac{-11}{9}, \frac{-8}{9})$.

63. Let $g(x, y) = 3x^2 + y^2$, so the constraint is $g(x, y) = 3x^2 + y^2 = 3$. Since $\operatorname{grad} f(x, y) = (6x - y)\vec{i} + (-x + 2y)\vec{j}$ and $\operatorname{grad} g(x, y) = 6x\,\vec{i} + 2y\,\vec{j}$, it follows that $\operatorname{grad} f(x, y) = \lambda \operatorname{grad} g(x, y)$ if

$$6x - y = 6x\lambda \quad\text{and}\quad -x + 2y = 2y\lambda$$

If $x = 0$, then by the first equation, $y = 0$, and the constraint is contradicted. Similarly, if $y = 0$, then $x = 0$ by the second equation, and the constraint is contradicted. Thus $x \neq 0$ and $y \neq 0$, so the two equations can be solved for λ:

$$\lambda = \frac{6x - y}{6x} = 1 - \frac{y}{6x} \quad \text{and} \quad \lambda = \frac{-x + 2y}{2y} = \frac{-x}{2y} + 1$$

so that $\frac{y}{6x} = \frac{x}{2y}$, and hence $y^2 = 3x^2$. The constraint becomes $3x^2 + 3x^2 = 3$, so $x = \frac{\pm 1}{\sqrt{2}}$, and therefore $y = \pm\sqrt{\frac{3}{2}}$. The possible extreme values of f are $f(\frac{1}{\sqrt{2}}, \sqrt{\frac{3}{2}}) = f(\frac{-1}{\sqrt{2}}, -\sqrt{\frac{3}{2}}) = 3 - \frac{\sqrt{3}}{2}$ and $f(\frac{-1}{\sqrt{2}}, \sqrt{\frac{3}{2}}) = f(\frac{1}{\sqrt{2}}, -\sqrt{\frac{3}{2}}) = 3 + \frac{\sqrt{3}}{2}$. The maximum value is $3 + \frac{\sqrt{3}}{2}$ and the minimum value is $3 - \frac{\sqrt{3}}{2}$.

64. First we use Lagrange multipliers to find the possible extreme values of f on the circle $x^2 + y^2 = 16$. Let $g(x, y) = x^2 + y^2$, so the constraint is $g(x, y) = x^2 + y^2 = 16$. Since grad $f(x, y) = (2x - 2)\vec{i} + (2y - 4)\vec{j}$ and grad $g(x, y) = 2x\vec{i} + 2y\vec{j}$, it follows that grad $f(x, y) = \lambda$grad $g(x, y)$ if

$$2x - 2 = 2x\lambda \quad \text{and} \quad 2y - 4 = 2y\lambda$$

The two equations imply that $x \neq 0$ and $y \neq 0$. Solving the equations for λ, we obtain

$$\lambda = \frac{x - 1}{x} = 1 - \frac{1}{x} \quad \text{and} \quad \lambda = \frac{y - 2}{y} = 1 - \frac{2}{y}$$

so that $\frac{1}{x} = \frac{2}{y}$, and hence $y = 2x$. The constraint becomes $x^2 + (2x)^2 = 16$, so that $x = \pm\frac{4}{\sqrt{5}}$, and $y = \pm\frac{8}{\sqrt{5}}$. The possible extreme values on the circle $x^2 + y^2 = 16$ are $f(\frac{4}{\sqrt{5}}, \frac{8}{\sqrt{5}}) = 10 - 8\sqrt{5}$, $f(\frac{-4}{\sqrt{5}}, \frac{8}{\sqrt{5}}) = 10 - \frac{24}{5}\sqrt{5}$, $f(\frac{4}{\sqrt{5}}, \frac{-8}{\sqrt{5}}) = 10 + \frac{24}{5}\sqrt{5}$, and $f(\frac{-4}{\sqrt{5}}, \frac{-8}{\sqrt{5}}) = 10 + 8\sqrt{5}$.

For the interior $x^2 + y^2 < 16$ of the circle we find that

$$f_x(x, y) = 2x - 2 \quad \text{and} \quad f_y(x, y) = 2y - 4$$

so that $f_x(x, y) = 0 = f_y(x, y)$ only if $x = 1$ and $y = 2$. But $f(1, 2) = -11$. Consequently the maximum and minimum values of f on $x^2 + y^2 \leq 16$ are $10 + 8\sqrt{5}$ and -11, respectively.

65. Let $g(x, y, z) = x^2 + y^2 - z$, so the constraint is $g(x, y, z) = x^2 + y^2 - z = 2$. Since grad $f(x, y, z) = \frac{2x}{z^2 + 5}\vec{i} + \frac{2y}{z^2 + 5}\vec{j} - \frac{2z(x^2 + y^2)}{(z^2 + 5)^2}\vec{k}$ and grad $g(x, y, z) = 2x\vec{i} + 2y\vec{j} - \vec{k}$, it follows that grad $f(x, y, z) = \lambda$grad $g(x, y, z)$ if

$$\frac{2x}{z^2 + 5} = 2x\lambda, \quad \frac{2y}{z^2 + 5} = 2y\lambda, \quad \text{and} \quad \frac{-2z(x^2 + y^2)}{(z^2 + 5)^2} = -\lambda \qquad (*)$$

From the first equation, $x = 0$ or $\lambda = \frac{1}{z^2 + 5}$. Assume that $\lambda = \frac{1}{z^2 + 5}$. Then the third equation is transformed into $2z(x^2 + y^2) = z^2 + 5$. With the help of the constraint this means that $2z(2 + z) = z^2 + 5$, so that $z^2 + 4z - 5 = 0$, and hence $z = 1$ or $z = -5$. If $z = 1$, then from the constraint, $x^2 + y^2 = 2 + 1 = 3$, so $f(x, y, 1) = \frac{x^2 + y^2}{1^2 + 5} = \frac{3}{6} = \frac{1}{2}$. If $z = -5$, then from the constraint, $x^2 + y^2 = 2 - 5 = -3$, which can't be true. Finally we assume that $\lambda \neq \frac{1}{z^2 + 5}$. Then by the first two equations in (*) we have $x = 0$ and $y = 0$, respectively. The constraint becomes $0^2 + 0^2 - z = 2$, so $z = -2$. But $f(0, 0, -2) = 0$. Consequently the maximum value of f is $\frac{1}{2}$ and the minimum value is 0.

66. Let D be the region consisting of all (x, y, z) such that $x^2 + y^2 - 2 \leq z \leq 6$. The boundary of D consists of the portion of the paraboloid $x^2 + y^2 - 2 = z$ for which $-2 \leq z \leq 6$ and the portion of the plane $z = 6$ for which $x^2 + y^2 \leq 8$. By the solution of Exercise 65, the extreme values on the portion of the boundary on the paraboloid $x^2 + y^2 - 2 = z$ (or $x^2 + y^2 - z = 2$) are $\frac{1}{2}$ and 0.

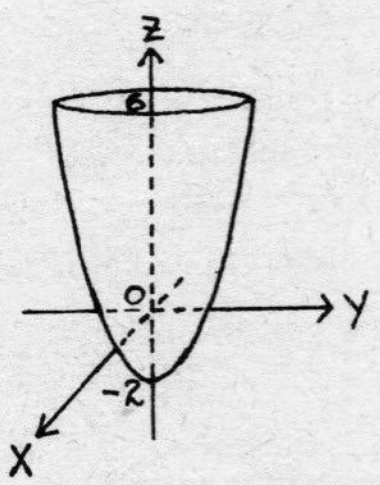

Since $f(x, y, z) = \frac{x^2 + y^2}{41}$ if $z = 6$, the extreme values of f on the part of the boundary on the plane $z = 6$ are 0 and $\frac{8}{41}$. Thus the extreme values of f on the boundary of D are $\frac{1}{2}$ and 0. Next we find the critical points of f in the interior of D. $f_x(x, y, z) = \frac{2x}{z^2 + 5}$, $f_y(x, y, z) = \frac{2y}{z^2 + 5}$, and $f_z(x, y, z) = \frac{-2z(x^2 + y^2)}{z^2 + 5}$. Thus $f_x(x, y, z) = f_y(x, y, z) = f_z(x, y, z) = 0$ if $x = 0$ and $y = 0$, so the critical points of f are of the form $(0, 0, z)$. Since $f(0, 0, z) = 0$, it follows that the maximum value of f on D is $\frac{1}{2}$ and the minimum value is 0.

67. Let (x, y, z) be a vertex of the parallelepiped that is on the ellipsoid and in the first octant. Let $V(x, y, z) = 8xyz$ denote the volume of the parallelepiped. Let $g(x, y, z) = x^2 + 4y^2 + 9z^2$, so the constraint is $g(x, y, z) = x^2 + 4y^2 + 9z^2 = 36$. Since grad $V(x, y, z) = 8yz\vec{i} + 8xz\vec{j} + 8xy\vec{k}$ and grad $g(x, y, z) = 2x\vec{i} + 8y\vec{j} + 18z\vec{k}$, it follows that grad $V(x, y, z) = \lambda$ grad $g(x, y, z)$ if

$$8yz = 2x\lambda, \quad 8xz = 8y\lambda, \quad \text{and} \quad 8xy = 18z\lambda$$

If x, y, or z is zero, then the volume is 0. Otherwise, $x > 0$, $y > 0$, and $z > 0$, and we can solve for λ in the three equations:

$$\lambda = \frac{4yz}{x}, \quad \lambda = \frac{xz}{y}, \quad \text{and} \quad \lambda = \frac{4xy}{9z} \qquad (*)$$

From the first two equations in (*) we obtain $\frac{4yz}{x} = \frac{xz}{y}$, so that $y = \frac{x}{2}$; from the first and third equations in (*) we obtain $\frac{4yz}{x} = \frac{4xy}{9z}$, so that $z = \frac{x}{3}$. The constraint becomes $x^2 + 4(\frac{x}{2})^2 + 9(\frac{x}{3})^2 = 36$, so that $x = 2\sqrt{3}$. Then $y = \sqrt{3}$ and $z = \frac{2\sqrt{3}}{3}$. Consequently the dimensions of the parallelepiped with largest volume are $4\sqrt{3}$, $2\sqrt{3}$, and $\frac{4}{3}\sqrt{3}$.

68. Notice that (p, f) is in the domain of q only if $p > f > 0$. Now $q_p(p, f) = \frac{f(p - f) - pf}{(p - f)^2} = \frac{f^2}{(p - f)^2}$ and $q_f(p, f) = \frac{p(p - f) - pf(-1)}{(p - f)^2} = \frac{p^2}{(p - f)^2}$. Thus $q_f(p, f) > q_p(p, f)$ for (p, f) in the domain of q.

69. $\frac{\partial T}{\partial \dot\theta} = m\ell^2\dot\theta$, so that $\frac{d}{dt}\left(\frac{\partial T}{\partial \dot\theta}\right) = \left[\frac{\partial}{\partial \dot\theta}\left(\frac{\partial T}{\partial \dot\theta}\right)\right]\frac{d\dot\theta}{dt} = \left[\frac{\partial}{\partial \dot\theta}(m\ell^2\dot\theta)\right]\frac{d\dot\theta}{dt} = m\ell^2\ddot\theta$.

Also $\frac{\partial V}{\partial \theta} = mg\ell\theta$. Thus Lagrange's equation becomes $m\ell^2\ddot\theta + mg\ell\theta = 0$, or rather, $\ddot\theta + \frac{g}{\ell}\theta = 0$.

70. Let x denote the number of pickers and y the number of hours that each picker harvests. The total cost to the farmer is the sum of the total wages $6xy$ of the pickers, the total wages $10y$ of the supervisor, the payment $10x$ to the union, and the service charge $\frac{50,000}{\sqrt{V}}$. Thus the total cost is given by $C(x, y, V) = 6xy + 10y + 10x + \frac{50,000}{\sqrt{V}}$. Since the volume $V = 625xy$, we let $g(x, y, V) = 625xy - V$, so the constraint is $g(x, y, V) = 625xy - V = 0$. Since $\text{grad } C(x, y, V) = (6y + 10)\,\vec{i} + (6x + 10)\,\vec{j} - \frac{50,000}{2V^{3/2}}\,\vec{k}$ and $\text{grad } g(x, y, V) = 625y\,\vec{i} + 625x\,\vec{j} - \vec{k}$, it follows that $\text{grad } C(x, y, V) = \lambda \text{ grad } g(x, y, V)$ if

$$6y + 10 = 625y\lambda\ , \quad 6x + 10 = 625x\lambda\ , \quad \text{and} \quad \frac{-50,000}{2V^{3/2}} = -\lambda \qquad (*)$$

From the first two equations, $6xy + 10x = 625xy\lambda = 6xy + 10y$, so that $x = y$. Using the constraint with $x = y$, we have $V = 625y^2$, so the third equation in (*) becomes

$$\lambda = \frac{25,000}{V^{3/2}} = \frac{25,000}{(625y^2)^{3/2}} = \frac{8}{5y^3}$$

Then the first equation in (*) becomes $6y + 10 = 625y\left(\frac{8}{5y^3}\right) = \frac{1000}{y^2}$, so that $3y^3 + 5y^2 - 500 = 0$. This equation holds if $y = 5$, and in fact, $3y^3 + 5y^2 - 500 = (y - 5)(3y^2 + 20y + 100)$. Since $3y^2 + 20y + 100 = 0$ has no zeros, $y = 5$ is the only solution of $3y^3 + 5y^2 - 500 = 0$. Since the minimum value of C exists by hypothesis, it occurs for $y = 5$ and thus $x = 5$. Then $V = 625(5)(5) = 15,625$. In this case 5 pickers are hired, and the volume is 15,625 tomatoes.

14

MULTIPLE INTEGRALS

Section 14.1

1. a. $\sum_{k=1}^{3} f(x_k,y_k)\Delta A_k = f(-2,0)\Delta A_1 + f(-2,1)\Delta A_2 + f(-1,0)\Delta A_3$

$= 4(1) + 3(1) + 4(1) = 11$

b. $\sum_{k=1}^{3} f(x_k,y_k)\Delta A_k = f(-1,1)\Delta A_1 + f(-1,2)\Delta A_2 + f(0,1)\Delta A_3$

$= 3(1) + 2(1) + 3(1) = 8$

2. Number the squares as in the diagram.

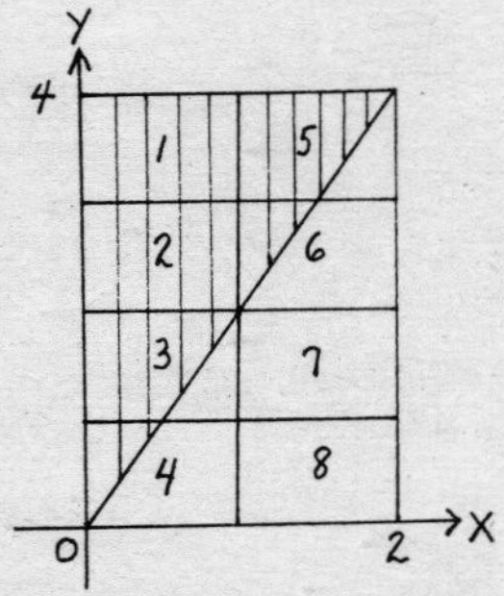

a. $L_f(\mathcal{P}) = f(0,3)\Delta A_1 + f(0,2)\Delta A_2$

$= 3(1) + 2(1) = 5$

b. $U_f(\mathcal{P}) = f(1,4)\Delta A_1 + f(1,3)\Delta A_2$

$+ f(1,2)\Delta A_3 + f(\frac{1}{2},1)\Delta A_4$

$+ f(2,4)\Delta A_5 + f(\frac{3}{2},3)\Delta A_6$

$+ f(1,2)\Delta A_7 = 5(1) + 4(1) + 3(1) + \frac{3}{2}(1) + 6(1)$

$+ \frac{9}{2}(1) + 3(1) = 27$

c. $\sum_{k=1}^{2} f(x_k,y_k)\Delta A_k = f(\frac{1}{2},\frac{7}{2})\Delta A_1 + f(\frac{1}{2},\frac{5}{2})\Delta A_2 = 4(1) + 3(1) = 7$

3. $\int_0^1\int_{-1}^1 x\,dy\,dx = \int_0^1 xy\Big|_{-1}^1 dx = \int_0^1 2x\,dx = x^2\Big|_0^1 = 1$

4. $\int_{-5}^{-3}\int_{-2}^{3} y\,dy\,dx = \int_{-5}^{-3} \frac{1}{2}y^2\Big|_{-2}^{3} dx = \int_{-5}^{-3}\frac{5}{2}\,dx = \frac{5}{2}x\Big|_{-5}^{-3} = 5$

5. $\int_0^1\int_0^1 e^{x+y}\,dy\,dx = \int_0^1 e^{x+y}\Big|_0^1 dx = \int_0^1 (e^{x+1} - e^x)\,dx$

$= (e^{x+1} - e^x)\Big|_0^1 = e^2 - 2e + 1$

6. $\int_0^1\int_1^5 \frac{1}{r}\,dr\,ds = \int_0^1 \ln r\Big|_1^5 ds = \int_0^1 \ln 5\,ds = s\ln 5\Big|_0^1 = \ln 5$

7. $\int_0^1\int_x^{x^2} 1\,dy\,dx = \int_0^1 y\Big|_x^{x^2} dx = \int_0^1 (x^2 - x)\,dx = (\frac{1}{3}x^3 - \frac{1}{2}x^2)\Big|_0^1$

$= -\frac{1}{6}$

8. $\int_0^1\int_0^3 x\sqrt{x^2 + y}\,dy\,dx = \int_0^1 \frac{2}{3}x(x^2 + y)^{3/2}\Big|_0^3 dx$

$= \int_0^1 [\frac{2}{3}x(x^2 + 3)^{3/2} - \frac{2}{3}x^4]\,dx$

$= [\frac{2}{15}(x^2 + 3)^{5/2} - \frac{2}{15}x^5]\Big|_0^1$

$= \frac{64}{15} - \frac{2}{15} - \frac{2}{15}(3)^{5/2} = \frac{62}{15} - \frac{6}{5}\sqrt{3}$

9. $\int_0^1\int_0^y x\sqrt{y^2 - x^2}\,dx\,dy = \int_0^1 -\frac{1}{3}(y^2 - x^2)^{3/2}\Big|_0^y dy = \int_0^1 \frac{1}{3}y^3\,dy$

$= \frac{1}{12}y^4\Big|_0^1 = \frac{1}{12}$

10. $\int_0^2\int_0^{\sqrt{4-y^2}} y\,dx\,dy = \int_0^2 yx\Big|_0^{\sqrt{4-y^2}} dy = \int_0^2 y\sqrt{4 - y^2}\,dy$

$= -\frac{1}{3}(4 - y^2)^{3/2}\Big|_0^2 = \frac{8}{3}$

11. $\displaystyle\int_0^2\int_0^{\sqrt{4-y^2}} x\,dx\,dy = \int_0^2 \frac{1}{2}x^2\Big|_0^{\sqrt{4-y^2}} dy = \int_0^2 \frac{1}{2}(4-y^2)dy$

$\displaystyle = (2y - \frac{1}{6}y^3)\Big|_0^2 = \frac{8}{3}$

12. $\displaystyle\int_0^{2\pi}\int_0^1 r\sin\theta\,dr\,d\theta = \int_0^{2\pi}\frac{1}{2}r^2\sin\theta\Big|_0^1 d\theta = \int_0^{2\pi}\frac{1}{2}\sin\theta\,d\theta$

$\displaystyle = -\frac{1}{2}\cos\theta\Big|_0^{2\pi} = 0$

13. $\displaystyle\int_0^{2\pi}\int_0^1 r\sqrt{1-r^2}\,dr\,d\theta = \int_0^{2\pi} -\frac{1}{3}(1-r^2)^{3/2}\Big|_0^1 d\theta = \int_0^{2\pi}\frac{1}{3}\,d\theta$

$\displaystyle = \frac{1}{3}\theta\Big|_0^{2\pi} = \frac{2\pi}{3}$

14. $\displaystyle\int_0^{2\pi}\int_0^{1+\cos\theta} r\,dr\,d\theta = \int_0^{2\pi}\frac{1}{2}r^2\Big|_0^{1+\cos\theta} d\theta$

$\displaystyle = \int_0^{2\pi}\frac{1}{2}(1 + 2\cos\theta + \cos^2\theta)d\theta$

$\displaystyle = \int_0^{2\pi}(\frac{1}{2} + \cos\theta + \frac{1}{4} + \frac{1}{4}\cos 2\theta)d\theta$

$\displaystyle = (\frac{3}{4}\theta + \sin\theta + \frac{1}{8}\sin 2\theta)\Big|_0^{2\pi} = \frac{3\pi}{2}$

15. $\displaystyle\int_1^3\int_0^x \frac{2}{x^2+y^2}\,dy\,dx = \int_1^3 \frac{2}{x}\arctan\frac{y}{x}\Big|_0^x dx = \int_1^3 \frac{\pi}{2x}\,dx$

$\displaystyle = \frac{\pi}{2}\ln x\Big|_1^3 = \frac{\pi}{2}\ln 3$

16. $\displaystyle\int_1^e\int_1^{\ln y} e^x\,dx\,dy = \int_1^e e^x\Big|_1^{\ln y} dy = \int_1^e (y-e)dy = (\frac{1}{2}y^2 - ey)\Big|_1^e$

$\displaystyle = e - \frac{1}{2}e^2 - \frac{1}{2}$

17. $\displaystyle\int_0^1\int_0^x e^{(x^2)}\,dy\,dx = \int_0^1 ye^{(x^2)}\Big|_0^x dx = \int_0^1 xe^{(x^2)}\,dx$

$\displaystyle = \frac{1}{2}e^{(x^2)}\Big|_0^1 = \frac{1}{2}(e-1)$

18. $\displaystyle\int_{\ln\pi/6}^{\ln\pi/2}\int_0^{e^y}\cos e^y\,dx\,dy = \int_{\ln\pi/6}^{\ln\pi/2} x\cos e^y\Big|_0^{e^y} dy$

$\displaystyle = \int_{\ln\pi/6}^{\ln\pi/2} e^y\cos e^y\,dy$

$\displaystyle = \sin e^y\Big|_{\ln\pi/6}^{\ln\pi/2} = \frac{1}{2}$

19. $\displaystyle\int_0^{\pi/4}\int_0^{\cos y} e^x\sin y\,dx\,dy = \int_0^{\pi/4} e^x\sin y\Big|_0^{\cos y} dy$

$\displaystyle = \int_0^{\pi/4}(e^{\cos y}\sin y - \sin y)dy$

$\displaystyle = (-e^{\cos y} + \cos y)\Big|_0^{\pi/4}$

$\displaystyle = e - e^{\sqrt{2}/2} + \frac{\sqrt{2}}{2} - 1$

20. $\displaystyle\iint_R (x+y)dA = \int_2^3\int_4^6 (x+y)\,dy\,dx$

$\displaystyle = \int_2^3 (xy + \frac{1}{2}y^2)\Big|_4^6 dx$

$\displaystyle = \int_2^3 (2x+10)dx$

$\displaystyle = (x^2 + 10x)\Big|_2^3 = 15$

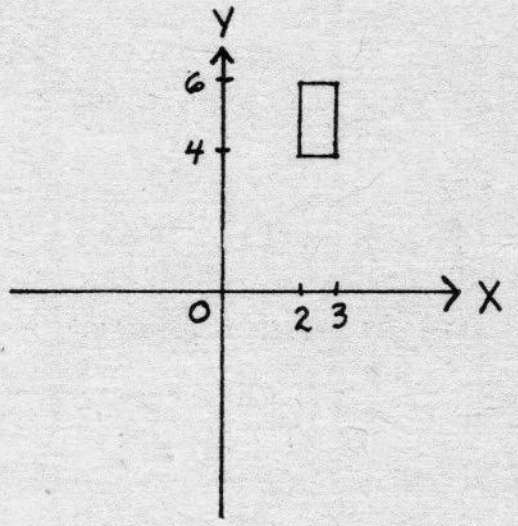

21. $\displaystyle\iint_R (x+y)dA = \int_0^2\int_{2x}^4 (x+y)dy\,dx$

$\displaystyle = \int_0^2 (xy + \frac{1}{2}y^2)\Big|_{2x}^4 dx$

$\displaystyle = \int_0^2 (4x + 8 - 4x^2)dx$

$\displaystyle = (2x^2 + 8x - \frac{4}{3}x^3)\Big|_0^2 = \frac{40}{3}$

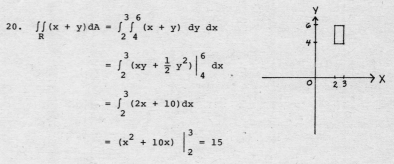

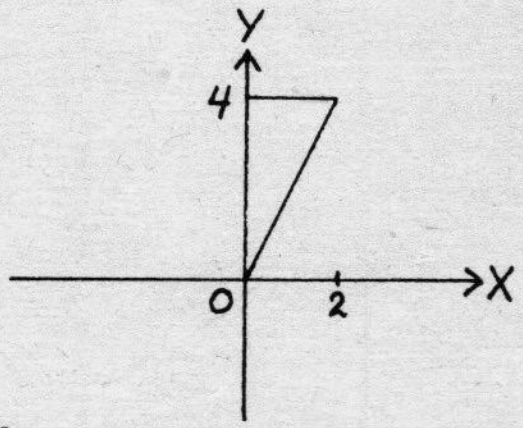

22. $\iint_R xy^2\,dA = \int_{-1}^{1}\int_0^{4-x^2} xy^2\,dy\,dx$

$= \int_{-1}^{1} \frac{1}{3}xy^3 \Big|_0^{4-x^2} dx$

$= \int_{-1}^{1} \frac{1}{3}x(4 - x^2)^3\,dx$

$= -\frac{1}{24}(4 - x^2)^4 \Big|_{-1}^{1} = 0$

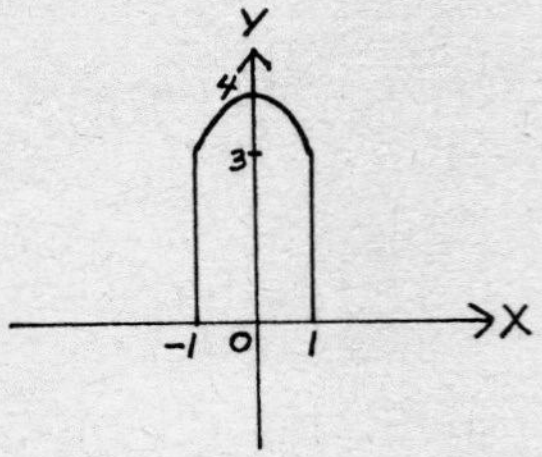

23. $\iint_R x\,dA = \int_3^5\int_1^x x\,dy\,dx = \int_3^5 xy \Big|_1^x dx$

$= \int_3^5 (x^2 - x)\,dx$

$= (\frac{1}{3}x^3 - \frac{1}{2}x^2)\Big|_3^5$

$= \frac{74}{3}$

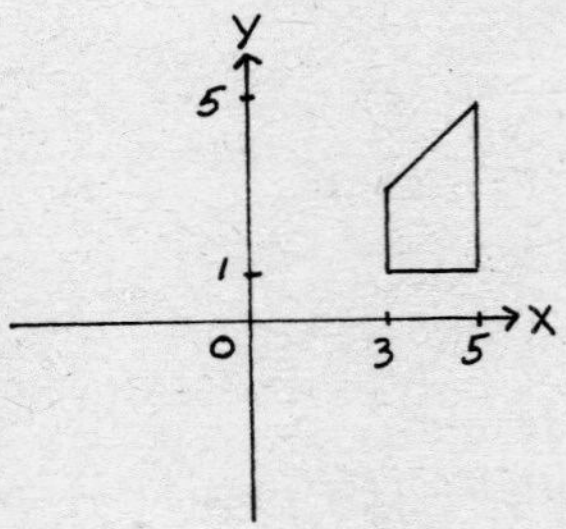

24. $\iint_R x(x - 1)e^{xy}\,dA = \int_0^2\int_0^{2-x} x(x - 1)e^{xy}\,dy\,dx$

$= \int_0^2 (x - 1)e^{xy}\Big|_0^{2-x} dx$

$= \int_0^2 [(x - 1)e^{2x-x^2}$

$- (x - 1)]dx$

$= (-\frac{1}{2}e^{2x-x^2} - \frac{1}{2}x^2$

$+ x)\Big|_0^2 = 0$

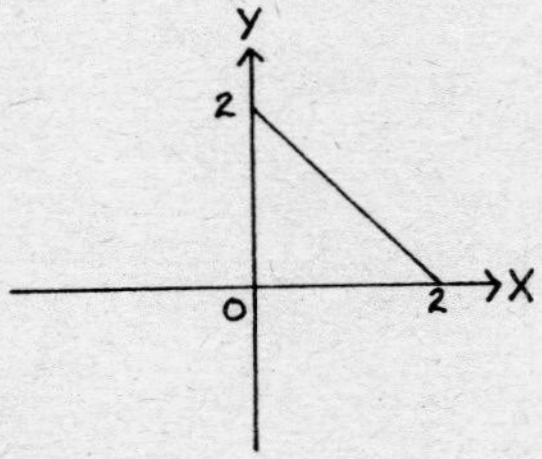

25. The lines intersect at (x,y) such that $5 + x = y = -x + 7$, so that $2x = 2$, or $x = 1$. Since $5 + x \geq 7 - x$ for x in $[1,10]$, we have

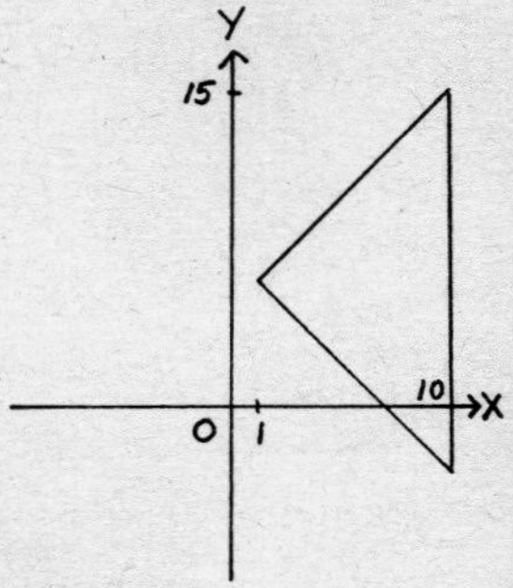

$\iint_R (3x - 5)\,dA = \int_1^{10}\int_{7-x}^{5+x} (3x - 5)\,dy\,dx$

$= \int_1^{10} (3x - 5)y \Big|_{7-x}^{5+x} dx$

$= \int_1^{10} (3x - 5)(2x - 2)\,dx$

$= \int_1^{10} (6x^2 - 16x + 10)\,dx$

$= (2x^3 - 8x^2 + 10x)\Big|_1^{10}$

$= 1296$

26. The graphs intersect at (x,y) such that $x = y = x^2$, so that $x = 0$ or $x = 1$. Thus

$\iint_R xy\,dA = \int_0^1\int_{x^2}^{x} xy\,dy\,dx = \int_0^1 \frac{1}{2}xy^2\Big|_{x^2}^{x} dx$

$= \int_0^1 (\frac{1}{2}x^3 - \frac{1}{2}x^5)\,dx$

$= (\frac{1}{8}x^4 - \frac{1}{12}x^6)\Big|_0^1 = \frac{1}{24}$

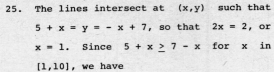

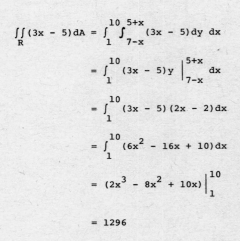

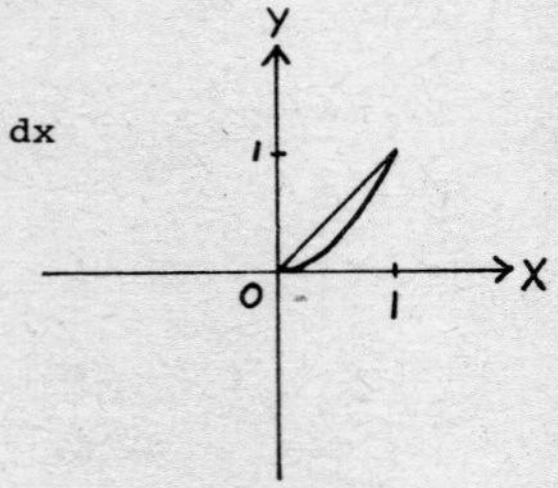

27. $\iint_R 1\,dA = \int_\pi^{2\pi}\int_{\sin x}^{1+x} 1\,dy\,dx = \int_\pi^{2\pi} y\Big|_{\sin x}^{1+x} dx$

$= \int_\pi^{2\pi} (1 + x - \sin x)dx$

$= (x + \frac{1}{2}x^2 + \cos x)\Big|_\pi^{2\pi} = \frac{3}{2}\pi^2$

$+ \pi + 2$

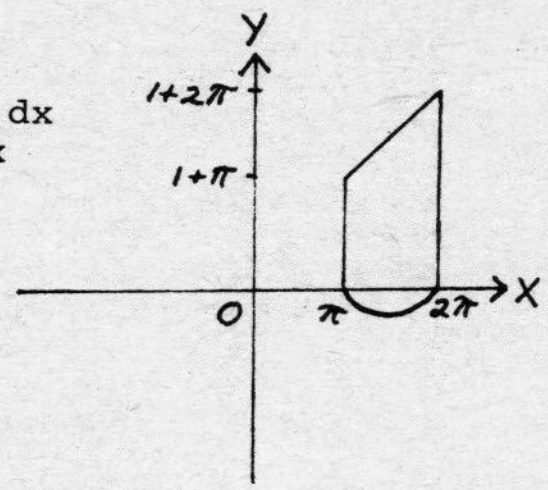

28. The graphs intersect at (x,y) such that $1 + x^2 = y = 9 - x^2$, so that $2x^2 = 8$, or $x = -2$ or $x = 2$. Thus

$\iint_R (4 + x^2)dA = \int_{-2}^{2}\int_{1+x^2}^{9-x^2} (4 + x^2)dy\,dx$

$= \int_{-2}^{2} (4 + x^2)y\Big|_{1+x^2}^{9-x^2} dx$

$= \int_{-2}^{2} (4 + x^2)(8 - 2x^2)dx$

$= \int_{-2}^{2} (32 - 2x^4)dx$

$= (32x - \frac{2}{5}x^5)\Big|_{-2}^{2} = \frac{512}{5}$

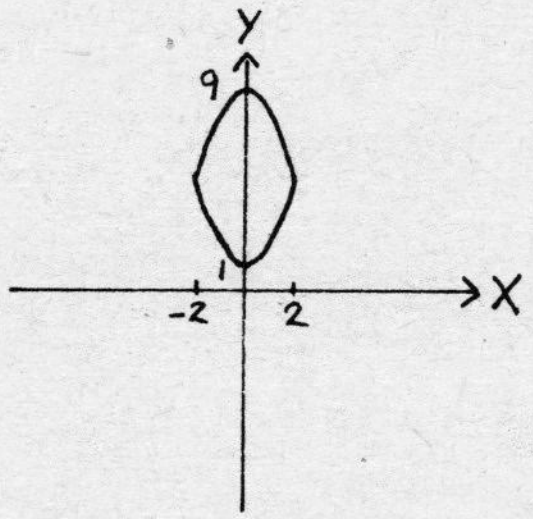

29. The graphs intersect at (x,y) such that $y^2 = x = 2 - y$, so that $y^2 + y - 2 = 0$, or $y = -2$ or $y = 1$. Thus

$\iint_R (1 - y)dA = \int_{-2}^{1}\int_{y^2}^{2-y} (1 - y)dx\,dy$

$= \int_{-2}^{1} (1 - y)x\Big|_{y^2}^{2-y} dy$

$= \int_{-2}^{1} (1 - y)(2 - y - y^2)dy$

$= \int_{-2}^{1} (2 - 3y + y^3)dy$

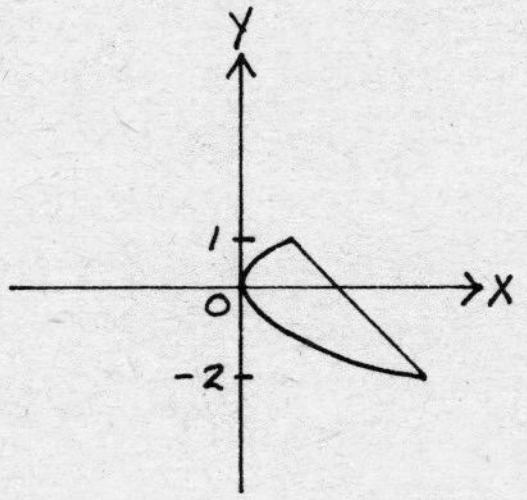

$= (2y - \frac{3}{2}y^2 + \frac{1}{4}y^4)\Big|_{-2}^{1}$

$= \frac{27}{4}$

30. R is the region bounded by the graphs of $y = \sqrt{16 - x^2}$ and $y = -\sqrt{16 - x^2}$. Thus

$\iint_R x\,dA = \int_{-4}^{4}\int_{-\sqrt{16-x^2}}^{\sqrt{16-x^2}} x\,dy\,dx$

$= \int_{-4}^{4} xy\Big|_{-\sqrt{16-x^2}}^{\sqrt{16-x^2}} dx$

$= \int_{-4}^{4} 2x\sqrt{16 - x^2}\,dx$

$= -\frac{2}{3}(16 - x^2)^{3/2}\Big|_{-4}^{4} = 0$

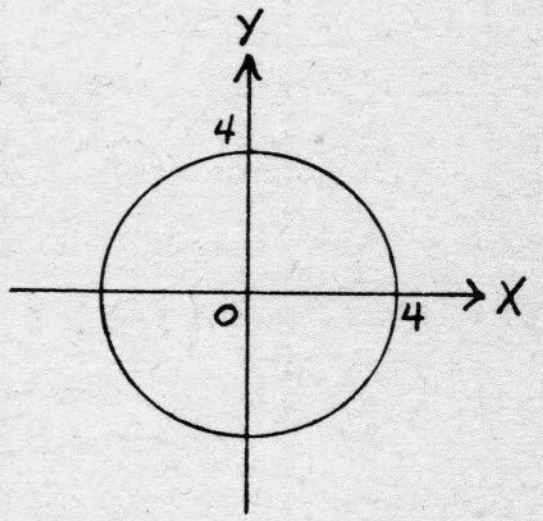

31. The line and the circle intersect at (x,y) such that $(1 - x)^2 = y^2 = 1 - x^2$, or $2x^2 - 2x = 0$, or $x = 0$ or $x = 1$. Since R lies above the line $y = 1 - x$, it follows that R lies above the x axis. Thus the part of the circle $x^2 + y^2 = 1$ that bounds R is the graph of $y = \sqrt{1 - x^2}$ for $0 \le x \le 1$. Thus

$\iint_R xy^2\,dA = \int_0^1\int_{1-x}^{\sqrt{1-x^2}} xy^2\,dy\,dx$

$= \int_0^1 \frac{1}{3}xy^3\Big|_{1-x}^{\sqrt{1-x^2}} dx$

$= \int_0^1 [\frac{1}{3}x(1 - x^2)^{3/2}$

$- \frac{1}{3}x(1 - x)^3]dx$

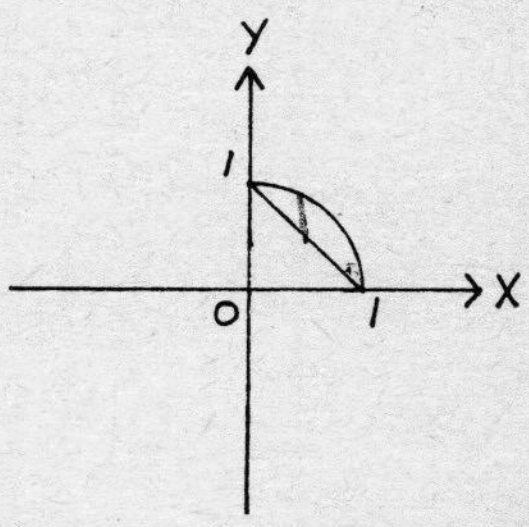

$$= \int_0^1 [\tfrac{1}{3} x(1 - x^2)^{3/2} - \tfrac{1}{3} x + x^2 - x^3 + \tfrac{1}{3} x^4]dx$$

$$= [-\tfrac{1}{15}(1 - x^2)^{5/2} - \tfrac{1}{6} x^2 + \tfrac{1}{3} x^3 - \tfrac{1}{4} x^4 + \tfrac{1}{15} x^5]\Big|_0^1 = \tfrac{1}{20}$$

32. Since $\sin x \geq 0$ for $0 \leq x \leq \pi$ and $\sin x \leq 0$ for $\pi \leq x \leq 2\pi$, we have

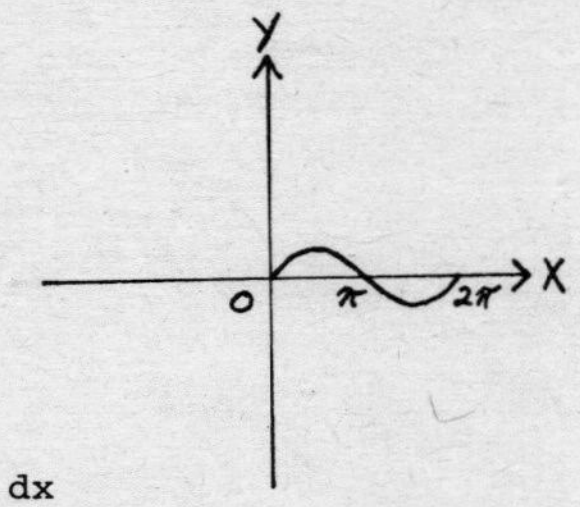

$$\iint_R 2y\, dA = \int_0^{\pi}\int_0^{\sin x} 2y\, dy\, dx + \int_{\pi}^{2\pi}\int_{\sin x}^{0} 2y\, dy\, dx$$

$$= \int_0^{\pi} y^2\Big|_0^{\sin x} dx + \int_{\pi}^{2\pi} y^2\Big|_{\sin x}^{0} dx$$

$$= \int_0^{\pi} \sin^2 x\, dx - \int_{\pi}^{2\pi} \sin^2 x\, dx$$

$$= \int_0^{\pi} (\tfrac{1}{2} - \tfrac{1}{2}\cos 2x)dx - \int_{\pi}^{2\pi} (\tfrac{1}{2} - \tfrac{1}{2}\cos 2x)dx$$

$$= (\tfrac{1}{2} x - \tfrac{1}{4}\sin 2x)\Big|_0^{\pi} - (\tfrac{1}{2} x - \tfrac{1}{4}\sin 2x)\Big|_{\pi}^{2\pi} = \tfrac{\pi}{2} - \tfrac{\pi}{2} = 0$$

33. The graphs intersect at (x,y) such that $x^3 + x^2 + 1 = y = x^3 + x + 1$, so that $x^2 = x$, or $x = 0$ or $x = 1$. Since $x^3 + x^2 + 1 \geq x^3 + x + 1$ for $-1 \leq x \leq 0$ and $x^3 + x + 1 \geq x^3 + x^2 + 1$ for $0 \leq x \leq 1$, we have

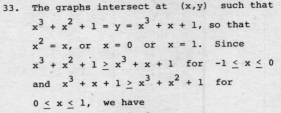

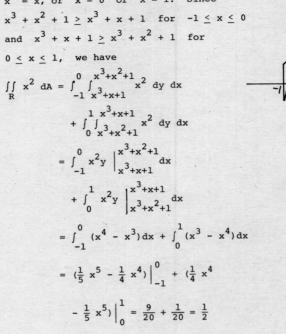

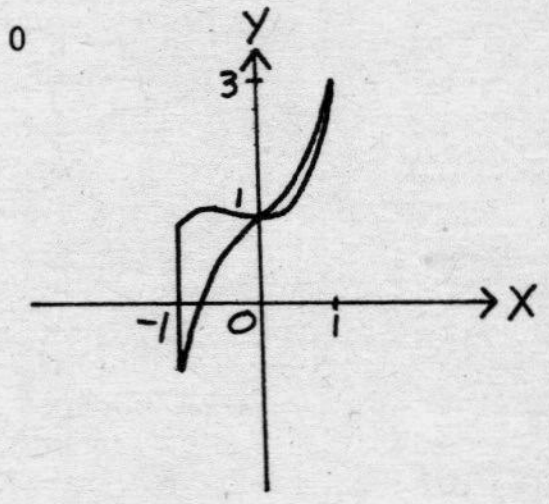

$$\iint_R x^2\, dA = \int_{-1}^{0}\int_{x^3+x+1}^{x^3+x^2+1} x^2\, dy\, dx + \int_0^1\int_{x^3+x^2+1}^{x^3+x+1} x^2\, dy\, dx$$

$$= \int_{-1}^{0} x^2 y\Big|_{x^3+x+1}^{x^3+x^2+1} dx + \int_0^1 x^2 y\Big|_{x^3+x^2+1}^{x^3+x+1} dx$$

$$= \int_{-1}^{0} (x^4 - x^3)dx + \int_0^1 (x^3 - x^4)dx$$

$$= (\tfrac{1}{5} x^5 - \tfrac{1}{4} x^4)\Big|_{-1}^{0} + (\tfrac{1}{4} x^4 - \tfrac{1}{5} x^5)\Big|_0^1 = \tfrac{9}{20} + \tfrac{1}{20} = \tfrac{1}{2}$$

34. The intersection of the solid region with the xy plane is the region R bounded by the lines $x = 0$, $x = 2$, $y = 0$, and $y = 1$. Thus

$$V = \iint_R (1 + x + y)dA = \int_0^2\int_0^1 (1 + x + y)dy\, dx$$

$$= \int_0^2 (y + xy + \tfrac{1}{2} y^2)\Big|_0^1 dx = \int_0^2 (\tfrac{3}{2} + x)dx = (\tfrac{3}{2} x + \tfrac{1}{2} x^2)\Big|_0^2 = 5$$

35. The intersection of the solid region with the xy plane is the region R bounded by the lines $x + 2y = 6$ (or $y = \frac{1}{2}(6 - x)$), $x = 0$, and $y = 0$. Thus

$$V = \iint_R \frac{1}{3}(6 - x - 2y)\,dA = \int_0^6 \int_0^{\frac{1}{2}(6-x)} \frac{1}{3}(6 - x - 2y)\,dy\,dx$$

$$= \int_0^6 \frac{1}{3}(6y - xy - y^2)\Big|_0^{\frac{1}{2}(6-x)} dx = \int_0^6 \frac{1}{12}(6 - x)^2\,dx$$

$$= -\frac{1}{36}(6 - x)^3\Big|_0^6 = 6$$

36. The intersection of the solid region with the xy plane is the region R bounded by the lines $x + y = 1$ (or $y = 1 - x$), $x = 0$, and $y = 0$. Thus

$$V = \iint_R \frac{1}{2}(6 - x - 4y)\,dA = \int_0^1 \int_0^{1-x} \frac{1}{2}(6 - x - 4y)\,dy\,dx$$

$$= \int_0^1 \frac{1}{2}(6y - xy - 2y^2)\Big|_0^{1-x} dx = \int_0^1 \frac{1}{2}[6(1-x) - x(1-x) - 2(1-x)^2]\,dx$$

$$= \int_0^1 (2 - \frac{3}{2}x - \frac{1}{2}x^2)\,dx = (2x - \frac{3}{4}x^2 - \frac{1}{6}x^3)\Big|_0^1 = \frac{13}{12}$$

37. The intersection of the solid region with the xy plane is the region R bounded by the lines $x + y = 1$ (or $y = 1 - x$), $x = 0$, and $y = 0$. Thus

$$V = \iint_R (x^2 + y^2)\,dA = \int_0^1 \int_0^{1-x} (x^2 + y^2)\,dy\,dx$$

$$= \int_0^1 (x^2y + \frac{1}{3}y^3)\Big|_0^{1-x} dx = \int_0^1 [x^2 - x^3 + \frac{1}{3}(1 - x)^3]\,dx$$

$$= [\frac{1}{3}x^3 - \frac{1}{4}x^4 - \frac{1}{12}(1 - x)^4]\Big|_0^1 = \frac{1}{6}$$

38. The intersection of the solid region with the xy plane is the region R bounded by the lines $x = 2y$ (or $y = \frac{1}{2}x$), $x = 0$, $x = 2$, and $y = 0$. Thus

$$V = \iint_R x^2\,dA = \int_0^2 \int_0^{\frac{1}{2}x} x^2\,dy\,dx = \int_0^2 x^2y\Big|_0^{\frac{1}{2}x} dx$$

$$= \int_0^2 \frac{1}{2}x^3\,dx = \frac{1}{8}x^4\Big|_0^2 = 2$$

39. The intersection of the solid region with the xy plane is the vertically simple region R between the graphs of $y = 0$ and $y = \sqrt{4 - x^2}$ on $[0,2]$. Thus

$$V = \iint_R y\,dA = \int_0^2 \int_0^{\sqrt{4-x^2}} y\,dy\,dx = \int_0^2 \frac{1}{2}y^2\Big|_0^{\sqrt{4-x^2}} dx$$

$$= \int_0^2 (2 - \frac{1}{2}x^2)\,dx = (2x - \frac{1}{6}x^3)\Big|_0^2 = \frac{8}{3}$$

40. The intersection of the solid region with the xy plane is the horizontally simple region R between the graphs of $x = 1 - (y - 1)^2$ and $x = y$. These intersect at (x,y) such that $1 - (y - 1)^2 = x = y$, so that $y^2 - y = 0$, and thus $y = 0$ or $y = 1$. Thus

$$V = \iint_R y^2\,dA = \int_0^1 \int_y^{1-(y-1)^2} y^2\,dx\,dy = \int_0^1 y^2x\Big|_y^{1-(y-1)^2} dy$$

$$= \int_0^1 [y^2 - y^2(y - 1)^2 - y^3]\,dy = \int_0^1 (-y^4 + y^3)\,dy$$

$$= (-\frac{1}{5}y^5 + \frac{1}{4}y^4)\Big|_0^1 = \frac{1}{20}$$

41. The intersection of the solid region with the xy plane is the region R in the first quadrant that lies inside the circle $x^2 + y^2 = 1$. Thus R is the vertically simple region between the graphs of $y = 0$ and $y = \sqrt{1 - x^2}$ on $[0,1]$, so that

$$V = \iint_R \sqrt{1 - x^2}\,dA = \int_0^1 \int_0^{\sqrt{1-x^2}} \sqrt{1 - x^2}\,dy\,dx = \int_0^1 y\sqrt{1 - x^2}\Big|_0^{\sqrt{1-x^2}} dx$$

$$= \int_0^1 (1 - x^2)\,dx = (x - \frac{1}{3}x^3)\Big|_0^1 = \frac{2}{3}$$

42. The intersection of the sphere $x^2 + y^2 + z^2 = 1$ with the xy plane is the circle $x^2 + y^2 = 1$, so that the intersection of the solid region with the xy plane is the vertically simple region R between the graphs of $y = -\sqrt{1 - x^2}$ and $y = \sqrt{1 - x^2}$ on

$[-1,1]$. Thus

$$V = \iint_R \sqrt{1 - x^2 - y^2}\, dA = \int_{-1}^{1} \int_{-\sqrt{1-x^2}}^{\sqrt{1-x^2}} \sqrt{1 - x^2 - y^2}\, dy\, dx$$

$$= \int_{-1}^{1} \int_{-\pi/2}^{\pi/2} \sqrt{1 - x^2 - (1 - x^2)\sin^2 u}\, \sqrt{1 - x^2} \cos u\, du\, dx$$

$$= \int_{-1}^{1} \int_{-\pi/2}^{\pi/2} (1 - x^2) \cos^2 u\, du\, dx = \int_{-1}^{1} \int_{-\pi/2}^{\pi/2} (1 - x^2)\left(\frac{1}{2}\right.$$

$$\left. + \frac{1}{2} \cos 2u\right) du\, dx = \int_{-1}^{1} (1 - x^2)\left(\frac{1}{2} u + \frac{1}{4} \sin 2u\right)\Big|_{-\pi/2}^{\pi/2} dx$$

$$= \int_{-1}^{1} \frac{\pi}{2}(1 - x^2)\, dx = \frac{\pi}{2}\left(x - \frac{1}{3} x^3\right)\Big|_{-1}^{1} = \frac{2}{3}\pi$$

43. The intersection of the solid region with the xy plane is the region R between the graphs of $y = x$ and $y = x^3$. These intersect at (x,y) such that $x = y = x^3$, so that $x = -1$, $x = 0$, or $x = 1$. Since $x^3 \geq x$ for $-1 \leq x \leq 0$ and $x \geq x^3$ for $0 \leq x \leq 1$, we have

$$V = \iint_R xy\, dA = \int_{-1}^{0} \int_{x}^{x^3} xy\, dy\, dx + \int_{0}^{1} \int_{x^3}^{x} xy\, dy\, dx = \int_{-1}^{0} \frac{1}{2} xy^2\Big|_{x}^{x^3} dx$$

$$+ \int_{0}^{1} \frac{1}{2} xy^2\Big|_{x^3}^{x} dx = \int_{-1}^{0} \frac{1}{2}(x^7 - x^3)\, dx + \int_{0}^{1} \frac{1}{2}(x^3 - x^7)\, dx$$

$$= \frac{1}{2}\left(\frac{1}{8} x^8 - \frac{1}{4} x^4\right)\Big|_{-1}^{0} + \frac{1}{2}\left(\frac{1}{4} x^4 - \frac{1}{8} x^8\right)\Big|_{0}^{1} = \frac{1}{8}$$

44. The intersection of the solid region with the xy plane is the vertically simple region R between the graphs of $y = x^2$ and $y = x$. These intersect at (x,y) such that $x = y = x^2$, so that $x = 0$ or $x = 1$. Thus

$$V = \iint_R (10 + 2x + 3y)\, dA = \int_{0}^{1} \int_{x^2}^{x} (10 + 2x + 3y)\, dy\, dx$$

$$= \int_{0}^{1} \left(10y + 2xy + \frac{3}{2} y^2\right)\Big|_{x^2}^{x} dx$$

$$= \int_{0}^{1} \left(10x + 2x^2 + \frac{3}{2} x^2 - 10x^2 - 2x^3 - \frac{3}{2} x^4\right) dx$$

$$= \int_{0}^{1} \left(10x - \frac{13}{2} x^2 - 2x^3 - \frac{3}{2} x^4\right) dx = \left(5x^2 - \frac{13}{6} x^3 - \frac{1}{2} x^4\right.$$

$$\left. - \frac{3}{10} x^5\right)\Big|_{0}^{1} = \frac{61}{30}$$

45.

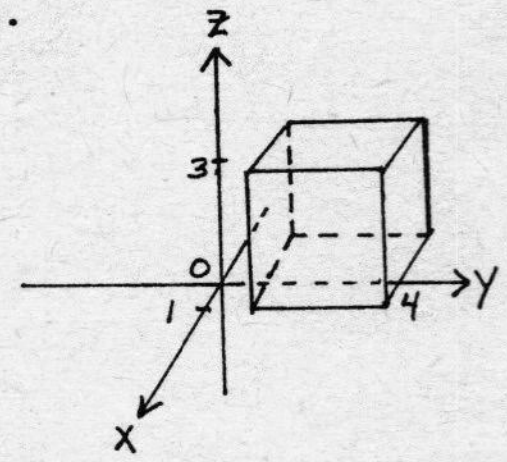

46.

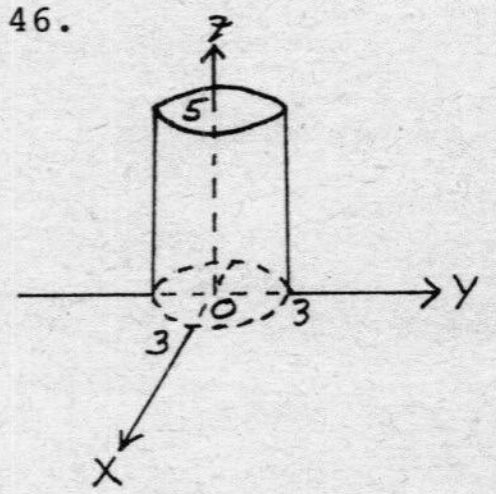

47.

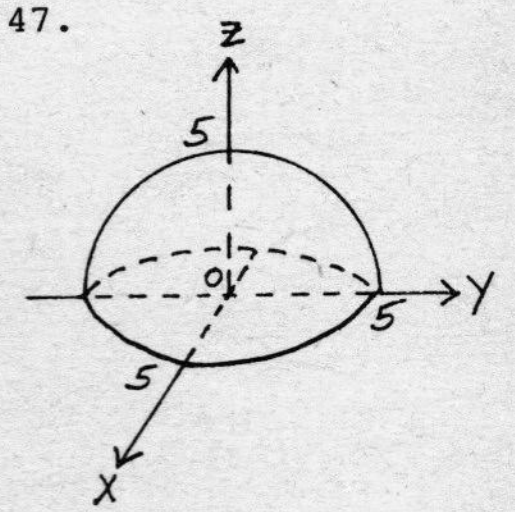

48.

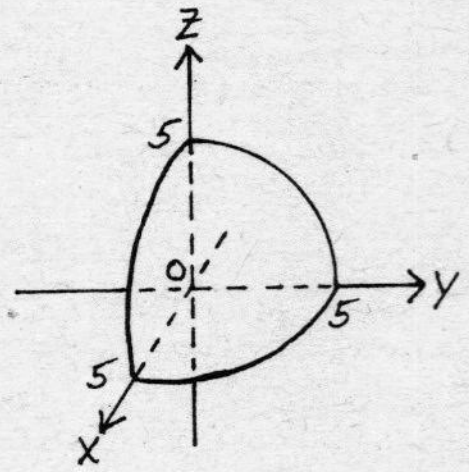

49.

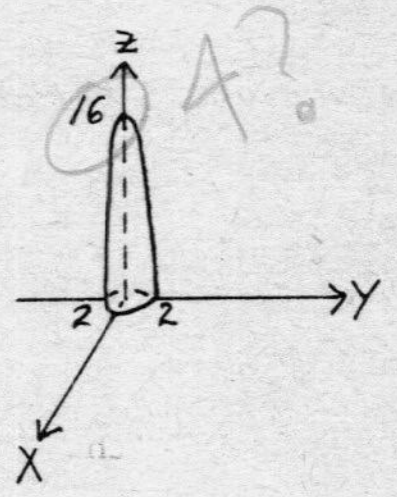

50.

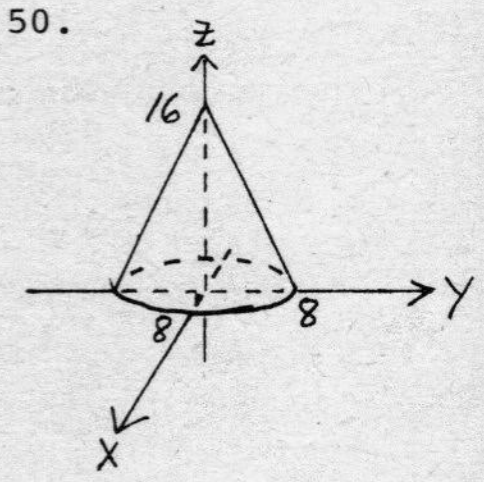

51. Since $x^2 \geq \sqrt{x}$ for $1 \leq x \leq 4$, we have

$$A = \int_{1}^{4} \int_{\sqrt{x}}^{x^2} 1\, dy\, dx = \int_{1}^{4} y\Big|_{\sqrt{x}}^{x^2} dx = \int_{1}^{4} (x^2 - \sqrt{x})\, dx$$

$$= \left(\frac{1}{3} x^3 - \frac{2}{3} x^{3/2}\right)\Big|_{1}^{4} = \frac{49}{3}$$

52. Since $\cosh x \geq \sinh x$ for all x, we have

$$A = \int_{-1}^{1} \int_{\sinh x}^{\cosh x} 1\, dy\, dx = \int_{-1}^{1} y\Big|_{\sinh x}^{\cosh x} dx$$

$$= \int_{-1}^{1} (\cosh x - \sinh x)\,dx = (\sinh x - \cosh x)\Big|_{-1}^{1} = 2 \sinh 1$$

53. The parabolas intersect at (x,y) such that $y^2 = x = 32 - y^2$, or $y^2 = 16$, or $y = -4$ or $y = 4$. Since $32 - y^2 \geq y^2$ for $-4 \leq y \leq 4$, we have

$$A = \int_{-4}^{4}\int_{y^2}^{32-y^2} 1\,dx\,dy = \int_{-4}^{4} x\Big|_{y^2}^{32-y^2} dy = \int_{-4}^{4} (32 - 2y^2)\,dy$$

$$= (32y - \tfrac{2}{3}y^3)\Big|_{-4}^{4} = \frac{512}{3}$$

54. The parabolas intersect at (x,y) such that $y^2 = x = 4y^2 - 3$, which means that $y^2 = 1$, or $y = -1$ or $y = 1$. Since $y^2 \geq 4y^2 - 3$ for $-1 \leq y \leq 1$, we have

$$A = \int_{-1}^{1}\int_{4y^2-3}^{y^2} 1\,dx\,dy = \int_{-1}^{1} x\Big|_{4y^2-3}^{y^2} dy = \int_{-1}^{1} (3 - 3y^2)\,dy$$

$$= (3y - y^3)\Big|_{-1}^{1} = 4$$

55. The line $y = x$ and the parabola $x = 2 - y^2$ intersect in the first quadrant at (x,y) such that $y \geq 0$ and $y = x = 2 - y^2$, or $y^2 + y - 2 = 0$, which means that $y = 1$. Since $x = 2 - y^2$ and $y \geq 0$ imply that $y = \sqrt{2 - x}$, and since $\sqrt{2 - x} \geq x$ for $-2 \leq x \leq 1$, we have

$$A = \int_{0}^{1}\int_{x}^{\sqrt{2-x}} 1\,dy\,dx = \int_{0}^{1} y\Big|_{x}^{\sqrt{2-x}} dx = \int_{0}^{1} (\sqrt{2 - x} - x)\,dx$$

$$= [-\tfrac{2}{3}(2 - x)^{3/2} - \tfrac{1}{2}x^2]\Big|_{0}^{1} = \tfrac{4}{3}\sqrt{2} - \tfrac{7}{6}$$

56. The graphs intersect at (x,y) such that $4 - x = y = \frac{3}{x}$, which means that $x^2 - 4x + 3 = 0$, or $x = 1$ or $x = 3$. Since $4 - x \geq \frac{3}{x}$ for $1 \leq x \leq 3$, we have

$$A = \int_{1}^{3}\int_{3/x}^{4-x} 1\,dy\,dx = \int_{1}^{3} y\Big|_{3/x}^{4-x} dx = \int_{1}^{3} (4 - x - \tfrac{3}{x})\,dx$$

$$= (4x - \tfrac{1}{2}x^2 - 3\ln x)\Big|_{1}^{3} = 4 - 3\ln 3$$

57. $$\int_{0}^{1}\int_{y}^{1} e^{(x^2)}\,dx\,dy = \int_{0}^{1}\int_{0}^{x} e^{(x^2)}\,dy\,dx$$

$$= \int_{0}^{1} y\,e^{(x^2)}\Big|_{0}^{x} dx$$

$$= \int_{0}^{1} x\,e^{(x^2)}\,dx$$

$$= \tfrac{1}{2} e^{(x^2)}\Big|_{0}^{1}$$

$$= \tfrac{1}{2}(e - 1)$$

58. $$\int_{1}^{4}\int_{\sqrt{y}}^{2} \sin(\tfrac{1}{3}x^3 - x)\,dx\,dy$$

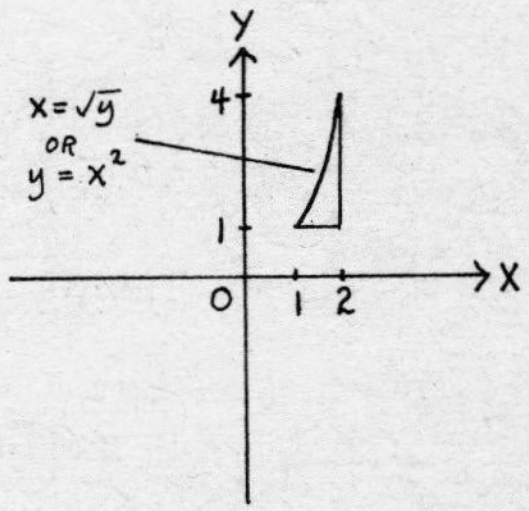

$$= \int_{1}^{2}\int_{1}^{x^2} \sin(\tfrac{1}{3}x^3 - x)\,dy\,dx$$

$$= \int_{1}^{2} y \sin(\tfrac{1}{3}x^3 - x)\Big|_{1}^{x^2} dx$$

$$= \int_{1}^{2} (x^2 - 1)\sin(\tfrac{1}{3}x^3 - x)\,dx$$

$$= -\cos(\tfrac{1}{3}x^3 - x)\Big|_{1}^{2} = 0$$

59. $$\int_{0}^{2}\int_{1+y^2}^{5} y\,e^{(x-1)^2}\,dx\,dy$$

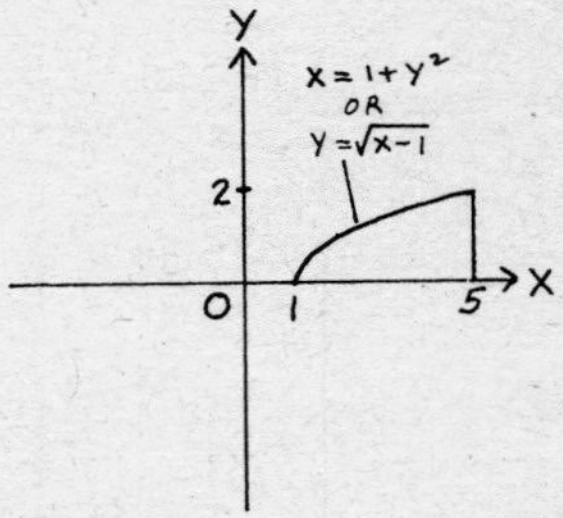

$$= \int_{1}^{5}\int_{0}^{\sqrt{x-1}} y\,e^{(x-1)^2}\,dy\,dx$$

$$= \int_{1}^{5} \tfrac{1}{2}y^2\,e^{(x-1)^2}\Big|_{0}^{\sqrt{x-1}} dx$$

$$= \int_{1}^{5} \tfrac{1}{2}(x - 1)\,e^{(x-1)^2}\,dx$$

$$= \frac{1}{4} e^{(x-1)^2}\Big|_1^5 = \frac{1}{4}(e^{16} - 1)$$

60. $$\int_0^1\int_{\arcsin y}^{\pi/2} \sec^2(\cos x)\,dx\,dy$$

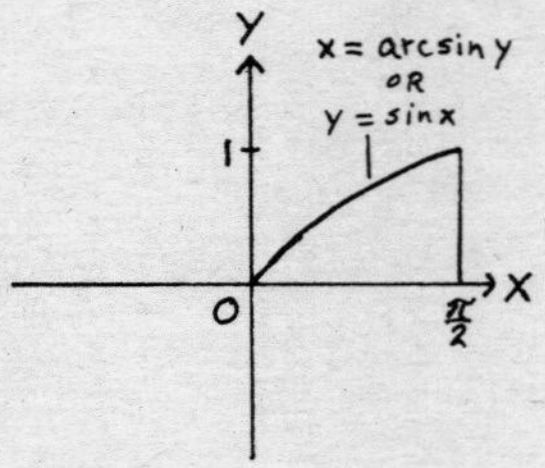

$$= \int_0^{\pi/2}\int_0^{\sin x} \sec^2(\cos x)\,dy\,dx$$

$$= \int_0^{\pi/2} y \sec^2(\cos x)\Big|_0^{\sin x} dx$$

$$= \int_0^{\pi/2} \sin x \sec^2(\cos x)\,dx$$

$$= -\tan(\cos x)\Big|_0^{\pi/2} = \tan 1$$

61. $$\int_1^e\int_0^{\ln x} y\,dy\,dx = \int_0^1\int_{e^y}^{e} y\,dx\,dy$$

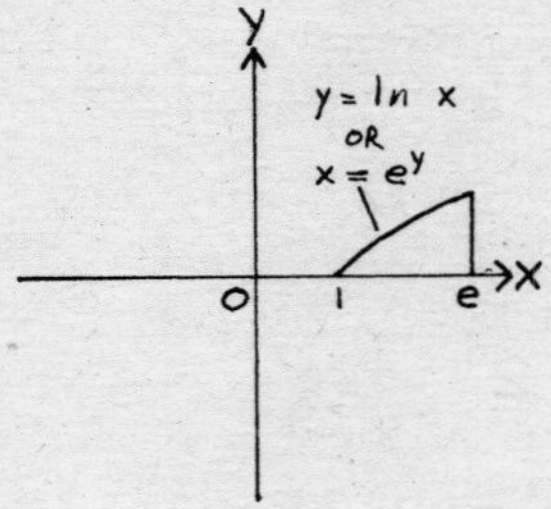

$$= \int_0^1 xy\Big|_{e^y}^{e} dy = \int_0^1 (ey - y\,e^y)\,dy$$

$$= \left(\tfrac{1}{2}e\,y^2 - y\,e^y + e^y\right)\Big|_0^1 = \tfrac{1}{2}e - 1$$

62. $$\int_1^e\int_{1/e}^{1/y} \cos(x - \ln x)\,dx\,dy$$

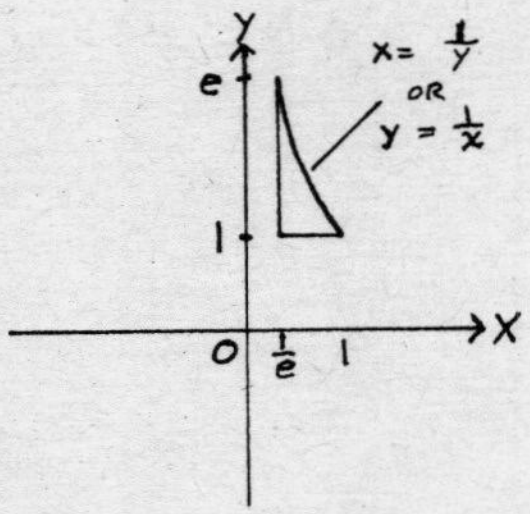

$$= \int_{1/e}^{1}\int_1^{1/x} \cos(x - \ln x)\,dy\,dx$$

$$= \int_{1/e}^{1} y\cos(x - \ln x)\Big|_1^{1/x} dx$$

$$= \int_{1/e}^{1} \left(\frac{1}{x} - 1\right)\cos(x - \ln x)\,dx$$

$$= -\sin(x - \ln x)\Big|_{1/e}^{1} = \sin\left(\frac{1}{e} + 1\right) - \sin 1$$

63. $$\int_0^{\pi^{1/3}}\int_{y^2}^{\pi^{2/3}} \sin x^{3/2}\,dx\,dy$$

$$= \int_0^{\pi^{2/3}}\int_0^{\sqrt{x}} \sin x^{3/2}\,dy\,dx$$

$$= \int_0^{\pi^{2/3}} y \sin x^{3/2}\Big|_0^{\sqrt{x}} dx$$

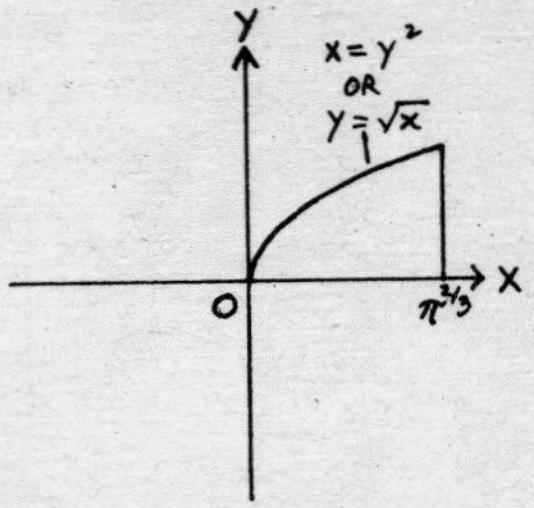

$$= \int_0^{\pi^{2/3}} \sqrt{x}\sin x^{3/2}\,dx$$

$$= -\frac{2}{3}\cos x^{3/2}\Big|_0^{\pi^{2/3}} = \frac{4}{3}$$

64. $$\int_0^{\sqrt{\pi/2}}\int_y^{\sqrt{\pi/2}} y^2 \sin x^2\,dx\,dy$$

$$= \int_0^{\sqrt{\pi/2}}\int_0^{x} y^2 \sin x^2\,dy\,dx$$

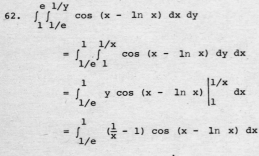

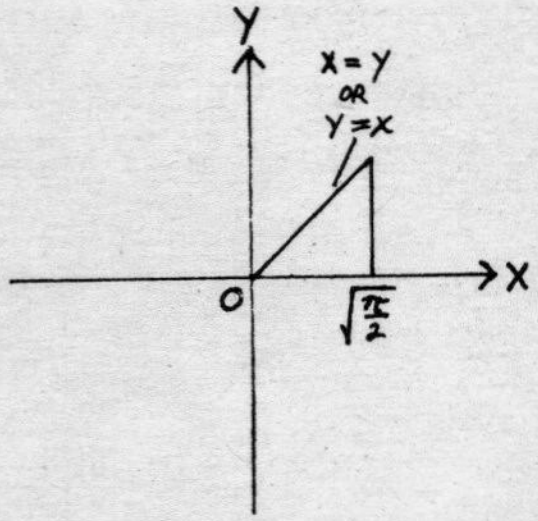

$$= \int_0^{\sqrt{\pi/2}} \frac{1}{3} y^3 \sin x^2\Big|_0^{x} dx$$

$$= \int_0^{\sqrt{\pi/2}} \frac{1}{3} x^3 \sin x^2\,dx$$

$$\overset{u=x^2}{=} \int_0^{\pi/2} \frac{1}{6} u \sin u\,du$$

$$= \left(-\frac{1}{6}u\cos u + \frac{1}{6}\sin u\right)\Big|_0^{\pi/2} = \frac{1}{6}$$

65. If $\mathcal{P} = \{R_1, R_2, \ldots, R_n\}$ and $L_f(\mathcal{P}) = U_f(\mathcal{P})$, then it follows from the definitions of $L_f(\mathcal{P})$ and $U_f(\mathcal{P})$ that $m_1 = M_1$, $m_2 = M_2$, ..., $m_n = M_n$. From these equations it follows that f is constant on R_1, R_2, ..., R_n, and hence on R. In that case, if a is any point in R, then for $1 \le k \le n$ we have $m_k = f(a) = M_k$, so that $L_f(\mathcal{P}) = m_1\Delta A_1 + m_2\Delta A_2 + \ldots + m_n\Delta A_n = f(a)\,(\Delta A_1 + \Delta A_2 + \ldots + \Delta A_n) = f(a)$ (area of R). Similarly, $U_f(\mathcal{P}) = f(a)$ (area of R).

66. Suppose $f(x_0,y_0) > 0$. Then since F is continuous at (x_0,y_0), we have $f(x,y) \ge \frac{1}{2} f(x_0,y_0)$ for all (x,y) in some rectangle R about (x_0,y_0). This and Exercise 65 imply that

$$0 = \iint_R f(x,y)\,dA \geq \iint_R \frac{1}{2} f(x_0,y_0)\,dA = \frac{1}{2} f(x_0,y_0)\,(\text{area of } R) > 0$$

which is a contradiction. Thus $f(x_0,y_0)$ cannot be positive. By an analogous argument, $f(x_0,y_0)$ cannot be negative. Consequently $f(x_0,y_0) = 0$.

Section 14.2

1. $\iint_R xy\,dA = \int_0^{2\pi}\int_0^5 (r\cos\theta)(r\sin\theta)r\,dr\,d\theta$

$= \int_0^{2\pi}\int_0^5 r^3\sin\theta\cos\theta\,dr\,d\theta = \int_0^{2\pi} (\frac{r^4}{4}\sin\theta\cos\theta)\Big|_0^5\,d\theta$

$= \int_0^{2\pi} \frac{625}{4}\sin\theta\cos\theta\,d\theta = \frac{625}{8}\sin^2\theta\Big|_0^{2\pi} = 0$

2. $\iint_R y\,dA = \int_{-\pi/2}^{\pi/2}\int_0^{\cos\theta} (r\sin\theta)r\,dr\,d\theta = \int_{-\pi/2}^{\pi/2}\int_0^{\cos\theta} r^2\sin\theta\,dr\,d\theta$

$= \int_{-\pi/2}^{\pi/2} (\frac{r^3}{3}\sin\theta)\Big|_0^{\cos\theta}\,d\theta = \frac{1}{3}\int_{-\pi/2}^{\pi/2} \cos^3\theta\sin\theta\,d\theta$

$= \frac{-1}{12}\cos^4\theta\Big|_{-\pi/2}^{\pi/2} = 0$

3. $\iint_R (x+y)\,dA = \int_0^{\pi/3}\int_0^2 (r\cos\theta + r\sin\theta)r\,dr\,d\theta$

$= \int_0^{\pi/3}\int_0^2 r^2(\cos\theta + \sin\theta)d\theta$

$= \int_0^{\pi/3} [\frac{r^3}{3}(\cos\theta + \sin\theta)]\Big|_0^2\,d\theta$

$= \frac{8}{3}\int_0^{\pi/3} (\cos\theta + \sin\theta)d\theta = \frac{8}{3}(\sin\theta - \cos\theta)\Big|_0^{\pi/3}$

$= \frac{8}{3}(\frac{\sqrt{3}}{2} + \frac{1}{2}) = \frac{4}{3}(\sqrt{3} + 1)$

4. $\iint_R (x^2+y^2)^{1/2}dA = \int_0^{2\pi}\int_0^{2+\cos\theta} r^2dr\,d\theta = \int_0^{2\pi} \frac{r^3}{3}\Big|_0^{2+\cos\theta} d\theta$

$= \frac{1}{3}\int_0^{2\pi} (8 + 12\cos\theta + 6\cos^2\theta + \cos^3\theta)d\theta$

$= \frac{1}{3}\int_0^{2\pi} [8 + 12\cos\theta + 3(1 + \cos 2\theta) + \cos\theta(1 - \sin^2\theta)]d\theta$

$$= \frac{1}{3}(11\theta + 12 \sin \theta + \frac{3}{2} \sin 2\theta + \sin \theta - \frac{1}{3} \sin^3\theta)\Big|_0^{2\pi} = \frac{22}{3}\pi$$

5. $$\iint_R (x^2 + y^2)dA = \int_0^{2\pi}\int_0^{2(1+\sin\theta)} r^3 dr\, d\theta = \int_0^{2\pi} \frac{r^4}{4}\Big|_0^{2(1+\sin\theta)} d\theta$$

$$= 4\int_0^{2\pi} (1 + \sin\theta)^4 d\theta$$

$$= 4\int_0^{2\pi} (1 + 4\sin\theta + 6\sin^2\theta + 4\sin^3\theta + \sin^4\theta)d\theta$$

$$= 4\int_0^{2\pi} [1 + 4\sin\theta + 3(1 - \cos 2\theta)$$

$$+ 4\sin\theta(1 - \cos^2\theta)]d\theta + 4\int_0^{2\pi} \sin^4\theta\, d\theta$$

$$= 4(4\theta - 4\cos\theta - \frac{3}{2}\sin 2\theta - 4\cos\theta$$

$$+ \frac{4}{3}\cos^3\theta)\Big|_0^{2\pi} + 4(\frac{-1}{4}\sin^3\theta\cos\theta$$

$$- \frac{3}{8}\sin\theta\cos\theta + \frac{3}{8}\theta)\Big|_0^{2\pi}$$

$$= 32\pi + 3\pi = 35\pi$$

with the next to last equality coming from (14) in Section 7.1.

6. $$\iint_R x^2 dA = \int_0^{\pi}\int_0^{4\sin\theta} (r^2\cos^2\theta)r\, dr\, d\theta = \int_0^{\pi}\int_0^{4\sin\theta} r^3\cos^2\theta\, dr\, d\theta$$

$$= \int_0^{\pi} \frac{r^4}{4}\cos^2\theta\Big|_0^{4\sin\theta} d\theta = 64\int_0^{\pi} \sin^4\theta\cos^2\theta\, d\theta$$

$$= 64\int_0^{\pi} (\sin^4\theta - \sin^6\theta)d\theta$$

From (10) in Section 7.1, $\int\sin^6\theta\, d\theta = -\frac{1}{6}\sin^5\theta\cos\theta + \frac{5}{6}\int\sin^4\theta\, d\theta$, so $64\int_0^{\pi}(\sin^4\theta - \sin^6\theta)d\theta = 64\int_0^{\pi}\sin^4\theta\, d\theta + \frac{32}{3}\sin^5\theta\cos\theta\Big|_0^{\pi} - \frac{160}{3}\int\sin^4\theta\, d\theta = \frac{32}{3}\int_0^{\pi}\sin^4\theta\, d\theta$ $= \frac{32}{3}(-\frac{1}{4}\sin^3\theta\cos\theta - \frac{3}{8}\sin\theta\cos\theta + \frac{3}{8}\theta)\Big|_0^{\pi} = 4\pi$, with the next to last equality coming from (14) in Section 7.1.

7. The hemisphere is bounded above by $z = \sqrt{9 - x^2 - y^2}$, and the region R over which the integral is to be taken is bounded by the circle $x^2 + y^2 = 9$. Thus

$$V = \iint_R \sqrt{9 - x^2 - y^2}\, dA = \int_0^{2\pi}\int_0^3 \sqrt{9 - r^2}\, r\, dr\, d\theta$$

$$= \frac{-1}{3}\int_0^{2\pi} (9 - r^2)^{3/2}\Big|_0^3 d\theta = \frac{-1}{3}\int_0^{2\pi} -27 d\theta = 18\pi$$

8. The region R over which the integral is to be taken is bounded by $r = 2\cos\theta$. Thus

$$V = \iint_R 4\, dA = \int_{-\pi/2}^{\pi/2}\int_0^{2\cos\theta} 4r\, dr\, d\theta = \int_{-\pi/2}^{\pi/2} 2r^2\Big|_0^{2\cos\theta} d\theta$$

$$= \int_{-\pi/2}^{\pi/2} 8\cos^2\theta\, d\theta = \int_{-\pi/2}^{\pi/2} (4 + 4\cos 2\theta)d\theta$$

$$= (4\theta + 2\sin 2\theta)\Big|_{-\pi/2}^{\pi/2} = 4\pi$$

9. The region R over which the integral is to be taken is bounded by $x^2 + y^2 = 1$. Thus

$$V = \iint_R (4 + x + 2y)dA = \int_0^{2\pi}\int_0^1 (4 + r\cos\theta + 2r\sin\theta)r\, dr\, d\theta$$

$$= \int_0^{2\pi}\int_0^1 (4r + r^2\cos\theta + 2r^2\sin\theta)dr\, d\theta$$

$$= \int_0^{2\pi} (2r^2 + \frac{r^3}{3}\cos\theta + \frac{2}{3}r^3\sin\theta)\Big|_0^1 d\theta$$

$$= \int_0^{2\pi} (2 + \frac{1}{3}\cos\theta + \frac{2}{3}\sin\theta)d\theta = (2\theta + \frac{1}{3}\sin\theta - \frac{2}{3}\cos\theta)\Big|_0^{2\pi}$$

$$= 4\pi$$

10. The region R over which the integral is taken is bounded by $x^2 + y^2 = x$, whose equation in polar coordinates is $r = \cos\theta$. Thus

$$V = \iint_R x\,dA = \int_{-\pi/2}^{\pi/2}\int_0^{\cos\theta} (r\cos\theta)r\,dr\,d\theta = \int_{-\pi/2}^{\pi/2}\int_0^{\cos\theta} r^2\cos\theta\,dr\,d\theta$$

$$= \int_{-\pi/2}^{\pi/2} \left(\frac{r^3}{3}\cos\theta\right)\Big|_0^{\cos\theta} d\theta = \frac{1}{3}\int_{-\pi/2}^{\pi/2}\cos^4\theta\,d\theta$$

$$= \frac{1}{3}\left(\frac{1}{4}\cos^3\theta\sin\theta + \frac{3}{8}\cos\theta\sin\theta + \frac{3}{8}\theta\right)\Big|_{-\pi/2}^{\pi/2} = \frac{1}{8}\pi$$

with the next to last equality coming from (15) in Section 7.1.

11. The solid region is bounded above by $z = \sqrt{4 - x^2 - y^2}$, and the region R over which the integral is to be taken is bounded by the circles $x^2 + y^2 = 1$ and $x^2 + y^2 = 4$. Thus

$$V = \iint_R \sqrt{4 - x^2 - y^2}\,dA = \int_0^{2\pi}\int_1^2 \sqrt{4 - r^2}\,r\,dr\,d\theta$$

$$= \int_0^{2\pi} -\frac{1}{3}(4 - r^2)^{3/2}\Big|_1^2 d\theta = \sqrt{3}\int_0^{2\pi} 1\,d\theta = 2\sqrt{3}\,\pi$$

12. The solid region is composed of two parts: one bounded above by $z = 3$, over the region R_1 bounded by $x^2 + y^2 = 1$; and the other bounded above by $z = 4 - x^2 - y^2$, over the region R_2 bounded by $x^2 + y^2 = 1$ and $x^2 + y^2 = 4$. Thus

$$V = \iint_{R_1} 3\,dA + \iint_{R_2} (4 - x^2 - y^2)\,dA$$

$$= \int_0^{2\pi}\int_0^1 3r\,dr\,d\theta + \int_0^{2\pi}\int_1^2 (4 - r^2)r\,dr\,d\theta$$

$$= \int_0^{2\pi} \frac{3}{2}r^2\Big|_0^1 d\theta + \int_0^{2\pi}\left(2r^2 - \frac{r^4}{4}\right)\Big|_1^2 d\theta = \int_0^{2\pi}\frac{3}{2}\,d\theta + \int_0^{2\pi}\frac{9}{4}\,d\theta$$

$$= 3\pi + \frac{9}{2}\pi = \frac{15}{2}\pi$$

13. The solid region is bounded above by $z^2 = x^2 + y^2$, whose equation can be rewritten as $z = r$. The region R over which the integral is to be taken is bounded by $x^2 + y^2 - 4x = 0$, whose equation in polar coordinates is $r = 4\cos\theta$. Thus

$$V = \iint_R \sqrt{x^2 + y^2}\,dA = \int_{-\pi/2}^{\pi/2}\int_0^{4\cos\theta} r^2\,dr\,d\theta = \int_{-\pi/2}^{\pi/2} \frac{r^3}{3}\Big|_0^{4\cos\theta} d\theta$$

$$= \int_{-\pi/2}^{\pi/2} \frac{64}{3}\cos^3\theta\,d\theta = \frac{64}{3}\int_{-\pi/2}^{\pi/2}\cos\theta(1 - \sin^2\theta)\,d\theta$$

$$= \frac{64}{3}\left(\sin\theta - \frac{1}{3}\sin^3\theta\right)\Big|_{-\pi/2}^{\pi/2} = \frac{256}{9}$$

14. $$A = \int_0^{\alpha}\int_0^1 r\,dr\,d\theta = \int_0^{\alpha} \frac{r^2}{2}\Big|_0^1 d\theta = \frac{1}{2}\int_0^{\alpha} 1\,d\theta = \frac{1}{2}\alpha$$

15. $$A = \int_0^{2\pi}\int_0^{2+\sin\theta} r\,dr\,d\theta = \int_0^{2\pi} \frac{r^2}{2}\Big|_0^{2+\sin\theta} d\theta$$

$$= \int_0^{2\pi} \left(2 + 2\sin\theta + \frac{1}{2}\sin^2\theta\right)d\theta$$

$$= \int_0^{2\pi} \left[2 + 2\sin\theta + \left(\frac{1}{4} - \frac{1}{4}\cos 2\theta\right)\right]d\theta$$

$$= \left(\frac{9}{4}\theta - 2\cos\theta - \frac{1}{8}\sin 2\theta\right)\Big|_0^{2\pi} = \frac{9}{2}\pi$$

16. One leaf is described by $r = 2\sin 3\theta$ for $0 \le \theta \le \frac{\pi}{3}$. Thus

$$A = \int_0^{\pi/3}\int_0^{2\sin 3\theta} r\,dr\,d\theta = \int_0^{\pi/3} \frac{r^2}{2}\Big|_0^{2\sin 3\theta} d\theta$$

$$= 2\int_0^{\pi/3}\sin^2 3\theta\,d\theta = 2\int_0^{\pi/3}\left(\frac{1}{2} - \frac{1}{2}\cos 6\theta\right)d\theta = \left(\theta - \frac{1}{6}\sin 6\theta\right)\Big|_0^{\pi/3}$$

$$= \frac{\pi}{3}$$

17. The area A is twice the area A_1 of the portion for which $-\frac{\pi}{4} \le \theta \le \frac{\pi}{4}$. Now

$$A_1 = \int_{-\pi/4}^{\pi/4}\int_0^{\sqrt{4\cos 2\theta}} r\,dr\,d\theta = \int_{-\pi/4}^{\pi/4} \frac{r^2}{2}\Big|_0^{\sqrt{4\cos 2\theta}} d\theta$$

$$= \int_{-\pi/4}^{\pi/4} 2\cos 2\theta\,d\theta = \sin 2\theta\Big|_{-\pi/4}^{\pi/4} = 2$$

Thus $A = 2A_1 = 4$.

18. The cardioid and circle intersect for (r,θ) such that $1 + \cos\theta = \frac{1}{2}$, so that $\cos\theta = \frac{-1}{2}$, and thus $\theta = \frac{-2\pi}{3}$ or $\theta = \frac{2\pi}{3}$. For $\frac{-2\pi}{3} \le \theta \le \frac{2\pi}{3}$, $\frac{1}{2} \le 1 + \cos\theta$, so the area A is given by

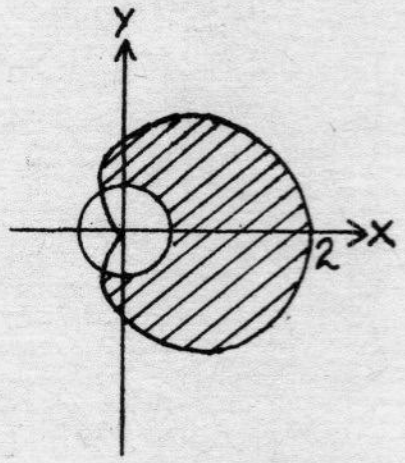

$$A = \int_{-2\pi/3}^{2\pi/3} \int_{1/2}^{1+\cos\theta} r\,dr\,d\theta$$

$$= \int_{-2\pi/3}^{2\pi/3} \frac{r^2}{2}\Big|_{1/2}^{1+\cos\theta} d\theta = \int_{-2\pi/3}^{2\pi/3} \left(\frac{3}{8} + \cos\theta + \frac{1}{2}\cos^2\theta\right)d\theta$$

$$= \int_{-2\pi/3}^{2\pi/3} \left[\frac{3}{8} + \cos\theta + \left(\frac{1}{4} + \frac{1}{4}\cos 2\theta\right)\right]d\theta$$

$$= \left(\frac{5}{8}\theta + \sin\theta + \frac{1}{8}\sin 2\theta\right)\Big|_{-2\pi/3}^{2\pi/3} = \frac{5}{6}\pi + \frac{7}{8}\sqrt{3}$$

19. The limaçon $r = 1 + 2\sin\theta$ intersects the origin for (r,θ) such that $1 + 2\sin\theta = 0$, so that $\sin\theta = -\frac{1}{2}$, and thus $\theta = \frac{-\pi}{6}, \frac{7\pi}{6}$, or $\frac{11\pi}{6}$. The area A_1 of the large loop is given by

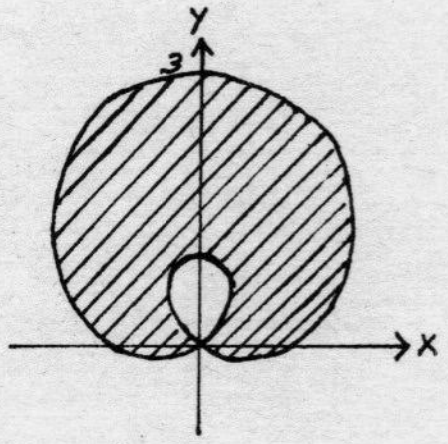

$$A_1 = \int_{-\pi/6}^{7\pi/6} \int_0^{1+2\sin\theta} r\,dr\,d\theta$$

$$= \int_{-\pi/6}^{7\pi/6} \frac{r^2}{2}\Big|_0^{1+2\sin\theta} d\theta = \int_{-\pi/6}^{7\pi/6} \left(\frac{1}{2} + 2\sin\theta + 2\sin^2\theta\right)d\theta$$

$$= \int_{-\pi/6}^{7\pi/6} \left[\frac{1}{2} + 2\sin\theta + (1 - \cos 2\theta)\right]d\theta$$

$$= \left(\frac{3}{2}\theta - 2\cos\theta - \frac{1}{2}\sin 2\theta\right)\Big|_{-\pi/6}^{7\pi/6} = 2\pi + \frac{3}{2}\sqrt{3}$$

For $\frac{7\pi}{6} \le \theta \le \frac{11\pi}{6}$, $1 + 2\sin\theta \le 0$, so the area A_2 of the small loop is given by

$$A_2 = \int_{7\pi/6}^{11\pi/6} \int_0^{-(1+2\sin\theta)} r\,dr\,d\theta = \int_{7\pi/6}^{11\pi/6} \frac{r^2}{2}\Big|_0^{-(1+2\sin\theta)} d\theta$$

$$= \int_{7\pi/6}^{11\pi/6} \left(\frac{1}{2} + 2\sin\theta + 2\sin^2\theta\right)d\theta$$

$$= \left(\frac{3}{2}\theta - 2\cos\theta - \frac{1}{2}\sin 2\theta\right)\Big|_{7\pi/6}^{11\pi/6} = \pi - \frac{3}{2}\sqrt{3}$$

Thus the area A of the region inside the large loop and outside the small loop is given by $A = A_1 - A_2 = \pi + 3\sqrt{3}$.

20. The graph of $r = \sin\theta - \cos\theta = \sqrt{2}\sin(\theta - \frac{\pi}{4})$ is a circle that intersects the origin for $\theta = \frac{\pi}{4}$ and $\theta = \frac{5\pi}{4}$. If $\frac{\pi}{4} \le \theta \le \frac{5\pi}{4}$, then $\sin\theta - \cos\theta \ge 0$. Thus the area is given by

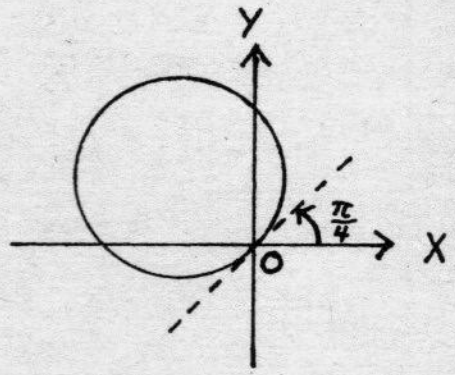

$$A = \int_{\pi/4}^{5\pi/4} \int_0^{\sin\theta - \cos\theta} r\,dr\,d\theta$$

$$= \int_{\pi/4}^{5\pi/4} \frac{r^2}{2}\Big|_0^{\sin\theta - \cos\theta} d\theta = \int_{\pi/4}^{5\pi/4} \left(\frac{1}{2}\sin^2\theta - \sin\theta\cos\theta + \frac{1}{2}\cos^2\theta\right)d\theta$$

$$= \int_{\pi/4}^{5\pi/4} \left(\frac{1}{2} - \sin\theta\cos\theta\right)d\theta = \left(\frac{1}{2}\theta - \frac{1}{2}\sin^2\theta\right)\Big|_{\pi/4}^{5\pi/4} = \frac{\pi}{2}$$

21. The spirals intersect on $[0, 3\pi]$ only for $\theta = 0$. Thus the area is given by

$$A = \int_0^{3\pi} \int_{e^\theta}^{e^{2\theta}} r\,dr\,d\theta = \int_0^{3\pi} \frac{r^2}{2}\Big|_{e^\theta}^{e^{2\theta}} d\theta$$

$$= \int_0^{3\pi} \frac{1}{2}(e^{4\theta} - e^{2\theta})d\theta$$

$$= \left(\frac{1}{8}e^{4\theta} - \frac{1}{4}e^{2\theta}\right)\Big|_0^{3\pi} = \frac{1}{8}(e^{12\pi} - 2e^{6\pi} + 1)$$

22. $\int_0^1 \int_0^{\sqrt{1-x^2}} 1 \, dy \, dx = \int_0^{\pi/2} \int_0^1 r \, dr \, d\theta$

$= \int_0^{\pi/2} \frac{r^2}{2} \Big|_0^1 d\theta = \int_0^{\pi/2} \frac{1}{2} \, d\theta$

$= \frac{1}{2} \theta \Big|_0^{\pi/2} = \frac{\pi}{4}$

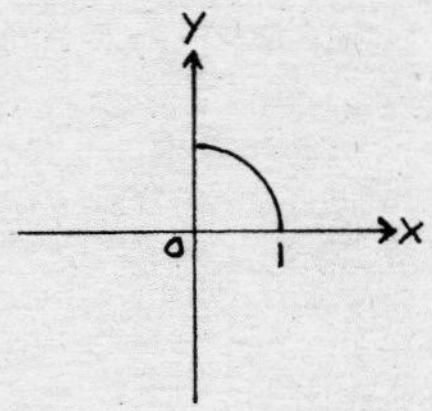

23. $\int_0^1 \int_y^{\sqrt{2-y^2}} 1 \, dx \, dy = \int_0^{\pi/4} \int_0^{\sqrt{2}} r \, dr \, d\theta$

$= \int_0^{\pi/4} \frac{r^2}{2} \Big|_0^{\sqrt{2}} d\theta = \int_0^{\pi/4} 1 \, d\theta$

$= \frac{\pi}{4}$

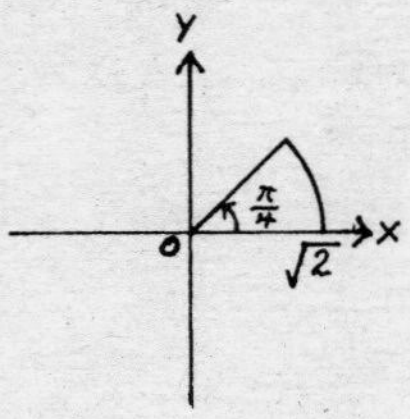

24. If (x,y) is on the circle $x^2 + y^2 = 9$ and $x = \frac{3}{\sqrt{2}}$, then $y = \sqrt{9 - \frac{9}{2}} = \frac{3}{\sqrt{2}}$. Thus the region over which the integral is to be taken consists of all (r,θ) such that $0 \le \theta \le \frac{\pi}{4}$ and $\frac{3}{\sqrt{2}} \sec\theta \le r \le 3$. Thus

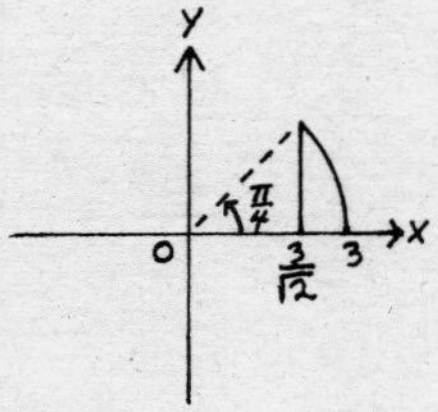

$\int_{3/\sqrt{2}}^{3} \int_0^{\sqrt{9-x^2}} \frac{1}{\sqrt{x^2 + y^2}} \, dy \, dx$

$= \int_0^{\pi/4} \int_{(3\sec\theta)/\sqrt{2}}^{3} \frac{1}{r} \, r \, dr \, d\theta = \int_0^{\pi/4} \int_{(3\sec\theta)/\sqrt{2}}^{3} 1 \, dr \, d\theta$

$= \int_0^{\pi/4} r \Big|_{(3\sec\theta)/\sqrt{2}}^{3} d\theta = \int_0^{\pi/4} (3 - \frac{3}{\sqrt{2}} \sec\theta) \, d\theta$

$= (3\theta - \frac{3}{\sqrt{2}} \ln |\sec\theta + \tan\theta|) \Big|_0^{\pi/4} = \frac{3\pi}{4} - \frac{3}{\sqrt{2}} \ln(\sqrt{2} + 1)$

25. $\int_0^1 \int_0^{\sqrt{1-y^2}} \sin(x^2 + y^2) \, dx \, dy$

$= \int_0^{\pi/2} \int_0^1 (\sin r^2) r \, dr \, d\theta$

$= \int_0^{\pi/2} \frac{-1}{2} \cos r^2 \Big|_0^1 d\theta$

$= \int_0^{\pi/2} (\frac{1}{2} - \frac{1}{2} \cos 1) \, d\theta$

$= \frac{\pi}{4}(1 - \cos 1)$

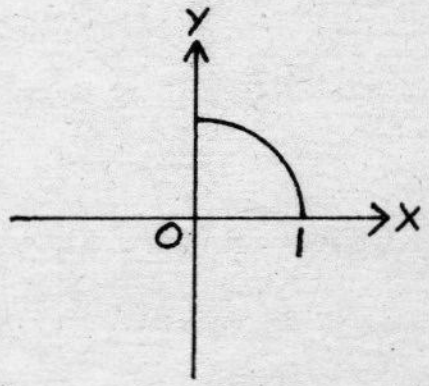

26. $\int_0^1 \int_0^{\sqrt{1-x^2}} e^{\sqrt{x^2+y^2}} \, dy \, dx$

$= \int_0^{\pi/2} \int_0^1 e^r \, r \, dr \, d\theta$

$= \int_0^{\pi/2} (r e^r - e^r) \Big|_0^1 d\theta$

$= \int_0^{\pi/2} 1 \, d\theta = \frac{\pi}{2}$

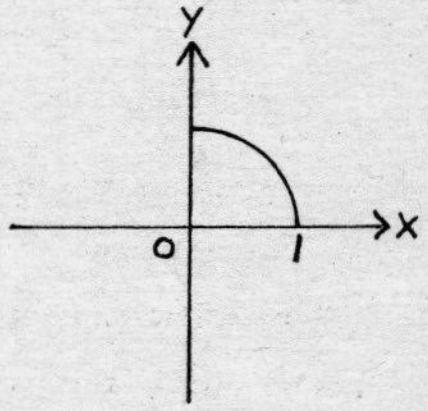

27. $\int_0^1 \int_0^{\sqrt{1-x^2}} e^{-(x^2+y^2)} \, dy \, dx$

$= \int_0^{\pi/2} \int_0^1 e^{-r^2} r \, dr \, d\theta$

$= \int_0^{\pi/2} \frac{-1}{2} e^{-r^2} \Big|_0^1 d\theta$

$= \int_0^{\pi/2} \frac{1}{2}(1 - e^{-1}) \, d\theta = \frac{\pi}{4}(1 - e^{-1})$

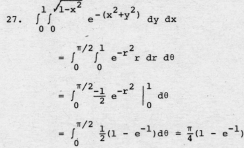

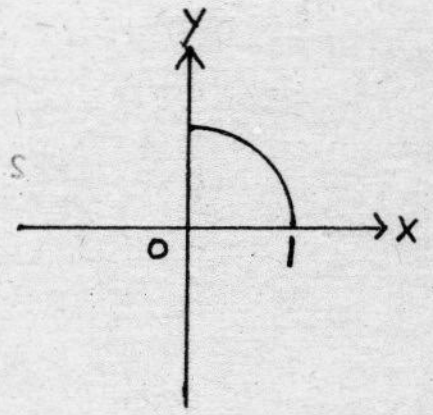

28. If $y = \sqrt{x - x^2}$, then $y^2 = x - x^2$, so $x^2 + y^2 = x$, which becomes $r = \cos\theta$ in polar coordinates. Thus

$\int_0^1 \int_{\sqrt{x-x^2}}^{\sqrt{1-x^2}} 1 \, dy \, dx = \int_0^{\pi/2} \int_{\cos\theta}^{1} r \, dr \, d\theta = \int_0^{\pi/2} \frac{r^2}{2} \Big|_{\cos\theta}^{1} d\theta$

$$= \int_0^{\pi/2} \tfrac{1}{2}(1 - \cos^2\theta)\,d\theta$$

$$= \int_0^{\pi/2} \tfrac{1}{2}[1 - (\tfrac{1}{2} + \tfrac{1}{2}\cos 2\theta)]\,d\theta$$

$$= (\tfrac{1}{4}\theta - \tfrac{1}{8}\sin 2\theta)\Big|_0^{\pi/2} = \tfrac{\pi}{8}$$

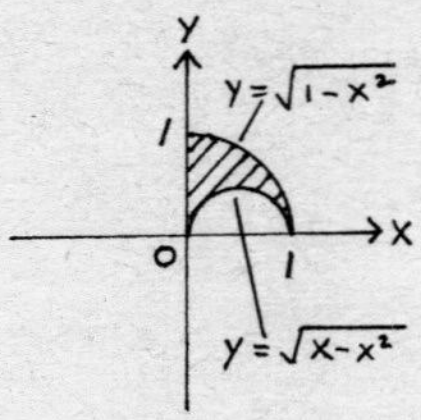

29. As in Exercise 28, in polar coordinates the the equation $y = \sqrt{x - x^2}$ becomes $r = \cos\theta$. Thus

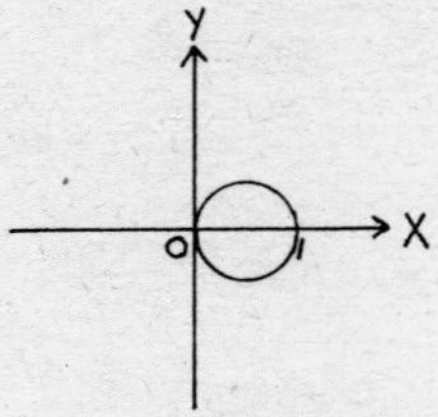

$$\int_0^1 \int_{-\sqrt{x-x^2}}^{\sqrt{x-x^2}} (x^2 + y^2)\,dy\,dx$$

$$= \int_{-\pi/2}^{\pi/2} \int_0^{\cos\theta} r^3\,dr\,d\theta$$

$$= \int_{-\pi/2}^{\pi/2} \frac{r^4}{4}\Big|_0^{\cos\theta} d\theta = \frac{1}{4}\int_{-\pi/2}^{\pi/2} \cos^4\theta\,d\theta$$

$$= \tfrac{1}{4}(\tfrac{1}{4}\cos^3\theta\sin\theta + \tfrac{3}{8}\cos\theta\sin\theta + \tfrac{3}{8}\theta)\Big|_{-\pi/2}^{\pi/2} = \tfrac{3}{32}\pi$$

with the next to last equality coming from (15) in Section 7.1.

30. a. $\int_0^\infty \int_0^\infty e^{-(x^2+y^2)}\,dx\,dy$

$$= \lim_{b\to\infty} \iint_{R_b} e^{-(x^2+y^2)}\,dA$$

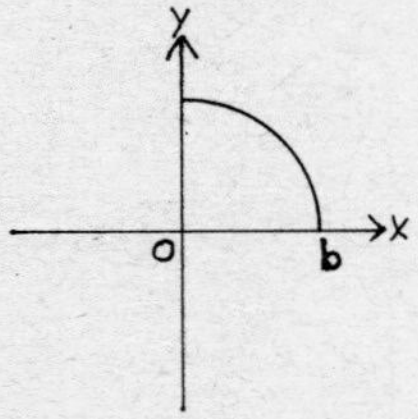

$$= \lim_{b\to\infty} \int_0^{\pi/2}\int_0^b e^{-r^2}\,r\,dr\,d\theta$$

$$= \lim_{b\to\infty} \int_0^{\pi/2} \frac{-1}{2}e^{-r^2}\Big|_0^b d\theta$$

$$= \lim_{b\to\infty} \int_0^{\pi/2} \tfrac{1}{2}(1 - e^{-b^2})\,d\theta = \lim_{b\to\infty} \tfrac{\pi}{4}(1 - e^{-b^2}) = \tfrac{\pi}{4}$$

b. By (a) and the assumption,

$$\left(\int_0^\infty e^{-x^2}\,dx\right)^2 = \int_0^\infty e^{-x^2}\,dx \int_0^\infty e^{-y^2}\,dy = \int_0^\infty\int_0^\infty e^{-x^2}e^{-y^2}\,dx\,dy$$

$$= \int_0^\infty\int_0^\infty e^{-(x^2+y^2)}\,dx\,dy = \frac{\pi}{4}$$

Therefore $\int_0^\infty e^{-x^2}\,dx = \sqrt{\frac{\pi}{4}} = \frac{1}{2}\sqrt{\pi}$.

c. Since e^{-x^2} is an even function, $\int_{-\infty}^0 e^{-x^2}\,dx = \int_0^\infty e^{-x^2}\,dx$. Thus by (b),

$$\int_{-\infty}^\infty e^{-x^2}\,dx = \int_{-\infty}^0 e^{-x^2}\,dx + \int_0^\infty e^{-x^2}\,dx = \tfrac{1}{2}\sqrt{\pi} + \tfrac{1}{2}\sqrt{\pi} = \sqrt{\pi}$$

31. Make the substitution $u = \frac{x}{\sqrt{2}}$ and use the result of Exercise 30(c):

$$\int_{-\infty}^\infty e^{-x^2/2}\,dx = \int_{-\infty}^\infty e^{-u^2}\sqrt{2}\,du = \sqrt{2}\,\sqrt{\pi} = \sqrt{2\pi}$$

Section 14.3

1. Let $f(x,y) = \frac{1}{3}(6 - x - 2y)$. Then $f_x(x,y) = -\frac{1}{3}$ and $f_y(x,y) = -\frac{2}{3}$. The portion of the plane $z = \frac{1}{3}(6 - x - 2y)$ in the first octant lies over the region R in the first quadrant of the xy plane bounded by the lines $x = 0$, $y = 0$, and $x + 2y = 6$. Thus by (1),

$$S = \iint_R \sqrt{(-\tfrac{1}{3})^2 + (-\tfrac{2}{3})^2 + 1}\, dA = \int_0^6 \int_0^{\frac{1}{2}(6-x)} \frac{\sqrt{14}}{3}\, dy\, dx$$

$$= \int_0^6 \frac{\sqrt{14}}{3} y \Big|_0^{\frac{1}{2}(6-x)} dx = \int_0^6 \frac{\sqrt{14}}{6}(6 - x)\,dx$$

$$= \frac{\sqrt{14}}{6}(6x - \tfrac{1}{2}x^2)\Big|_0^6 = 3\sqrt{14}$$

2. Let $f(x,y) = 9 - x^2 - y^2$. Then $f_x(x,y) = -2x$ and $f_y(x,y) = -2y$. The portion of the paraboloid $z = 9 - x^2 - y^2$ above the xy plane lies above the region R in the xy plane bounded by the circle $x^2 + y^2 = 9$. Thus by (1),

$$S = \iint_R \sqrt{4x^2 + 4y^2 + 1}\, dA = \int_0^{2\pi}\int_0^3 r\sqrt{4r^2 + 1}\, dr\, d\theta$$

$$= \int_0^{2\pi} \frac{1}{12}(4r^2 + 1)^{3/2}\Big|_0^3 d\theta = \int_0^{2\pi} \frac{1}{12}(37^{3/2} - 1)d\theta$$

$$= \frac{\pi}{6}(37^{3/2} - 1)$$

3. Let $f(x,y) = 9 - x^2 - y^2$. Then $f_x(x,y) = -2x$ and $f_y(x,y) = -2y$. The paraboloid $z = 9 - x^2 - y^2$ intersects the plane $z = 5$ over the circle $5 = 9 - x^2 - y^2$, or $x^2 + y^2 = 4$. Thus the portion of the paraboloid above the plane $z = 5$ lies above the region in the xy plane bounded by the circle $x^2 + y^2 = 4$. Thus by (1),

$$S = \iint_R \sqrt{4x^2 + 4y^2 + 1}\, dA = \int_0^{2\pi}\int_0^2 r\sqrt{4r^2 + 1}\, dr\, d\theta$$

$$= \int_0^{2\pi} \frac{1}{12}(4r^2 + 1)^{3/2}\Big|_0^2 d\theta = \int_0^{2\pi} \frac{1}{12}(17^{3/2} - 1)d\theta$$

$$= \frac{\pi}{6}(17^{3/2} - 1)$$

4. Let $f(x,y) = \sqrt{4 - x^2 - y^2}$. Then $f_x(x,y) = \frac{-x}{\sqrt{4 - x^2 - y^2}}$ and $f_y(x,y) = \frac{-y}{\sqrt{4 - x^2 - y^2}}$. The portion of the hemisphere $z = \sqrt{4 - x^2 - y^2}$ that lies inside the cylinder $x^2 + y^2 = 1$ and above the xy plane lies over the region R in the xy plane bounded by the circle $x^2 + y^2 = 1$. Thus by (1), the surface area S of that portion of the hemisphere is given by

$$S = \iint_R \sqrt{\frac{x^2}{4 - x^2 - y^2} + \frac{y^2}{4 - x^2 - y^2} + 1}\, dA = \iint_R \frac{2}{\sqrt{4 - x^2 - y^2}}\, dA$$

$$= \int_0^{2\pi}\int_0^1 \frac{2r}{\sqrt{4 - r^2}}\, dr\, d\theta = \int_0^{2\pi} -2\sqrt{4 - r^2}\Big|_0^1 d\theta$$

$$= \int_0^{2\pi} 2(2 - \sqrt{3})d\theta = 4\pi(2 - \sqrt{3})$$

Thus the surface area of the entire portion of the sphere $x^2 + y^2 + z^2 = 4$ that is inside the cylinder $x^2 + y^2 = 1$ is $2[4\pi(2 - \sqrt{3})] = 8\pi(2 - \sqrt{3})$.

5. Let $f(x,y) = \sqrt{16 - x^2 - y^2}$. Then $f_x(x,y) = \frac{-x}{\sqrt{16 - x^2 - y^2}}$ and $f_y(x,y) = \frac{-y}{\sqrt{16 - x^2 - y^2}}$. The portion of the hemisphere $z = \sqrt{16 - x^2 - y^2}$ that lies inside the cylinder $x^2 - 4x + y^2 = 0$ and above the xy plane lies over the region R in the xy plane bounded by the circle $x^2 - 4x + y^2 = 0$, whose equation in polar coordinates is $r = 4\cos\theta$. Thus by (1),

the surface area S of that portion of the hemisphere is given as an improper integral by

$$S = \iint_R \sqrt{\frac{x^2}{16 - x^2 - y^2} + \frac{y^2}{16 - x^2 - y^2} + 1}\, dA = \iint_R \frac{4}{\sqrt{16 - x^2 - y^2}}\, dA$$

$$= \int_{-\pi/2}^{\pi/2} \int_0^{4\cos\theta} \frac{4r}{\sqrt{16 - r^2}}\, dr\, d\theta = \int_{-\pi/2}^{\pi/2} -4\sqrt{16 - r^2}\,\Big|_0^{4\cos\theta}\, d\theta$$

$$= \int_{-\pi/2}^{\pi/2} 16(1 - \sin\theta)\, d\theta = 16(\theta + \cos\theta)\,\Big|_{-\pi/2}^{\pi/2} = 16\pi$$

Thus the surface area of the entire portion of the sphere that is inside the cylinder is $2(16\pi) = 32\pi$.

6. Let $f(x,y) = \sqrt{9 - x^2}$. Then $f_x(x,y) = \dfrac{-x}{\sqrt{9 - x^2}}$ and $f_y(x,y) = 0$.

The portion of the cylinder whose surface area we seek lies above the region R in the xy plane bounded by the lines $x = 1$, $y = 0$ and $x = y$. Thus by (1), the surface area S of that portion of the cylinder is given by

$$S = \iint_R \sqrt{\frac{x^2}{9 - x^2} + 0^2 + 1}\, dA = \iint_R \frac{3}{\sqrt{9 - x^2}}\, dA$$

$$= \int_0^1 \int_0^x \frac{3}{\sqrt{9 - x^2}}\, dy\, dx = \int_0^1 \frac{3y}{\sqrt{9 - x^2}}\,\Big|_0^x\, dx$$

$$= \int_0^1 \frac{3x}{\sqrt{9 - x^2}}\, dx = -3\sqrt{9 - x^2}\,\Big|_0^1 = 9 - 6\sqrt{2}$$

7. Let $f(x,y) = x^2$. Then $f_x(x,y) = 2x$ and $f_y(x,y) = 0$. The region R bounded by the given triangle is bounded by the lines $y = 0$, $x = 1$, and $y = x$. Thus by (1),

$$S = \iint_R \sqrt{4x^2 + 0^2 + 1}\, dA = \int_0^1 \int_0^x \sqrt{4x^2 + 1}\, dy\, dx$$

$$= \int_0^1 y\sqrt{4x^2 + 1}\,\Big|_0^x\, dx = \int_0^1 x\sqrt{4x^2 + 1}\, dx = \frac{1}{12}(4x^2 + 1)^{3/2}\,\Big|_0^1$$

$$= \frac{1}{12}(5^{3/2} - 1)$$

8. Let $f(x,y) = \sqrt{9 - x^2 - y^2}$. Then $f_x(x,y) = \dfrac{-x}{\sqrt{9 - x^2 - y^2}}$ and $f_y(x,y) = \dfrac{-y}{\sqrt{9 - x^2 - y^2}}$. The sphere and the paraboloid intersect at (x,y,z) such that $8z = x^2 + y^2 = 9 - z^2$, so that $z \geq 0$ and $z^2 + 8z - 9 = 0$. It follows that $z = 1$ and hence $x^2 + y^2 = 8$. Thus the portion of the sphere that is inside the paraboloid lies over the region R in the xy plane bounded by the circle $x^2 + y^2 = 8$. Thus by (1),

$$S = \iint_R \sqrt{\frac{x^2}{9 - x^2 - y^2} + \frac{y^2}{9 - x^2 - y^2} + 1}\, dA = \iint_R \frac{3}{\sqrt{9 - x^2 - y^2}}\, dA$$

$$= \int_0^{2\pi} \int_0^{\sqrt{8}} \frac{3r}{\sqrt{9 - r^2}}\, dr\, d\theta = \int_0^{2\pi} -3\sqrt{9 - r^2}\,\Big|_0^{\sqrt{8}}\, d\theta$$

$$= \int_0^{2\pi} 6\, d\theta = 12\pi$$

9. If $x^2 + y^2 + z^2 = 14z$, then $x^2 + y^2 + (z - 7)^2 = 49$, or $z = 7 \pm \sqrt{49 - x^2 - y^2}$. The sphere and the paraboloid intersect at (x,y,z) such that $5z = x^2 + y^2 = 14z - z^2$, so that $z^2 - 9z = 0$, or $z = 0$ or $z = 9$, and consequently $x^2 + y^2 = 0$ or $x^2 + y^2 = 45$. Thus the portion of the sphere that is inside the paraboloid lies over the region R in the xy plane bounded by the circle $x^2 + y^2 = 45$. Since $z \geq 7$ if (x,y,z) is a point on the sphere inside the given paraboloid, we let $f(x,y) = 7 + \sqrt{49 - x^2 - y^2}$. Then

$$f_x(x,y) = \frac{-x}{\sqrt{49 - x^2 - y^2}} \quad \text{and} \quad f_y(x,y) = \frac{-y}{\sqrt{49 - x^2 - y^2}}.$$

Thus by (1),

$$S = \iint_R \sqrt{\frac{x^2}{49 - x^2 - y^2} + \frac{y^2}{49 - x^2 - y^2} + 1}\, dA = \iint_R \frac{7}{\sqrt{49 - x^2 - y^2}}\, dA$$

$$= \int_0^{2\pi}\int_0^{\sqrt{45}} \frac{7r}{\sqrt{49 - r^2}}\, dr\, d\theta = \int_0^{2\pi} -7\sqrt{49 - r^2}\,\Big|_0^{\sqrt{45}}\, d\theta$$

$$= \int_0^{2\pi} 35\, d\theta = 70\pi$$

10. Let $f(x,y) = \frac{2}{3}\sqrt{2}\, x^{3/2} + \frac{2}{3}\, y^{3/2}$. Then $f_x(x,y) = \sqrt{2}\, x^{1/2}$ and $f_y(x,y) = y^{1/2}$. The portion of the surface whose surface area we seek lies above the region R in the xy plane bounded by the lines $x = 1$ and $y = 0$ and the parabola $y = x^2$. Thus by (1), the surface area S of that surface is given by

$$S = \iint_R \sqrt{(\sqrt{2}\, x^{1/2})^2 + (y^{1/2})^2 + 1}\, dA = \iint_R \sqrt{2x + y + 1}\, dA$$

$$= \int_0^1\int_0^{x^2} \sqrt{2x + y + 1}\, dy\, dx = \int_0^1 \frac{2}{3}(2x + y + 1)^{3/2}\,\Big|_0^{x^2} dx$$

$$= \int_0^1 \frac{2}{3}[(2x + x^2 + 1)^{3/2} - (2x + 1)^{3/2}]\, dx$$

$$= \int_0^1 \frac{2}{3}[(x + 1)^3 - (2x - 1)^{3/2}]\, dx$$

$$= \frac{2}{3}\left[\frac{1}{4}(x + 1)^4 - \frac{1}{25}(2x + 1)^{5/2}\right]\Big|_0^1 = \frac{379}{150} - \frac{6}{25}\sqrt{3}$$

Section 14.4

1. $$\int_0^3\int_{-1}^1\int_2^4 (y - xz)\,dz\,dy\,dx = \int_0^3\int_{-1}^1 \left(yz - \frac{xz^2}{2}\right)\Big|_2^4 dy\,dx$$

$$= \int_0^3\int_{-1}^1 (2y - 6x)\,dy\,dx = \int_0^3 (y^2 - 6xy)\Big|_{-1}^1 dx$$

$$= \int_0^3 (-12x)\,dx = -6x^2\,\Big|_0^3 = -54$$

2. $$\int_0^3\int_{-1}^1\int_2^4 (y - xz)\,dy\,dx\,dz = \int_0^3\int_{-1}^1 \left(\frac{y^2}{2} - xzy\right)\Big|_2^4 dx\,dz$$

$$= \int_0^3\int_{-1}^1 (6 - 2xz)\,dx\,dz = \int_0^3 (6x - x^2 z)\Big|_{-1}^1 dz = \int_0^3 12\,dz = 36$$

3. $$\int_{-1}^1\int_0^x\int_{x-y}^{x+y} (z - 2x - y)\,dz\,dy\,dx = \int_{-1}^1\int_0^x \left(\frac{z^2}{2} - 2xz - yz\right)\Big|_{x-y}^{x+y} dy\,dx$$

$$= \int_{-1}^1\int_0^x \Big[\frac{(x + y)^2}{2} - 2x(x + y) - y(x + y) - \frac{(x - y)^2}{2}$$

$$+ 2x(x - y) + y(x - y)\Big]dy\,dx$$

$$= \int_{-1}^1\int_0^x (-2xy - 2y^2)\,dy\,dx = \int_{-1}^1 \left(-xy^2 - \frac{2}{3}y^3\right)\Big|_0^x dx$$

$$= \int_{-1}^1 \frac{-5}{3}x^3\,dx = \frac{-5}{12}x^4\,\Big|_{-1}^1 = 0$$

4. $$\int_0^{\pi/2}\int_0^1\int_0^{\sqrt{1-x^2}} x\cos z\,dy\,dx\,dz = \int_0^{\pi/2}\int_0^1 x(\cos z)y\Big|_0^{\sqrt{1-x^2}} dx\,dz$$

$$= \int_0^{\pi/2}\int_0^1 x\sqrt{1 - x^2}\cos z\,dx\,dz = \int_0^{\pi/2} \left(\frac{-1}{3}(1 - x^2)^{3/2}\cos z\right)\Big|_0^1 dz$$

$$= \frac{1}{3}\int_0^{\pi/2} \cos z\,dz = \frac{1}{3}\sin z\,\Big|_0^{\pi/2} = \frac{1}{3}$$

5. $$\int_0^{\ln 3}\int_0^1\int_0^y (z^2 + 1)e^{(y^2)}\,dx\,dz\,dy = \int_0^{\ln 3}\int_0^1 (z^2 + 1)e^{(y^2)}x\,\Big|_0^y dz\,dy$$

$$= \int_0^{\ln 3} \int_0^1 (z^2 + 1)y\, e^{(y^2)} dz\, dy$$

$$= \int_0^{\ln 3} \left[\left(\frac{z^3}{3} + z\right)y\, e^{(y^2)}\right]\Big|_0^1 dy = \frac{4}{3} \int_0^{\ln 3} y\, e^{(y^2)} dy$$

$$= \frac{2}{3} e^{(y^2)} \Big|_0^{\ln 3} = \frac{2}{3} e^{(\ln 3)^2} - \frac{2}{3}$$

6. $$\int_0^{\sqrt{\pi/6}} \int_0^y \int_0^y (1 + y^2 z \cos xz)\, dx\, dz\, dy$$

$$= \int_0^{\sqrt{\pi/6}} \int_0^y (x + y^2 \sin xz)\Big|_0^y dz\, dy$$

$$= \int_0^{\sqrt{\pi/6}} \int_0^y (y + y^2 \sin yz)\, dz\, dy = \int_0^{\sqrt{\pi/6}} (yz - y \cos yz)\Big|_0^y dy$$

$$= \int_0^{\sqrt{\pi/6}} (y^2 - y \cos y^2 + y)\, dy = \left(\frac{y^3}{3} - \frac{1}{2} \sin y^2 + \frac{y^2}{2}\right)\Big|_0^{\sqrt{\pi/6}}$$

$$= \frac{1}{3}\left(\frac{\pi}{6}\right)^{3/2} - \frac{1}{4} + \frac{\pi}{12}$$

7. $$\int_{-15}^{13} \int_1^e \int_0^{1/\sqrt{x}} z(\ln x)^2 dz\, dx\, dy = \int_{-15}^{13} \int_1^e \frac{z^2}{2}(\ln x)^2 \Big|_0^{1/\sqrt{x}} dx\, dy$$

$$= \int_{-15}^{13} \int_1^e \frac{1}{2x}(\ln x)^2 dx\, dy = \int_{-15}^{13} \frac{1}{6}(\ln x)^3 \Big|_1^e dy$$

$$= \int_{-15}^{13} \frac{1}{6}\, dy = \frac{14}{3}$$

8. $$\int_{-1}^2 \int_1^{y+2} \int_e^{e^2} \frac{x + y}{z}\, dz\, dx\, dy = \int_{-1}^2 \int_1^{y+2} (x + y)(\ln z)\Big|_e^{e^2} dx\, dy$$

$$= \int_{-1}^2 \int_1^{y+2} (x + y)\, dx\, dy = \int_{-1}^2 \left(\frac{x^2}{2} + yx\right)\Big|_1^{y+2} dy$$

$$= \int_{-1}^2 \left[\frac{(y + 2)^2}{2} - \frac{1}{2} + y^2 + y\right] dy$$

$$= \left(\frac{(y + 2)^3}{6} - \frac{y}{2} + \frac{y^3}{3} + \frac{y^2}{2}\right)\Big|_{-1}^2 = \frac{27}{2}$$

9. $$\int_0^{\pi/2} \int_0^{\pi/2} \int_0^{\sin z} x^2 \sin y\, dx\, dy\, dz = \int_0^{\pi/2} \int_0^{\pi/2} \frac{x^3}{3} \sin y \Big|_0^{\sin z} dy\, dz$$

$$= \int_0^{\pi/2} \int_0^{\pi/2} \frac{1}{3} \sin^3 z \sin y\, dy\, dz = \frac{1}{3}\int_0^{\pi/2} (-\sin^3 z \cos y)\Big|_0^{\pi/2} dz$$

$$= \frac{1}{3}\int_0^{\pi/2} \sin^3 z\, dz = \frac{1}{3}\int_0^{\pi/2} \sin z(1 - \cos^2 z)\, dz$$

$$= \frac{1}{3}\left(-\cos z + \frac{1}{3} \cos^3 z\right)\Big|_0^{\pi/2} = \frac{2}{9}$$

10. $$\int_{-\pi/2}^{\pi/2} \int_{-\cos z}^{\cos z} \int_{-\cos zy}^{\cos zy} x \cos zy\, dx\, dy\, dz$$

$$= \int_{-\pi/2}^{\pi/2} \int_{-\cos z}^{\cos z} \frac{x^2}{2} \cos zy \Big|_{-\cos zy}^{\cos zy} dy\, dz$$

$$= \int_{-\pi/2}^{\pi/2} \int_{-\cos z}^{\cos z} 0\, dy\, dz = 0$$

11. The region R in the xy plane is the horizontally simple region between the graphs of $x = -y$ and $x = y$ on $[0,1]$; D is the solid region between the graphs of $z = 0$ and $z = y$ on R . Thus

$$\iiint_D e^y dV = \int_0^1 \int_{-y}^y \int_0^y e^y\, dz\, dx\, dy = \int_0^1 \int_{-y}^y z e^y \Big|_0^y dx\, dy$$

$$= \int_0^1 \int_{-y}^y y\, e^y\, dx\, dy = \int_0^1 xy\, e^y \Big|_{-y}^y dy$$

$$= \int_0^1 2y^2 e^y\, dy \overset{\text{parts}}{=} 2y^2 e^y \Big|_0^1 - \int_0^1 4y\, e^y\, dy$$

$$\overset{\text{parts}}{=} 2e - \left(4y\, e^y \Big|_0^1\right) + 4\int_0^1 e^y\, dy = 2e - 4e + \left(4e^y \Big|_0^1\right)$$

$$= 2e - 4$$

12. The region R in the xy plane is the vertically simple region between the graphs of $y = 0$ and $y = x$ on $[1,2]$; D is the solid region between the graphs of $z = 0$ and $z = 4 - x - y$

on R . Thus

$$\iiint_D \frac{1}{x}\,dV = \int_1^2\int_0^x\int_0^{4-x-y} \frac{1}{x}\,dz\,dy\,dx = \int_1^2\int_0^x \frac{z}{x}\Big|_0^{4-x-y} dy\,dx$$

$$= \int_1^2\int_0^x \left(\frac{4}{x} - 1 - \frac{y}{x}\right)dy\,dx = \int_1^2 \left(\frac{4y}{x} - y - \frac{y^2}{2x}\right)\Big|_0^x dx$$

$$= \int_1^2 \left(4 - \frac{3}{2}x\right)dx = \left(4x - \frac{3}{4}x^2\right)\Big|_1^2 = \frac{7}{4}$$

13. The region R in the xy plane is the horizontally simple region between the graph of $x = 1$ and $x = 3$ on $[0,2]$; D is the solid region between the graphs of $z = -2$ and $z = 0$ on R . Thus

$$\iiint_D y\,e^{xy}\,dV = \int_0^2\int_1^3\int_{-2}^0 y\,e^{xy}\,dz\,dx\,dy = \int_0^2\int_1^3 zy\,e^{xy}\Big|_{-2}^0 dx\,dy$$

$$= 2\int_0^2\int_1^3 ye^{xy}dx\,dy = 2\int_0^2 e^{xy}\Big|_1^3 dy = 2\int_0^2 (e^{3y} - e^y)\,dy$$

$$= \left(\frac{2}{3}e^{3y} - 2e^y\right)\Big|_0^2 = \frac{2}{3}e^6 - 2e^2 + \frac{4}{3}$$

14. The region R in the xy plane is the vertically simple region between the graphs of $y = -\sqrt{4 - x^2}$ and $y = \sqrt{4 - x^2}$ on $[-2,2]$; D is the solid region between the graphs of $z = 0$ and $z = \sqrt{4 - x^2 - y^2}$ on R . Thus

$$\iiint_D xy\,dV = \int_{-2}^2\int_{-\sqrt{4-x^2}}^{\sqrt{4-x^2}}\int_0^{\sqrt{4-x^2-y^2}} xy\,dz\,dy\,dx$$

$$= \int_{-2}^2\int_{-\sqrt{4-x^2}}^{\sqrt{4-x^2}} xyz\Big|_0^{\sqrt{4-x^2-y^2}} dy\,dx$$

$$= \int_{-2}^2\int_{-\sqrt{4-x^2}}^{\sqrt{4-x^2}} xy\sqrt{4 - x^2 - y^2}\,dy\,dx$$

$$= \int_{-2}^2 \frac{-1}{3}x\,(4 - x^2 - y^2)^{3/2}\Big|_{-\sqrt{4-x^2}}^{\sqrt{4-x^2}} dx = \int_{-2}^2 0\,dx = 0$$

15. The region R in the xy plane is bounded by the circle $x^2 + y^2 = 1$, and hence is the vertically simple region between the graphs of $y = -\sqrt{1 - x^2}$ and $y = \sqrt{1 - x^2}$ on $[-1,1]$; D is the solid region between the graphs of $z = \sqrt{x^2 + y^2}$ and $z = 1$. Thus

$$\iiint_D zy\,dV = \int_{-1}^1\int_{-\sqrt{1-x^2}}^{\sqrt{1-x^2}}\int_{\sqrt{x^2+y^2}}^1 zy\,dz\,dy\,dx$$

$$= \int_{-1}^1\int_{-\sqrt{1-x^2}}^{\sqrt{1-x^2}} \frac{z^2}{2}y\,\Big|_{\sqrt{x^2+y^2}}^1 dy\,dx$$

$$= \frac{1}{2}\int_{-1}^1\int_{-\sqrt{1-x^2}}^{\sqrt{1-x^2}} [y - y(x^2 + y^2)]\,dy\,dx$$

$$= \frac{1}{2}\int_{-1}^1\int_{-\sqrt{1-x^2}}^{\sqrt{1-x^2}} (y - x^2y - y^3)\,dy\,dx$$

$$= \frac{1}{2}\int_{-1}^1 \left(\frac{y^2}{2} - \frac{x^2y^2}{2} - \frac{y^4}{4}\right)\Big|_{-\sqrt{1-x^2}}^{\sqrt{1-x^2}} dx = \frac{1}{2}\int_{-1}^1 0\,dx = 0$$

16. The region R in the xy plane is the horizontally simple region between the lines $x = 0$ and $x = 1$ on $[-4,5]$; D is the solid region between the graphs of $z = -\sqrt{1 - x^2}$ and $z = \sqrt{1 - x^2}$ on R . Thus

$$\iiint_D (x + z)\,dV = \int_{-4}^5\int_0^1\int_{-\sqrt{1-x^2}}^{\sqrt{1-x^2}} (x + z)\,dz\,dx\,dy$$

$$= \int_{-4}^5\int_0^1 \left(xz + \frac{z^2}{2}\right)\Big|_{-\sqrt{1-x^2}}^{\sqrt{1-x^2}} dx\,dy$$

$$= \int_{-4}^5\int_0^1 2x\sqrt{1 - x^2}\,dx\,dy = \int_{-4}^5 \frac{-2}{3}(1 - x^2)^{3/2}\Big|_0^1 dy$$

$$= \int_{-4}^5 \frac{2}{3}\,dy = 6$$

17. The region R in the xy plane is a square, and is the horizontally simple region between the graphs of $y = -1$ and

$y = 1$ on $[-1,1]$; D is the solid region between the graphs of $z = 0$ and $z = \sqrt{9 - x^2 - y^2}$ on R . Thus

$$\iiint_D z\,dV = \int_{-1}^{1}\int_{-1}^{1}\int_{0}^{\sqrt{9-x^2-y^2}} z\,dz\,dy\,dx = \int_{-1}^{1}\int_{-1}^{1} \frac{z^2}{2}\Big|_0^{\sqrt{9-x^2-y^2}} dy\,dx$$

$$= \frac{1}{2}\int_{-1}^{1}\int_{-1}^{1}(9 - x^2 - y^2)dy\,dx = \frac{1}{2}\int_{-1}^{1}(9y - x^2y - \frac{y^3}{3})\Big|_{-1}^{1} dx$$

$$= \int_{-1}^{1}(\frac{26}{3} - x^2)dx = (\frac{26}{3}x - \frac{x^3}{3})\Big|_{-1}^{1} = \frac{50}{3}$$

18. The region R in the xy plane is bounded by a quarter circle, and is the horizontally simple region between the graphs of $x = 0$ and $x = \sqrt{1 - y^2}$ on $[0,1]$; D is the solid region between the graphs of $z = 0$ and $z = \sqrt{4 - x^2 - y^2}$ on R . Thus

$$\iiint_D xz\,dV = \int_0^1\int_0^{\sqrt{1-y^2}}\int_0^{\sqrt{4-x^2-y^2}} xz\,dz\,dx\,dy$$

$$= \int_0^1\int_0^{\sqrt{1-y^2}} \frac{xz^2}{2}\Big|_0^{\sqrt{4-x^2-y^2}} dx\,dy$$

$$= \int_0^1\int_0^{\sqrt{1-y^2}} \frac{x}{2}(4 - x^2 - y^2)dx\,dy$$

$$= \int_0^1 (x^2 - \frac{x^4}{8} - \frac{x^2y^2}{4})\Big|_0^{\sqrt{1-y^2}} dy$$

$$= \int_0^1 [1 - y^2 - \frac{(1-y^2)^2}{8} - \frac{y^2(1-y^2)}{4}]dy$$

$$= \int_0^1 (\frac{7}{8} - y^2 + \frac{y^4}{8})dy = (\frac{7}{8}y - \frac{y^3}{3} + \frac{y^5}{40})\Big|_0^1 = \frac{17}{30}$$

19. At any point (x,y,z) of intersection of the cone and cylinder, x and y must satisfy

$$x^2 + y^2 = z^2 = 1 - x^2$$

so that $y^2 = 1 - 2x^2$, and thus $y = -\sqrt{1 - 2x^2}$ or $y = \sqrt{1 - 2x^2}$ for $\frac{-1}{\sqrt{2}} \le x \le \frac{1}{\sqrt{2}}$. Therefore the region R in the xy plane is the vertically simple region between the graphs of $y = -\sqrt{1 - 2x^2}$ and $y = \sqrt{1 - 2x^2}$ on $[\frac{-1}{\sqrt{2}}, \frac{1}{\sqrt{2}}]$. Then D is the solid region between the graphs of $z = \sqrt{x^2 + y^2}$ and $z = \sqrt{1 - x^2}$ on R . Thus

$$\iiint_D 3xy\,dV = \int_{-1/\sqrt{2}}^{1/\sqrt{2}}\int_{-\sqrt{1-2x^2}}^{\sqrt{1-2x^2}}\int_{\sqrt{x^2+y^2}}^{\sqrt{1-x^2}} 3xy\,dz\,dy\,dx$$

$$= \int_{-1/\sqrt{2}}^{1/\sqrt{2}}\int_{-\sqrt{1-2x^2}}^{\sqrt{1-2x^2}} 3xyz\Big|_{\sqrt{x^2+y^2}}^{\sqrt{1-x^2}} dy\,dx$$

$$= \int_{-1/\sqrt{2}}^{1/\sqrt{2}}\int_{-\sqrt{1-2x^2}}^{\sqrt{1-2x^2}} 3xy(\sqrt{1 - x^2} - \sqrt{x^2 + y^2})dy\,dx$$

$$= \int_{-1/\sqrt{2}}^{1/\sqrt{2}} \left[\frac{3}{2}xy^2\sqrt{1 - x^2} - x(x^2 + y^2)^{3/2}\right]\Big|_{-\sqrt{1-2x^2}}^{\sqrt{1-2x^2}} dx$$

$$= \int_{-1/\sqrt{2}}^{1/\sqrt{2}} 0\,dx = 0$$

20. The intersection of the plane $x + 3y + 6z = 1$ and the xy plane is the line $x + 3y = 1$, so the region R in the xy plane is the horizontally simple region between the graphs of $x = 0$ and $x = 1 - 3y$ on $[0,\frac{1}{3}]$; D is the solid region between the graphs of $z = 0$ and $z = \frac{1}{6} - \frac{1}{6}x - \frac{1}{2}y$ on R . Thus

$$V = \iiint_D 1\,dV = \int_0^{1/3}\int_0^{1-3y}\int_0^{1/6-x/6-y/2} 1\,dz\,dx\,dy$$

$$= \int_0^{1/3}\int_0^{1-3y} z\Big|_0^{1/6-x/6-y/2} dx\,dy$$

$$= \int_0^{1/3}\int_0^{1-3y} (\frac{1}{6} - \frac{1}{6}x - \frac{1}{2}y)dx\,dy$$

$$= \frac{1}{6}\int_0^{1/3}\int_0^{1-3y}(1 - x - 3y)\,dx\,dy$$

$$= \frac{1}{6}\int_0^{1/3} \frac{-1}{2}(1 - x - 3y)^2 \Big|_0^{1-3y} dy$$

$$= \frac{-1}{12}\int_0^{1/3}(1 - 3y)^2 dy = \frac{-1}{108}(1 - 3y)^3\Big|_0^{1/3} = \frac{1}{108}$$

21. Since the graphs of $y = x$ and $y = 2 - x$ intersect for (x,y) such that $x = y = 2 - x$, so that $x = 1$, the region R in the xy plane is the vertically simple region between the graphs of $y = x$ and $y = 2 - x$ on $[0,1]$. Then D is the solid region between the graphs of $z = 0$ and $z = 10 + x + y$ on R. Thus

$$V = \iiint_D 1\,dV = \int_0^1\int_x^{2-x}\int_0^{10+x+y} 1\,dz\,dy\,dx$$

$$= \int_0^1\int_x^{2-x} z\Big|_0^{10+x+y} dy\,dx = \int_0^1\int_x^{2-x}(10 + x + y)\,dy\,dx$$

$$= \int_0^1 (10y + xy + \frac{y^2}{2})\Big|_x^{2-x} dx$$

$$= \int_0^1 [10(2 - x) + x(2 - x) + \frac{(2 - x)^2}{2} - 10x - x^2 - \frac{x^2}{2}]dx$$

$$= \int_0^1 (22 - 20x - 2x^2)dx = (22x - 10x^2 - \frac{2}{3}x^3)\Big|_0^1 = \frac{34}{3}$$

22. The region R in the xy plane is elliptical and is the vertically simple region between the graphs of $y = 0$ and $y = \sqrt{1 - 2x^2}$ on $[0, \frac{1}{\sqrt{2}}]$; D is the solid region between the graphs of $z = 0$ and $z = 2x$ on R. Thus

$$V = \iiint_D 1\,dV = \int_0^{1/\sqrt{2}}\int_0^{\sqrt{1-2x^2}}\int_0^{2x} 1\,dz\,dy\,dx$$

$$= \int_0^{1/\sqrt{2}}\int_0^{\sqrt{1-2x^2}} z\Big|_0^{2x} dy\,dx = \int_0^{1/\sqrt{2}}\int_0^{\sqrt{1-2x^2}} 2x\,dy\,dx$$

$$= \int_0^{1/\sqrt{2}} 2xy\Big|_0^{\sqrt{1-2x^2}} dx = \int_0^{1/\sqrt{2}} 2x\sqrt{1 - 2x^2}\,dx$$

$$= \frac{-1}{3}(1 - 2x^2)^{3/2}\Big|_0^{1/\sqrt{2}} = \frac{1}{3}$$

23. Since the graphs of $y = x^2$ and $y = x$ intersect for (x,y) such that $x^2 = y = x$, so that $x = 0$ or $x = 1$, the region R in the xy plane is the vertically simple region between the graphs of $y = x^2$ and $y = x$ on $[0,1]$. Then D is the solid region between the graphs of $z = -2$ and $z = 4(x^2 + y^2)$ on R. Thus

$$V = \iiint_D 1\,dV = \int_0^1\int_{x^2}^{x}\int_{-2}^{4(x^2+y^2)} 1\,dz\,dy\,dx$$

$$= \int_0^1\int_{x^2}^{x} z\Big|_{-2}^{4(x^2+y^2)} dy\,dx = \int_0^1\int_{x^2}^{x}(4x^2 + 4y^2 + 2)dy\,dx$$

$$= \int_0^1 (4x^2y + \frac{4}{3}y^3 + 2y)\Big|_{x^2}^{x} dx$$

$$= \int_0^1 [4x^2(x - x^2) + \frac{4}{3}(x^3 - x^6) + 2(x - x^2)]dx$$

$$= \int_0^1 (\frac{-4}{3}x^6 - 4x^4 + \frac{16}{3}x^3 - 2x^2 + 2x)dx$$

$$= (\frac{-4}{21}x^7 - \frac{4}{5}x^5 + \frac{4}{3}x^4 - \frac{2}{3}x^3 + x^2)\Big|_0^1 = \frac{71}{105}$$

24. The region R in the xy plane is the horizontally simple region between the graphs of $x = 0$ and $x = 1 - y^2$ on $[-1,1]$; D is the solid region between the graphs of $z = 0$ and $z = 2x^2 + 3y^2$ on R. Thus

$$V = \iiint_D 1\,dV = \int_{-1}^1\int_0^{1-y^2}\int_0^{2x^2+3y^2} 1\,dz\,dx\,dy$$

$$= \int_{-1}^1\int_0^{1-y^2} z\Big|_0^{2x^2+3y^2} dx\,dy = \int_{-1}^1\int_0^{1-y^2}(2x^2 + 3y^2)\,dx\,dy$$

$$= \int_{-1}^{1} \left(\frac{2}{3}x^3 + 3xy^2\right) \Big|_0^{1-y^2} dy$$

$$= \int_{-1}^{1} \left[\frac{2}{3}(1-y^2)^3 + 3y^2(1-y^2)\right] dy$$

$$= \int_{-1}^{1} \left(\frac{2}{3} + y^2 - y^4 - \frac{2}{3}y^6\right) dy = \left(\frac{2}{3}y + \frac{1}{3}y^3 - \frac{1}{5}y^5 - \frac{2}{21}y^7\right)\Big|_{-1}^{1}$$

$$= \frac{148}{105}$$

25. The cone and plane intersect for (x,y,z) such that $h^2(x^2+y^2) = z^2 = h^2$, so that $x^2 + y^2 = 1$. Thus the region R in the xy plane is circular, and is the vertically simple region between the graphs of $y = -\sqrt{1-x^2}$ and $y = \sqrt{1-x^2}$ on $[-1,1]$. Then D is the solid region between the graphs of $z = h\sqrt{x^2+y^2}$ and $z = h$ on R. Thus

$$V = \iiint_D 1\, dV = \int_{-1}^{1}\int_{-\sqrt{1-x^2}}^{\sqrt{1-x^2}}\int_{h\sqrt{x^2+y^2}}^{h} 1\, dz\, dy\, dx$$

$$= \int_{-1}^{1}\int_{-\sqrt{1-x^2}}^{\sqrt{1-x^2}} z \Big|_{h\sqrt{x^2+y^2}}^{h} dy\, dx$$

$$= \int_{-1}^{1}\int_{-\sqrt{1-x^2}}^{\sqrt{1-x^2}} (h - h\sqrt{x^2+y^2})\, dy\, dx$$

$$= \int_{-1}^{1}\int_{-\sqrt{1-x^2}}^{\sqrt{1-x^2}} h\, dy\, dx - \int_{-1}^{1}\int_{-\sqrt{1-x^2}}^{\sqrt{1-x^2}} h\sqrt{x^2+y^2}\, dy\, dx$$

Now

$$\int_{-1}^{1}\int_{-\sqrt{1-x^2}}^{\sqrt{1-x^2}} h\, dy\, dx = \int_{-1}^{1} hy \Big|_{-\sqrt{1-x^2}}^{\sqrt{1-x^2}} dx = \int_{-1}^{1} 2h\sqrt{1-x^2}\, dx$$

($x = \sin u$)

$$= 2h\int_{-\pi/2}^{\pi/2} \sqrt{1-\sin^2 u}\cos u\, du = 2h\int_{-\pi/2}^{\pi/2} \cos^2 u\, du$$

$$= 2h\int_{-\pi/2}^{\pi/2} \left(\frac{1}{2} + \frac{1}{2}\cos 2u\right) du = h\left(u + \frac{1}{2}\sin 2u\right)\Big|_{-\pi/2}^{\pi/2} = \pi h$$

Next, by changing to polar coordinates we find that

$$\int_{-1}^{1}\int_{-\sqrt{1-x^2}}^{\sqrt{1-x^2}} h\sqrt{x^2+y^2}\, dy\, dx = \int_0^{2\pi}\int_0^1 hr^2\, dr\, d\theta = \int_0^{2\pi} \frac{hr^3}{3}\Big|_0^1 d\theta$$

$$= \int_0^{2\pi} \frac{h}{3}\, d\theta = \frac{2\pi}{3}h$$

Adding our results, we conclude that $V = \pi h - \frac{2\pi}{3}h = \frac{1}{3}\pi h$.

26. Proceeding as the hint suggests, we find that an equation of the plane that forms the part of the boundary in the first octant is $\frac{\sqrt{2}}{s}x + \frac{\sqrt{2}}{s}y + \frac{1}{h}z = 1$, so that $z = h(1 - \frac{\sqrt{2}}{s}x - \frac{\sqrt{2}}{s}y)$. The plane intersects the xy plane for (x,y,z) such that $0 = z = h(1 - \frac{\sqrt{2}}{s}x - \frac{\sqrt{2}}{s}y)$, so that $\frac{\sqrt{2}}{s}x + \frac{\sqrt{2}}{s}y = 1$ for $0 \le x \le \frac{s}{\sqrt{2}}$.

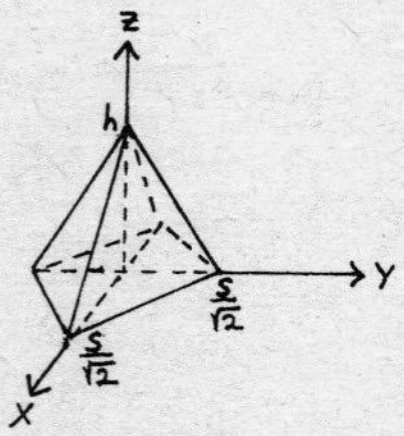

Thus the region R in the xy plane is the vertically simple region between the graphs of $y = 0$ and $y = \frac{s}{\sqrt{2}} - x$ on $[0, \frac{s}{\sqrt{2}}]$. Then D is the solid region between the graphs of $z = 0$ and $z = h(1 - \frac{\sqrt{2}}{s}x - \frac{\sqrt{2}}{s}y)$ on R. Therefore the volume of the portion D in the first octant is given by

$$\frac{1}{4}V = \iiint_D 1\, dV = \int_0^{s/\sqrt{2}}\int_0^{s/\sqrt{2}-x}\int_0^{h(1-\sqrt{2}x/s-\sqrt{2}y/s)} 1\, dz\, dy\, dx$$

$$= \int_0^{s/\sqrt{2}}\int_0^{s/\sqrt{2}-x} z \Big|_0^{h(1-\sqrt{2}x/s-\sqrt{2}y/s)} dy\, dx$$

$$= \int_0^{s/\sqrt{2}}\int_0^{s/\sqrt{2}-x} h\left(1 - \frac{\sqrt{2}}{s}x - \frac{\sqrt{2}}{s}y\right) dy\, dx$$

$$= h\int_0^{s/\sqrt{2}} \left[\left(1 - \frac{\sqrt{2}}{s}x\right)y - \frac{\sqrt{2}}{2s}y^2\right]\Big|_0^{s/\sqrt{2}-x} dx$$

$$= h \int_0^{s/\sqrt{2}} [(1 - \frac{\sqrt{2}}{s} x)(\frac{s}{\sqrt{2}} - x) - \frac{\sqrt{2}}{2s}(\frac{s}{\sqrt{2}} - x)^2]dx$$

$$= h \int_0^{s/\sqrt{2}} (\frac{s}{2\sqrt{2}} - x + \frac{\sqrt{2}}{2s} x^2)dx$$

$$= h(\frac{s}{2\sqrt{2}} x - \frac{x^2}{2} + \frac{\sqrt{2}}{6s} x^3)\Big|_0^{s/\sqrt{2}} = \frac{1}{12} hs^2$$

Consequently $V = \frac{1}{3} hs^2$.

27. The plane $2x + y + z = 1$ intersects the xy plane for (x,y,z) such that $0 = z = 1 - 2x - y$, so that $y = 1 - 2x$. Thus the region R in the xy plane is the vertically simple region between the graphs of $y = 0$ and $y = 1 - 2x$ on $[0,\frac{1}{2}]$. Then D is the solid region between the graphs of $z = 0$ and $z = 1 - 2x - y$ on R .

a. Since $\delta(x,y,z) = z$, the total mass m is given by

$$m = \int_0^{1/2} \int_0^{1-2x} \int_0^{1-2x-y} z \, dz \, dy \, dx$$

$$= \int_0^{1/2} \int_0^{1-2x} \frac{z^2}{2}\Big|_0^{1-2x-y} dy \, dx$$

$$= \frac{1}{2} \int_0^{1/2} \int_0^{1-2x} (1 - 2x - y)^2 \, dy \, dx$$

$$= \frac{1}{2} \int_0^{1/2} \frac{-1}{3}(1 - 2x - y)^3 \Big|_0^{1-2x} dx$$

$$= \frac{1}{6} \int_0^{1/2} (1 - 2x)^3 dx = \frac{-1}{48}(1 - 2x)^4 \Big|_0^{1/2} = \frac{1}{48}$$

b. Since $\delta(x,y,z) = 2y$, the total mass m is given by

$$m = \int_0^{1/2} \int_0^{1-2x} \int_0^{1-2x-y} 2y \, dz \, dy \, dx$$

$$= \int_0^{1/2} \int_0^{1-2x} 2yz \Big|_0^{1-2x-y} dy \, dx$$

$$= \int_0^{1/2} \int_0^{1-2x} 2y(1 - 2x - y) \, dy \, dx$$

$$= \int_0^{1/2} \int_0^{1-2x} [2y(1 - 2x) - 2y^2] \, dy \, dx$$

$$= \int_0^{1/2} [y^2(1 - 2x) - \frac{2}{3} y^3]\Big|_0^{1-2x} dx$$

$$= \int_0^{1/2} [(1 - 2x)^3 - \frac{2}{3}(1 - 2x)^3]dx$$

$$= \int_0^{1/2} \frac{1}{3}(1 - 2x)^3 dx = \frac{-1}{24}(1 - 2x)^4 \Big|_0^{1/2} = \frac{1}{24}$$

c. Since $\delta(x,y,z) = x$, the total mass m is given by

$$m = \int_0^{1/2} \int_0^{1-2x} \int_0^{1-2x-y} x \, dz \, dy \, dx$$

$$= \int_0^{1/2} \int_0^{1-2x} xz \Big|_0^{1-2x-y} dy \, dx$$

$$= \int_0^{1/2} \int_0^{1-2x} x(1 - 2x - y) \, dy \, dx$$

$$= \int_0^{1/2} \int_0^{1-2x} [x(1 - 2x) - xy] \, dy \, dx$$

$$= \int_0^{1/2} [x(1 - 2x)y - \frac{xy^2}{2}]\Big|_0^{1-2x} dx$$

$$= \int_0^{1/2} [x(1 - 2x)^2 - \frac{x}{2}(1 - 2x)^2]dx$$

$$= \int_0^{1/2} (\frac{x}{2} - 2x^2 + 2x^3)dx = (\frac{x^2}{4} - \frac{2}{3} x^3 + \frac{1}{2} x^4)\Big|_0^{1/2} = \frac{1}{96}$$

28. First, $\delta(x,y,z) = x^2 + y^2 + z^2$. Next, let the cube be D , and let it be situated in the first octant. Then the total mass m is given by

$$m = \iiint_D (x^2 + y^2 + z^2)\,dV = \int_0^2 \int_0^2 \int_0^2 (x^2 + y^2 + z^2)\,dz\,dy\,dx$$

$$= \int_0^2 \int_0^2 \left(x^2 z + y^2 z + \frac{z^3}{3}\right)\Big|_0^2 \,dy\,dx$$

$$= \int_0^2 \int_0^2 \left(2x^2 + 2y^2 + \frac{8}{3}\right)dy\,dx = \int_0^2 \left(2x^2 y + \frac{2}{3}y^3 + \frac{8}{3}y\right)\Big|_0^2 \,dx$$

$$= \int_0^2 \left(4x^2 + \frac{32}{3}\right)dx = \left(\frac{4}{3}x^3 + \frac{32}{3}x\right)\Big|_0^2 = 32$$

29. First, $\rho(x,y,z) = z$. Next, R is circular, and is the vertically simple region between the graphs of $y = -\sqrt{9 - x^2}$ and $y = \sqrt{9 - x^2}$ on $[-3,3]$. Finally, D is the solid region between the graphs of $z = 0$ and $z = \sqrt{9 - x^2 - y^2}$ on R. Thus the total charge is given by

$$q = \iiint_D z\,dV = \int_{-3}^{3} \int_{-\sqrt{9-x^2}}^{\sqrt{9-x^2}} \int_0^{\sqrt{9-x^2-y^2}} z\,dz\,dy\,dx$$

$$= \int_{-3}^{3} \int_{-\sqrt{9-x^2}}^{\sqrt{9-x^2}} \frac{z^2}{2}\Big|_0^{\sqrt{9-x^2-y^2}} dy\,dx$$

$$= \frac{1}{2}\int_{-3}^{3} \int_{-\sqrt{9-x^2}}^{\sqrt{9-x^2}} (9 - x^2 - y^2)\,dy\,dx$$

$$= \frac{1}{2}\int_{-3}^{3} \left[(9 - x^2)y - \frac{y^3}{3}\right]\Big|_{-\sqrt{9-x^2}}^{\sqrt{9-x^2}} dx$$

$$= \frac{1}{2}\int_{-3}^{3} \frac{4}{3}(9 - x^2)^{3/2}dx \overset{x = 3\sin u}{=} \frac{2}{3}\int_{-\pi/2}^{\pi/2} 27\cos^3 u(3\cos u)\,du$$

$$= 54\int_{-\pi/2}^{\pi/2} \cos^4 u\,du = 54\left(\frac{1}{4}\cos^3 u \sin u + \frac{3}{8}\cos u \sin u + \frac{3}{8}u\right)\Big|_{-\pi/2}^{\pi/2}$$

$$= \frac{81}{4}\pi$$

with the next to last equality coming from (15) in Section 7.1.

30. First, $\rho(x,y,z) = x$. Next, R is bounded by a quarter circle, and is the horizontally simple region between the graphs of $x = 0$ and $x = \sqrt{4 - y^2}$ on $[0,2]$. Finally, D is the solid region between the graphs of $z = 0$ and $z = \sqrt{4 - y^2}$ on R . Thus the total charge is given by

$$q = \iiint_D x\,dV = \int_0^2 \int_0^{\sqrt{4-y^2}} \int_0^{\sqrt{4-y^2}} x\,dz\,dx\,dy$$

$$= \int_0^2 \int_0^{\sqrt{4-y^2}} xz\Big|_0^{\sqrt{4-y^2}} dx\,dy = \int_0^2 \int_0^{\sqrt{4-y^2}} x\sqrt{4 - y^2}\,dx\,dy$$

$$= \int_0^2 \frac{x^2}{2}\sqrt{4 - y^2}\Big|_0^{\sqrt{4-y^2}} dy = \frac{1}{2}\int_0^2 (4 - y^2)^{3/2}dy$$

$$\overset{y = 2\sin u}{=} \frac{1}{2}\int_0^{\pi/2} 8\cos^3 u(2\cos u)\,du = 8\int_0^{\pi/2} \cos^4 u\,du$$

$$= 8\left(\frac{1}{4}\cos^3 u \sin u + \frac{3}{8}\cos u \sin u + \frac{3}{8}u\right)\Big|_0^{\pi/2} = \frac{3}{2}\pi$$

with the next to last equality coming from (15) in Section 7.1.

31. a. The sheet and the plane $z = x$ intersect for (x,y,z) such that $x^2 = z = x$, so that $x = 0$ or $x = 1$. Thus the region R in the xy plane is the square bounded by the lines $y = 0$ and $y = 1$ on $[0,1]$. Finally, D is the solid region between the graphs of $z = x^2$ and $z = x$ on R . Therefore the volume is given by

$$V = \iiint_D 1\,dV = \int_0^1 \int_0^1 \int_{x^2}^{x} 1\,dz\,dy\,dx = \int_0^1 \int_0^1 z\Big|_{x^2}^{x} dy\,dx$$

$$= \int_0^1 \int_0^1 (x - x^2)\,dy\,dx = \int_0^1 (x - x^2)y\Big|_0^1 dx$$

$$= \int_0^1 (x - x^2)\,dx = \left(\frac{x^2}{2} - \frac{x^3}{3}\right)\Big|_0^1 = \frac{1}{6}$$

Consequently the average value of f on D is given by

$$\frac{1}{V}\iiint_D (x+y+z)\,dV = 6\int_0^1\int_0^1\int_{x^2}^{x} (x+y+z)\,dz\,dy\,dx$$

$$= 6\int_0^1\int_0^1 \left[(x+y)z + \frac{1}{2}z^2\right]\Big|_{x^2}^{x} dy\,dx$$

$$= 6\int_0^1\int_0^1 \left[\frac{-1}{2}x^4 - x^3 + \frac{3}{2}x^2 + (x-x^2)y\right]dy\,dx$$

$$= 6\int_0^1 \left[\left(\frac{-1}{2}x^4 - x^3 + \frac{3}{2}x^2\right)y + (x-x^2)\left(\frac{1}{2}y^2\right)\right]\Big|_0^1 dx$$

$$= 6\int_0^1 \left(\frac{-1}{2}x^4 - x^3 + x^2 + \frac{1}{2}x\right)dx$$

$$= 6\left(\frac{-1}{10}x^5 - \frac{1}{4}x^4 + \frac{1}{3}x^3 + \frac{1}{4}x^2\right)\Big|_0^1 = \frac{7}{5}$$

b. The paraboloids intersect for (x,y,z) such that $-1 + x^2 + y^2 = z = 1 - x^2 - y^2$, or rather, $x^2 + y^2 = 1$. Thus R is circular, and is the vertically simple region between the graphs of $y = -\sqrt{1-x^2}$ and $y = \sqrt{1-x^2}$ on $[-1,1]$. Finally, D is the solid region between the graphs of $z = -1 + x^2 + y^2$ and $z = 1 - x^2 - y^2$ on R. Therefore the average value of f is given by

$$\frac{1}{V}\iiint_D xy\,dV = \frac{1}{V}\int_{-1}^{1}\int_{-\sqrt{1-x^2}}^{\sqrt{1-x^2}}\int_{-1+x^2+y^2}^{1-x^2-y^2} xy\,dz\,dy\,dx$$

$$= \frac{1}{V}\int_{-1}^{1}\int_{-\sqrt{1-x^2}}^{\sqrt{1-x^2}} xyz\Big|_{-1+x^2+y^2}^{1-x^2-y^2} dy\,dx$$

$$= \frac{1}{V}\int_{-1}^{1}\int_{-\sqrt{1-x^2}}^{\sqrt{1-x^2}} (2xy - 2x^3y - 2xy^3)\,dy\,dx$$

$$= \frac{1}{V}\int_{-1}^{1} \left(xy^2 - x^3y^2 - \frac{1}{2}xy^4\right)\Big|_{-\sqrt{1-x^2}}^{\sqrt{1-x^2}} dx$$

$$= \frac{1}{V}\int_{-1}^{1} 0\,dx = 0$$

Section 14.5

1. $r\sin\theta = -4$

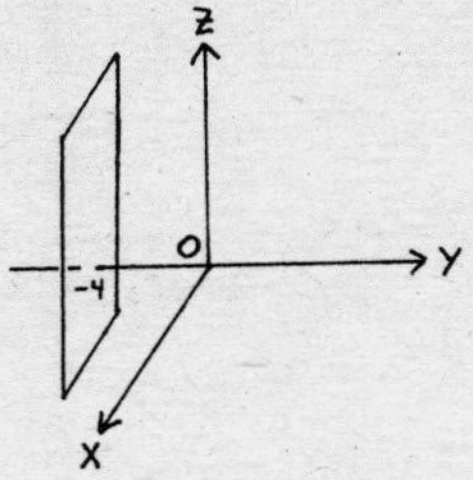

2. $r\cos\theta = 5z$

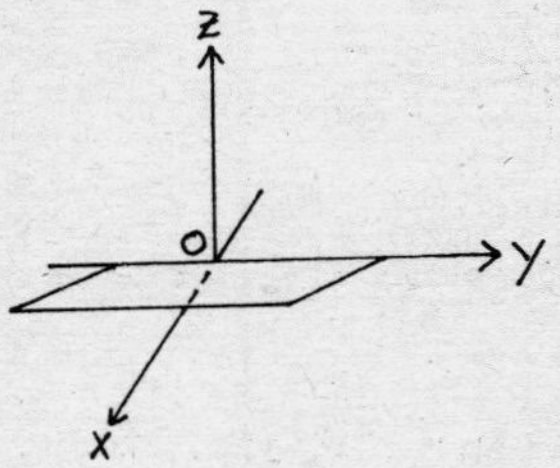

3. $r(\cos\theta + \sin\theta) + z = 3$

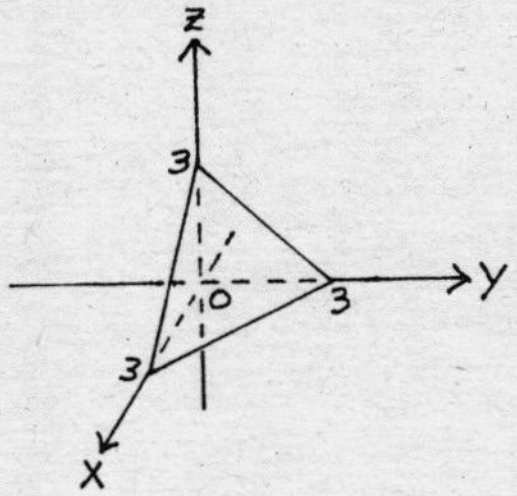

4. $r^2 + z^2 = 16$

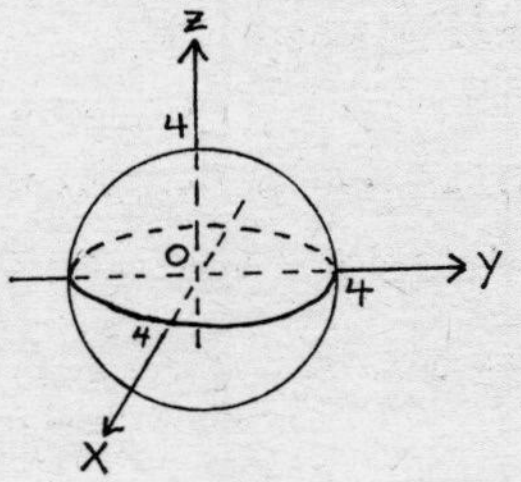

5. $r^2 + z = 1$

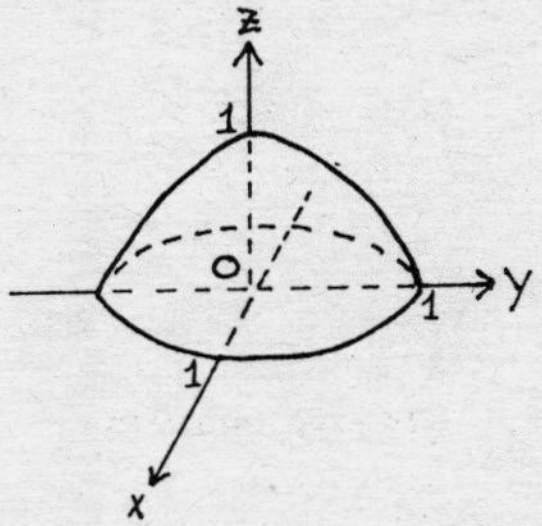

6. $r^2 + z^2 = 0$

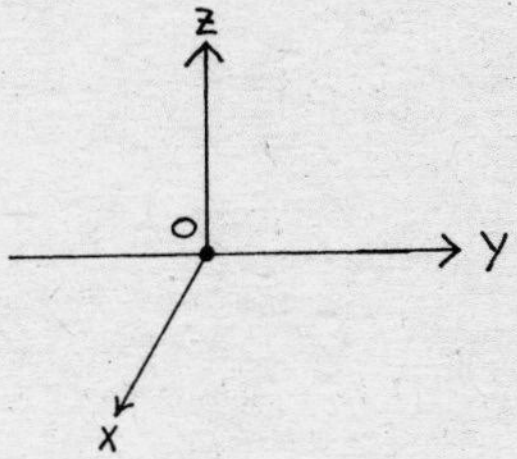

7. $4r^2 = z^2$, or $z = 2r$

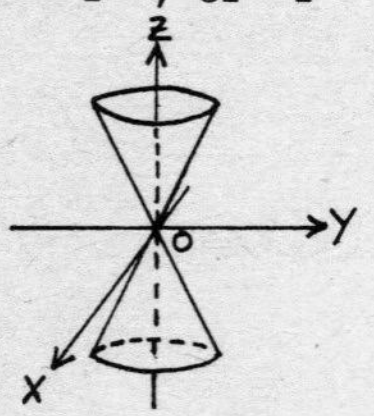

8. $r^2 + 3z^2 = 9$

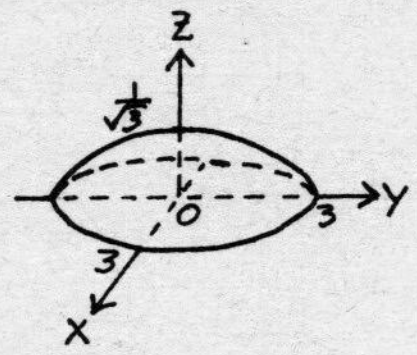

9. $\int_0^{2\pi}\int_1^2\int_0^5 e^z r\,dz\,dr\,d\theta = \int_0^{2\pi}\int_1^2 e^z r\Big|_0^5 dr\,d\theta$

$= \int_0^{2\pi}\int_1^2 (e^5 - 1)r\,dr\,d\theta = \int_0^{2\pi}\frac{1}{2}(e^5 - 1)r^2\Big|_1^2 d\theta$

$= \int_0^{2\pi}\frac{3}{2}(e^5 - 1)d\theta = 3\pi(e^5 - 1)$

10. $\int_0^{\pi/2}\int_0^1\int_0^{\sqrt{1-r^2}} r\sin\theta\,dz\,dr\,d\theta = \int_0^{\pi/2}\int_0^1 zr\sin\theta\Big|_0^{\sqrt{1-r^2}} dr\,d\theta$

$= \int_0^{\pi/2}\int_0^1 r\sqrt{1-r^2}\sin\theta\,dr\,d\theta$

$= \int_0^{\pi/2}\frac{-1}{3}(1 - r^2)^{3/2}\sin\theta\Big|_0^1 d\theta = \int_0^{\pi/2}\frac{1}{3}\sin\theta\,d\theta$

$= \frac{-1}{3}\cos\theta\Big|_0^{\pi/2} = \frac{1}{3}$

11. $\int_{-\pi/2}^0\int_0^{2\sin\theta}\int_0^{r^2} r^2\cos\theta\,dz\,dr\,d\theta = \int_{-\pi/2}^0\int_0^{2\sin\theta} zr^2\cos\theta\Big|_0^{r^2} dr\,d\theta$

$= \int_{-\pi/2}^0\int_0^{2\sin\theta} r^4\cos\theta\,dr\,d\theta = \int_{-\pi/2}^0 \frac{1}{5}r^5\cos\theta\Big|_0^{2\sin\theta} d\theta$

$= \int_{-\pi/2}^0 \frac{32}{5}\sin^5\theta\cos\theta\,d\theta = \frac{16}{15}\sin^6\theta\Big|_{-\pi/2}^0 = \frac{-16}{15}$

12. $\int_0^{\pi/4}\int_0^{1+\cos\theta}\int_0^r 1\,dz\,dr\,d\theta = \int_0^{\pi/4}\int_0^{1+\cos\theta} z\Big|_0^r dr\,d\theta$

$= \int_0^{\pi/4}\int_0^{1+\cos\theta} r\,dr\,d\theta = \int_0^{\pi/4}\frac{1}{2}r^2\Big|_0^{1+\cos\theta} d\theta$

$= \int_0^{\pi/4}(\frac{1}{2} + \cos\theta + \frac{1}{2}\cos^2\theta)d\theta$

$= \int_0^{\pi/4}(1 + \cos\theta + \frac{1}{2}\cos 2\theta)d\theta$

$= (\theta + \sin\theta + \frac{1}{4}\sin 2\theta)\Big|_0^{\pi/4} = \frac{\pi}{4} + \frac{\sqrt{2}}{2} + \frac{1}{4}$

13. $\int_{-\pi/4}^{\pi/4}\int_0^{1-2\cos^2\theta}\int_0^1 r\sin\theta\,dz\,dr\,d\theta$

$= \int_{-\pi/4}^{\pi/4}\int_0^{1-2\cos^2\theta} zr\sin\theta\Big|_0^1 dr\,d\theta$

$= \int_{-\pi/4}^{\pi/4}\int_0^{1-2\cos^2\theta} r\sin\theta\,dr\,d\theta$

$= \int_{-\pi/4}^{\pi/4}\frac{1}{2}r^2\sin\theta\Big|_0^{1-2\cos^2\theta} d\theta$

$= \int_{-\pi/4}^{\pi/4}(\frac{1}{2} - 2\cos^2\theta + 2\cos^4\theta)\sin\theta\,d\theta$

$= (-\frac{1}{2}\cos\theta + \frac{2}{3}\cos^3\theta - \frac{2}{5}\cos^5\theta)\Big|_{-\pi/4}^{\pi/4} = 0$

14. D is the solid region between the graphs of $z = 0$ and $z = 4$ on the disk $0 \le r \le 1$. Therefore

$\iiint_D (x^2 + y^2)dV = \int_0^{2\pi}\int_0^1\int_0^4 r^3 dz\,dr\,d\theta = \int_0^{2\pi}\int_0^1 r^3 z\Big|_0^4 dr\,d\theta$

$= \int_0^{2\pi}\int_0^1 4r^3 dr\,d\theta = \int_0^{2\pi} r^4\Big|_0^1 d\theta = \int_0^{2\pi} 1\,d\theta = 2\pi$

15. D is the solid region between the graphs of $z = 0$ and $z = \sqrt{1 - r^2}$ on the region bounded by the polar graphs of $r = 0$ and $r = 1$ for $0 \le \theta \le \frac{\pi}{2}$. Therefore

$$\iiint_D z\,dV = \int_0^{\pi/2}\int_0^1\int_0^{\sqrt{1-r^2}} zr\,dz\,dr\,d\theta$$

$$= \int_0^{\pi/2}\int_0^1 \frac{1}{2} z^2 r \,\Big|_0^{\sqrt{1-r^2}} dr\,d\theta$$

$$= \int_0^{\pi/2}\int_0^1 \left(\frac{1}{2} r - \frac{1}{2} r^3\right)dr\,d\theta$$

$$= \int_0^{\pi/2} \left(\frac{1}{4} r^2 - \frac{1}{8} r^4\right)\Big|_0^1 d\theta = \int_0^{\pi/2} \frac{1}{8}\,d\theta = \frac{\pi}{16}$$

16. D is the solid region between the graphs of $z = -\sqrt{4 - r^2}$ and $z = \sqrt{4 - r^2}$ on the disk $0 \le r \le 1$. Therefore

$$\iiint_D y^2 dV = \int_0^{2\pi}\int_0^1\int_{-\sqrt{4-r^2}}^{\sqrt{4-r^2}} r^3\sin^2\theta\,dz\,dr\,d\theta$$

$$= \int_0^{2\pi}\int_0^1 z\,r^3\sin^2\theta\,\Big|_{-\sqrt{4-r^2}}^{\sqrt{4-r^2}} dr\,d\theta$$

$$= \int_0^{2\pi}\int_0^1 2r^3\sqrt{4 - r^2}\,\sin^2\theta\,dr\,d\theta$$

$$= \int_0^{2\pi}\int_4^3 (u - 4)u^{1/2}\sin^2\theta\,du\,d\theta$$

$$= \int_0^{2\pi}\left(\frac{2}{5}u^{5/2} - \frac{8}{3}u^{3/2}\right)\sin^2\theta\,\Big|_4^3 d\theta$$

$$= \int_0^{2\pi} \frac{2}{15}(64 - 33\sqrt{3})\sin^2\theta\,d\theta$$

$$= \int_0^{2\pi} \frac{2}{15}(64 - 33\sqrt{3})\left(\frac{1}{2} - \frac{1}{2}\cos 2\theta\right)d\theta$$

$$= \frac{2}{15}(64 - 33\sqrt{3})\left(\frac{1}{2}\theta - \frac{1}{4}\sin 2\theta\right)\Big|_0^{2\pi} = \frac{2\pi}{15}(64 - 33\sqrt{3})$$

17. D is the solid region between the graphs of $z = -\sqrt{4 - r^2}$ and $z = \sqrt{4 - r^2}$ on the disk $0 \le r \le 2$. Therefore

$$\iiint_D xz\,dV = \int_0^{2\pi}\int_0^2\int_{-\sqrt{4-r^2}}^{\sqrt{4-r^2}} r^2 z\cos\theta\,dz\,dr\,d\theta$$

$$= \int_0^{2\pi}\int_0^2 \frac{1}{2} r^2 z^2\cos\theta\,\Big|_{-\sqrt{4-r^2}}^{\sqrt{4-r^2}} dr\,d\theta$$

$$= \int_0^{2\pi}\int_0^2 (4r^2 - r^4)\cos\theta\,dr\,d\theta$$

$$= \int_0^{2\pi}\left(\frac{4}{3}r^3 - \frac{1}{5}r^5\right)\cos\theta\,\Big|_0^2 d\theta$$

$$= \int_0^{2\pi}\frac{64}{15}\cos\theta\,d\theta = \frac{64}{15}\sin\theta\,\Big|_0^{2\pi} = 0$$

18. D is the solid region between the graphs of $z = -\sqrt{1 - r^2}$ and $z = \sqrt{1 - r^2}$ on the region in the xy plane bounded by the circle $r = \cos\theta$. Therefore

$$\iiint_D yz\,dV = \int_{-\pi/2}^{\pi/2}\int_0^{\cos\theta}\int_{-\sqrt{1-r^2}}^{\sqrt{1-r^2}} r^2 z\sin\theta\,dz\,dr\,d\theta$$

$$= \int_{-\pi/2}^{\pi/2}\int_0^{\cos\theta}\frac{1}{2} r^2 z^2\sin\theta\,\Big|_{-\sqrt{1-r^2}}^{\sqrt{1-r^2}} dr\,d\theta$$

$$= \int_{-\pi/2}^{\pi/2}\int_0^{\cos\theta}(r^2 - r^4)\sin\theta\,dr\,d\theta$$

$$= \int_{-\pi/2}^{\pi/2}\left(\frac{1}{3}r^3 - \frac{1}{5}r^5\right)\sin\theta\,\Big|_0^{\cos\theta} d\theta$$

$$= \int_{-\pi/2}^{\pi/2}\left(\frac{1}{3}\cos^3\theta - \frac{1}{5}\cos^5\theta\right)\sin\theta\,d\theta$$

$$= \left(-\frac{1}{12}\cos^4\theta + \frac{1}{30}\cos^6\theta\right)\Big|_{-\pi/2}^{\pi/2} = 0$$

19. The surface $z = \sqrt{r}$ and the plane $z = 1$ intersect over the circle $r = 1$ in the xy plane. Thus the given region D is the solid region between the graphs of $z = \sqrt{r}$ and $z = 1$ on the disk $0 \le r \le 1$. Therefore

$$V = \iiint_D 1\,dV = \int_0^{2\pi}\int_0^1\int_{\sqrt{r}}^1 r\,dz\,dr\,d\theta = \int_0^{2\pi}\int_0^1 rz\,\Big|_{\sqrt{r}}^1 dr\,d\theta$$

$$= \int_0^{2\pi}\int_0^1 (r - r^{3/2})dr\,d\theta = \int_0^{2\pi}\left(\frac{1}{2}r^2 - \frac{2}{5}r^{5/2}\right)\Big|_0^1 d\theta$$

$$= \int_0^{2\pi} \frac{1}{10}\, d\theta = \frac{\pi}{5}$$

20. At any point (x,y,z) of intersection of the sphere $x^2 + y^2 + z^2 = 2$ and the paraboloid $z = x^2 + y^2$, z must satisfy $z + z^2 = 2$ and $z \geq 0$, so that $z = 1$. Thus the sphere and the paraboloid intersect over the circle $x^2 + y^2 = 1$, or $r = 1$, in the xy plane, so that the given region D is the solid region between the graphs of $z = r^2$ and $z = \sqrt{2 - r^2}$ on the disk $0 \leq r \leq 1$. Therefore

$$V = \iiint_D 1\, dV = \int_0^{2\pi} \int_0^1 \int_{r^2}^{\sqrt{2-r^2}} r\, dz\, dr\, d\theta = \int_0^{2\pi} \int_0^1 rz \Big|_{r^2}^{\sqrt{2-r^2}} dr\, d\theta$$

$$= \int_0^{2\pi} \int_0^1 (r\sqrt{2 - r^2} - r^3) dr\, d\theta = \int_0^{2\pi} [\tfrac{-1}{3}(2 - r^2)^{3/2} - \tfrac{1}{4} r^4]\Big|_0^1 d\theta$$

$$= \int_0^{2\pi} (\tfrac{2\sqrt{2}}{3} - \tfrac{7}{12}) d\theta = 2\pi(\tfrac{2\sqrt{2}}{3} - \tfrac{7}{12})$$

21. The given region D is the solid region between the graphs of $z = 0$ and $z = e^{-r^2}$ on the disk $0 \leq r \leq 1$. Therefore

$$V = \iiint_D 1\, dV = \int_0^{2\pi} \int_0^1 \int_0^{e^{-r^2}} r\, dz\, dr\, d\theta = \int_0^{2\pi} \int_0^1 rz \Big|_0^{e^{-r^2}} dr\, d\theta$$

$$= \int_0^{2\pi} \int_0^1 re^{-r^2} dr\, d\theta = \int_0^{2\pi} \frac{-1}{2} e^{-r^2} \Big|_0^1 d\theta = \int_0^{2\pi} \tfrac{1}{2}(1 - e^{-1}) d\theta$$

$$= \pi(1 - e^{-1})$$

22. At any point (x,y,z) of intersection of the plane $z = 1$ with the sphere $x^2 + y^2 + z^2 = 2$, x and y must satisfy $x^2 + y^2 + 1 = 2$, or $r = 1$. Thus the given region D is the solid region between the graphs of $z = 1$ and $z = \sqrt{2 - r^2}$ on the disk $0 \leq r \leq 1$. Therefore

$$V = \iiint_D 1\, dV = \int_0^{2\pi} \int_0^1 \int_1^{\sqrt{2-r^2}} r\, dz\, dr\, d\theta = \int_0^{2\pi} \int_0^1 rz \Big|_1^{\sqrt{2-r^2}} dr\, d\theta$$

$$= \int_0^{2\pi} \int_0^1 (r\sqrt{2 - r^2} - r) dr\, d\theta = \int_0^{2\pi} [\tfrac{-1}{3}(2 - r^2)^{3/2} - \tfrac{1}{2} r^2]\Big|_0^1 d\theta$$

$$= \int_0^{2\pi} (\tfrac{2\sqrt{2}}{3} - \tfrac{5}{6}) d\theta = 2\pi(\tfrac{2\sqrt{2}}{3} - \tfrac{5}{6})$$

23. At any point (x,y,z) of intersection of the sphere $x^2 + y^2 + z^2 = 4$ and the cone $z^2 = 3x^2 + 3y^2$, x and y must satisfy $x^2 + y^2 + 3x^2 + 3y^2 = 4$, or $r = 1$. Thus the given region D is the solid region between the graphs of $z = \sqrt{3}\, r$ and $z = \sqrt{4 - r^2}$ on the disk $0 \leq r \leq 1$. Therefore

$$V = \iiint_D 1\, dV = \int_0^{2\pi} \int_0^1 \int_{\sqrt{3}\, r}^{\sqrt{4-r^2}} r\, dz\, dr\, d\theta$$

$$= \int_0^{2\pi} \int_0^1 rz \Big|_{\sqrt{3}\, r}^{\sqrt{4-r^2}} dr\, d\theta = \int_0^{2\pi} \int_0^1 (r\sqrt{4 - r^2} - \sqrt{3}\, r^2) dr\, d\theta$$

$$= \int_0^{2\pi} [\tfrac{-1}{3}(4 - r^2)^{3/2} - \tfrac{\sqrt{3}}{3} r^3] \Big|_0^1 d\theta = \int_0^{2\pi} (\tfrac{8}{3} - \tfrac{4\sqrt{3}}{3}) d\theta$$

$$= \frac{8\pi}{3}(2 - \sqrt{3})$$

24. At any point (x,y,z) of intersection of the paraboloid $z = 1 - x^2 - y^2$ and the plane $z = -3$, x , y , and z must satisfy $-3 = z = 1 - x^2 - y^2$, or $r = 2$. Thus the given region D is the solid region between the graphs of $z = -3$ and $z = 1 - r^2$ on the disk $0 \leq r \leq 2$. Therefore

$$V = \iiint_D 1\, dV = \int_0^{2\pi} \int_0^2 \int_{-3}^{1-r^2} r\, dz\, dr\, d\theta = \int_0^{2\pi} \int_0^2 rz \Big|_{-3}^{1-r^2} dr\, d\theta$$

$$= \int_0^{2\pi} \int_0^2 (4r - r^3) dr\, d\theta = \int_0^{2\pi} (2r^2 - \tfrac{1}{4} r^4) \Big|_0^2 d\theta = \int_0^{2\pi} 4\, d\theta = 8\pi$$

25. The cone $z = r$ intersects the planes $z = 1$ and $z = 2$ over the circles $r = 1$ and $r = 2$, respectively, in the xy plane. Thus the given solid region D consists of the regions D_1 and D_2 , where D_1 is the solid region between the graphs

of $z = 1$ and $z = 2$ on the disk $0 \le r \le 1$, and D_2 in the solid region between the graphs of $z = r$ and $z = 2$ on the ring $1 \le r \le 2$. Therefore

$$V = \iiint_D 1\,dV = \iiint_{D_1} 1\,dV + \iiint_{D_2} 1\,dV$$

$$= \int_0^{2\pi}\int_0^1\int_1^2 r\,dz\,dr\,d\theta + \int_0^{2\pi}\int_1^2\int_r^2 r\,dz\,dr\,d\theta$$

$$= \int_0^{2\pi}\int_0^1 rz\Big|_1^2 dr\,d\theta + \int_0^{2\pi}\int_1^2 rz\Big|_r^2 dr\,d\theta$$

$$= \int_0^{2\pi}\int_0^1 r\,dr\,d\theta + \int_0^{2\pi}\int_1^2 (2r - r^2)dr\,d\theta$$

$$= \int_0^{2\pi} \frac{1}{2}r^2\Big|_0^1 d\theta + \int_0^{2\pi} (r^2 - \frac{1}{3}r^3)\Big|_1^2 d\theta$$

$$= \int_0^{2\pi} \frac{1}{2}\,d\theta + \int_0^{2\pi} \frac{2}{3}\,d\theta = \pi + \frac{4\pi}{3} = \frac{7\pi}{3}$$

26. In cylindrical coordinates the equation $x^2 + y^2 = 2x$ of the cylinder becomes $r^2 = 2r\cos\theta$, or $r = 2\cos\theta$. Thus the given region D is the solid region between the graphs of $z = 0$ and $z = 8 - r$ on the region bounded by the circle $r = 2\cos\theta$. Therefore

$$V = \iiint_D 1\,dV = \int_{-\pi/2}^{\pi/2}\int_0^{2\cos\theta}\int_0^{8-r} r\,dz\,dr\,d\theta$$

$$= \int_{-\pi/2}^{\pi/2}\int_0^{2\cos\theta} rz\Big|_0^{8-r} dr\,d\theta = \int_{-\pi/2}^{\pi/2}\int_0^{2\cos\theta} (8r - r^2)dr\,d\theta$$

$$= \int_{-\pi/2}^{\pi/2} (4r^2 - \frac{1}{3}r^3)\Big|_0^{2\cos\theta} d\theta = \int_{-\pi/2}^{\pi/2} (16\cos^2\theta - \frac{8}{3}\cos^3\theta)d\theta$$

$$= \int_{-\pi/2}^{\pi/2} [8 + 8\cos 2\theta - \frac{8}{3}(1 - \sin^2\theta)\cos\theta]d\theta$$

$$= (8\theta + 4\sin 2\theta - \frac{8}{3}\sin\theta + \frac{8}{9}\sin^3\theta)\Big|_{-\pi/2}^{\pi/2} = 8\pi - \frac{32}{9}$$

27. At any point (x,y,z) of intersection of the plane $z = y$ and the paraboloid $z = x^2 + y^2$, x, y, and z must satisfy $y = z = x^2 + y^2$, or $r\sin\theta = r^2$, or $r = \sin\theta$. Thus the given region D is the solid region between the graphs of $z = r^2$ and $z = r\sin\theta$ on the region bounded by the circle $r = \sin\theta$. Therefore

$$V = \iiint_D 1\,dV = \int_0^{\pi}\int_0^{\sin\theta}\int_{r^2}^{r\sin\theta} r\,dz\,dr\,d\theta$$

$$= \int_0^{\pi}\int_0^{\sin\theta} rz\Big|_{r^2}^{r\sin\theta} dr\,d\theta = \int_0^{\pi}\int_0^{\sin\theta} (r^2\sin\theta - r^3)dr\,d\theta$$

$$= \int_0^{\pi} (\frac{1}{3}r^3\sin\theta - \frac{1}{4}r^4)\Big|_0^{\sin\theta} d\theta = \int_0^{\pi} \frac{1}{12}\sin^4\theta\,d\theta$$

$$= \frac{1}{12}(\frac{-1}{4}\sin^3\theta\cos\theta - \frac{3}{8}\sin\theta\cos\theta + \frac{3}{8}\theta)\Big|_0^{\pi} = \frac{\pi}{32}$$

with the next to last equality coming from (14) in Section 7.1.

28. The given region D is the solid region between the graphs of $z = -\sqrt{4a^2 - r^2}$ and $z = \sqrt{4a^2 - r^2}$ on the disk $0 \le r \le a$. Therefore

$$V = \iiint_D 1\,dV = \int_0^{2\pi}\int_0^a\int_{-\sqrt{4a^2-r^2}}^{\sqrt{4a^2-r^2}} r\,dz\,dr\,d\theta$$

$$= \int_0^{2\pi}\int_0^a rz\Big|_{-\sqrt{4a^2-r^2}}^{\sqrt{4a^2-r^2}} dr\,d\theta = \int_0^{2\pi}\int_0^a 2r\sqrt{4a^2 - r^2}\,dr\,d\theta$$

$$= \int_0^{2\pi} \frac{-2}{3}(4a^2 - r^2)^{3/2}\Big|_0^a d\theta = \int_0^{2\pi} (\frac{16}{3}a^3 - 2\sqrt{3}\,a^3)d\theta$$

$$= \frac{4\pi a^3}{3}(8 - 3\sqrt{3})$$

29. The given region D is the solid region between the graphs of $z = -\sqrt{a^2 - r^2}$ and $z = \sqrt{a^2 - r^2}$ on the region bounded by

the circle $r = a\sin\theta$. Therefore

$$V = \iiint_D 1\,dV = \int_0^{\pi}\int_0^{a\sin\theta}\int_{-\sqrt{a^2-r^2}}^{\sqrt{a^2-r^2}} r\,dz\,dr\,d\theta$$

$$= \int_0^{\pi}\int_0^{a\sin\theta} rz\Big|_{-\sqrt{a^2-r^2}}^{\sqrt{a^2-r^2}} dr\,d\theta = \int_0^{\pi}\int_0^{a\sin\theta} 2r\sqrt{a^2-r^2}\,dr\,d\theta$$

$$= \int_0^{\pi} \frac{-2}{3}(a^2-r^2)^{3/2}\Big|_0^{a\sin\theta} d\theta = \int_0^{\pi} \frac{2}{3}a^3(1-|\cos^3\theta|)d\theta$$

$$= \int_0^{\pi/2} \frac{2}{3}a^3(1-\cos^3\theta)d\theta + \int_{\pi/2}^{\pi} \frac{2}{3}a^3(1+\cos^3\theta)d\theta$$

$$= \frac{2}{3}a^3\int_0^{\pi/2}[1-(1-\sin^2\theta)\cos\theta]d\theta + \frac{2}{3}a^3\int_{\pi/2}^{\pi}[1+(1-\sin^2\theta)\cos\theta]d\theta$$

$$= \frac{2}{3}a^3(\theta-\sin\theta+\frac{1}{3}\sin^3\theta)\Big|_0^{\pi/2} + \frac{2}{3}a^3(\theta+\sin\theta-\frac{1}{3}\sin^3\theta)\Big|_{\pi/2}^{\pi}$$

$$= \frac{2}{3}a^3(\frac{\pi}{2}-\frac{2}{3}) + \frac{2}{3}a^3(\frac{\pi}{2}-\frac{2}{3}) = \frac{4}{3}a^3(\frac{\pi}{2}-\frac{2}{3})$$

30. The given region D is the solid region between the graphs of $z = 0$ and $z = r$ on the region bounded by the cardioid $r = 1 + \cos\theta$. Therefore

$$V = \iiint_D 1\,dV = \int_0^{2\pi}\int_0^{1+\cos\theta}\int_0^{r} r\,dz\,dr\,d\theta$$

$$= \int_0^{2\pi}\int_0^{1+\cos\theta} rz\Big|_0^{r} dr\,d\theta = \int_0^{2\pi}\int_0^{1+\cos\theta} r^2dr\,d\theta$$

$$= \int_0^{2\pi} \frac{1}{3}r^3\Big|_0^{1+\cos\theta} d\theta = \int_0^{2\pi} (\frac{1}{3}+\cos\theta+\cos^2\theta+\frac{1}{3}\cos^3\theta)d\theta$$

$$= \int_0^{2\pi} [\frac{1}{3}+\cos\theta+\frac{1}{2}+\frac{1}{2}\cos 2\theta+\frac{1}{3}(1-\sin^2\theta)\cos\theta]d\theta$$

$$= (\frac{1}{3}\theta+\sin\theta+\frac{1}{2}\theta+\frac{1}{4}\sin 2\theta+\frac{1}{3}\sin\theta-\frac{1}{9}\sin^3\theta)\Big|_0^{2\pi} = \frac{5\pi}{3}$$

31. The given region D is the solid region between the graphs of $z = 0$ and $z = r^2$ on the region in the first quadrant bounded by the x axis and the polar graph of $r = 2\sqrt{\cos\theta}$. Therefore

$$V = \iiint_D 1\,dV = \int_0^{\pi/2}\int_0^{2\sqrt{\cos\theta}}\int_0^{r^2} r\,dz\,dr\,d\theta$$

$$= \int_0^{\pi/2}\int_0^{2\sqrt{\cos\theta}} rz\Big|_0^{r^2} dr\,d\theta = \int_0^{\pi/2}\int_0^{2\sqrt{\cos\theta}} r^3dr\,d\theta$$

$$= \int_0^{\pi/2} \frac{1}{4}r^4\Big|_0^{2\sqrt{\cos\theta}} d\theta = \int_0^{\pi/2} 4\cos^2\theta\,d\theta$$

$$= \int_0^{\pi/2} (2+2\cos 2\theta)d\theta = (2\theta+\sin 2\theta)\Big|_0^{\pi/2} = \pi$$

32. The region D occupied by the solid is the solid region between the graphs of $z = 0$ and $z = 5$ on the disk $0 \le r \le 3$. Since the mass density is given by $\delta(x,y,z) = \sqrt{x^2+y^2}$, the total mass m of the object is given by

$$m = \iiint_D \sqrt{x^2+y^2}\,dV = \int_0^{2\pi}\int_0^{3}\int_0^{5} r^2dz\,dr\,d\theta$$

$$= \int_0^{2\pi}\int_0^{3} r^2z\Big|_0^{5} dr\,d\theta = \int_0^{2\pi}\int_0^{3} 5r^2dr\,d\theta = \int_0^{2\pi} \frac{5}{3}r^3\Big|_0^{3} d\theta$$

$$= \int_0^{2\pi} 45\,d\theta = 90\pi$$

33. At any point (x,y,z) of intersection of the cone $z^2 = 9x^2 + 9y^2$ and the plane $z = 9$, x , y , and z must satisfy $81 = z^2 = 9x^2 + 9y^2$, or $r = 3$. Thus the object occupies the solid region D between the graphs of $z = 3r$ and $z = 9$ on the disk $0 \le r \le 3$. Since the mass density is given by $\delta(x,y,z) = 9 - z$, the total mass m is given by

$$m = \iiint_D (9-z)dV = \int_0^{2\pi}\int_0^{3}\int_{3r}^{9} (9-z)r\,dz\,dr\,d\theta$$

$$= \int_0^{2\pi}\int_0^{3} (9z-\frac{1}{2}z^2)r\Big|_{3r}^{9} dr\,d\theta$$

$$= \int_0^{2\pi} \int_0^3 \left(\frac{81}{2} r - 27r^2 + \frac{9}{2} r^3\right) dr\, d\theta$$

$$= \int_0^{2\pi} \left(\frac{81}{4} r^2 - 9r^3 + \frac{9}{8} r^4\right) \Big|_0^3 d\theta = \int_0^{2\pi} \frac{243}{8}\, d\theta = \frac{243\pi}{4}$$

34. The remaining part occupies the solid region D between the graphs of $z = -\sqrt{a^2 - r^2}$ and $z = \sqrt{a^2 - r^2}$ on the ring $b \le r \le a$. Therefore

$$V = \iiint_D 1\, dV = \int_0^{2\pi} \int_b^a \int_{-\sqrt{a^2-r^2}}^{\sqrt{a^2-r^2}} r\, dz\, dr\, d\theta$$

$$= \int_0^{2\pi} \int_b^a rz \Big|_{-\sqrt{a^2-r^2}}^{\sqrt{a^2-r^2}} dr\, d\theta = \int_0^{2\pi} \int_b^a 2r\sqrt{a^2 - r^2}\, dr\, d\theta$$

$$= \int_0^{2\pi} \frac{-2}{3}(a^2 - r^2)^{3/2} \Big|_b^a d\theta = \int_0^{2\pi} \frac{2}{3}(a^2 - b^2)^{3/2} d\theta = \frac{4\pi}{3}(a^2 - b^2)^{3/2}$$

35. At any point (x,y,z) of intersection of the plane $z = h$ and the cone $z^2 = h^2(x^2 + y^2)$, x, y, and z must satisfy $h^2 = z^2 = h^2(x^2 + y^2)$, or $x^2 + y^2 = 1$, or $r = 1$. Thus the given region D is the solid region between the graphs of $z = hr$ and $z = h$ on the disk $0 \le r \le 1$. Therefore

$$V = \iiint_D 1\, dV = \int_0^{2\pi} \int_0^1 \int_{hr}^h r\, dz\, dr\, d\theta = \int_0^{2\pi} \int_0^1 rz \Big|_{hr}^h dr\, d\theta$$

$$= \int_0^{2\pi} \int_0^1 (hr - hr^2) dr\, d\theta = \int_0^{2\pi} \left(\frac{1}{2} hr^2 - \frac{1}{3} hr^3\right) \Big|_0^1 d\theta$$

$$= \int_0^{2\pi} \frac{1}{6} h\, d\theta = \frac{\pi h}{3}$$

Section 14.6

1. a. $x = 1(1)\left(\frac{\sqrt{3}}{2}\right) = \frac{\sqrt{3}}{2}$, $y = 1(1)\left(\frac{1}{2}\right) = \frac{1}{2}$, $z = 1(0) = 0$; $\left(\frac{\sqrt{3}}{2}, \frac{1}{2}, 0\right)$

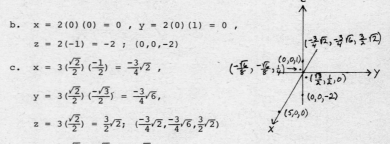

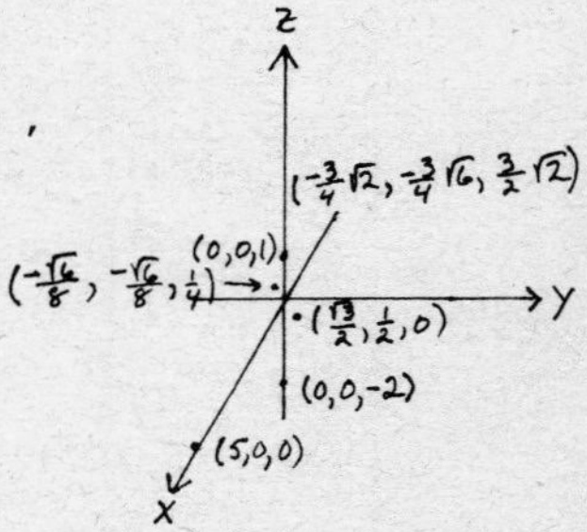

b. $x = 2(0)(0) = 0$, $y = 2(0)(1) = 0$, $z = 2(-1) = -2$; $(0,0,-2)$

c. $x = 3\left(\frac{\sqrt{2}}{2}\right)\left(\frac{-1}{2}\right) = \frac{-3}{4}\sqrt{2}$,

$y = 3\left(\frac{\sqrt{2}}{2}\right)\left(\frac{-\sqrt{3}}{2}\right) = \frac{-3}{4}\sqrt{6}$,

$z = 3\left(\frac{\sqrt{2}}{2}\right) = \frac{3}{2}\sqrt{2}$; $\left(\frac{-3}{4}\sqrt{2}, \frac{-3}{4}\sqrt{6}, \frac{3}{2}\sqrt{2}\right)$

d. $x = \frac{1}{2}\left(\frac{\sqrt{3}}{2}\right)\left(\frac{-\sqrt{2}}{2}\right) = \frac{-\sqrt{6}}{8}$,

$y = \frac{1}{2}\left(\frac{\sqrt{3}}{2}\right)\left(\frac{-\sqrt{2}}{2}\right) = \frac{-\sqrt{6}}{8}$,

$z = \frac{1}{2}\left(\frac{1}{2}\right) = \frac{1}{4}$; $\left(\frac{-\sqrt{6}}{8}, \frac{-\sqrt{6}}{8}, \frac{1}{4}\right)$

e. $x = 1(0)\left(\frac{-\sqrt{3}}{2}\right) = 0$, $y = 1(0)\left(\frac{-1}{2}\right) = 0$, $z = 1(1) = 1$; $(0,0,1)$

f. $x = 5(1)(1) = 5$, $y = 5(1)(0) = 0$, $z = 5(0) = 0$; $(5,0,0)$

2. a. $\rho = \sqrt{x^2 + y^2 + z^2} = \sqrt{1^2 + 0^2 + 1^2} = \sqrt{2}$; $\tan\phi = \frac{\sqrt{x^2 + y^2}}{z} = \frac{\sqrt{1^2 + 0^2}}{1} = 1$, so $\phi = \frac{\pi}{4}$; $\tan\theta = \frac{y}{x} = \frac{0}{1} = 0$ and the point lies in the first octant, so $\theta = 0$. Thus a set of spherical coordinates for $(1,0,1)$ is $\left(\sqrt{2}, \frac{\pi}{4}, 0\right)$.

b. $\rho = \sqrt{x^2 + y^2 + z^2} = \sqrt{3^2 + 0^2 + 0^2} = 3$; $\phi = \frac{\pi}{2}$; $\tan\theta = \frac{y}{x} = \frac{0}{3} = 0$ and the point lies in the first octant, so $\theta = 0$. Thus a set of spherical coordinates for $(3,0,0)$ is $\left(3, \frac{\pi}{2}, 0\right)$.

c. $\rho = \sqrt{x^2+y^2+z^2} = \sqrt{2^2+2^2+(2\sqrt{2}/\sqrt{3})^2} = \frac{4\sqrt{2}}{\sqrt{3}}$;

$\tan\phi = \frac{\sqrt{x^2+y^2}}{z} = \frac{\sqrt{2^2+2^2}}{2\sqrt{2}/\sqrt{3}} = \sqrt{3}$, so $\phi = \frac{\pi}{3}$; $\tan\theta = \frac{y}{x}$

$= \frac{2}{2} = 1$ and the point lies in the first octant, so $\theta = \frac{\pi}{4}$. Thus a set of spherical coordinates for $(2,2,2\sqrt{2}/\sqrt{3})$ is $(\frac{4\sqrt{2}}{\sqrt{3}},\frac{\pi}{3},\frac{\pi}{4})$.

d. $\rho = \sqrt{x^2+y^2+z^2} = \sqrt{(2\sqrt{2})^2+(-2\sqrt{2})^2+(-4\sqrt{3})^2} = 8$;

$\tan\phi = \frac{\sqrt{x^2+y^2}}{z} = \frac{\sqrt{(2\sqrt{2})^2+(2\sqrt{2})^2}}{-4\sqrt{3}} = \frac{-1}{\sqrt{3}}$, so $\phi = \frac{5\pi}{6}$;

$\tan\theta = \frac{y}{x} = \frac{-2\sqrt{2}}{2\sqrt{2}} = -1$, so since (x,y) lies in the fourth quadrant, $\theta = \frac{7\pi}{4}$. Thus a set of spherical coordinates for $(2\sqrt{2},-2\sqrt{2},-4\sqrt{3})$ is $(8,\frac{5\pi}{6},\frac{7\pi}{4})$.

3. $\int_0^{2\pi}\int_0^{\pi/4}\int_0^1 \rho^2\sin\phi\, d\rho\, d\phi\, d\theta = \int_0^{2\pi}\int_0^{\pi/4} (\frac{\rho^3}{3}\sin\phi)\Big|_0^1 d\phi\, d\theta$

$= \int_0^{2\pi}\int_0^{\pi/4} \frac{1}{3}\sin\phi\, d\phi\, d\theta = \int_0^{2\pi} (\frac{-1}{3}\cos\phi)\Big|_0^{\pi/4} d\theta$

$= \int_0^{2\pi} \frac{1}{6}(2-\sqrt{2})d\theta = \frac{\pi}{3}(2-\sqrt{2})$

4. $\int_0^{2\pi}\int_0^{\pi/2}\int_1^3 \rho^3\cos\phi\sin\phi\, d\rho\, d\phi\, d\theta$

$= \int_0^{2\pi}\int_0^{\pi/2} (\frac{\rho^4}{4}\cos\phi\sin\phi)\Big|_1^3 d\phi\, d\theta$

$= \int_0^{2\pi}\int_0^{\pi/2} 20\cos\phi\sin\phi\, d\phi\, d\theta = \int_0^{2\pi} (10\sin^2\phi)\Big|_0^{\pi/2} d\theta$

$= \int_0^{2\pi} 10\, d\theta = 20\pi$

5. $\int_0^{\pi}\int_{\pi/2}^{\pi}\int_1^2 \rho^4\sin^2\phi\cos^2\theta\, d\rho\, d\phi\, d\theta$

$= \int_0^{\pi}\int_{\pi/2}^{\pi} (\frac{\rho^5}{5}\sin^2\phi\cos^2\theta)\Big|_1^2 d\phi\, d\theta$

$= \frac{31}{5}\int_0^{\pi}\int_{\pi/2}^{\pi} \sin^2\phi\cos^2\theta\, d\phi\, d\theta$

$= \frac{31}{5}\int_0^{\pi}\int_{\pi/2}^{\pi} (\frac{1}{2}-\frac{1}{2}\cos 2\phi)\cos^2\theta\, d\phi\, d\theta$

$= \frac{31}{5}\int_0^{\pi} [(\frac{1}{2}\phi - \frac{1}{4}\sin 2\phi)\cos^2\theta]\Big|_{\pi/2}^{\pi} d\theta$

$= \frac{31}{20}\pi\int_0^{\pi} \cos^2\theta\, d\theta = \frac{31}{20}\pi\int_0^{\pi} (\frac{1}{2}+\frac{1}{2}\cos 2\theta)d\theta$

$= \frac{31}{20}\pi(\frac{1}{2}\theta + \frac{1}{4}\sin 2\theta)\Big|_0^{\pi} = \frac{31}{40}\pi^2$

6. $\int_0^{\pi}\int_0^{\pi/2}\int_0^{\sin\phi} \rho^2\sin\phi\, d\rho\, d\phi\, d\theta = \int_0^{\pi}\int_0^{\pi/2} (\frac{\rho^3}{3}\sin\phi)\Big|_0^{\sin\phi} d\phi\, d\theta$

$= \int_0^{\pi}\int_0^{\pi/2} \frac{1}{3}\sin^4\phi\, d\phi\, d\theta$

$= \frac{1}{3}\int_0^{\pi} (\frac{-1}{4}\sin^3\phi\cos\phi - \frac{3}{8}\sin\phi\cos\phi + \frac{3}{8}\phi)\Big|_0^{\pi/2} d\theta$

$= \frac{1}{3}\int_0^{\pi} \frac{3}{16}\pi\, d\theta = \frac{\pi^2}{16}$

with the third from last equality coming from (14) in Section 7.1.

7. $\int_{\pi/4}^{\pi/3}\int_0^{\theta}\int_0^{9\sec\phi} \rho\cos^2\phi\cos\theta\, d\rho\, d\phi\, d\theta$

$= \int_{\pi/4}^{\pi/3}\int_0^{\theta} (\frac{\rho^2}{2}\cos^2\phi\cos\theta)\Big|_0^{9\sec\phi} d\phi\, d\theta$

$= \int_{\pi/4}^{\pi/3}\int_0^{\theta} \frac{81}{2}\cos\theta\, d\phi\, d\theta = \int_{\pi/4}^{\pi/3} (\phi\,\frac{81}{2}\cos\theta)\Big|_0^{\theta} d\theta$

$= \frac{81}{2}\int_{\pi/4}^{\pi/3} \theta\cos\theta\, d\theta \overset{\text{parts}}{=} \frac{81}{2}(\theta\sin\theta)\Big|_{\pi/4}^{\pi/3} - \frac{81}{2}\int_{\pi/4}^{\pi/3} \sin\theta\, d\theta$

$$= \frac{81}{2}(\theta \sin \theta)\Big|_{\pi/4}^{\pi/3} + \frac{81}{2} \cos \theta\Big|_{\pi/4}^{\pi/3}$$

$$= \frac{27}{4}\pi(\sqrt{3} - \tfrac{3}{4}\sqrt{2}) + \frac{81}{4}(1 - \sqrt{2})$$

8. D is the collection of all points with spherical coordinates (ρ,ϕ,θ) such that $0 \le \theta \le 2\pi$, $0 \le \phi \le \pi$, and $0 \le \rho \le 1$. Since $x^2 + y^2 = \rho^2\sin^2\phi$, we find that

$$\iiint_D (x^2 + y^2)dV = \int_0^{2\pi}\int_0^{\pi}\int_0^{1}(\rho^2\sin^2\phi)\rho^2\sin\phi\, d\rho\, d\phi\, d\theta$$

$$= \int_0^{2\pi}\int_0^{\pi}(\frac{\rho^5}{5}\sin^3\phi)\Big|_0^1 d\phi\, d\theta = \frac{1}{5}\int_0^{2\pi}\int_0^{\pi}\sin^3\phi\, d\phi\, d\theta$$

$$= \frac{1}{5}\int_0^{2\pi}\int_0^{\pi}\sin\phi(1 - \cos^2\phi)d\phi\, d\theta$$

$$= \frac{1}{5}\int_0^{2\pi}(-\cos\phi + \frac{1}{3}\cos^3\phi)\Big|_0^{\pi} d\theta = \frac{1}{5}\int_0^{2\pi}\frac{4}{3}\, d\theta = \frac{8\pi}{15}$$

9. D is the collection of all points with spherical coordinates (ρ,ϕ,θ) such that $0 \le \theta \le 2\pi$, $0 \le \phi \le \pi$, and $2 \le \rho \le 3$. Since $x^2 = \rho^2\sin^2\phi\cos^2\theta$, we find that

$$\iiint_D x^2 dV = \int_0^{2\pi}\int_0^{\pi}\int_2^{3}(\rho^2\sin^2\phi\cos^2\theta)\rho^2\sin\phi\, d\rho\, d\phi\, d\theta$$

$$= \int_0^{2\pi}\int_0^{\pi}(\frac{\rho^5}{5}\sin^3\phi\cos^2\theta)\Big|_2^3 d\phi\, d\theta$$

$$= \frac{211}{5}\int_0^{2\pi}\int_0^{\pi}\sin^3\phi\cos^2\theta\, d\phi\, d\theta$$

$$= \frac{211}{5}\int_0^{2\pi}\int_0^{\pi}\sin\phi(1 - \cos^2\phi)\cos^2\theta\, d\phi\, d\theta$$

$$= \frac{211}{5}\int_0^{2\pi}(-\cos\phi + \frac{1}{3}\cos^3\phi)\cos^2\theta\Big|_0^{\pi} d\theta = \frac{844}{15}\int_0^{2\pi}\cos^2\theta\, d\theta$$

$$= \frac{844}{15}\int_0^{2\pi}(\frac{1}{2} + \frac{1}{2}\cos 2\theta)d\theta = \frac{844}{15}(\frac{1}{2}\theta + \frac{1}{4}\sin 2\theta)\Big|_0^{2\pi} = \frac{844}{15}\pi$$

10. The sphere and cone intersect for (x,y,z) such that $x^2 + y^2 = z^2 = 1 - x^2 - y^2$, so that $\frac{1}{2} = x^2 + y^2 = \rho^2\sin^2\phi$. Since $\rho = 1$ for each point (ρ,ϕ,θ) on the sphere, it follows that $\frac{1}{2} = \sin^2\phi$, so that $\phi = \frac{\pi}{4}$. Thus D is the collection of all points with spherical coordinates (ρ,ϕ,θ) such that $0 \le \theta \le 2\pi$, $0 \le \phi \le \frac{\pi}{4}$, and $0 \le \rho \le 1$. Since $(x^2 + y^2 + z^2)^2 = \rho^4$, we find that

$$\iiint_D (x^2 + y^2 + z^2)^2 dV = \int_0^{2\pi}\int_0^{\pi/4}\int_0^{1}\rho^4(\rho^2\sin\phi)d\rho\, d\phi\, d\theta$$

$$= \int_0^{2\pi}\int_0^{\pi/4}(\frac{\rho^7}{7}\sin\phi)\Big|_0^1 d\phi\, d\theta = \int_0^{2\pi}\int_0^{\pi/4}\frac{1}{7}\sin\phi\, d\phi\, d\theta$$

$$= \frac{1}{7}\int_0^{2\pi}(-\cos\phi)\Big|_0^{\pi/4} d\theta = \frac{1}{7}\int_0^{2\pi}(1 - \frac{\sqrt{2}}{2})d\theta = \frac{\pi}{7}(2 - \sqrt{2})$$

11. In spherical coordinates the cone has equation $\rho\cos\phi = \sqrt{3}\rho\sin\phi$, so that $\cot\phi = \sqrt{3}$, and hence $\phi = \frac{\pi}{6}$. Then D is the collection of all points with spherical coordinates (ρ,ϕ,θ) such that $0 \le \theta \le 2\pi$, $0 \le \phi \le \frac{\pi}{6}$, and $3 \le \rho \le 9$. Since $\frac{1}{x^2 + y^2 + z^2} = \frac{1}{\rho^2}$, we find that

$$\iiint_D \frac{1}{x^2 + y^2 + z^2} dV = \int_0^{2\pi}\int_0^{\pi/6}\int_3^{9}\frac{1}{\rho^2}(\rho^2\sin\phi)d\rho\, d\phi\, d\theta$$

$$= \int_0^{2\pi}\int_0^{\pi/6}(\rho\sin\phi)\Big|_3^9 d\phi\, d\theta = \int_0^{2\pi}\int_0^{\pi/6}6\sin\phi\, d\phi\, d\theta$$

$$= 6\int_0^{2\pi}(-\cos\phi)\Big|_0^{\pi/6} d\theta = 6\int_0^{2\pi}(1 - \frac{\sqrt{3}}{2})d\theta = 6\pi(2 - \sqrt{3})$$

12. D is the collection of all points with spherical coordinates (ρ,ϕ,θ) such that $0 \le \theta \le \frac{\pi}{2}$, $0 \le \phi \le \frac{\pi}{2}$, and $1 \le \rho \le \sqrt{2}$. Since $z^2 + 1 = \rho^2\cos^2\phi + 1$, we find that

$$\iiint_D (z^2 + 1)dV = \int_0^{\pi/2}\int_0^{\pi/2}\int_1^{\sqrt{2}}(\rho^2\cos^2\phi + 1)(\rho^2\sin\phi)d\rho\, d\phi\, d\theta$$

$$= \int_0^{\pi/2}\int_0^{\pi/2}(\frac{\rho^5}{5}\cos^2\phi\sin\phi + \frac{\rho^3}{3}\sin\phi)\Big|_1^{\sqrt{2}} d\phi\, d\theta$$

$$= \int_0^{\pi/2}\int_0^{\pi/2}\left(\frac{4\sqrt{2}-1}{5}\cos^2\phi\,\sin\phi + \frac{2\sqrt{2}-1}{3}\sin\phi\right)d\phi\,d\theta$$

$$= \int_0^{\pi/2}\left[\frac{4\sqrt{2}-1}{5}\left(\frac{-1}{3}\cos^3\phi\right) - \frac{2\sqrt{2}-1}{3}\cos\phi\right]\Bigg|_0^{\pi/2} d\theta$$

$$= \int_0^{\pi/2}\left(\frac{4\sqrt{2}-1}{15} + \frac{2\sqrt{2}-1}{3}\right)d\theta = \frac{\pi}{2}\left(\frac{4\sqrt{2}-1}{15} + \frac{2\sqrt{2}-1}{3}\right)$$

$$= \frac{\pi}{10}(7\sqrt{2} - 2)$$

13. In spherical coordinates the planes $x = \sqrt{3}\,y$ and $x = y$ have equations $\theta = \frac{\pi}{6}$ and $\theta = \frac{\pi}{4}$, respectively. Thus D is the collection of all points with spherical coordinates (ρ, ϕ, θ) such that $\frac{\pi}{6} \le \theta \le \frac{\pi}{4}$, $0 \le \phi \le \frac{\pi}{2}$, and $0 \le \rho \le 4$. Since $\sqrt{z} = \sqrt{\rho\cos\phi}$, we find that

$$\iiint_D \sqrt{z}\,dV = \int_{\pi/6}^{\pi/4}\int_0^{\pi/2}\int_0^4 \sqrt{\rho\cos\phi}\,(\rho^2\sin\phi)\,d\rho\,d\phi\,d\theta$$

$$= \int_{\pi/6}^{\pi/4}\int_0^{\pi/2}\left(\frac{2}{7}\rho^{7/2}\cos^{1/2}\phi\,\sin\phi\right)\Bigg|_0^4 d\phi\,d\theta$$

$$= \int_{\pi/6}^{\pi/4}\int_0^{\pi/2}\frac{256}{7}\cos^{1/2}\phi\,\sin\phi\,d\phi\,d\theta$$

$$= \frac{256}{7}\int_{\pi/6}^{\pi/4}\frac{-2}{3}\cos^{3/2}\phi\Bigg|_0^{\pi/2} d\theta = \frac{512}{21}\int_{\pi/6}^{\pi/4} 1\,d\theta = \left(\frac{512}{21}\right)\left(\frac{\pi}{12}\right)$$

$$= \frac{128}{63}\pi$$

14. D is the collection of all points with spherical coordinates (ρ, ϕ, θ) such that $0 \le \theta \le \frac{\pi}{2}$, $0 \le \phi \le \frac{\pi}{2}$, and $1 \le \rho \le 3$. Thus

$$V = \iiint_D 1\,dV = \int_0^{\pi/2}\int_0^{\pi/2}\int_1^3 \rho^2\sin\phi\,d\rho\,d\phi\,d\theta$$

$$= \int_0^{\pi/2}\int_0^{\pi/2}\left(\frac{\rho^3}{3}\sin\phi\right)\Bigg|_1^3 d\phi\,d\theta = \int_0^{\pi/2}\int_0^{\pi/2}\frac{26}{3}\sin\phi\,d\phi\,d\theta$$

$$= \int_0^{\pi/2}\left(\frac{-26}{3}\cos\phi\right)\Bigg|_0^{\pi/2} d\theta = \int_0^{\pi/2}\frac{26}{3}\,d\theta = \frac{13}{3}\pi$$

15. In spherical coordinates the cone has equation $\rho^2\cos^2\phi = \rho^2\sin^2\phi$, so that $\phi = \frac{\pi}{4}$. D is the collection of all points with spherical coordinates (ρ, ϕ, θ) such that $0 \le \theta \le 2\pi$, $0 \le \phi \le \frac{\pi}{4}$, and $0 \le \rho \le 2$. Thus

$$V = \iiint_D 1\,dV = \int_0^{2\pi}\int_0^{\pi/4}\int_0^2 \rho^2\sin\phi\,d\rho\,d\phi\,d\theta$$

$$= \int_0^{2\pi}\int_0^{\pi/4}\left(\frac{\rho^3}{3}\sin\phi\right)\Bigg|_0^2 d\phi\,d\theta = \int_0^{2\pi}\int_0^{\pi/4}\frac{8}{3}\sin\phi\,d\phi\,d\theta$$

$$= \int_0^{2\pi}\left(\frac{-8}{3}\cos\phi\right)\Bigg|_0^{\pi/4} d\theta = \int_0^{2\pi}\left(\frac{8}{3} - \frac{4}{3}\sqrt{2}\right)d\theta = \frac{8}{3}\pi(2 - \sqrt{2})$$

16. In spherical coordinates the cone has equation $\rho^2\cos^2\phi = 3\rho^2\sin^2\phi$, so that $\cot\phi = \sqrt{3}$, and thus $\phi = \frac{\pi}{6}$. Therefore D is the collection of all points with spherical coordinates (ρ, ϕ, θ) such that $0 \le \theta \le 2\pi$, $0 \le \phi \le \frac{\pi}{6}$, and $0 \le \rho \le 2$. Thus

$$V = \iiint_D 1\,dV = \int_0^{2\pi}\int_0^{\pi/6}\int_0^2 \rho^2\sin\phi\,d\rho\,d\phi\,d\theta$$

$$= \int_0^{2\pi}\int_0^{\pi/6}\left(\frac{\rho^3}{3}\sin\phi\right)\Bigg|_0^2 d\phi\,d\theta = \int_0^{2\pi}\int_0^{\pi/6}\frac{8}{3}\sin\phi\,d\phi\,d\theta$$

$$= \int_0^{2\pi}\left(\frac{-8}{3}\cos\phi\right)\Bigg|_0^{\pi/6} d\theta = \int_0^{2\pi}\left(\frac{8}{3} - \frac{4}{3}\sqrt{3}\right)d\theta = \frac{8}{3}\pi(2 - \sqrt{3})$$

17. In spherical coordinates the cone has equation $3\rho^2\cos^2\phi = \rho^2\sin^2\phi$, so that $\cot\phi = \frac{1}{\sqrt{3}}$, and thus $\phi = \frac{\pi}{3}$. Therefore D is the collection of all points with spherical coordinates (ρ, ϕ, θ) such that $0 \le \theta \le 2\pi$, $\frac{\pi}{3} \le \phi \le \pi$, and $1 \le \rho \le 2$. Thus

$$V = \iiint_D 1\,dV = \int_0^{2\pi}\int_{\pi/3}^{\pi}\int_1^2 \rho^2\sin\phi\,d\rho\,d\phi\,d\theta$$

$$= \int_0^{2\pi}\int_{\pi/3}^{\pi}\left(\frac{\rho^3}{3}\sin\phi\right)\Bigg|_1^2 d\phi\,d\theta = \int_0^{2\pi}\int_{\pi/3}^{\pi}\frac{7}{3}\sin\phi\,d\phi\,d\theta$$

$$= \int_0^{2\pi} \left(\frac{-7}{3}\cos\phi\right)\Big|_{\pi/3}^{\pi} d\theta = \int_0^{2\pi} \frac{7}{2}\, d\theta = 7\pi$$

18. In spherical coordinates the sphere has equation $\rho^2 = 4\rho\cos\phi$, so that $\rho = 4\cos\phi$, and the cone has equation $\rho^2\cos^2\phi = \rho^2\sin^2\phi$, so that $\phi = \frac{\pi}{4}$. Therefore D is the collection of all points with spherical coordinates (ρ,ϕ,θ) such that $0 \le \theta \le 2\pi$, $0 \le \phi \le \frac{\pi}{4}$, and $0 \le \rho \le 4\cos\phi$. Thus

$$V = \iiint_D 1\, dV = \int_0^{2\pi}\int_0^{\pi/4}\int_0^{4\cos\phi} \rho^2\sin\phi\, d\rho\, d\phi\, d\theta$$

$$= \int_0^{2\pi}\int_0^{\pi/4} \left(\frac{\rho^3}{3}\sin\phi\right)\Big|_0^{4\cos\phi} d\phi\, d\theta$$

$$= \int_0^{2\pi}\int_0^{\pi/4} \frac{64}{3}\cos^3\phi\sin\phi\, d\phi\, d\theta = \int_0^{2\pi} \left(\frac{-64}{12}\cos^4\phi\right)\Big|_0^{\pi/4} d\theta$$

$$= \int_0^{2\pi} 4\, d\theta = 8\pi$$

19. In spherical coordinates the cone has equation $\rho^2\sin^2\phi = \rho^2\cos^2\phi$, so that $\phi = \frac{\pi}{4}$, and the cylinder has equation $\rho^2\sin^2\phi = 4$, so that $\rho\sin\phi = 2$, and thus $\rho = 2\csc\phi$. Therefore D is the collection of all points with spherical coordinates (ρ,ϕ,θ) such that $0 \le \theta \le 2\pi$, $\frac{\pi}{4} \le \phi \le \frac{\pi}{2}$, and $0 \le \rho \le 2\csc\phi$. Thus

$$V = \iiint_D 1\, dV = \int_0^{2\pi}\int_{\pi/4}^{\pi/2}\int_0^{2\csc\phi} \rho^2\sin\phi\, d\rho\, d\phi\, d\theta$$

$$= \int_0^{2\pi}\int_{\pi/4}^{\pi/2} \left(\frac{\rho^3}{3}\sin\phi\right)\Big|_0^{2\csc\phi} d\phi\, d\theta = \int_0^{2\pi}\int_{\pi/4}^{\pi/2} \frac{8}{3}\csc^2\phi\, d\phi\, d\theta$$

$$= \int_0^{2\pi} \left(\frac{-8}{3}\cot\phi\right)\Big|_{\pi/4}^{\pi/2} d\theta = \int_0^{2\pi} \frac{8}{3}\, d\theta = \frac{16}{3}\pi$$

20. D is the collection of all points with spherical coordinates (ρ,ϕ,θ) such that $\frac{\pi}{6} \le \theta \le \frac{\pi}{3}$, $0 \le \phi \le \pi$, and $0 \le \rho \le 5$. Thus

$$V = \iiint_D 1\, dV = \int_{\pi/6}^{\pi/3}\int_0^{\pi}\int_0^{5} \rho^2\sin\phi\, d\rho\, d\phi\, d\theta$$

$$= \int_{\pi/6}^{\pi/3}\int_0^{\pi} \left(\frac{\rho^3}{3}\sin\phi\right)\Big|_0^5 d\phi\, d\theta = \int_{\pi/6}^{\pi/3}\int_0^{\pi} \frac{125}{3}\sin\phi\, d\phi\, d\theta$$

$$= \int_{\pi/6}^{\pi/3} \left(\frac{-125}{3}\cos\phi\right)\Big|_0^{\pi} d\theta = \int_{\pi/6}^{\pi/3} \frac{250}{3}\, d\theta = \frac{125}{9}\pi$$

21. In spherical coordinates the plane $z = -4\sqrt{3}$ has equation $\rho\cos\phi = -4\sqrt{3}$, or $\rho = -4\sqrt{3}\sec\phi$. Thus the plane $z = -4\sqrt{3}$ and the sphere $x^2 + y^2 + z^2 = 64$ intersect at points having spherical coordinates (ρ,ϕ,θ) satisfying $8 = \rho = -4\sqrt{3}\sec\phi$, so that $\sec\phi = -\frac{2}{\sqrt{3}}$, or $\phi = \frac{5\pi}{6}$. Thus the points that are inside the sphere $x^2 + y^2 + z^2 = 8$ and lie below the plane $z = -4\sqrt{3}$ have spherical coordinates (ρ,ϕ,θ) such that $0 \le \theta \le 2\pi$, $\frac{5\pi}{6} \le \phi \le \pi$, and $-4\sqrt{3}\sec\phi \le \rho \le 8$. The volume V_1 of the set of such points is given by

$$V_1 = \int_0^{2\pi}\int_{5\pi/6}^{\pi}\int_{-4\sqrt{3}\sec\phi}^{8} \rho^2\sin\phi\, d\rho\, d\phi\, d\theta$$

$$= \int_0^{2\pi}\int_{5\pi/6}^{\pi} \frac{\rho^3}{3}\sin\phi\,\Big|_{-4\sqrt{3}\sec\phi}^{8} d\phi\, d\theta$$

$$= \int_0^{2\pi}\int_{5\pi/6}^{\pi} \left(\frac{512}{3}\sin\phi + 64\sqrt{3}\sec^3\phi\sin\phi\right) d\phi\, d\theta$$

$$= \int_0^{2\pi}\int_{5\pi/6}^{\pi} \left(\frac{512}{3}\sin\phi + 64\sqrt{3}\,\frac{\sin\phi}{\cos^3\phi}\right) d\phi\, d\theta$$

$$= \int_0^{2\pi} \left(\frac{-512}{3}\cos\phi - \frac{32\sqrt{3}}{\cos^2\phi}\right)\Big|_{5\pi/6}^{\pi} d\theta$$

$$= \int_0^{2\pi} \frac{1}{3}(512 - 224\sqrt{3})\, d\theta = \frac{2\pi}{3}(512 - 224\sqrt{3})$$

Thus $V = \frac{4}{3}\pi 8^3 - V_1 = \frac{64\pi}{3}(16 + 7\sqrt{3})$.

22. D is the collection of all points with spherical coordinates (ρ,ϕ,θ) such that $0 \le \theta \le 2\pi$, $0 \le \phi \le \frac{\pi}{2}$, and

$0 \le \rho \le 1+\cos\phi$. Thus

$$V = \iiint_D 1\,dV = \int_0^{2\pi}\int_0^{\pi/2}\int_0^{1+\cos\phi} \rho^2 \sin\phi\, d\rho\, d\phi\, d\theta$$

$$= \int_0^{2\pi}\int_0^{\pi/2} \left(\frac{\rho^3}{3}\sin\phi\right)\Big|_0^{1+\cos\phi} d\phi\, d\theta$$

$$= \int_0^{2\pi}\int_0^{\pi/2} \frac{1}{3}(1+\cos\phi)^3 \sin\phi\, d\phi\, d\theta$$

$$= \int_0^{2\pi} \frac{-1}{12}(1+\cos\phi)^4\Big|_0^{\pi/2} d\theta = \int_0^{2\pi}\frac{5}{4}\,d\theta = \frac{5}{2}\pi$$

23. Since $\rho \ge 0$ and $0 \le \phi \le \pi$, it follows that if $\rho = \cos\phi$, then $0 \le \phi \le \frac{\pi}{2}$, Thus D is the collection of all points with spherical coordinates (ρ,ϕ,θ) such that $0 \le \theta \le 2\pi$, $0 \le \phi \le \frac{\pi}{2}$, and $0 \le \rho \le \cos\phi$. Thus

$$V = \iiint_D 1\,dV = \int_0^{2\pi}\int_0^{\pi/2}\int_0^{\cos\phi} \rho^2\sin\phi\, d\rho\, d\phi\, d\theta$$

$$= \int_0^{2\pi}\int_0^{\pi/2}\left(\frac{\rho^3}{3}\sin\phi\right)\Big|_0^{\cos\phi} d\phi\, d\theta$$

$$= \int_0^{2\pi}\int_0^{\pi/2}\frac{1}{3}\cos^3\phi\,\sin\phi\, d\phi\, d\theta = \int_0^{2\pi}\left(\frac{-1}{12}\cos^4\phi\right)\Big|_0^{\pi/2} d\theta$$

$$= \int_0^{2\pi}\frac{1}{12}\,d\theta = \frac{1}{6}\pi$$

Notice that D is a ball with radius $\frac{1}{2}$, centered at $(0,0,\frac{1}{2})$.

24. In spherical coordinates the cone has equation $\rho^2\sin^2\phi = \rho^2\cos^2\phi$, so that $\phi = \frac{\pi}{4}$. Thus D is the collection of all points with spherical coordinates (ρ,ϕ,θ) such that $0 \le \theta \le 2\pi$, $0 \le \phi \le \frac{\pi}{4}$, and $0 \le \rho \le 2$. Next, $\delta(x,y,z) = \sqrt{x^2+y^2+z^2}$, so that the total mass m is given by

$$m = \iiint_D \sqrt{x^2+y^2+z^2}\,dV = \int_0^{2\pi}\int_0^{\pi/4}\int_0^2 \rho(\rho^2\sin\phi)\,d\rho\, d\phi\, d\theta$$

$$= \int_0^{2\pi}\int_0^{\pi/4}\left(\frac{\rho^4}{4}\sin\phi\right)\Big|_0^2 d\phi\, d\theta = \int_0^{2\pi}\int_0^{\pi/4} 4\sin\phi\, d\phi\, d\theta$$

$$= \int_0^{2\pi}(-4\cos\phi)\Big|_0^{\pi/4} d\theta = \int_0^{2\pi}(4-2\sqrt{2})\,d\theta = 4\pi(2-\sqrt{2})$$

25. D is the collection of all points with spherical coordinates (ρ,ϕ,θ) such that $0 \le \theta \le 2\pi$, $0 \le \phi \le \pi$, and $2 \le \rho \le 4$. Since $\delta(x,y,z) = \dfrac{1}{\sqrt{x^2+y^2+z^2}}$, the total mass m is given by

$$m = \int_0^{2\pi}\int_0^{\pi}\int_2^4 \frac{1}{\rho}(\rho^2\sin\phi)\,d\rho\, d\phi\, d\theta = \int_0^{2\pi}\int_0^{\pi}\left(\frac{\rho^2}{2}\sin\phi\right)\Big|_2^4 d\phi\, d\theta$$

$$= \int_0^{2\pi}\int_0^{\pi} 6\sin\phi\, d\phi\, d\theta = \int_0^{2\pi}(-6\cos\phi)\Big|_0^{\pi} d\theta = \int_0^{2\pi} 12\, d\theta = 24\pi$$

Section 14.7

1. By symmetry, $\bar{x} = 0$. The graphs of $y = 5$ and $y = 1 + x^2$ intersect at (x,y) such that $5 = y = 1 + x^2$, so that $x = -2$ or $x = 2$. Consequently $\mathcal{M}_x = \iint_R y\,dA$

$$= \int_{-2}^{2}\int_{1+x^2}^{5} y\,dy\,dx = \int_{-2}^{2} \frac{1}{2}y^2\Big|_{1+x^2}^{5} dx = \int_{-2}^{2} (12 - x^2 - \tfrac{1}{2}x^4)\,dx$$

$$= (12x - \tfrac{1}{3}x^3 - \tfrac{1}{10}x^5)\Big|_{-2}^{2} = \frac{544}{15}. \text{ Since } A = \int_{-2}^{2}\int_{1+x^2}^{5} 1\,dy\,dx$$

$$= \int_{-2}^{2} y\Big|_{1+x^2}^{5} dx = \int_{-2}^{2} (4 - x^2)dx = (4x - \tfrac{1}{3}x^3)\Big|_{-2}^{2} = \frac{32}{3}, \text{ it}$$

follows that $\bar{y} = \frac{\mathcal{M}_x}{A} = \frac{544/15}{32/3} = \frac{17}{5}$. Thus $(\bar{x},\bar{y}) = (0,\frac{17}{5})$.

2. By symmetry, $\bar{x} = 0$. The graphs of $y = x^2$ and $y = x^4$ intersect at (x,y) such that $x^2 = y = x^4$, so that $x = -1$, $x = 0$, or $x = 1$. Consequently $\mathcal{M}_x = \iint_R y\,dA$

$$= \int_{-1}^{1}\int_{x^4}^{x^2} y\,dy\,dx = \int_{-1}^{1} \frac{1}{2}y^2\Big|_{x^4}^{x^2} dx = \int_{-1}^{1} (\tfrac{1}{2}x^4 - \tfrac{1}{2}x^8)dx$$

$$= (\tfrac{1}{10}x^5 - \tfrac{1}{18}x^9)\Big|_{-1}^{1} = \frac{4}{45}. \text{ Since } A = \int_{-1}^{1}\int_{x^4}^{x^2} 1\,dy\,dx$$

$$= \int_{-1}^{1} y\Big|_{x^4}^{x^2} dx = \int_{-1}^{1} (x^2 - x^4)dx = (\tfrac{1}{3}x^3 - \tfrac{1}{5}x^5)\Big|_{-1}^{1} = \frac{4}{15}, \text{ it}$$

follows that $\bar{y} = \frac{\mathcal{M}_x}{A} = \frac{4/45}{4/15} = \frac{1}{3}$. Thus $(\bar{x},\bar{y}) = (0,\frac{1}{3})$.

3. The given region is symmetric with respect to the lines $y = x$ and $x + y = 1$. Thus $\bar{x} = \bar{y}$ and $\bar{x} + \bar{y} = 1$, so that

$$(\bar{x},\bar{y}) = (\tfrac{1}{2},\tfrac{1}{2}).$$

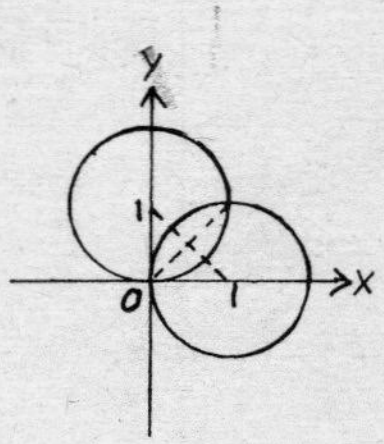

4. The given region R is symmetric with respect to the line $y = x$, so that $\bar{x} = \bar{y}$. Now $\mathcal{M}_x = \iint_R y\,dA$

$$= \int_0^{\pi/2}\int_0^{\sin 2\theta} r^2 \sin\theta\,dr\,d\theta = \int_0^{\pi/2} \frac{1}{3}r^3\sin\theta\Big|_0^{\sin 2\theta} d\theta$$

$$= \int_0^{\pi/2} \frac{1}{3}\sin^3 2\theta \sin\theta\,d\theta = \int_0^{\pi/2} \frac{8}{3}\sin^4\theta\cos^3\theta\,d\theta$$

$$= \int_0^{\pi/2} \frac{8}{3}\sin^4\theta(1 - \sin^2\theta)\cos\theta\,d\theta = (\tfrac{8}{15}\sin^5\theta - \tfrac{8}{21}\sin^7\theta)\Big|_0^{\pi/2}$$

$$= \frac{16}{105}. \text{ Since } A = \int_0^{\pi/2}\int_0^{\sin 2\theta} r\,dr\,d\theta = \int_0^{\pi/2} \frac{1}{2}r^2\Big|_0^{\sin 2\theta} d\theta$$

$$= \int_0^{\pi/2} \frac{1}{2}\sin^2 2\theta\,d\theta = \int_0^{\pi/2} (\tfrac{1}{4} - \tfrac{1}{4}\cos 4\theta)d\theta = (\tfrac{1}{4}\theta - \tfrac{1}{16}\sin 4\theta)\Big|_0^{\pi/2}$$

$= \frac{\pi}{8}$, we have $\bar{x} = \bar{y} = \frac{\mathcal{M}_x}{A} = \frac{16/105}{\pi/8} = \frac{128}{105\pi}$. Thus $(\bar{x},\bar{y})$ $= (\frac{128}{105\pi},\frac{128}{105\pi})$.

5. By symmetry, $\bar{y} = 0$. Now $\mathcal{M}_y = \iint_R x\,dA$

$$= \int_0^{2\pi}\int_0^{1+\cos\theta} r^2\cos\theta\,dr\,d\theta = \int_0^{2\pi} \frac{1}{3}r^3\cos\theta\Big|_0^{1+\cos\theta} d\theta$$

$$= \int_0^{2\pi} (\tfrac{1}{3}\cos\theta + \cos^2\theta + \cos^3\theta + \tfrac{1}{3}\cos^4\theta)d\theta$$

$$= \int_0^{2\pi} [\tfrac{1}{3}\cos\theta + \tfrac{1}{2} + \tfrac{1}{2}\cos 2\theta + (1 - \sin^2\theta)\cos\theta]d\theta$$

$$+ \int_0^{2\pi} \frac{1}{3}\cos^4\theta\,d\theta$$

$$= \left(\frac{1}{3}\sin\theta + \frac{1}{2}\theta + \frac{1}{4}\sin 2\theta + \sin\theta - \frac{1}{3}\sin^3\theta\right)\Big|_0^{2\pi}$$

$$+ \left(\frac{1}{12}\cos^3\theta\sin\theta + \frac{1}{8}\cos\theta\sin\theta + \frac{1}{8}\theta\right)\Big|_0^{2\pi}$$

$= \frac{5}{4}\pi$, with the next to last equality coming from (15) in Section 7.1. Since $A = \int_0^{2\pi}\int_0^{1+\cos\theta} r\,dr\,d\theta = \int_0^{2\pi}\frac{1}{2}r^2\Big|_0^{1+\cos\theta} d\theta$

$$= \int_0^{2\pi}\left(\frac{1}{2} + \cos\theta + \frac{1}{2}\cos^2\theta\right)d\theta = \int_0^{2\pi}\left(\frac{1}{2} + \cos\theta + \frac{1}{4} + \frac{1}{4}\cos 2\theta\right)d\theta$$

$= \left(\frac{3}{4}\theta + \sin\theta + \frac{1}{8}\sin 2\theta\right)\Big|_0^{2\pi} = \frac{3}{2}\pi$, it follows that

$\bar{x} = \frac{\mathcal{M}_y}{A} = \frac{5\pi/4}{3\pi/2} = \frac{5}{6}$. Thus $(\bar{x},\bar{y}) = (\frac{5}{6},0)$.

6. By symmetry, $\bar{x} = 0$. The circles $r = 2\sin\theta$ and $r = 1$ intersect at (r,θ) such that $2\sin\theta = r = 1$, so that $\theta = \frac{\pi}{6}$ or $\theta = \frac{5}{6}\pi$. Now $\mathcal{M}_x = \iint_R y\,dA$

$$= \int_{\pi/6}^{5\pi/6}\int_1^{2\sin\theta} r^2\sin\theta\,dr\,d\theta = \int_{\pi/6}^{5\pi/6}\frac{1}{3}r^3\sin\theta\Big|_1^{2\sin\theta} d\theta$$

$$= \int_{\pi/6}^{5\pi/6}\left(\frac{8}{3}\sin^4\theta - \frac{1}{3}\sin\theta\right)d\theta$$

$$= \left(-\frac{2}{3}\sin^3\theta\cos\theta - \sin\theta\cos\theta + \theta + \frac{1}{3}\cos\theta\right)\Big|_{\pi/6}^{5\pi/6}$$

$= \frac{2}{3}\pi + \frac{\sqrt{3}}{4}$, with the next to last equality coming from (14) in Section 7.1. Since

$$A = \int_{\pi/6}^{5\pi/6}\int_1^{2\sin\theta} r\,dr\,d\theta = \int_{\pi/6}^{5\pi/6}\frac{1}{2}r^2\Big|_1^{2\sin\theta} d\theta$$

$$= \int_{\pi/6}^{5\pi/6}\left(2\sin^2\theta - \frac{1}{2}\right)d\theta = \int_{\pi/6}^{5\pi/6}\left(\frac{1}{2} - \cos 2\theta\right)d\theta$$

$= \left(\frac{1}{2}\theta - \frac{1}{2}\sin 2\theta\right)\Big|_{\pi/6}^{5\pi/6} = \frac{1}{3}\pi + \frac{\sqrt{3}}{2}$, it follows that

$\bar{y} = \frac{\mathcal{M}_x}{A} = \frac{2\pi/3 + \sqrt{3}/4}{\pi/3 + \sqrt{3}/2} = \frac{8\pi + 3\sqrt{3}}{4\pi + 6\sqrt{3}}$. Thus $(\bar{x},\bar{y}) = \left(0,\frac{8\pi + 3\sqrt{3}}{4\pi + 6\sqrt{3}}\right)$.

7. By symmetry, $\bar{x} = \bar{y} = 0$. Taking $\delta = 1$, we have $\mathcal{M}_{xy} =$

$$\iiint_D z\,dV = \int_0^{2\pi}\int_0^a\int_0^{\sqrt{a^2-r^2}} zr\,dz\,dr\,d\theta$$

$$= \int_0^{2\pi}\int_0^a \frac{1}{2}z^2 r\Big|_0^{\sqrt{a^2-r^2}} dr\,d\theta = \int_0^{2\pi}\int_0^a\left(\frac{1}{2}a^2 r - \frac{1}{2}r^3\right)dr\,d\theta$$

$$= \int_0^{2\pi}\left(\frac{1}{4}a^2r^2 - \frac{1}{8}r^4\right)\Big|_0^a d\theta = \int_0^{2\pi}\frac{1}{8}a^4\,d\theta = \frac{1}{4}\pi a^4 .$$

Since $m = \frac{2}{3}\pi a^3$, it follows that $\bar{z} = \frac{\mathcal{M}_{xy}}{m} = \frac{\pi a^4/4}{2\pi a^3/3} = \frac{3}{8}a$. Thus $(\bar{x},\bar{y},\bar{z}) = (0,0,\frac{3}{8}a)$.

8. By symmetry, $\bar{x} = \bar{y} = 0$. The paraboloid $z = 4x^2 + 4y^2$ and the plane $z = 2$ intersect over the circle $x^2 + y^2 = \frac{1}{2}$. Taking $\delta = 1$, we have

$$\mathcal{M}_{xy} = \iiint_D z\,dV = \int_0^{2\pi}\int_0^{1/\sqrt{2}}\int_{4r^2}^{2} zr\,dz\,dr\,d\theta$$

$$= \int_0^{2\pi}\int_0^{1/\sqrt{2}}\frac{1}{2}z^2 r\Big|_{4r^2}^{2} dr\,d\theta = \int_0^{2\pi}\int_0^{1/\sqrt{2}}(2r - 8r^5)dr\,d\theta$$

$$= \int_0^{2\pi}\left(r^2 - \frac{4}{3}r^6\right)\Big|_0^{1/\sqrt{2}} d\theta = \int_0^{2\pi}\frac{1}{3}d\theta = \frac{2}{3}\pi$$

Since $m = \iiint_D 1\,dV = \int_0^{2\pi}\int_0^{1/\sqrt{2}}\int_{4r^2}^{2} r\,dz\,dr\,d\theta$

$$= \int_0^{2\pi}\int_0^{1/\sqrt{2}} rz\Big|_{4r^2}^{2} dr\,d\theta = \int_0^{2\pi}\int_0^{1/\sqrt{2}}(2r - 4r^3)dr\,d\theta$$

$$= \int_0^{2\pi}(r^2 - r^4)\Big|_0^{1/\sqrt{2}} d\theta = \int_0^{2\pi}\frac{1}{4}d\theta = \frac{1}{2}\pi ,$$

it follows that $\bar{z} = \frac{\mathcal{M}_{xy}}{m} = \frac{2\pi/3}{\pi/2} = \frac{4}{3}$. Thus $(\bar{x},\bar{y},\bar{z}) = (0,0,\frac{4}{3})$.

9. By symmetry, $\bar{x} = \bar{y} = 0$. The plane $z = 1$ and the cone $z^2 = 9x^2 + 9y^2$ intersect over the circle $x^2 + y^2 = \frac{1}{9}$. Taking

$\delta = 1$, we have $\mathcal{M}_{xy} = \iiint\limits_D z\,dV$

$= \int_0^{2\pi}\int_0^{1/3}\int_{3r}^{1} zr\,dz\,dr\,d\theta = \int_0^{2\pi}\int_0^{1/3} \frac{1}{2} z^2 r \Big|_{3r}^{1} dr\,d\theta$

$= \int_0^{2\pi}\int_0^{1/3} (\frac{1}{2} r - \frac{9}{2} r^3)\,dr\,d\theta = \int_0^{2\pi} (\frac{1}{4} r^2 - \frac{9}{8} r^4)\Big|_0^{1/3} d\theta$

$= \int_0^{2\pi} \frac{1}{72}\,d\theta = \frac{1}{36}\pi$. Since $m = \iiint\limits_D 1\,dV$

$= \int_0^{2\pi}\int_0^{1/3}\int_{3r}^{1} r\,dz\,dr\,d\theta = \int_0^{2\pi}\int_0^{1/3} rz \Big|_{3r}^{1} dr\,d\theta$

$= \int_0^{2\pi}\int_0^{1/3} (r - 3r^2)dr\,d\theta = \int_0^{2\pi} (\frac{1}{2} r^2 - r^3)\Big|_0^{1/3} d\theta = \int_0^{2\pi} \frac{1}{54}\,d\theta$

$= \frac{1}{27}\pi$, it follows that $\bar{z} = \frac{\mathcal{M}_{xy}}{m} = \frac{\pi/36}{\pi/27} = \frac{3}{4}$. Thus

$(\bar{x},\bar{y},\bar{z}) = (0,0,\frac{3}{4})$.

10. By symmetry, $\bar{x} = \bar{y} = 0$. The sphere $x^2 + y^2 + z^2 = 1$ and the cone $z = \sqrt{x^2 + y^2}$ intersect at (x,y,z) such that $1 - x^2 - y^2 = z^2 = x^2 + y^2$ so that $x^2 + y^2 = \frac{1}{2}$. Taking $\delta = 1$, we have $\mathcal{M}_{xy} = \iiint\limits_D z\,dV$

$= \int_0^{2\pi}\int_0^{1/\sqrt{2}}\int_r^{\sqrt{1-r^2}} zr\,dz\,dr\,d\theta = \int_0^{2\pi}\int_0^{1/\sqrt{2}} \frac{1}{2} z^2 r \Big|_r^{\sqrt{1-r^2}} dr\,d\theta$

$= \int_0^{2\pi}\int_0^{1/\sqrt{2}} (\frac{1}{2} r - r^3)dr\,d\theta = \int_0^{2\pi} (\frac{1}{4} r^2 - \frac{1}{4} r^4)\Big|_0^{1/\sqrt{2}} d\theta$

$= \int_0^{2\pi} \frac{1}{16}\,d\theta = \frac{1}{8}\pi$. Since $m = \iiint\limits_D 1\,dV$

$= \int_0^{2\pi}\int_0^{1/\sqrt{2}}\int_r^{\sqrt{1-r^2}} r\,dz\,dr\,d\theta = \int_0^{2\pi}\int_0^{1/\sqrt{2}} rz \Big|_r^{\sqrt{1-r^2}} dr\,d\theta$

$= \int_0^{2\pi}\int_0^{1/\sqrt{2}} (r\sqrt{1 - r^2} - r^2)dr\,d\theta = \int_0^{2\pi} [\frac{-1}{3}(1 - r^2)^{3/2} - \frac{1}{3} r^3]\Big|_0^{1/\sqrt{2}} d\theta$

$= \int_0^{2\pi} \frac{1}{6}(2 - \sqrt{2})d\theta = \frac{\pi}{3}(2 - \sqrt{2})$, it follows that

$\bar{z} = \frac{\mathcal{M}_{xy}}{m} = \frac{\pi/8}{\pi(2 - \sqrt{2})/3} = \frac{3}{8(2 - \sqrt{2})}$. Thus $(\bar{x},\bar{y},\bar{z})$

$= (0,0,\frac{3}{8(2-\sqrt{2})})$.

11. The paraboloids $z = 1 - x^2 - y^2$ and $z = x^2 + y^2$ intersect at (x,y,z) such that $1 - x^2 - y^2 = z = x^2 + y^2$, so that $x^2 + y^2 = \frac{1}{2}$. Taking $\delta = 1$, we have $\mathcal{M}_{xy} = \iiint\limits_D z\,dV$

$= \int_0^{\pi/2}\int_0^{1/\sqrt{2}}\int_{r^2}^{1-r^2} zr\,dz\,dr\,d\theta = \int_0^{\pi/2}\int_0^{1/\sqrt{2}} \frac{1}{2} z^2 r \Big|_{r^2}^{1-r^2} dr\,d\theta$

$= \int_0^{\pi/2}\int_0^{1/\sqrt{2}} (\frac{1}{2} r - r^3)dr\,d\theta = \int_0^{\pi/2} (\frac{1}{4} r^2 - \frac{1}{4} r^4)\Big|_0^{1/\sqrt{2}} d\theta$

$= \int_0^{\pi/2} \frac{1}{16}\,d\theta = \frac{1}{32}\pi$,

$\mathcal{M}_{xz} = \iiint\limits_D y\,dV = \int_0^{\pi/2}\int_0^{1/\sqrt{2}}\int_{r^2}^{1-r^2} r^2 \sin\theta\,dz\,dr\,d\theta$

$= \int_0^{\pi/2}\int_0^{1/\sqrt{2}} r^2 z \sin\theta \Big|_{r^2}^{1-r^2} dr\,d\theta$

$= \int_0^{\pi/2}\int_0^{1/\sqrt{2}} (r^2 - 2r^4)\sin\theta\,dr\,d\theta$

$= \int_0^{\pi/2} (\frac{1}{3} r^3 - \frac{2}{5} r^5)\sin\theta \Big|_0^{1/\sqrt{2}} d\theta = \int_0^{\pi/2} \frac{\sqrt{2}}{30} \sin\theta\,d\theta$

$= \frac{-\sqrt{2}}{30} \cos\theta \Big|_0^{\pi/2} = \frac{\sqrt{2}}{30}$, and $\mathcal{M}_{yz} = \iiint\limits_D x\,dV$

$= \int_0^{\pi/2}\int_0^{1/\sqrt{2}}\int_{r^2}^{1-r^2} r^2 \cos\theta\,dz\,dr\,d\theta$

$= \int_0^{\pi/2}\int_0^{1/\sqrt{2}} r^2 z \cos\theta \Big|_{r^2}^{1-r^2} dr\,d\theta$

$= \int_0^{\pi/2}\int_0^{1/\sqrt{2}} (r^2 - 2r^4)\cos\theta\,dr\,d\theta = \int_0^{\pi/2} (\frac{1}{3} r^3 - \frac{2}{5} r^5)\cos\theta \Big|_0^{1/\sqrt{2}} d\theta$

$= \int_0^{\pi/2} \frac{\sqrt{2}}{30} \cos\theta\,d\theta = \frac{\sqrt{2}}{30} \sin\theta \Big|_0^{\pi/2} = \frac{\sqrt{2}}{30}$. Since

$$m = \iiint_D 1\, dV = \int_0^{\pi/2} \int_0^{1/\sqrt{2}} \int_{r^2}^{1-r^2} r\, dz\, dr\, d\theta$$

$$= \int_0^{\pi/2} \int_0^{1/\sqrt{2}} rz \Big|_{r^2}^{1-r^2} dr\, d\theta = \int_0^{\pi/2} \int_0^{1/\sqrt{2}} (r - 2r^3) dr\, d\theta$$

$$= \int_0^{\pi/2} (\tfrac{1}{2} r^2 - \tfrac{1}{2} r^4) \Big|_0^{1/\sqrt{2}} d\theta = \int_0^{\pi/2} \tfrac{1}{8}\, d\theta = \tfrac{1}{16}\pi ,$$

it follows that $\bar{x} = \frac{\mathcal{M}_{yz}}{m} = \frac{\sqrt{2}/30}{\pi/16} = \frac{8\sqrt{2}}{15\pi}$, $\bar{y} = \frac{\mathcal{M}_{xz}}{m} = \frac{\sqrt{2}/30}{\pi/16} = \frac{8\sqrt{2}}{15\pi}$,

and $\bar{z} = \frac{\mathcal{M}_{xy}}{m} = \frac{\pi/32}{\pi/16} = \frac{1}{2}$. Thus $(\bar{x},\bar{y},\bar{z}) = (\frac{8\sqrt{2}}{15\pi}, \frac{8\sqrt{2}}{15\pi}, \frac{1}{2})$.

12. Taking $\delta = 1$, we have $\mathcal{M}_{xy} = \iiint_D z\, dV = \int_0^1 \int_0^1 \int_0^{1+x+2y} z\, dz\, dy\, dx$

$$= \int_0^1 \int_0^1 \tfrac{1}{2} z^2 \Big|_0^{1+x+2y} dy\, dx = \int_0^1 \int_0^1 \tfrac{1}{2}(1 + x + 2y)^2\, dy\, dx$$

$$= \int_0^1 \tfrac{1}{12}(1 + x + 2y)^3 \Big|_0^1 dx = \tfrac{1}{12} \int_0^1 [(3 + x)^3 - (1 + x)^3] dx$$

$$= \tfrac{1}{48}[(3 + x)^4 - (1 + x)^4] \Big|_0^1 = \tfrac{10}{3} , \quad \mathcal{M}_{xz} = \iiint_D y\, dV$$

$$= \int_0^1 \int_0^1 \int_0^{1+x+2y} y\, dz\, dy\, dx = \int_0^1 \int_0^1 yz \Big|_0^{1+x+2y} dy\, dx$$

$$= \int_0^1 \int_0^1 (y + xy + 2y^2) dy\, dx = \int_0^1 (\tfrac{1}{2} y^2 + \tfrac{1}{2} xy^2 + \tfrac{2}{3} y^3) \Big|_0^1 dx$$

$$= \int_0^1 (\tfrac{7}{6} + \tfrac{1}{2} x) dx = (\tfrac{7}{6} x + \tfrac{1}{4} x^2) \Big|_0^1 = \tfrac{17}{12} , \text{ and } \mathcal{M}_{yz} = \iiint_D x\, dV$$

$$= \int_0^1 \int_0^1 \int_0^{1+x+2y} x\, dz\, dy\, dx = \int_0^1 \int_0^1 xz \Big|_0^{1+x+2y} dy\, dx$$

$$= \int_0^1 \int_0^1 (x + x^2 + 2xy) dy\, dx = \int_0^1 (xy + x^2y + xy^2) \Big|_0^1 dx$$

$$= \int_0^1 (2x + x^2) dx = (x^2 + \tfrac{1}{3} x^3) \Big|_0^1 = \tfrac{4}{3} . \quad \text{Since } m = \iiint_D 1\, dV$$

$$= \int_0^1 \int_0^1 \int_0^{1+x+2y} 1\, dz\, dy\, dx = \int_0^1 \int_0^1 z \Big|_0^{1+x+2y} dy\, dx$$

$$= \int_0^1 \int_0^1 (1 + x + 2y) dy\, dx = \int_0^1 (y + xy + y^2) \Big|_0^1 dx$$

$$= \int_0^1 (2 + x) dx = (2x + \tfrac{1}{2} x^2) \Big|_0^1 = \tfrac{5}{2} , \text{ it follows that}$$

$\bar{x} = \frac{\mathcal{M}_{yz}}{m} = \frac{4/3}{5/2} = \frac{8}{15}$, $\bar{y} = \frac{\mathcal{M}_{xz}}{m} = \frac{17/12}{5/2} = \frac{17}{30}$, and $\bar{z} = \frac{\mathcal{M}_{xy}}{m}$

$= \frac{10/3}{5/2} = \frac{4}{3}$. Thus $(\bar{x},\bar{y},\bar{z}) = (\frac{8}{15}, \frac{17}{30}, \frac{4}{3})$.

13. By symmetry, $\bar{x} = \bar{y} = 0$. An equation of the plane that contains the face of the pyramid in the first octant is $x + y + \frac{z}{2} = 1$, or $z = 2(1 - x - y)$. Thus, taking $\delta = 1$, we have

$$\mathcal{M}_{xy} = \iiint_D z\, dV = 4 \int_0^1 \int_0^{1-x} \int_0^{2(1-x-y)} z\, dz\, dy\, dx$$

$$= \int_0^1 \int_0^{1-x} 2z^2 \Big|_0^{2(1-x-y)} dy\, dx = \int_0^1 \int_0^{1-x} 8(1 - x - y)^2 dy\, dx$$

$$= \int_0^1 \tfrac{-8}{3}(1 - x - y)^3 \Big|_0^{1-x} dx = \int_0^1 \tfrac{8}{3}(1 - x)^3 dx$$

$$= \tfrac{-2}{3}(1 - x)^4 \Big|_0^1 = \tfrac{2}{3} . \quad \text{Since } m = \iiint_D 1\, dV$$

$$= 4 \int_0^1 \int_0^{1-x} \int_0^{2(1-x-y)} 1\, dz\, dy\, dx = \int_0^1 \int_0^{1-x} 4z \Big|_0^{2(1-x-y)} dy\, dx$$

$$= \int_0^1 \int_0^{1-x} 8(1 - x - y) dy\, dx = \int_0^1 -4(1 - x - y)^2 \Big|_0^{1-x} dx$$

$$= \int_0^1 4(1 - x)^2 dx = \tfrac{-4}{3}(1 - x)^3 \Big|_0^1 = \tfrac{4}{3} , \text{ it follows that}$$

$\bar{z} = \frac{\mathcal{M}_{xy}}{m} = \frac{2/3}{4/3} = \frac{1}{2}$. Thus $(\bar{x},\bar{y},\bar{z}) = (0, 0, \frac{1}{2})$.

14. a. Since $\delta(x,y,z) = \sqrt{x^2 + y^2 + z^2}$ and since the given region is symmetric with respect to the coordinate planes, we have

$$\mathcal{M}_{xy} = \iiint_D z\delta(x,y,z) dV = \iiint_D z\sqrt{x^2 + y^2 + z^2}\, dV = 0 , \text{ and}$$

similarly $\mathcal{M}_{xz} = 0 = \mathcal{M}_{yz}$. Thus $\bar{x} = \frac{\mathcal{M}_{yz}}{m} = \frac{0}{m} = 0$,

$\bar{y} = \frac{\mathcal{M}_{xz}}{m} = \frac{0}{m} = 0$, and $\bar{z} = \frac{\mathcal{M}_{xy}}{m} = \frac{0}{m} = 0$, so that

$(\bar{x},\bar{y},\bar{z}) = (0,0,0)$.

b. Since $\delta(x,y,z)$ does not depend on x or y and since the given region is symmetric with respect to the yz plane and the xz plane, we have $\bar{x} = 0 = \bar{y}$. Next by symmetry we have $\mathcal{M}_{xy} = \iiint_D z\delta(x,y,z)dV = \iiint_D z(1 + z^2)dV$ $= 0$, so that $\bar{z} = \frac{\mathcal{M}_{xy}}{m} = \frac{0}{m} = 0$. Thus $(\bar{x},\bar{y},\bar{z}) = (0,0,0)$.

15. Since $\delta(x,y,z)$ does not depend on x or y and since the given region is symmetric with respect to the yz plane and the xz plane, we have $\bar{x} = 0 = \bar{y}$. Next
$\mathcal{M}_{xy} = \iiint_D z\delta(x,y,z)dV = \iiint_D z(z^2 + 1)dV = 0$, so that
$\bar{z} = \frac{\mathcal{M}_{xy}}{m} = \frac{0}{m} = 0$. Thus $(\bar{x},\bar{y},\bar{z}) = (0,0,0)$.

16. Since $\delta(x,y,z)$ does not depend on either x or y , the symmetry of the given region implies that $\bar{x} = \bar{y} = 0$. The two paraboloids intersect at (x,y,z) such that $1 - x^2 - y^2 = z = x^2 + y^2$, so that $x^2 + y^2 = \frac{1}{2}$. Thus

$$\mathcal{M}_{xy} = \iiint_D z\,\delta(x,y,z)dV = \int_0^{2\pi}\int_0^{1/\sqrt{2}}\int_{r^2}^{1-r^2} z(2 - z)r\,dz\,dr\,d\theta$$

$$= \int_0^{2\pi}\int_0^{1/\sqrt{2}} (z^2 - \tfrac{1}{3}z^3)r\Big|_{r^2}^{1-r^2} dr\,d\theta$$

$$= \int_0^{2\pi}\int_0^{1/\sqrt{2}} (\tfrac{2}{3}r - r^3 - r^5 + \tfrac{2}{3}r^7)dr\,d\theta$$

$$= \int_0^{2\pi} (\tfrac{1}{3}r^2 - \tfrac{1}{4}r^4 - \tfrac{1}{6}r^6 + \tfrac{1}{12}r^8)\Big|_0^{1/\sqrt{2}} d\theta = \int_0^{2\pi}\frac{17}{192}d\theta = \frac{17}{96}\pi .$$

Since $m = \iiint_D \delta(x,y,z)dV = \int_0^{2\pi}\int_0^{1/\sqrt{2}}\int_{r^2}^{1-r^2} (2 - z)r\,dz\,dr\,d\theta$

$$= \int_0^{2\pi}\int_0^{1/\sqrt{2}} (2z - \tfrac{1}{2}z^2)r\Big|_{r^2}^{1-r^2} dr\,d\theta = \int_0^{2\pi}\int_0^{1/\sqrt{2}} (\tfrac{3}{2}r - 3r^3)dr\,d\theta$$

$= \int_0^{2\pi} (\frac{3}{4}r^2 - \frac{3}{4}r^4)\Big|_0^{1/\sqrt{2}} d\theta = \int_0^{2\pi}\frac{3}{16}d\theta = \frac{3}{8}\pi$, it follows that

$\bar{z} = \frac{\mathcal{M}_{xy}}{m} = \frac{17\pi/96}{3\pi/8} = \frac{17}{36}$. Thus $(\bar{x},\bar{y},\bar{z}) = (0,0,\frac{17}{36})$.

17. $\mathcal{M}_{xy} = \iiint_D z\delta(x,y,z)dV = \int_0^2\int_0^2\int_0^2 z(1 + x)dz\,dy\,dx$

$$= \int_0^2\int_0^2 \tfrac{1}{2}z^2(1 + x)\Big|_0^2 dy\,dx = \int_0^2\int_0^2 2(1 + x)dy\,dx$$

$= \int_0^2 2(1 + x)y\Big|_0^2 dx = \int_0^2 4(1 + x)dx = (4x + 2x^2)\Big|_0^2 = 16$,

$$\mathcal{M}_{xz} = \iiint_D y\delta(x,y,z)dV = \int_0^2\int_0^2\int_0^2 y(1 + x)dz\,dy\,dx$$

$$= \int_0^2\int_0^2 y(1 + x)z\Big|_0^2 dy\,dx = \int_0^2\int_0^2 2y(1 + x)dy\,dx$$

$= \int_0^2 y^2(1 + x)\Big|_0^2 dx = \int_0^2 4(1 + x)dx = (4x + 2x^2)\Big|_0^2 = 16$, and

$$\mathcal{M}_{yz} = \iiint_D x\delta(x,y,z)dV = \int_0^2\int_0^2\int_0^2 x(1 + x)dz\,dy\,dx$$

$$= \int_0^2\int_0^2 x(1 + x)z\Big|_0^2 dy\,dx = \int_0^2\int_0^2 2x(1 + x)dy\,dx$$

$$= \int_0^2 2x(1 + x)y\Big|_0^2 dx = \int_0^2 4x(1 + x)dx = (2x^2 + \tfrac{4}{3}x^3)\Big|_0^2$$

$= \frac{56}{3}$. Since $m = \iiint_D \delta(x,y,z)dV = \int_0^2\int_0^2\int_0^2 (1 + x)dz\,dy\,dx$

$$= \int_0^2\int_0^2 (1 + x)z\Big|_0^2 dy\,dx = \int_0^2\int_0^2 2(1 + x)dy\,dx$$

$= \int_0^2 2(1 + x)y\Big|_0^2 dx = \int_0^2 4(1 + x)dx = (4x + 2x^2)\Big|_0^2 = 16$,

it follows that $\bar{x} = \frac{\mathcal{M}_{yz}}{m} = \frac{56/3}{16} = \frac{7}{6}$, $\bar{y} = \frac{\mathcal{M}_{xz}}{m} = \frac{16}{16} = 1$, and

$\bar{z} = \frac{\mathcal{M}_{xy}}{m} = \frac{16}{16} = 1$. Thus $(\bar{x},\bar{y},\bar{z}) = (\frac{7}{6},1,1)$.

18. Since $\delta(x,y,z)$ does not depend on x and since the given region is symmetric with respect to the yz plane, we have $\bar{x} = 0$. Since the sheet $z = 1 - x^2$ intersects the plane $z = 0$ in the lines $x = -1$ and $x = 1$, the base of the solid is bounded by the lines $x = -1$, $x = 1$, $y = -1$, and $y = 1$. Thus $\mathcal{M}_{xy} = \iiint_D z\,\delta(x,y,z)\,dV$

$$= \int_{-1}^{1}\int_{-1}^{1}\int_{0}^{1-x^2} z^2(y+2)\,dz\,dy\,dx = \int_{-1}^{1}\int_{-1}^{1} \frac{1}{3}z^3(y+2)\Big|_0^{1-x^2} dy\,dx$$

$$= \int_{-1}^{1}\int_{-1}^{1} \frac{1}{3}(1-x^2)^3(y+2)\,dy\,dx = \int_{-1}^{1} \frac{1}{3}(1-x^2)^3\left(\frac{1}{2}y^2+2y\right)\Big|_{-1}^{1} dx$$

$$= \int_{-1}^{1} \frac{4}{3}(1-x^2)^3\,dx = \int_{-1}^{1}\left(\frac{4}{3} - 4x^2 + 4x^4 - \frac{4}{3}x^6\right)dx$$

$$= \left(\frac{4}{3}x - \frac{4}{3}x^3 + \frac{4}{5}x^5 - \frac{4}{21}x^7\right)\Big|_{-1}^{1} = \frac{128}{105}\text{, and}$$

$$\mathcal{M}_{xz} = \iiint_D y\,\delta(x,y,z)\,dV = \int_{-1}^{1}\int_{-1}^{1}\int_{0}^{1-x^2} zy(y+2)\,dz\,dy\,dx$$

$$= \int_{-1}^{1}\int_{-1}^{1} \frac{1}{2}z^2y(y+2)\Big|_0^{1-x^2} dy\,dx$$

$$= \int_{-1}^{1}\int_{-1}^{1} \frac{1}{2}(1-x^2)^2y(y+2)\,dy\,dx$$

$$= \int_{-1}^{1} \frac{1}{2}(1-x^2)^2\left(\frac{1}{3}y^3+y^2\right)\Big|_{-1}^{1} dx = \int_{-1}^{1}\frac{1}{3}(1-x^2)^2\,dx$$

$$= \int_{-1}^{1}\left(\frac{1}{3} - \frac{2}{3}x^2 + \frac{1}{3}x^4\right)dx = \left(\frac{1}{3}x - \frac{2}{9}x^3 + \frac{1}{15}x^5\right)\Big|_{-1}^{1} = \frac{16}{45}.$$

Since $m = \iiint_D \delta(x,y,z)\,dV = \int_{-1}^{1}\int_{-1}^{1}\int_{0}^{1-x^2} z(y+2)\,dz\,dy\,dx$

$$= \int_{-1}^{1}\int_{-1}^{1}\frac{1}{2}z^2(y+2)\Big|_0^{1-x^2} dy\,dx = \int_{-1}^{1}\int_{-1}^{1}\frac{1}{2}(1-x^2)^2(y+2)\,dy\,dx$$

$$= \int_{-1}^{1}\frac{1}{2}(1-x^2)^2\left(\frac{1}{2}y^2+2y\right)\Big|_{-1}^{1} dx = \int_{-1}^{1} 2(1-x^2)^2\,dx$$

$= \int_{-1}^{1}(2 - 4x^2 + 2x^4)\,dx = \left(2x - \frac{4}{3}x^3 + \frac{2}{5}x^5\right)\Big|_{-1}^{1} = \frac{32}{15}$, it follows that $\bar{y} = \frac{\mathcal{M}_{xz}}{m} = \frac{16/45}{32/15} = \frac{1}{6}$ and $\bar{z} = \frac{\mathcal{M}_{xy}}{m} = \frac{128/105}{32/15} = \frac{4}{7}$. Thus $(\bar{x},\bar{y},\bar{z}) = (0,\frac{1}{6},\frac{4}{7})$

19. Since $\delta(x,y,z) = \sqrt{x^2+y^2}$, we have $\mathcal{M}_{xy} = \iiint_D z\,\delta(x,y,z)\,dV$

$$= \iiint_D z\sqrt{x^2+y^2}\,dV = \int_0^{2\pi}\int_0^3\int_0^{\sqrt{9-r^2}} zr^2\,dz\,dr\,d\theta$$

$$= \int_0^{2\pi}\int_0^3 \frac{1}{2}z^2r^2\Big|_0^{\sqrt{9-r^2}} dr\,d\theta = \int_0^{2\pi}\int_0^3\left(\frac{9}{2}r^2 - \frac{1}{2}r^4\right)dr\,d\theta$$

$= \int_0^{2\pi}\left(\frac{3}{2}r^3 - \frac{1}{10}r^5\right)\Big|_0^3 d\theta = \int_0^{2\pi}\frac{81}{5}\,d\theta = \frac{162}{5}\pi$. By symmetry

$\mathcal{M}_{xz} = \iiint_D y\,\delta(x,y,z)\,dV = \iiint_D y\sqrt{x^2+y^2}\,dV = 0$ and

$\mathcal{M}_{yz} = \iiint_D x\,\delta(x,y,z)\,dV = \iiint_D x\sqrt{x^2+y^2}\,dV = 0$. Since

$$m = \iiint_D \delta(x,y,z)\,dV = \iiint_D \sqrt{x^2+y^2}\,dV = \int_0^{2\pi}\int_0^3\int_0^{\sqrt{9-r^2}} r^2\,dz\,dr\,d\theta$$

$$= \int_0^{2\pi}\int_0^3 r^2z\Big|_0^{\sqrt{9-r^2}} dr\,d\theta = \int_0^{2\pi}\int_0^3 r^2\sqrt{9-r^2}\,dr\,d\theta$$

(r = 3 sin u)

$$= \int_0^{2\pi}\int_0^{\pi/2}(9\sin^2 u)(3\cos u)(3\cos u)\,du\,d\theta$$

$$= \int_0^{2\pi}\int_0^{\pi/2}\frac{81}{4}\sin^2 2u\,du\,d\theta = \int_0^{2\pi}\int_0^{\pi/2}\frac{81}{4}\left(\frac{1}{2} - \frac{1}{2}\cos 4u\right)du\,d\theta$$

$= \int_0^{2\pi}\frac{81}{4}\left(\frac{1}{2}u - \frac{1}{8}\sin 4u\right)\Big|_0^{\pi/2} d\theta = \int_0^{2\pi}\frac{81}{16}\pi\,d\theta = \frac{81}{8}\pi^2$, it follows that $\bar{x} = \frac{\mathcal{M}_{yz}}{m} = \frac{0}{m} = 0$, $\bar{y} = \frac{\mathcal{M}_{xz}}{m} = \frac{0}{m} = 0$, and $\bar{z}$

$= \frac{\mathcal{M}_{xy}}{m} = \frac{162\pi/5}{81\pi^2/8} = \frac{16}{5\pi}$. Thus $(\bar{x},\bar{y},\bar{z}) = (0,0,\frac{16}{5\pi})$.

20. Since the given region is symmetric with respect to the yz plane and the xz plane, we have $\mathcal{M}_{yz} = \iiint_D x\,\delta(x,y,z)\,dV$

$= \iiint_D xz^2(x^2 + y^2 + z^2)\,dV = 0$ and $\mathcal{M}_{xz} = \iiint_D y\,\delta(x,y,z)\,dV$

$= \iiint_D yz^2(x^2 + y^2 + z^2)\,dV = 0$. The sphere $x^2 + y^2 + z^2 = 4$ and the cone $z^2 = x^2 + y^2$ intersect at points (x,y,z) such that $4 - x^2 - y^2 = z^2 = x^2 + y^2$ and $z \geq 0$, so that $x^2 + y^2 = 2$ and thus $z = \sqrt{2}$. This means that $\cos\phi = \frac{z}{\rho}$ $= \frac{\sqrt{2}}{2}$, which implies that $\phi = \frac{\pi}{4}$. Thus

$\mathcal{M}_{xy} = \iiint_D z\,\delta(x,y,z)\,dV = \iiint_D z^3(x^2 + y^2 + z^2)\,dV$

$= \int_0^{2\pi}\int_0^{\pi/4}\int_0^2 (\rho^3\cos^3\phi)(\rho^2)(\rho^2\sin\phi)\,d\rho\,d\phi\,d\theta$

$= \int_0^{2\pi}\int_0^{\pi/4} \frac{1}{8}\rho^8\cos^3\phi\,\sin\phi\,\Big|_0^2\,d\phi\,d\theta$

$= \int_0^{2\pi}\int_0^{\pi/4} 32\cos^3\phi\,\sin\phi\,d\phi\,d\theta = \int_0^{2\pi} -8\cos^4\phi\Big|_0^{\pi/4}\,d\theta$

$= \int_0^{2\pi} 6\,d\theta = 12\pi$. Since $m = \iiint_D \delta(x,y,z)\,dV$

$= \iiint_D z^2(x^2 + y^2 + z^2)\,dV$

$= \int_0^{2\pi}\int_0^{\pi/4}\int_0^2 (\rho^2\cos^2\phi)(\rho^2)(\rho^2\sin\phi)\,d\rho\,d\phi\,d\theta$

$= \int_0^{2\pi}\int_0^{\pi/4} \frac{1}{7}\rho^7\cos^2\phi\,\sin\phi\,\Big|_0^2\,d\phi\,d\theta$

$= \int_0^{2\pi}\int_0^{\pi/4} \frac{128}{7}\cos^2\phi\,\sin\phi\,d\phi\,d\theta = \int_0^{2\pi} -\frac{128}{21}\cos^3\phi\Big|_0^{\pi/4}\,d\theta$

$= \int_0^{2\pi} \frac{32}{21}(4 - \sqrt{2})\,d\theta = \frac{64\pi}{21}(4 - \sqrt{2})$, it follows that $\bar{x} = \frac{\mathcal{M}_{yz}}{m} = \frac{0}{m}$

$= 0$, $\bar{y} = \frac{\mathcal{M}_{xz}}{m} = \frac{0}{m} = 0$, and $\bar{z} = \frac{\mathcal{M}_{xy}}{m} = \frac{12\pi}{64\pi(4 - \sqrt{2})/21}$

$= \frac{63}{16(4 - \sqrt{2})}$. Thus $(\bar{x},\bar{y},\bar{z}) = (0,0,\frac{63}{16(4 - \sqrt{2})})$.

21. Since $\delta(x,y,z)$ does not depend on x or y and since the region occupied by the juice is symmetric with respect to the yz plane and the xz plane, we have $\bar{x} = 0 = \bar{y}$. Next,

$\mathcal{M}_{xy} = \iiint_D z\,\delta(x,y,z)\,dV = \iiint_D az(40 - z)\,dV$

$= \int_0^{2\pi}\int_0^4\int_0^{20} az(40 - z)r\,dz\,dr\,d\theta$

$= a\int_0^{2\pi}\int_0^4 (20z^2 - \frac{1}{3}z^3)r\,\Big|_0^{20}\,dr\,d\theta$

$= a\int_0^{2\pi}\int_0^4 \frac{16{,}000}{3}r\,dr\,d\theta = a\int_0^{2\pi} \frac{8{,}000}{3}r^2\Big|_0^4\,d\theta$

$= a\int_0^{2\pi} \frac{128{,}000}{3}\,d\theta = \frac{256{,}000}{3}\pi a$. Since $m = \iiint_D \delta(x,y,z)\,dV$

$= \iiint_D a(40 - z)\,dV = \int_0^{2\pi}\int_0^4\int_0^{20} a(40 - z)r\,dz\,dr\,d\theta$

$= a\int_0^{2\pi}\int_0^4 (40z - \frac{1}{2}z^2)r\,\Big|_0^{20}\,dr\,d\theta = a\int_0^{2\pi}\int_0^4 600r\,dr\,d\theta$

$= a\int_0^{2\pi} 300r^2\Big|_0^4\,d\theta = a\int_0^{2\pi} 4800\,d\theta = 9600\pi a$, it follows that

$\bar{z} = \frac{\mathcal{M}_{xy}}{m} = \frac{256{,}000\pi a/3}{9600\pi a} = \frac{80}{9}$. Thus $(\bar{x},\bar{y},\bar{z}) = (0,0,\frac{80}{9})$.

22. Set up a coordinate system with the origin at the center of the base of the top cube and with the positive z axis passing through the top cube. By symmetry $\bar{x} = \bar{y} = 0$. Since the center of gravity of each cube is located at its center, we find that the total moment of the two cubes about the xy plane

is given by $\mathcal{M}_{xy} = (1)(\frac{1}{2}) + (10)(-\frac{1}{2}) = -\frac{9}{2}$. Since the total mass m is $1 + 10 = 11$, we have $\bar{z} = \frac{\mathcal{M}_{xy}}{m} = \frac{-9/2}{11} = -\frac{9}{22}$. Thus $(\bar{x},\bar{y},\bar{z}) = (0,0,\frac{-9}{22})$, so that the center of gravity lies on the line joining the centers of the cubes, $\frac{9}{22}$ units below the base of the top cube.

23. $I_x = \iiint_D (y^2 + z^2)5\, dV$

$$= \int_0^{2\pi}\int_0^{\pi}\int_0^5 (\rho^2\sin^2\phi\, \sin^2\theta + \rho^2\cos^2\phi)5\rho^2\sin\phi\, d\rho\, d\phi\, d\theta$$

$$= \int_0^{2\pi}\int_0^{\pi} \rho^5(\sin^2\phi\, \sin^2\theta + \cos^2\phi)\sin\phi\Big|_0^5 d\phi\, d\theta$$

$$= \int_0^{2\pi}\int_0^{\pi} 3125[(1 - \cos^2\phi)\sin^2\theta + \cos^2\phi]\sin\phi\, d\phi\, d\theta$$

$$= 3125\int_0^{2\pi} [(-\cos\phi + \frac{1}{3}\cos^3\phi)\sin^2\theta - \frac{1}{3}\cos^3\phi]\Big|_0^{\pi} d\theta$$

$$= 3125\int_0^{2\pi} (\frac{4}{3}\sin^2\theta + \frac{2}{3})d\theta = 3125\int_0^{2\pi}(\frac{2}{3} - \frac{2}{3}\cos 2\theta + \frac{2}{3})d\theta$$

$$= 3125(\frac{4}{3}\theta - \frac{1}{3}\sin 2\theta)\Big|_0^{2\pi} = \frac{25{,}000}{3}\pi$$

By the symmetry of the region and the mass density, $I_y = \frac{25{,}000}{3}\pi = I_z$.

24. $I_x = \iiint_D (y^2 + z^2)(x^2 + y^2 + z^2)dV$

$$= \int_0^{2\pi}\int_0^{\pi}\int_0^2 (\rho^2\sin^2\phi\, \sin^2\theta + \rho^2\cos^2\phi)\rho^4\sin\phi\, d\rho\, d\phi\, d\theta$$

$$= \int_0^{2\pi}\int_0^{\pi} \frac{1}{7}\rho^7(\sin^2\phi\, \sin^2\theta + \cos^2\phi)\sin\phi\Big|_0^2 d\phi\, d\theta$$

$$= \int_0^{2\pi}\int_0^{\pi} \frac{128}{7}[(1 - \cos^2\phi)\sin^2\theta + \cos^2\phi]\sin\phi\, d\phi\, d\theta$$

$$= \frac{128}{7}(\frac{4}{3}\theta - \frac{1}{3}\sin 2\theta)\Big|_0^{2\pi} = \frac{1024}{7}\pi$$

where the next to last equality follows as in the solution of Exercise 23. By the symmetry of the region and the mass density, $I_y = \frac{1024}{7}\pi = I_z$.

25. $I_x = \iiint_D (y^2 + z^2)2\, dV = \int_0^{2\pi}\int_0^2\int_0^6 2(r^2\sin^2\theta + z^2)r\, dz\, dr\, d\theta$

$$= \int_0^{2\pi}\int_0^2 (2r^3z\sin^2\theta + \frac{2}{3}z^3r)\Big|_0^6 dr\, d\theta$$

$$= \int_0^{2\pi}\int_0^2 (12r^3\sin^2\theta + 144r)dr\, d\theta = \int_0^{2\pi}(3r^4\sin^2\theta + 72r^2)\Big|_0^2 d\theta$$

$$= \int_0^{2\pi}(48\sin^2\theta + 288)d\theta = \int_0^{2\pi}(24 - 24\cos 2\theta + 288)d\theta$$

$$= (312\theta - 12\sin 2\theta)\Big|_0^{2\pi} = 624\pi$$

By the symmetry of the region and the mass density, $I_y = 624\pi$. Finally,

$$I_z = \iiint_D (x^2 + y^2)2dV = \int_0^{2\pi}\int_0^2\int_0^6 2r^3\, dz\, dr\, d\theta$$

$$= \int_0^{2\pi}\int_0^2 2r^3z\Big|_0^6 dr\, d\theta = \int_0^{2\pi}\int_0^2 12r^3\, dr\, d\theta$$

$$= \int_0^{2\pi} 3r^4\Big|_0^2 d\theta = \int_0^{2\pi} 48\, d\theta = 96\pi$$

26. $I_x = \iiint_D (y^2 + z^2)(x^2 + y^2)\, dV$

$$= \int_0^{2\pi}\int_0^2\int_r^4 (r^2\sin^2\theta + z^2)r^3\, dz\, dr\, d\theta$$

$$= \int_0^{2\pi}\int_0^2 (zr^5\sin^2\theta + \frac{1}{3}z^3r^3)\Big|_r^4 dr\, d\theta$$

$$= \int_0^{2\pi}\int_0^2 (4r^5\sin^2\theta + \frac{64}{3}r^3 - r^6\sin^2\theta - \frac{1}{3}r^6)dr\, d\theta$$

$$= \int_0^{2\pi}(\frac{2}{3}r^6\sin^2\theta + \frac{16}{3}r^4 - \frac{1}{7}r^7\sin^2\theta - \frac{1}{21}r^7)\Big|_0^2 d\theta$$

$$= \int_0^{2\pi} \left(\frac{512}{21}\sin^2\theta + \frac{1664}{21}\right)d\theta = \int_0^{2\pi}\left(\frac{256}{21} - \frac{256}{21}\cos 2\theta + \frac{1664}{21}\right)d\theta$$

$$= \left(\frac{640}{7}\theta - \frac{128}{21}\sin 2\theta\right)\Big|_0^{2\pi} = \frac{1280}{7}\pi$$

By the symmetry of the region and the mass density, $I_y = \frac{1280}{7}\pi$.

Finally,

$$I_z = \iiint_D (x^2+y^2)(x^2+y^2)\,dV = \int_0^{2\pi}\int_0^2\int_r^4 r^5\,dz\,dr\,d\theta$$

$$= \int_0^{2\pi}\int_0^2 r^5 z\Big|_r^4 dr\,d\theta = \int_0^{2\pi}\int_0^2 (4r^5 - r^6)\,dr\,d\theta$$

$$= \int_0^{2\pi}\left(\frac{2}{3}r^6 - \frac{1}{7}r^7\right)\Big|_0^2 d\theta = \int_0^{2\pi}\frac{512}{21}\,d\theta = \frac{1024}{21}\pi$$

Section 14.8

1. $$\frac{\partial(x,y)}{\partial(u,v)} = \begin{vmatrix} \frac{\partial x}{\partial u} & \frac{\partial x}{\partial v} \\ \frac{\partial y}{\partial u} & \frac{\partial y}{\partial v}\end{vmatrix} = \begin{vmatrix} 3 & -4 \\ \frac{1}{2} & \frac{1}{6}\end{vmatrix} = (3)(\tfrac{1}{6}) - (-4)(\tfrac{1}{2}) = \frac{5}{2}$$

2. $$\frac{\partial(x,y)}{\partial(u,v)} = \begin{vmatrix} \frac{\partial x}{\partial u} & \frac{\partial x}{\partial v} \\ \frac{\partial y}{\partial u} & \frac{\partial y}{\partial v}\end{vmatrix} = \begin{vmatrix} 3 & -6 \\ -2 & 4\end{vmatrix} = (3)(4) - (-6)(-2) = 0$$

3. $$\frac{\partial(x,y)}{\partial(u,v)} = \begin{vmatrix} \frac{\partial x}{\partial u} & \frac{\partial x}{\partial v} \\ \frac{\partial y}{\partial u} & \frac{\partial y}{\partial v}\end{vmatrix} = \begin{vmatrix} v & u \\ 2u & 2v\end{vmatrix} = (v)(2v) - (u)(2u) = 2v^2 - 2u^2$$

4. $$\frac{\partial(x,y)}{\partial(u,v)} = \begin{vmatrix} \frac{\partial x}{\partial u} & \frac{\partial x}{\partial v} \\ \frac{\partial y}{\partial u} & \frac{\partial y}{\partial v}\end{vmatrix} = \begin{vmatrix} -\sin u & \cos v \\ -\cos u & -\sin v\end{vmatrix} = (-\sin u)(-\sin v) -$$

$$(\cos v)(-\cos u) = \sin u \sin v + \cos u \cos v = \cos(u - v)$$

5. $$\frac{\partial(x,y)}{\partial(u,v)} = \begin{vmatrix} \frac{\partial x}{\partial u} & \frac{\partial x}{\partial v} \\ \frac{\partial y}{\partial u} & \frac{\partial y}{\partial v}\end{vmatrix} = \begin{vmatrix} 0 & e^v \\ e^v & ue^v\end{vmatrix} = (0)(ue^v) - (e^v)(e^v) = -e^{2v}$$

6. $$\frac{\partial(x,y)}{\partial(u,v)} = \begin{vmatrix} \frac{\partial x}{\partial u} & \frac{\partial x}{\partial v} \\ \frac{\partial y}{\partial u} & \frac{\partial y}{\partial v}\end{vmatrix} = \begin{vmatrix} 1 & -\frac{1}{v} \\ \frac{1}{u} & 1\end{vmatrix} = (1)(1) - (-\tfrac{1}{v})(\tfrac{1}{u}) = 1 + \frac{1}{uv}$$

7. $$\frac{\partial(x,y,z)}{\partial(u,v,w)} = \begin{vmatrix} \frac{\partial x}{\partial u} & \frac{\partial x}{\partial v} & \frac{\partial x}{\partial w} \\ \frac{\partial y}{\partial u} & \frac{\partial y}{\partial v} & \frac{\partial y}{\partial w} \\ \frac{\partial z}{\partial u} & \frac{\partial z}{\partial v} & \frac{\partial z}{\partial w}\end{vmatrix} = \begin{vmatrix} a & 0 & 0 \\ 0 & b & 0 \\ 0 & 0 & 1\end{vmatrix} = a[(b)(1) - (0)(0)] +$$

$$0[(0)(0) - (0)(1)] + 0[(0)(0) - (b)(0)] = ab$$

8. $$\frac{\partial(x,y,z)}{\partial(u,v,w)} = \begin{vmatrix} \frac{\partial x}{\partial u} & \frac{\partial x}{\partial v} & \frac{\partial x}{\partial w} \\ \frac{\partial y}{\partial u} & \frac{\partial y}{\partial v} & \frac{\partial y}{\partial w} \\ \frac{\partial z}{\partial u} & \frac{\partial z}{\partial v} & \frac{\partial z}{\partial w} \end{vmatrix} = \begin{vmatrix} \frac{1}{v^2} & -\frac{2u}{v^3} & 0 \\ 0 & \frac{1}{w^2} & -\frac{2v}{w^3} \\ -\frac{2w}{u^3} & 0 & \frac{1}{u^2} \end{vmatrix}$$

$$= \frac{1}{v^2}\left[\left(\frac{1}{w^2}\right)\left(\frac{1}{u^2}\right) - \left(-\frac{2v}{w^3}\right)(0)\right] + \left(-\frac{2u}{v^3}\right)\left[\left(-\frac{2v}{w^3}\right)\left(-\frac{2w}{u^3}\right) - (0)\left(-\frac{1}{u^2}\right)\right] + 0\left[(0)(0) - \left(\frac{1}{w^2}\right)\left(-\frac{2w}{u^3}\right)\right] = \frac{1}{u^2v^2w^2} - \frac{8uvw}{u^3v^3w^3}$$

$$= -\frac{7}{u^2v^2w^2}$$

9. First,

$$\frac{\partial(x,y)}{\partial(u,v)} = \begin{vmatrix} \frac{\partial x}{\partial u} & \frac{\partial x}{\partial v} \\ \frac{\partial y}{\partial u} & \frac{\partial y}{\partial v} \end{vmatrix} = \begin{vmatrix} 3 & 1 \\ 1 & 0 \end{vmatrix} = (3)(0) - (1)(1) = -1$$

To find S we observe that for $y = 1$ we have $1 = y = u$; for $y = \frac{1}{4}x$ we have $u = \frac{1}{4}(3u + v)$, so that $\frac{1}{4}u = \frac{1}{4}v$, or $u = v$; for $x - 3y = e$ we have $(3u + v) - 3u = e$, or $v = e$. Consequently S is the region in the uv plane bounded by the lines $u = 1$, $u = v$, and $v = e$ (see the figure). By (9),

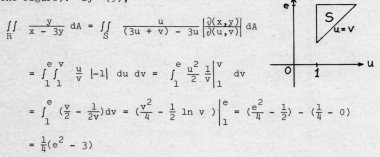

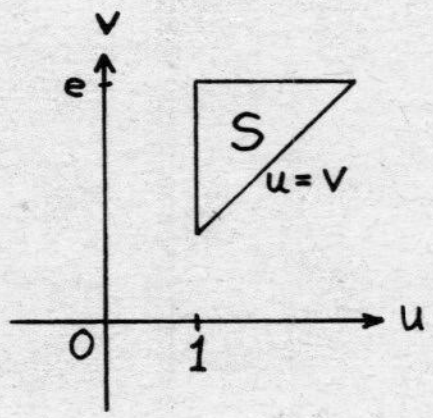

$$\iint_R \frac{y}{x - 3y}\, dA = \iint_S \frac{u}{(3u + v) - 3u}\left|\frac{\partial(x,y)}{\partial(u,v)}\right| dA$$

$$= \int_1^e \int_1^v \frac{u}{v}\,|-1|\,du\,dv = \int_1^e \frac{u^2}{2}\frac{1}{v}\bigg|_1^v dv$$

$$= \int_1^e \left(\frac{v}{2} - \frac{1}{2v}\right)dv = \left(\frac{v^2}{4} - \frac{1}{2}\ln v\right)\bigg|_1^e = \left(\frac{e^2}{4} - \frac{1}{2}\right) - \left(\frac{1}{4} - 0\right)$$

$$= \frac{1}{4}(e^2 - 3)$$

10. First,

$$\frac{\partial(x,y)}{\partial(u,v)} = \begin{vmatrix} \frac{\partial x}{\partial u} & \frac{\partial x}{\partial v} \\ \frac{\partial y}{\partial u} & \frac{\partial y}{\partial v} \end{vmatrix} = \begin{vmatrix} \frac{1}{2} & 0 \\ 0 & \frac{1}{3} \end{vmatrix} = \left(\frac{1}{2}\right)\left(\frac{1}{3}\right) - (0)(0) = \frac{1}{6}$$

To find S we observe that for $4x^2 + 9y^2 = 1$ we obtain $1 = 4x^2 + 9y^2 = 4(\frac{1}{2}u)^2 + 9(\frac{1}{3}v)^2 = u^2 + v^2$, so that S is the unit disk $u^2 + v^2 \le 1$. By (9),

$$\iint_R y^2\,dA = \iint_S \left(\frac{1}{3}v\right)^2 \left|\frac{\partial(x,y)}{\partial(u,v)}\right| dA = \iint_S \frac{1}{9}v^2\left(\frac{1}{6}\right) dA$$

Converting to polar coordinates with $u = r\cos\theta$ and $v = r\sin\theta$, we obtain

$$\iint_R y^2\,dA = \iint_S \frac{1}{54}v^2\,dA = \frac{1}{54}\int_0^{2\pi}\int_0^1 r^2(\sin^2\theta)r\,dr\,d\theta$$

$$= \frac{1}{54}\int_0^{2\pi}(\sin^2\theta)\frac{r^4}{4}\bigg|_0^1 d\theta = \frac{1}{216}\int_0^{2\pi}\left(\frac{1}{2} - \frac{1}{2}\cos 2\theta\right)d\theta$$

$$= \frac{1}{216}\left(\frac{1}{2}\theta - \frac{1}{4}\sin 2\theta\right)\bigg|_0^{2\pi} = \frac{\pi}{216}$$

11. First,

$$\frac{\partial(x,y)}{\partial(u,v)} = \begin{vmatrix} \frac{\partial x}{\partial u} & \frac{\partial x}{\partial v} \\ \frac{\partial y}{\partial u} & \frac{\partial y}{\partial v} \end{vmatrix} = \begin{vmatrix} \frac{3}{5} & \frac{1}{5} \\ -\frac{2}{5} & \frac{1}{5} \end{vmatrix} = \left(\frac{3}{5}\right)\left(\frac{1}{5}\right) - \left(\frac{1}{5}\right)\left(-\frac{2}{5}\right) = \frac{1}{5}$$

To find S we observe that for $x - y = 2$ we have $\frac{1}{5}(3u + v) - \frac{1}{5}(v - 2u) = 2$, so that $u = 2$; for $x - y = -1$ we have $\frac{1}{5}(3u + v) - \frac{1}{5}(v - 2u) = -1$, so that $u = -1$; for $2x + 3y = 1$ we have $\frac{2}{5}(3u + v) + \frac{3}{5}(v - 2u) = 1$, so that $v = 1$; for $2x + 3y = 0$ we have $\frac{2}{5}(3u + v) + \frac{3}{5}(v - 2u) = 0$, so that $v = 0$. Thus S is the square region bounded by the lines $u = -1$, $u = 2$, $v = 1$ and $v = 0$. By (9),

$$\iint_R xy^2\,dA = \iint_S \left[\tfrac{1}{5}(3u+v)\right]\left[\tfrac{1}{5}(v-2u)\right]^2 \left|\frac{\partial(x,y)}{\partial(u,v)}\right| dA$$

$$= \iint_S \frac{1}{125}(3u+v)(v^2-4uv+4u^2)(\tfrac{1}{5})\,dA$$

$$= \frac{1}{625}\int_0^1\int_{-1}^2 (12u^3 - 8u^2v - uv^2 + v^3)\,du\,dv$$

$$= \frac{1}{625}\int_0^1 \left(3u^4 - \tfrac{8}{3}u^3v - \tfrac{1}{2}u^2v^2 + uv^3\right)\Big|_{-1}^{2} dv$$

$$= \frac{1}{625}\int_0^1 (45 - 24v - \tfrac{3}{2}v^2 + 3v^3)\,dv$$

$$= \frac{1}{625}\left(45v - 12v^2 - \tfrac{1}{2}v^3 + \tfrac{3}{4}v^4\right)\Big|_0^1 = \frac{133}{2500}$$

12. First,

$$\frac{\partial(x,y)}{\partial(u,v)} = \begin{vmatrix} \frac{\partial x}{\partial u} & \frac{\partial x}{\partial v} \\ \frac{\partial y}{\partial u} & \frac{\partial y}{\partial v} \end{vmatrix} = \begin{vmatrix} 1 & 1 \\ 1 & 2 \end{vmatrix} = (1)(2) - (1)(1) = 1$$

To find S we observe that for $y = \frac{3}{2}x$ we have $u + 2v = \frac{3}{2}(u+v)$, so that $u = v$; for $y = 2x$ we have $u + 2v = 2(u+v)$, so that $u = 0$; for $y = x + 1$ we have $u + 2v = (u+v) + 1$, so that $v = 1$. Consequently S is the triangular region in the uv plane bounded by the lines $u = v$, $u = 0$ and $v = 1$ (see the figure). By (9),

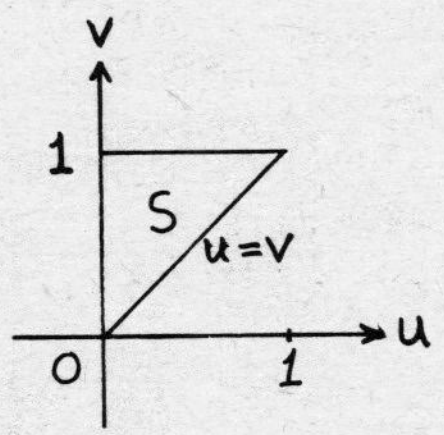

$$\iint_R e^{(y-x)^2}\,dA = \iint_R e^{[(u+2v)-(u+v)]^2}\left|\frac{\partial(x,y)}{\partial(u,v)}\right| dA$$

$$= \int_0^1\int_0^v e^{v^2}\,du\,dv = \int_0^1 e^{v^2}\,u\Big|_0^v dv = \int_0^1 e^{v^2}\,v\,dv$$

$$= \tfrac{1}{2}e^{v^2}\Big|_0^1 = \tfrac{1}{2}(e^1 - e^0) = \tfrac{1}{2}(e-1)$$

13. First,

$$\frac{\partial(x,y)}{\partial(u,v)} = \begin{vmatrix} \frac{\partial x}{\partial u} & \frac{\partial x}{\partial v} \\ \frac{\partial y}{\partial u} & \frac{\partial y}{\partial v} \end{vmatrix} = \begin{vmatrix} \sec v & u\sec v\tan v \\ \tan v & u\sec^2 v \end{vmatrix}$$

$$= (\sec v)(u\sec^2 v) - (u\sec v\tan v)(\tan v)$$

$$= u\sec v\,(\sec^2 v - \tan^2 v) = u\sec v$$

To find S we observe that for $x^2 - y^2 = 1$ we have $1 = x^2 - y^2 = u^2\sec^2 v - u^2\tan^2 v = u^2$, and since $u > 0$ by hypothesis, $u = 1$; similarly, for $x^2 - y^2 = 4$ we have $u = 2$; for $x = 2y$ we have $u\sec v = 2u\tan v$, or $\frac{u}{\cos v} = \frac{2u\sin v}{\cos v}$; since $u > 0$ by hypothesis, we have $\sin v = \frac{1}{2}$, and since $0 < v < \frac{\pi}{2}$, $v = \frac{\pi}{6}$; similarly, for $x = \sqrt{2}\,y$ we have $\sin v = \frac{1}{\sqrt{2}} = \frac{1}{2}\sqrt{2}$, and thus $v = \frac{\pi}{4}$. Consequently S is the rectangular region in the uv plane bounded by the lines $u = 1$, $u = 2$, $v = \frac{\pi}{6}$ and $v = \frac{\pi}{4}$. By (9),

$$\iint_R \frac{y}{x}e^{x^2-y^2}\,dA = \iint_S \frac{u\tan v}{u\sec v}e^{u^2\sec^2 v - u^2\tan^2 v}\left|\frac{\partial(x,y)}{\partial(u,v)}\right| dA$$

$$= \iint_S \frac{\tan v}{\sec v}e^{u^2}\,u\sec v\,dA = \iint_S u\,e^{u^2}\tan v\,dA$$

$$= \int_{\pi/6}^{\pi/4}\int_1^2 u\,e^{u^2}\tan v\,du\,dv = \int_{\pi/6}^{\pi/4} \tfrac{1}{2}e^{u^2}\tan v\Big|_1^2 dv$$

$$= \int_{\pi/6}^{\pi/4} \tfrac{1}{2}(e^4 - e)\tan v\,dv = -\tfrac{1}{2}(e^4 - e)\ln\cos v\Big|_{\pi/6}^{\pi/4}$$

$$= -\tfrac{1}{2}(e^4 - e)\left(\ln\frac{\sqrt{2}}{2} - \ln\frac{\sqrt{3}}{2}\right) = \tfrac{1}{2}(e^4 - e)\ln\sqrt{\frac{3}{2}}$$

$$= \tfrac{1}{4}(e^4 - e)\ln\tfrac{3}{2}$$

14. First,

$$\frac{\partial(x,y)}{\partial(u,v)} = \begin{vmatrix} \frac{\partial x}{\partial u} & \frac{\partial x}{\partial v} \\ \frac{\partial y}{\partial u} & \frac{\partial y}{\partial v} \end{vmatrix} = \begin{vmatrix} -\frac{2v}{(u+v)^2} & \frac{2u}{(u+v)^2} \\ 1 & 1 \end{vmatrix}$$

$$= \left(-\frac{2v}{(u+v)^2}\right)(1) - \left(\frac{2u}{(u+v)^2}\right)(1) = -\frac{2}{u+v}$$

To find S we observe that for $xy = \pi/2$ we have $\frac{\pi}{2} = xy = \frac{2v}{u+v}(u+v) = 2v$, so that $v = \pi/4$; similarly, for $xy = \pi$ we have $v = \pi/2$; for $y(2-x) = 2$ we have $2 = (u+v)(2 - \frac{2v}{u+v}) = 2u$, so that $u = 1$; similarly, for $y(2-x) = 4$ we have $u = 2$. Consequently S is the rectangular region in the uv plane bounded by the lines $v = \frac{\pi}{4}$, $v = \frac{\pi}{2}$, $u = 1$ and $u = 2$. By (9),

$$\iint_R y \cos xy \, dA = \iint_S (u+v)\cos\left[\frac{2v}{u+v}(u+v)\right]\left|\frac{\partial(x,y)}{\partial(u,v)}\right| dA$$

$$= \int_1^2 \int_{\pi/4}^{\pi/2} 2\cos 2v \, dv \, du = \int_1^2 \sin 2v \Big|_{\pi/4}^{\pi/2} du$$

$$= \int_1^2 -1 \, du = -1$$

15. First,

$$\frac{\partial(x,y)}{\partial(u,v)} = \begin{vmatrix} \frac{\partial x}{\partial u} & \frac{\partial x}{\partial v} \\ \frac{\partial y}{\partial u} & \frac{\partial y}{\partial v} \end{vmatrix} = \begin{vmatrix} \cosh v & u \sinh v \\ \sinh v & u \cosh v \end{vmatrix} = (\cosh v)(u \cosh v)$$

$$- (u \sinh v)(\sinh v) = u(\cosh^2 v - \sinh^2 v) = u$$

To find S we observe that for $x^2 - y^2 = 1$ we have $1 = u^2\cosh^2 v - u^2 \sinh^2 v = u^2$, and since $u > 0$ by hypothesis, $u = 1$; similarly, for $x^2 - y^2 = 4$ we have $u = 2$; for $y = 0$ we have $0 = y = u \sinh v$, and since $u > 0$ by hypothesis, $v = 0$; for $y = \frac{3}{5}x$ we have $u \sinh v = \frac{3}{5}u \cosh v$, and since $u > 0$ by hypothesis, $5 \sinh v = 3 \cosh v$, or $5(e^v - e^{-v}) = 3(e^v + e^{-v})$, or $2e^v = 8e^{-v}$, or $e^{2v} = 4$, so $v = \ln 2$. Consequently S is the rectangular region in the uv plane bounded by the lines $u = 1$, $u = 2$, $v = 0$ and $v = \ln 2$. By (9),

$$\iint_R e^{x^2-y^2} dA = \iint_S e^{u^2\cosh^2 v - u^2 \sinh^2 v}\left|\frac{\partial(x,y)}{\partial(u,v)}\right| dA$$

$$= \iint_S e^{u^2}(u)\, dA = \int_0^{\ln 2}\int_1^2 u e^{u^2} du\, dv = \int_0^{\ln 2} \frac{1}{2} e^{u^2}\Big|_1^2 dv$$

$$= \int_0^{\ln 2} \frac{1}{2}(e^4 - e)\, dv = \frac{v}{2}(e^4 - e)\Big|_0^{\ln 2} = \frac{1}{2}(e^4 - e)\ln 2$$

16. First,

$$\frac{\partial(x,y,z)}{\partial(u,v,w)} = \begin{vmatrix} \frac{\partial x}{\partial u} & \frac{\partial x}{\partial v} & \frac{\partial x}{\partial w} \\ \frac{\partial y}{\partial u} & \frac{\partial y}{\partial v} & \frac{\partial y}{\partial w} \\ \frac{\partial z}{\partial u} & \frac{\partial z}{\partial v} & \frac{\partial z}{\partial w} \end{vmatrix} = \begin{vmatrix} 2 & 0 & 0 \\ 0 & 3 & 0 \\ 0 & 0 & 1 \end{vmatrix} = 2[(3)(1) - (0)(0)]$$

$$+ 0[(0)(0) - (0)(1)] + 0[(0)(0) - (3)(0)] = 6$$

To find E we observe that for $\frac{x^2}{4} + \frac{y^2}{9} + z^2 = 1$ we obtain $1 = \frac{(2u)^2}{4} + \frac{(3v)^2}{9} + w^2 = u^2 + v^2 + w^2$, so that since $x \geq 0$, $y \geq 0$, and $z \geq 0$, E is the portion of the unit ball $u^2 + v^2 + w^2 \leq 1$ in the first octant. By (15),

$$\iiint_D x \, dV = \iiint_E 2u\left|\frac{\partial(x,y,z)}{\partial(u,v,w)}\right| dV = \iiint_E 12u\, dV$$

Converting to spherical coordinates with $u = \rho \sin\phi \cos\theta$, $v = \rho \sin\phi \sin\theta$, and $w = \rho\cos\phi$, we conclude from Theorem 14.11 that

$$\iiint_D x\, dV = \iiint_E 12u\, dV = \int_0^{\pi/2}\int_0^{\pi/2}\int_0^1 12\rho \sin\phi\cos\theta\,(\rho^2\sin\phi)\,d\rho\, d\phi\, d\theta$$

$$= \int_0^{\pi/2}\int_0^{\pi/2}\int_0^1 12\rho^3 \sin^2\phi \cos\theta\, d\rho\, d\phi\, d\theta$$

$$= \int_0^{\pi/2}\int_0^{\pi/2} \left(3\rho^4\Big|_0^1\right)\sin^2\phi \cos\theta\, d\phi\, d\theta$$

$$= \int_0^{\pi/2}\int_0^{\pi/2} 3\left(\tfrac{1}{2} - \tfrac{1}{2}\cos 2\phi\right)\cos\theta\, d\phi\, d\theta$$

$$= \int_0^{\pi/2} 3\left(\tfrac{\phi}{2} - \tfrac{1}{4}\sin 2\phi\right)\Big|_0^{\pi/2} \cos\theta\, d\theta = \int_0^{\pi/2} \tfrac{3\pi}{4}\cos\theta\, d\theta$$

$$= \tfrac{3\pi}{4}\sin\theta\Big|_0^{\pi/2} = \tfrac{3\pi}{4}$$

17. First,

$$\frac{\partial(x,y,z)}{\partial(u,v,w)} = \begin{vmatrix} \frac{\partial x}{\partial u} & \frac{\partial x}{\partial v} & \frac{\partial x}{\partial w} \\ \frac{\partial y}{\partial u} & \frac{\partial y}{\partial v} & \frac{\partial y}{\partial w} \\ \frac{\partial z}{\partial u} & \frac{\partial z}{\partial v} & \frac{\partial z}{\partial w} \end{vmatrix} = \begin{vmatrix} -\frac{v}{u^2}\cos w & \frac{1}{u}\cos w & -\frac{v}{u}\sin w \\ -\frac{v}{u^2}\sin w & \frac{1}{u}\sin w & \frac{v}{u}\cos w \\ 0 & 2v & 0 \end{vmatrix}$$

$$= -\frac{v}{u^2}\cos w\left[\left(\tfrac{1}{u}\sin w\right)(0) - \left(\tfrac{v}{u}\cos w\right)(2v)\right]$$

$$+ \frac{1}{u}\cos w\left[\left(\tfrac{v}{u}\cos w\right)(0) - \left(-\tfrac{v}{u^2}\sin w\right)(0)\right]$$

$$- \frac{v}{u}\sin w\left[\left(-\tfrac{v}{u^2}\sin w\right)(2v) - \left(\tfrac{1}{u}\sin w\right)(0)\right]$$

$$= \frac{2v^3}{u^3}\cos^2 w + \frac{2v^3}{u^3}\sin^2 w = \frac{2v^3}{u^3}$$

To find E we observe that for $z = x^2 + y^2$ we have $v^2 = \left(\frac{v}{u}\cos w\right)^2 + \left(\frac{v}{u}\sin w\right)^2 = \frac{v^2}{u^2}$, so since $u > 0$ and $1 \le z = v^2 \le 4$ by hypothesis, $u = 1$; similarly, for $z = 4(x^2 + y^2)$ we have $u = 2$; for $z = 1$ we have $v^2 = 1$, so $v = 1$; similarly, for $z = 4$ we have $v = 2$. Consequently E is the solid region in space bounded by the planes $u = 1$, $u = 2$, $v = 1$, and $v = 2$, and such that $0 \le w \le \pi/2$. By (15),

$$\iiint_D (x^2 + y^2)\, dV = \iiint_E \left[\left(\tfrac{v}{u}\cos w\right)^2 + \left(\tfrac{v}{u}\sin w\right)^2\right]\left|\frac{\partial(x,y,z)}{\partial(u,v,w)}\right| dV$$

$$= \iiint_E \frac{v^2}{u^2}\frac{2v^3}{u^3}\, dV = \int_0^{\pi/2}\int_1^2\int_1^2 2\frac{v^5}{u^5}\, du\, dv\, dw$$

$$= \int_0^{\pi/2}\int_1^2 \left(2v^5\left(-\frac{1}{4u^4}\right)\Big|_1^2\right) dv\, dw = \int_0^{\pi/2}\int_1^2 \frac{15}{32}v^5\, dv\, dw$$

$$= \int_0^{\pi/2} \frac{5}{64}v^6\Big|_1^2\, dw = \int_0^{\pi/2}\frac{315}{64}\, dw = \frac{315}{128}\pi$$

18. Let T_R be defined by $u = 2x - y$ and $v = x + 3y$. To find S we observe that for $2x - y = 1$ we have $u = 1$; for $2x - y = -2$ we have $u = -2$; for $x + 3y = 0$ we have $v = 0$; for $x + 3y = 1$ we have $v = 1$. Consequently S is the rectangular region in the uv plane bounded by the lines $u = -2$, $u = 1$, $v = 0$ and $v = 1$. Solving for x and y, we find that $u - 2v = (2x - y) - 2(x + 3y) = -7y$, so $y = -\frac{1}{7}(u - 2v)$, and $3u + v = 3(2x - y) + (x + 3y) = 7x$, so $x = \frac{1}{7}(3u + v)$. Then T is defined by $x = \frac{1}{7}(3u + v)$ and $y = -\frac{1}{7}(u - 2v)$. Thus

$$\frac{\partial(x,y)}{\partial(u,v)} = \begin{vmatrix} \frac{\partial x}{\partial u} & \frac{\partial x}{\partial v} \\ \frac{\partial y}{\partial u} & \frac{\partial y}{\partial v} \end{vmatrix} = \begin{vmatrix} \frac{3}{7} & \frac{1}{7} \\ -\frac{1}{7} & \frac{2}{7} \end{vmatrix} = \left(\tfrac{3}{7}\right)\left(\tfrac{2}{7}\right) - \left(\tfrac{1}{7}\right)\left(-\tfrac{1}{7}\right) = \tfrac{1}{7}$$

By (9),

$$\iint_R 49x^2y\, dA = \iint_S 49\left[\tfrac{1}{7}(3u + v)\right]^2\left[-\tfrac{1}{7}(u - 2v)\right]\left|\frac{\partial(x,y)}{\partial(u,v)}\right| dA$$

$$= \int_0^1\int_{-2}^1 49\left[\tfrac{1}{7}(3u + v)\right]^2\left[-\tfrac{1}{7}(u - 2v)\right]\left(\tfrac{1}{7}\right) du\, dv$$

$$= \int_0^1 \int_{-2}^1 \frac{1}{49}\left(-\frac{9}{4}u^4 + 4u^3v + \frac{11}{2}u^2v^2 + 2uv^3\right)\Big|_{-2}^1 dv$$

$$= \int_0^1 \frac{1}{49}\left(\frac{135}{4} + 36v - \frac{33}{2}v^2 + 6v^3\right) dv$$

$$= \frac{1}{49}\left(\frac{135}{4}v + 18v^2 - \frac{11}{2}v^3 + \frac{3}{2}v^4\right)\Big|_0^1 = \frac{1}{49}\left(\frac{191}{4}\right) = \frac{191}{196}$$

19. Let T_R be defined by $u = x - 2y$ and $v = x + 2y$. To find S we observe that for $x - 2y = 1$ we have $u = 1$; for $x - 2y = 2$ we have $u = 2$; for $x + 2y = 1$ we have $v = 1$; for $x + 2y = 3$ we have $v = 3$. Consequently S is the rectangular region in the uv plane bounded by the lines $u = 1$, $u = 2$, $v = 1$ and $v = 3$. Next,

$$\frac{\partial(u,v)}{\partial(x,y)} = \begin{vmatrix} \frac{\partial u}{\partial x} & \frac{\partial u}{\partial y} \\ \frac{\partial v}{\partial x} & \frac{\partial v}{\partial y} \end{vmatrix} = \begin{vmatrix} 1 & -2 \\ 1 & 2 \end{vmatrix} = (1)(2) - (-2)(1) = 4$$

By (9) and (14),

$$\iint_R \left(\frac{x - 2y}{x + 2y}\right)^3 dA = \iint_S \left(\frac{u}{v}\right)^3 \left|\frac{\partial(x,y)}{\partial(u,v)}\right| dA = \int_1^3 \int_1^2 \frac{u^3}{v^3}\frac{1}{4}\,du\,dv$$

$$= \int_1^3 \frac{1}{v^3}\frac{u^4}{16}\Big|_1^2 dv = \int_1^3 \frac{15}{16}\frac{1}{v^3}\,dv = -\frac{15}{32}\frac{1}{v^2}\Big|_1^3 = -\frac{15}{32}\left(\frac{1}{9} - 1\right)$$

$$= \frac{5}{12}$$

20. Let T_R be defined by $u = x/4$ and $v = y/5$. To find S we observe that for $\frac{x^2}{16} + \frac{y^2}{25} = 1$ we have $u^2 + v^2 = 1$, so that S is the unit disk $u^2 + v^2 \le 1$ in the uv plane. Next,

$$\frac{\partial(u,v)}{\partial(x,y)} = \begin{vmatrix} \frac{\partial u}{\partial x} & \frac{\partial u}{\partial y} \\ \frac{\partial v}{\partial x} & \frac{\partial v}{\partial y} \end{vmatrix} = \begin{vmatrix} \frac{1}{4} & 0 \\ 0 & \frac{1}{5} \end{vmatrix} = \left(\frac{1}{4}\right)\left(\frac{1}{5}\right) - (0)(0) = \frac{1}{20}$$

By (9) and (14),

$$\iint_R \left(1 + \frac{x^2}{16} + \frac{y^2}{25}\right)^{3/2} dA = \iint_S (1 + u^2 + v^2)^{3/2} \left|\frac{\partial(x,y)}{\partial(u,v)}\right| dA$$

$$= \iint_S (1 + u^2 + v^2)^{3/2}\, 20\, dA$$

Converting to polar coordinates with $u = r\cos\theta$ and $v = r\sin\theta$, we find that

$$\iint_R \left(1 + \frac{x^2}{16} + \frac{y^2}{25}\right)^{3/2} dA = \iint_S 20(1 + u^2 + v^2)^{3/2}\, dA$$

$$= \int_0^{2\pi}\int_0^1 20(1 + r^2)^{3/2}\, r\,dr\,d\theta = \int_0^{2\pi} 20\left(\frac{1}{5}\right)(1 + r^2)^{5/2}\Big|_0^1 d\theta$$

$$= \int_0^{2\pi} 4(4\sqrt{2} - 1)\,d\theta = 8\pi(4\sqrt{2} - 1)$$

21. Let T_R be defined by $u = x/a$ and $v = y/b$. To find S we observe that for $\frac{x^2}{a^2} + \frac{y^2}{b^2} = 1$ we have $u^2 + v^2 = 1$, so that S is the unit disk $u^2 + v^2 \le 1$ in the uv plane. Next,

$$\frac{\partial(u,v)}{\partial(x,y)} = \begin{vmatrix} \frac{\partial u}{\partial x} & \frac{\partial u}{\partial y} \\ \frac{\partial v}{\partial x} & \frac{\partial v}{\partial y} \end{vmatrix} = \begin{vmatrix} \frac{1}{a} & 0 \\ 0 & \frac{1}{b} \end{vmatrix} = \left(\frac{1}{a}\right)\left(\frac{1}{b}\right) - (0)(0) = \frac{1}{ab}$$

Solving for x in terms of a, we have $x = au$. Then by (9) and (14),

$$\iint_R x^2\,dA = \iint_S (au)^2 \left|\frac{\partial(x,y)}{\partial(u,v)}\right| dA = \iint_S a^2u^2(ab)\,dA$$

$$= \iint_S a^3bu^2\,dA$$

Converting to polar coordinates with $u = r\cos\theta$ and $v = r\sin\theta$, we find that

$$\iint_R x^2\,dA = \iint_S a^3bu^2\,dA = \int_0^{2\pi}\int_0^1 a^3b(r^2\cos^2\theta)r\,dr\,d\theta$$

$$= \int_0^{2\pi} a^3b(\cos^2\theta)\frac{r^4}{4}\Big|_0^1 d\theta = \int_0^{2\pi}\frac{a^3b}{4}\cos^2\theta\,d\theta$$

$$= \int_0^{2\pi}\frac{a^3b}{4}\left(\frac{1}{2} + \frac{1}{2}\cos 2\theta\right)d\theta = \frac{a^3b}{4}\left(\frac{\theta}{2} + \frac{1}{4}\sin 2\theta\right)\Big|_0^{2\pi} = \frac{a^3b\pi}{4}$$

22. Let T_R be defined by $u = x$ and $v = 2y$. To find S we observe that for $x^2 + 4y^2 = 1$ we have $u^2 + v^2 = 1$, so S is the semicircular region in the uv plane bounded

by $u^2 + v^2 = 1$ and $v = 0$. Next

$$\frac{\partial(u,v)}{\partial(x,y)} = \begin{vmatrix} \frac{\partial u}{\partial x} & \frac{\partial u}{\partial y} \\ \frac{\partial v}{\partial x} & \frac{\partial v}{\partial y} \end{vmatrix} = \begin{vmatrix} 1 & 0 \\ 0 & 2 \end{vmatrix} = (1)(2) - (0)(0) = 2$$

By (9) and (14),

$$\iint_R \cos(x^2 + 4y^2 + \pi - 1)\, dA = \iint_S \cos(u^2 + v^2 + \pi - 1)\left|\frac{\partial(x,y)}{\partial(u,v)}\right| dA$$

$$= \iint_S \cos(u^2 + v^2 + \pi - 1)\left(\tfrac{1}{2}\right) dA$$

Converting to polar coordinates with $u = r\cos\theta$ and $v = r\sin\theta$, we find that

$$\iint_R \cos(x^2 + 4y^2 + \pi - 1)\, dA = \iint_S \tfrac{1}{2}\cos(u^2 + v^2 + \pi - 1)\, dA$$

$$= \int_0^{\pi}\int_0^1 \tfrac{1}{2}[\cos(r^2 + \pi - 1)]\, r\, dr\, d\theta$$

$$= \int_0^{\pi} \tfrac{1}{4}\sin(r^2 + \pi - 1)\Big|_0^1 d\theta = \int_0^{\pi} -\tfrac{1}{4}\sin(\pi - 1)\, d\theta$$

$$= -\tfrac{\pi}{4}\sin(\pi - 1) = -\tfrac{\pi}{4}\sin 1$$

23. Let T_R be defined by $u = y - x$ and $v = y + x$. To find S we observe that for $x + y = 1$ we have $v = 1$; for $x + y = 2$ we have $v = 2$; for $x = 0$ we have $u = y$ and $v = y$, so that $u = v$; for $y = 0$ we have $u = -x$ and $v = x$, so that $u = -v$. Consequently S is the trapezoidal region region in the uv plane bounded by the lines $v = 1$, $v = 2$, $u = v$ and $u = -v$ (see the figure). Next,

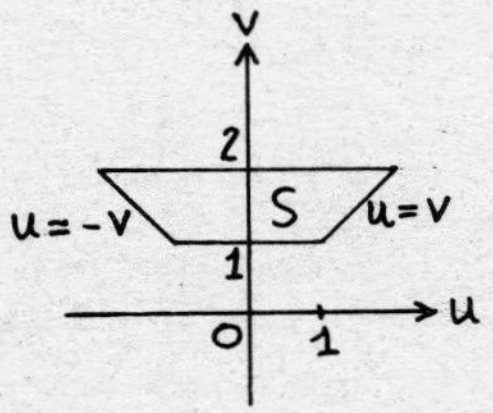

$$\frac{\partial(u,v)}{\partial(x,y)} = \begin{vmatrix} \frac{\partial u}{\partial x} & \frac{\partial u}{\partial y} \\ \frac{\partial v}{\partial x} & \frac{\partial v}{\partial y} \end{vmatrix} = \begin{vmatrix} -1 & 1 \\ 1 & 1 \end{vmatrix} = (-1)(1) - (1)(1) = -2$$

By (9) and (14),

$$\iint_R \sin\left[\pi\left(\frac{y-x}{y+x}\right)\right] dA = \iint_S \sin\left(\pi\frac{u}{v}\right)\left|\frac{\partial(x,y)}{\partial(u,v)}\right| dA$$

$$= \int_1^2\int_{-v}^{v} \tfrac{1}{2}\sin\left(\pi\frac{u}{v}\right) du\, dv = \int_1^2 -\frac{v}{2\pi}\cos\left(\pi\frac{u}{v}\right)\Big|_{-v}^{v} dv$$

$$= \int_1^2 -\frac{v}{2\pi}(\cos\pi - \cos(-\pi))\, dv = \int_1^2 0\, dv = 0$$

24. From the figure we see that ℓ_1, ℓ_2, ℓ_3, and ℓ_4 are given by $x - y = \pi$, $x + y = 3\pi$, $x - y = -\pi$, and $x + y = \pi$, respectively. Let T_R be defined by $u = x + y$ and $v = x - y$. To find S we observe that for $x - y = \pi$ we have $v = \pi$; for $x + y = 3\pi$ we have $u = 3\pi$; for $x - y = -\pi$ we have $v = -\pi$; for $x + y = \pi$ we have $u = \pi$. Consequently S is the square region in the uv plane bounded by the lines $u = \pi$, $u = 3\pi$, $v = -\pi$ and $v = \pi$. Next,

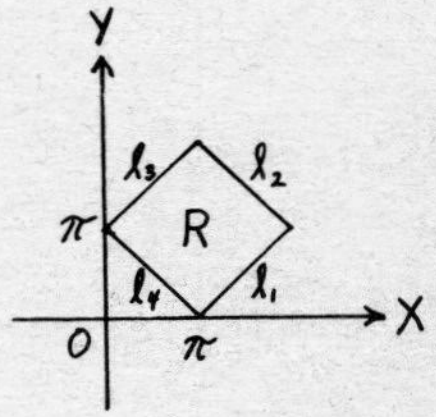

$$\frac{\partial(u,v)}{\partial(x,y)} = \begin{vmatrix} \frac{\partial u}{\partial x} & \frac{\partial u}{\partial y} \\ \frac{\partial v}{\partial x} & \frac{\partial v}{\partial y} \end{vmatrix} = \begin{vmatrix} 1 & 1 \\ 1 & -1 \end{vmatrix} = (1)(-1) - (1)(1) = -2$$

By (9) and (14),

$$\iint_R (x - y)^2\sin^2(x + y)\, dA = \iint_S v^2\sin^2 u\left|\frac{\partial(x,y)}{\partial(u,v)}\right| dA$$

$$= \int_{\pi}^{3\pi}\int_{-\pi}^{\pi} \tfrac{1}{2}v^2\sin^2 u\, dv\, du = \int_{\pi}^{3\pi} (\sin^2 u)\left(\tfrac{1}{6}v^3\right)\Big|_{-\pi}^{\pi} du$$

$$= \int_{\pi}^{3\pi} \frac{\pi^3}{3}\sin^2 u\, du = \int_{\pi}^{3\pi} \frac{\pi^3}{3}\left(\tfrac{1}{2} - \tfrac{1}{2}\cos 2u\right) du$$

$$= \frac{\pi^3}{3}\left(\frac{u}{2} - \tfrac{1}{4}\sin 2u\right)\Big|_{\pi}^{3\pi} = \frac{\pi^4}{3}$$

25. Let T_R be defined by $u = 2x - y$ and $v = x + y$. To find S, we observe that for $y = 2x$ we have $2x - y = 0$, so that

$u = 0$; for $x + y = 1$ we have $v = 1$; for $x + y = 2$ we have $v = 2$. For $x = 2y$ we solve for x and y in terms of u and v to obtain $u + v = (2x - y) + (x + y) = 3x$, so that $x = \frac{1}{3}(u + v)$, and $2v - u = 2(x + y) - (2x - y) = 3y$, so that $y = \frac{1}{3}(2v - u)$. Thus for $x = 2y$ we have $\frac{1}{3}(u + v) = \frac{2}{3}(2v - u)$, so that $u = v$. Consequently S is the trapezoidal region in the uv plane bounded by the lines $u = 0$, $v = 1$, $v = 2$ and $u = v$ (see the figure). Next,

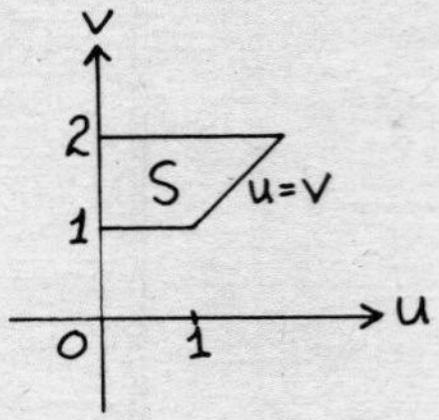

$$\frac{\partial(x,y)}{\partial(u,v)} = \begin{vmatrix} \frac{\partial x}{\partial u} & \frac{\partial x}{\partial v} \\ \frac{\partial y}{\partial u} & \frac{\partial y}{\partial v} \end{vmatrix} = \begin{vmatrix} \frac{1}{3} & \frac{1}{3} \\ -\frac{1}{3} & \frac{2}{3} \end{vmatrix} = (\tfrac{1}{3})(\tfrac{2}{3}) - (\tfrac{1}{3})(-\tfrac{1}{3}) = \frac{1}{3}$$

By (9),

$$\iint_R e^{(2x-y)/(x+y)}\, dA = \iint_S e^{u/v} \left|\frac{\partial(x,y)}{\partial(u,v)}\right| dA = \int_1^2 \int_0^v e^{u/v} \frac{1}{3}\, du\, dv$$

$$= \int_1^2 \frac{v}{3} e^{u/v} \Big|_0^v dv = \int_1^2 \frac{e - 1}{3} v\, dv = \frac{1}{6}(e - 1)v^2 \Big|_1^2 = \frac{1}{2}(e - 1)$$

26. First, $A = \iint_R 1\, dA$. Next,

$$\frac{\partial(x,y)}{\partial(u,v)} = \begin{vmatrix} \frac{\partial x}{\partial u} & \frac{\partial x}{\partial v} \\ \frac{\partial y}{\partial u} & \frac{\partial y}{\partial v} \end{vmatrix} = \begin{vmatrix} \frac{1}{v} & -\frac{u}{v^2} \\ 0 & 1 \end{vmatrix} = \frac{1}{v}$$

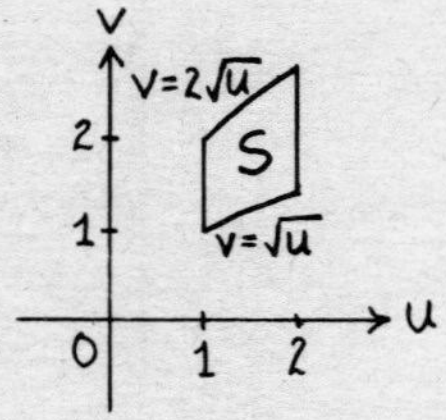

To find S we observe that for $xy = 1$ we have $\frac{u}{v} v = 1$, or $u = 1$; for $xy = 2$ we have $\frac{u}{v} v = 2$, or $u = 2$; for $y = x$ we have $v = \frac{u}{v}$, so since $u > 0$ and $v > 0$, we have $v = \sqrt{u}$; for $y = 4x$ we have $v = 4\frac{u}{v}$, so since $u > 0$ and $v > 0$, we have $v = 2\sqrt{u}$. Consequently S is the region in the uv plane bounded by the lines $u = 1$ and $u = 2$, and the parabolas $v = \sqrt{u}$ and $v = 2\sqrt{u}$ (see the figure). By (9) and (14),

$$A = \iint_R 1\, dA = \iint_S \left|\frac{\partial(x,y)}{\partial(u,v)}\right| dA = \int_1^2 \int_{\sqrt{u}}^{2\sqrt{u}} \frac{1}{v}\, dv\, du$$

$$= \int_1^2 \ln v \Big|_{\sqrt{u}}^{2\sqrt{u}} du = \int_1^2 (\ln 2\sqrt{u} - \ln \sqrt{u})\, du$$

$$= \int_1^2 \ln 2\, du = \ln 2$$

27. First, $A = \iint_R 1\, dA$. Next,

$$\frac{\partial(x,y)}{\partial(u,v)} = \begin{vmatrix} \frac{\partial x}{\partial u} & \frac{\partial x}{\partial v} \\ \frac{\partial y}{\partial u} & \frac{\partial x}{\partial v} \end{vmatrix} = \begin{vmatrix} \cosh v & u \sinh v \\ \sinh v & u \cosh v \end{vmatrix}$$

$$= (\cosh v)(u \cosh v) - (u \sinh v)(\sinh v) = u$$

Since $a > 0$, we have $x^2 \geq x^2 - y^2 \geq a^2 > 0$, so that $u > 0$.

To find S we observe that for $x^2 - y^2 = a^2$ we have $a^2 = u^2\cosh^2 v - u^2\sinh^2 v = u^2$, so since $a \geq 0$ and $u \geq 0$ we have $u = a$; similarly, if $x^2 - y^2 = b^2$ we have $u = b$; for $y = 0$ we have $0 = u \sinh v$, so since $u \geq 0$ we have $v = 0$; for $y = \frac{1}{2}x$ we have $u \sinh v = \frac{1}{2} u \cosh v$, so since $u > 0$ we have $\sinh v = \frac{1}{2}\cosh v$, so that $e^v - e^{-v} = \frac{1}{2}(e^v + e^{-v})$, or $\frac{1}{2}e^v = \frac{3}{2}e^{-v}$, or $e^{2v} = 3$, or $v = \frac{1}{2}\ln 3$. Consequently S is the rectangular region in the uv plane bounded by the lines $u = a$, $u = b$, $v = 0$ and $v = \frac{1}{2}\ln 3$. By (9) and (14),

$$A = \iint_R 1\, dA = \iint_S \left|\frac{\partial(x,y)}{\partial(u,v)}\right| dA = \int_a^b \int_0^{(1/2)\ln 3} u\, dv\, du$$

$$= \int_a^b \frac{1}{2}(\ln 3)\, u\, du = \frac{1}{2}(\ln 3) \frac{u^2}{2}\Big|_a^b = \frac{1}{4}(b^2 - a^2) \ln 3$$

28. First, note that $V = \iiint_D 1\,dV$. Next, let $x = u$, $y = \frac{1}{\sqrt{2}}v$, and $z = \frac{1}{2}w$. Then

$$\frac{\partial(x,y,z)}{\partial(u,v,w)} = \begin{vmatrix} \frac{\partial x}{\partial u} & \frac{\partial x}{\partial v} & \frac{\partial x}{\partial z} \\ \frac{\partial y}{\partial u} & \frac{\partial y}{\partial v} & \frac{\partial y}{\partial w} \\ \frac{\partial z}{\partial u} & \frac{\partial z}{\partial v} & \frac{\partial z}{\partial w} \end{vmatrix} = \begin{vmatrix} 1 & 0 & 0 \\ 0 & \frac{1}{\sqrt{2}} & 0 \\ 0 & 0 & 2 \end{vmatrix} = \sqrt{2}$$

and E is the unit ball in uvw space, with volume $\frac{4}{3}\pi$. Thus by (15),

$$V = \iiint_D 1\,dV = \iiint_E 1 \left|\frac{\partial(x,y,z)}{\partial(u,v,w)}\right| dV = \iiint_E \sqrt{2}\,dV$$

$$= \sqrt{2}\left(\frac{4}{3}\pi\right) = \frac{4}{3}\sqrt{2}\,\pi$$

Chapter 14 - Review

1. $\int_0^1 \int_x^{3x} ye^{(x^3)}\,dy\,dx = \int_0^1 \frac{y^2}{2} e^{(x^3)} \Big|_x^{3x} dx = \int_0^1 4x^2 e^{(x^3)}\,dx$

$$= \frac{4}{3} e^{(x^3)} \Big|_0^1 = \frac{4}{3}(e - 1)$$

2. $\int_0^{\sqrt{\pi}} \int_0^x \sin x^2\,dy\,dx = \int_0^{\sqrt{\pi}} y \sin x^2 \Big|_0^x dx = \int_0^{\sqrt{\pi}} x \sin x^2\,dx$

$$= \frac{-1}{2} \cos x^2 \Big|_0^{\sqrt{\pi}} = 1$$

3. $\int_{-1}^1 \int_0^2 \int_{2x}^{5x} e^{xy}\,dz\,dy\,dx = \int_{-1}^1 \int_0^2 z\,e^{xy} \Big|_{2x}^{5x} dy\,dx$

$$= \int_{-1}^1 \int_0^2 3x\,e^{xy}\,dy\,dx = \int_{-1}^1 3e^{xy} \Big|_0^2 dx = \int_{-1}^1 3(e^{2x} - 1)dx$$

$$= \left(\frac{3}{2} e^{2x} - 3x\right)\Big|_{-1}^1 = \frac{3}{2}(e^2 - e^{-2}) - 6$$

4. $\int_1^e \int_0^x \int_0^{1/(x+y)} \ln(x + y)dz\,dy\,dx = \int_1^e \int_0^x z \ln(x + y)\Big|_0^{1/(x+y)} dy\,dx$

$$= \int_1^e \int_0^x \frac{\ln(x + y)}{x + y}\,dy\,dx = \int_1^e \frac{1}{2}[\ln(x + y)]^2\Big|_0^x dx$$

$$= \frac{1}{2}\int_1^e [(\ln 2x)^2 - (\ln x)^2]dx$$

$$= \frac{1}{2}\int_1^e [(\ln 2 + \ln x)^2 - (\ln x)^2]dx$$

$$= \frac{1}{2}\int_1^e [(\ln 2)^2 + 2 \ln 2 \ln x]dx$$

$$= \frac{1}{2}\int_1^e (\ln 2)^2 dx + \ln 2 \int_1^e \ln x\,dx$$

parts

$$= \frac{1}{2}(\ln 2)^2 x \Big|_1^e + (\ln 2)(x \ln x)\Big|_1^e - \ln 2 \int_1^e 1\,dx$$

$$= \frac{1}{2}(\ln 2)^2(e-1) + e\ln 2 - (\ln 2)(e-1)$$

$$= \frac{1}{2}(e-1)(\ln 2)(\ln 2 - 2) + e\ln 2$$

5. The region R of integration is the vertically simple region between the graphs of $y = \sqrt{x}$ and $y = 1$ on $[0,1]$. It is also the horizontally simple region between the graphs of $x = 0$ and $x = y^2$ on $[0,1]$. Thus

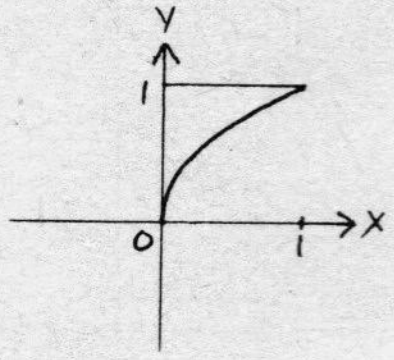

$$\int_0^1 \int_{\sqrt{x}}^1 e^{(y^3)}\,dy\,dx = \int_0^1 \int_0^{y^2} e^{(y^3)}\,dx\,dy$$

$$= \int_0^1 xe^{(y^3)}\Big|_0^{y^2} dy = \int_0^1 y^2 e^{(y^3)}\,dy = \frac{1}{3}e^{(y^3)}\Big|_0^1 = \frac{1}{3}(e-1)$$

6. The region R of integration is the horizontally simple region between the graphs of $x = \sqrt{y}$ and $x = 3$ on $[1,9]$. It is also the vertically simple region between the graphs of $y = 1$ and $y = x^2$ on $[1,3]$. Thus

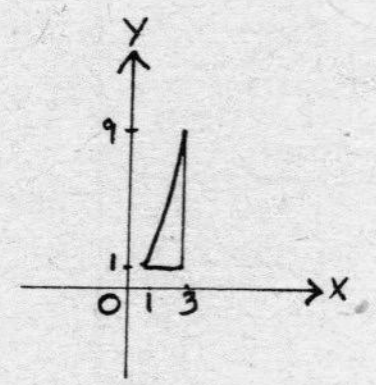

$$\int_1^9 \int_{\sqrt{y}}^3 \frac{e^{(x^2-2x)}}{x+1}\,dx\,dy = \int_1^3 \int_1^{x^2} \frac{e^{(x^2-2x)}}{x+1}\,dy\,dx = \int_1^3 \frac{ye^{(x^2-2x)}}{x+1}\Bigg|_1^{x^2} dx$$

$$= \int_1^3 (x-1)e^{(x^2-2x)}\,dx$$

$$= \frac{1}{2}e^{(x^2-2x)}\Big|_1^3 = \frac{1}{2}(e^3 - e^{-1})$$

7. The region R of integration is the vertically simple region between the graphs of $y = x$ and $y = \sqrt{3}$ on $[1,\sqrt{3}]$. It is also the horizontally simple region between the graphs of $x = 1$ and $x = y$ on $[1,\sqrt{3}]$. Thus

$$\int_1^{\sqrt{3}} \int_x^{\sqrt{3}} \frac{x}{(x^2+y^2)^{3/2}}\,dy\,dx$$

$$= \int_1^{\sqrt{3}} \int_1^y \frac{x}{(x^2+y^2)^{3/2}}\,dx\,dy$$

$$= \int_1^{\sqrt{3}} \frac{-1}{(x^2+y^2)^{1/2}}\Bigg|_1^y dy$$

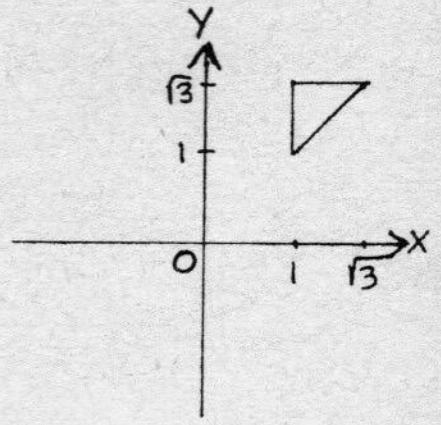

$$= \int_1^{\sqrt{3}} \left[\frac{1}{(1+y^2)^{1/2}} - \frac{1}{\sqrt{2}\,y}\right] dy$$

$$= \int_1^{\sqrt{3}} \frac{1}{(1+y^2)^{1/2}}\,dy - \frac{\sqrt{2}}{2}\int_1^{\sqrt{3}} \frac{1}{y}\,dy$$

$$\overset{y=\tan u}{=} \int_{\pi/4}^{\pi/3} \sec u\,du - \frac{\sqrt{2}}{2}\ln y\Big|_1^{\sqrt{3}}$$

$$= \ln|\sec u + \tan u|\Big|_{\pi/4}^{\pi/3} - \frac{\sqrt{2}}{2}\ln\sqrt{3}$$

$$= \ln\frac{2+\sqrt{3}}{1+\sqrt{2}} - \frac{\sqrt{2}}{4}\ln 3$$

8. The graphs of $y^2 = x$ and $y = x^3$ intersect for (x,y) such that $x = y^2 = x^6$, so that $x = 0$ or $x = 1$. Since $\sqrt{x} \ge x^3$ for $0 \le x \le 1$, we have

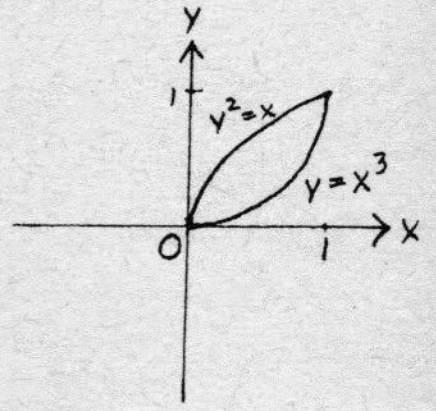

$$A = \int_0^1 \int_{x^3}^{\sqrt{x}} 1\,dy\,dx = \int_0^1 y\Big|_{x^3}^{\sqrt{x}} dx$$

$$= \int_0^1 (\sqrt{x} - x^3)\,dx = \left(\frac{2}{3}x^{3/2} - \frac{1}{4}x^4\right)\Big|_0^1 = \frac{5}{12}$$

9. The graphs of $\sqrt{x} + \sqrt{y} = \sqrt{a}$ and $x + y = a$ intersect for (x,y) such that $a - x = y = (\sqrt{a} - \sqrt{x})^2 = a + x - 2\sqrt{a}\sqrt{x}$, so that $x = \sqrt{a}\,\sqrt{x}$, and thus $x = 0$ or $x = a$. Since $a - x \ge (\sqrt{a} - \sqrt{x})^2$ for $0 \le x \le a$, we have

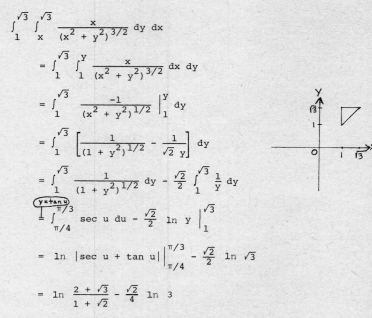

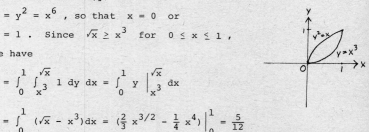

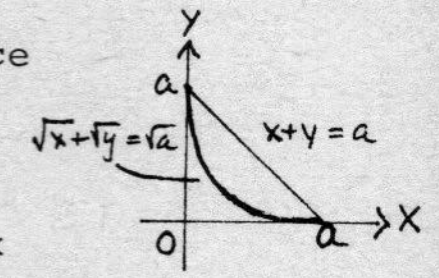

$$A = \int_0^a \int_{(\sqrt{a}-\sqrt{x})^2}^{a-x} 1\,dy\,dx = \int_0^a y\Big|_{(\sqrt{a}-\sqrt{x})^2}^{a-x} dx$$

$$= \int_0^a [(a - x) - (a + x - 2\sqrt{a}\sqrt{x})]dx = \int_0^a (-2x + 2\sqrt{a}\sqrt{x})dx$$

$$= (-x^2 + \frac{4}{3}\sqrt{a}\, x^{3/2})\Big|_0^a = \frac{1}{3}a^2$$

10. The two cardioids intersect for (r,θ) such that $1 + \sin\theta = r = 1 + \cos\theta$, so that $\sin\theta = \cos\theta$, and thus $\theta = \frac{\pi}{4}$ or $\frac{5\pi}{4}$. Therefore

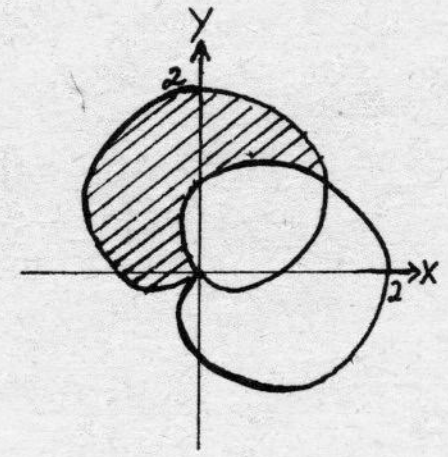

$$A = \int_{\pi/4}^{5\pi/4} \int_{1+\cos\theta}^{1+\sin\theta} r\, dr\, d\theta$$

$$= \int_{\pi/4}^{5\pi/4} \frac{1}{2} r^2 \Big|_{1+\cos\theta}^{1+\sin\theta} d\theta$$

$$= \int_{\pi/4}^{5\pi/4} [\sin\theta - \cos\theta + \frac{1}{2}(\sin^2\theta - \cos^2\theta)]d\theta$$

$$= \int_{\pi/4}^{5\pi/4} (\sin\theta - \cos\theta - \frac{1}{2}\cos 2\theta)d\theta$$

$$= (-\cos\theta - \sin\theta - \frac{1}{4}\sin 2\theta)\Big|_{\pi/4}^{5\pi/4} = 2\sqrt{2}$$

11. The limaçon and the circle intersect for (r,θ) such that $3 - \sin\theta = r = 5\sin\theta$, so that $\sin\theta = \frac{1}{2}$, and thus $\theta = \frac{\pi}{6}$ or $\theta = \frac{5\pi}{6}$. Therefore

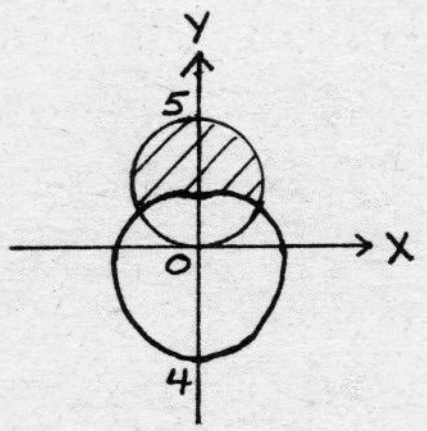

$$A = \int_{\pi/6}^{5\pi/6} \int_{3-\sin\theta}^{5\sin\theta} r\, dr\, d\theta$$

$$= \int_{\pi/6}^{5\pi/6} \frac{1}{2} r^2 \Big|_{3-\sin\theta}^{5\sin\theta} d\theta$$

$$= \int_{\pi/6}^{5\pi/6} (12\sin^2\theta + 3\sin\theta - \frac{9}{2})d\theta$$

$$= \int_{\pi/6}^{5\pi/6} (6 - 6\cos 2\theta + 3\sin\theta - \frac{9}{2})d\theta$$

$$= (\frac{3}{2}\theta - 3\sin 2\theta - 3\cos\theta)\Big|_{\pi/6}^{5\pi/6} = \pi + 6\sqrt{3}$$

12. R is the vertically simple region between the graphs of $y = 0$ and $y = x$ on $[0,\frac{\pi}{2}]$. Thus

$$\iint_R \sin(x + y)dA = \int_0^{\pi/2} \int_0^x \sin(x + y)dy\, dx = \int_0^{\pi/2} [-\cos(x + y)]\Big|_0^x dx$$

$$= \int_0^{\pi/2} (\cos x - \cos 2x)dx = (\sin x - \frac{1}{2}\sin 2x)\Big|_0^{\pi/2} = 1$$

13. The lines $y = 5 + x$ and $y = -x + 7$ intersect for (x,y) such that $5 + x = y = -x + 7$, so that $x = 1$. Thus R is the vertically simple region between the graphs of $y = 5 + x$ and $y = -x + 7$ on $[0,1]$. Therefore

$$\iint_R (3x - 5)dA = \int_0^1 \int_{5+x}^{-x+7} (3x - 5)dy\, dx = \int_0^1 (3x - 5)y \Big|_{5+x}^{-x+7} dx$$

$$= \int_0^1 (3x - 5)(2 - 2x)dx = \int_0^1 (-6x^2 + 16x - 10)dx$$

$$= (-2x^3 + 8x^2 - 10x)\Big|_0^1 = -4$$

14. The parabolas intersect for (x,y) such that $1 + x^2 = y = 3 - x^2$, so that $x = -1$ or $x = 1$. Thus R is the vertically simple region between the graphs of $y = 1 + x^2$ and $y = 3 - x^2$ on $[-1,1]$. Therefore

$$\iint_R (4 + x^2)dA = \int_{-1}^1 \int_{1+x^2}^{3-x^2} (4 + x^2)dy\, dx = \int_{-1}^1 (4 + x^2)y \Big|_{1+x^2}^{3-x^2} dx$$

$$= \int_{-1}^1 (4 + x^2)(2 - 2x^2)dx = \int_{-1}^1 (-2x^4 - 6x^2 + 8)dx$$

$$= (\frac{-2}{5}x^5 - 2x^3 + 8x)\Big|_{-1}^1 = \frac{56}{5}$$

15. In spherical coordinates the cone has equation $\rho^2\cos^2\phi = 3\rho^2\sin^2\phi$, so that $\cot\phi = \sqrt{3}$, and thus $\phi = \frac{\pi}{6}$. Thus

D is the collection of all points with spherical coordinates (ρ,ϕ,θ) such that $0 \le \theta \le 2\pi$, $0 \le \phi \le \frac{\pi}{6}$, and $0 \le \rho \le 2$. Since $z^2 + 1 = \rho^2\cos^2\phi + 1$, we find that

$$\iiint_D (z^2 + 1)\,dV = \int_0^{2\pi}\int_0^{\pi/6}\int_0^2 (\rho^2\cos^2\phi + 1)\rho^2\sin\phi\,d\rho\,d\phi\,d\theta$$

$$= \int_0^{2\pi}\int_0^{\pi/6} \left(\frac{\rho^5}{5}\cos^2\phi\sin\phi + \frac{\rho^3}{3}\sin\phi\right)\Big|_0^2 d\phi\,d\theta$$

$$= \int_0^{2\pi}\int_0^{\pi/6} \left(\frac{32}{5}\cos^2\phi\sin\phi + \frac{8}{3}\sin\phi\right)d\phi\,d\theta$$

$$= \int_0^{2\pi} \left(\frac{-32}{15}\cos^3\phi - \frac{8}{3}\cos\phi\right)\Big|_0^{\pi/6} d\theta$$

$$= \int_0^{2\pi} \left[\frac{32}{15}\left(1 - \frac{3\sqrt{3}}{8}\right) + \frac{8}{3}\left(1 - \frac{\sqrt{3}}{2}\right)\right] d\theta = \left(\frac{72 - 32\sqrt{3}}{15}\right)2\pi$$

$$= \frac{16\pi}{15}(9 - 4\sqrt{3})$$

16. The region R in the xy plane is the horizontally simply region between the graphs of $x = 0$ and $x = \sqrt{1 - y^2}$ on $[0,1]$; D is the solid region between the graphs of $z = 0$ and $z = \sqrt{1 - x^2}$ on R . Thus

$$\iiint_D xy\,dV = \int_0^1\int_0^{\sqrt{1-y^2}}\int_0^{\sqrt{1-x^2}} xy\,dz\,dx\,dy$$

$$= \int_0^1\int_0^{\sqrt{1-y^2}} xyz\Big|_0^{\sqrt{1-x^2}} dx\,dy = \int_0^1\int_0^{\sqrt{1-y^2}} xy\sqrt{1 - x^2}\,dx\,dy$$

$$= \int_0^1 \frac{-1}{3}y(1 - x^2)^{3/2}\Big|_0^{\sqrt{1-y^2}} dy = \int_0^1 \frac{-1}{3}y(y^3 - 1)dy$$

$$= \frac{-1}{3}\int_0^1 (y^4 - y)dy = \frac{-1}{3}\left(\frac{y^5}{5} - \frac{y^2}{2}\right)\Big|_0^1 = \frac{1}{10}$$

17. The region R in the xy plane is the vertically simple circular region in the xy plane between the graphs of $y = -\sqrt{9 - x^2}$ and $y = \sqrt{9 - x^2}$ on $[-3,3]$; D is the solid region between the graphs of $z = -\sqrt{9 - x^2 - y^2}$ and $z = 0$ on R . Thus

$$\iiint_D xyz\,dV = \int_{-3}^3\int_{-\sqrt{9-x^2}}^{\sqrt{9-x^2}}\int_{-\sqrt{9-x^2-y^2}}^0 xyz\,dz\,dy\,dx$$

$$= \int_{-3}^3\int_{-\sqrt{9-x^2}}^{\sqrt{9-x^2}} \frac{1}{2}xyz^2\Big|_{-\sqrt{9-x^2-y^2}}^0 dy\,dx$$

$$= \int_{-3}^3\int_{-\sqrt{9-x^2}}^{\sqrt{9-x^2}} \frac{-1}{2}xy(9 - x^2 - y^2)dy\,dx$$

$$= \int_{-3}^3 \frac{1}{8}x(9 - x^2 - y^2)^2 \Big|_{-\sqrt{9-x^2}}^{\sqrt{9-x^2}} dx = \int_{-3}^3 0\,dx = 0$$

18. Let $f(x,y) = \frac{1}{2}y^2$. Then $f_x(x,y) = 0$ and $f_y(x,y) = y$. The portion of the parabolic sheet $z = \frac{1}{2}y^2$ cut out by the planes $y = x$, $y = 2\sqrt{2}$, and $x = 0$ lies over the horizontally simple region R in the xy plane between the graphs of $x = 0$ and $x = y$ on $[0,2\sqrt{2}]$. Thus

$$S = \iint_R \sqrt{0^2 + y^2 + 1}\,dA = \int_0^{2\sqrt{2}}\int_0^y \sqrt{y^2 + 1}\,dx\,dy$$

$$= \int_0^{2\sqrt{2}} x\sqrt{y^2 + 1}\Big|_0^y dy = \int_0^{2\sqrt{2}} y\sqrt{y^2 + 1}\,dy = \frac{1}{3}(y^2 + 1)^{3/2}\Big|_0^{2\sqrt{2}} = \frac{26}{3}$$

19. Let $f(x,y) = xy$. Then $f_x(x,y) = y$ and $f_x(x,y) = x$. The portion of the surface $z = xy$ that is inside the cylinder $x^2 + y^2 = 1$ lies over the disk R in the xy plane bounded by the circle $r = 1$. Thus

$$S = \iint_R \sqrt{y^2 + x^2 + 1}\,dA = \int_0^{2\pi}\int_0^1 \sqrt{r^2 + 1}\,r\,dr\,d\theta$$

$$= \int_0^{2\pi} \frac{1}{3}(r^2 + 1)^{3/2}\Big|_0^1 d\theta = \int_0^{2\pi} \frac{1}{3}(2\sqrt{2} - 1)d\theta = \frac{2\pi}{3}(2\sqrt{2} - 1)$$

20. Let $f(x,y) = \frac{2}{3}(x^{3/2} + y^{3/2})$. Then $f_x(x,y) = x^{1/2}$ and $f_y(x,y) = y^{1/2}$. The portion of the surface whose surface area we seek lies above the region R in the xy plane bounded by the lines $x = 0$, $y = 1$ and $x = 7y$. Thus

$$S = \iint_R \sqrt{(x^{1/2})^2 + (y^{1/2})^2 + 1}\; dA = \iint_R \sqrt{x + y + 1}\; dA$$

$$= \int_0^1 \int_0^{7y} \sqrt{x + y + 1}\, dx\, dy = \int_0^1 \frac{2}{3}(x + y + 1)^{3/2} \Big|_0^{7y} dy$$

$$= \int_0^1 \frac{2}{3}[(8y + 1)^{3/2} - (y + 1)^{3/2}]dy$$

$$= \frac{4}{15}[\tfrac{1}{8}(8y + 1)^{5/2} - (y + 1)^{5/2}]\Big|_0^1 = \frac{25}{3} - \frac{16\sqrt{2}}{15}$$

21. The paraboloid and cone intersect for (x,y,z) such that $z = x^2 + y^2 = z^2$, so that $z = 0$ or $z = 1$, and thus $x^2 + y^2 = 0$ or $x^2 + y^2 = 1$. In polar coordinates R is the region in the xy plane between the graphs of $r = 0$ and $r = 1$ on $[0,2\pi]$. Then D is the solid region between the graphs of $z = x^2 + y^2 = r^2$ and $z = \sqrt{x^2 + y^2} = r$ on R. Therefore

$$V = \iiint_D 1\, dV = \int_0^{2\pi}\int_0^1\int_{r^2}^{r} r\, dz\, dr\, d\theta = \int_0^{2\pi}\int_0^1 rz\Big|_{r^2}^{r} dr\, d\theta$$

$$= \int_0^{2\pi}\int_0^1 (r^2 - r^3)dr\, d\theta = \int_0^{2\pi}\left(\frac{r^3}{3} - \frac{r^4}{4}\right)\Big|_0^1 d\theta = \int_0^{2\pi} \frac{1}{12}\, d\theta = \frac{1}{6}\pi$$

22. The region R in the xy plane is the vertically simple region between the graphs of $y = 0$ and $y = x$ on $[0,1]$; D is the solid region between the graphs of $z = 0$ and $z = e^x$ on R. Thus

$$V = \iiint_D 1\, dV = \int_0^1\int_0^x\int_0^{e^x} 1\, dz\, dy\, dx = \int_0^1\int_0^x z\Big|_0^{e^x} dy\, dx$$

$$= \int_0^1\int_0^x e^x\, dy\, dx = \int_0^1 ye^x\Big|_0^x dx = \int_0^1 x e^x\, dx$$

(parts)

$$= x e^x\Big|_0^1 - \int_0^1 e^x\, dx = e - \left(e^x\Big|_0^1\right) = 1$$

23. In polar coordinates R is the region in the xy plane between the graphs of $r = 0$ and $r = 4 \sin\theta$ on $[0,\pi]$; D is the solid region between the graphs of $z = 0$ and $z = r$ on R. Thus

$$V = \iiint_D 1\, dV = \int_0^{\pi}\int_0^{4\sin\theta}\int_0^{r} r\, dz\, dr\, d\theta = \int_0^{\pi}\int_0^{4\sin\theta} rz\Big|_0^{r} dr\, d\theta$$

$$= \int_0^{\pi}\int_0^{4\sin\theta} r^2 dr\, d\theta = \int_0^{\pi} \frac{r^3}{3}\Big|_0^{4\sin\theta} d\theta = \int_0^{\pi} \frac{64}{3}\sin^3\theta\, d\theta$$

$$= \frac{64}{3}\int_0^{\pi}(1 - \cos^2\theta)\sin\theta\, d\theta = \frac{64}{3}\left(-\cos\theta + \frac{1}{3}\cos^3\theta\right)\Big|_0^{\pi} = \frac{256}{9}$$

24. In polar coordinates R is the region in the xy plane between the graphs of $r^2 = 5r\sin\theta$, or rather $r = 5\sin\theta$, and $r = 5$ on $[0,\frac{\pi}{2}]$; D is the solid region between the graphs of $z = 0$ and $z = \sqrt{25 - x^2 - y^2} = \sqrt{25 - r^2}$ on R. Thus

$$V = \iiint_D 1\, dV = \int_0^{\pi/2}\int_{5\sin\theta}^{5}\int_0^{\sqrt{25-r^2}} r\, dz\, dr\, d\theta$$

$$= \int_0^{\pi/2}\int_{5\sin\theta}^{5} rz\Big|_0^{\sqrt{25-r^2}} dr\, d\theta = \int_0^{\pi/2}\int_{5\sin\theta}^{5} r\sqrt{25 - r^2}\, dr\, d\theta$$

$$= \int_0^{\pi/2} \frac{-1}{3}(25 - r^2)^{3/2}\Big|_{5\sin\theta}^{5} d\theta = \int_0^{\pi/2}\frac{125}{3}\cos^3\theta\, d\theta$$

$$= \frac{125}{3}\int_0^{\pi/2}(1 - \sin^2\theta)\cos\theta\, d\theta = \frac{125}{3}\left(\sin\theta - \frac{1}{3}\sin^3\theta\right)\Big|_0^{\pi/2} = \frac{250}{9}$$

25. The paraboloid and sheet intersect for (x,y,z) such that $4x^2 + y^2 = z = 16 - 3y^2$, so that $x^2 + y^2 = 4$. In polar coordinates R is the circular region in the xy plane between the graphs of $r = 0$ and $r = 2$ on $[0,2\pi]$. Then D is the solid region between the graphs of $z = 4x^2 + y^2$ and $z = 16 - 3y^2$ on R. Thus

$$V = \iiint_D 1\, dV = \int_0^{2\pi}\int_0^{2}\int_{r^2+3r^2\cos^2\theta}^{16-3r^2\sin^2\theta} r\, dz\, dr\, d\theta$$

$$= \int_0^{2\pi}\int_0^2 rz \Big|_{r^2+3r^2\cos^2\theta}^{16-3r^2\sin^2\theta} dr\, d\theta = \int_0^{2\pi}\int_0^2 r(16-4r^2)dr\, d\theta$$

$$= \int_0^{2\pi} (8r^2 - r^4)\Big|_0^2 d\theta = \int_0^{2\pi} 16\, d\theta = 32\pi$$

26. The paraboloids intersect for (x,y,z) such that $-18 + 2x^2 + 2y^2 = z = 9 - x^2 - y^2$, so that $x^2 + y^2 = 9$. In polar coordinates R is the circular region in the xy plane between the graphs of $r = 0$ and $r = 3$ on $[0,2\pi]$. Then D is the solid region between the graphs of $z = -18 + 2r^2$ and $z = 9 - r^2$ on R. Thus

$$V = \iiint_D 1\, dV = \int_0^{2\pi}\int_0^3\int_{-18+2r^2}^{9-r^2} r\, dz\, dr\, d\theta$$

$$= \int_0^{2\pi}\int_0^3 rz\Big|_{-18+2r^2}^{9-r^2} dr\, d\theta = \int_0^{2\pi}\int_0^3 r(27-3r^2)dr\, d\theta$$

$$= \int_0^{2\pi} \left(\frac{27}{2} r^2 - \frac{3}{4} r^4\right)\Big|_0^3 d\theta = \int_0^{2\pi} \frac{243}{4}\, d\theta = \frac{243}{2}\pi$$

27. The region R in the xy plane is the horizontally simple region between the lines $x = 0$ and $x = 6 - 3y$ on $[0,2]$; D is the solid region between the graphs of $z = 0$ and $z = x + 2y$ on R. Thus

$$V = \iiint_D 1\, dV = \int_0^2\int_0^{6-3y}\int_0^{x+2y} 1\, dz\, dx\, dy$$

$$= \int_0^2\int_0^{6-3y} z\Big|_0^{x+2y} dx\, dy = \int_0^2\int_0^{6-3y} (x+2y)dx\, dy$$

$$= \int_0^2 \left(\frac{x^2}{2} + 2yx\right)\Big|_0^{6-3y} dy = \int_0^2 \left[\frac{1}{2}(6-3y)^2 + 12y - 6y^2\right]dy$$

$$= \left[\frac{-1}{18}(6-3y)^3 + 6y^2 - 2y^3\right]\Big|_0^2 = 20$$

28. The cone and the plane $z = 3$ intersect for (x,y,z) such that $x^2 + y^2 = 27$, and the angle that the line $x = \sqrt{3}\, y$ makes with the positive x axis is $\frac{\pi}{6}$. Thus in polar coordinates R is the region in the xy plane between the graphs of $r = 0$ and $r = \sqrt{27} = 3\sqrt{3}$ on $[0,\frac{\pi}{6}]$. Then D is the solid region between the graphs of $x^2 + y^2 = 3z^2$, or rather, $z = \frac{1}{\sqrt{3}}\sqrt{x^2+y^2} = \frac{1}{\sqrt{3}} r$, and $z = 3$ on R. Therefore

$$V = \iiint_D 1\, dV = \int_0^{\pi/6}\int_0^{3\sqrt{3}}\int_{r/\sqrt{3}}^3 r\, dz\, dr\, d\theta$$

$$= \int_0^{\pi/6}\int_0^{3\sqrt{3}} rz\Big|_{r/\sqrt{3}}^3 dr\, d\theta = \int_0^{\pi/6}\int_0^{3\sqrt{3}} \left(3r - \frac{r^2}{\sqrt{3}}\right)dr\, d\theta$$

$$= \int_0^{\pi/6} \left(\frac{3}{2} r^2 - \frac{r^3}{3\sqrt{3}}\right)\Big|_0^{3\sqrt{3}} d\theta = \int_0^{\pi/6} \frac{27}{2}\, d\theta = \frac{9}{4}\pi$$

29. The sphere and paraboloid intersect for (x,y,z) such that $3z + 21 = 49 - z^2$, so that $z^2 + 3z - 28 = 0$, and thus $z = -7$ or $z = 4$. If $z = -7$, then $x^2 + y^2 = 0$, so that $r = 0$, and if $z = 4$, then $x^2 + y^2 = 33$, so that $r = \sqrt{33}$. In polar coordinates R is the circular region in the xy plane between the graphs of $r = 0$ and $r = \sqrt{33}$ on $[0,2\pi]$. Then D is the solid region between the graphs of $z = \frac{1}{3} r^2 - 7$ and $z = \sqrt{49 - r^2}$ on R. Thus

$$V = \iiint_D 1\, dV = \int_0^{2\pi}\int_0^{\sqrt{33}}\int_{(r^2/3)-7}^{\sqrt{49-r^2}} r\, dz\, dr\, d\theta$$

$$= \int_0^{2\pi}\int_0^{\sqrt{33}} rz\Big|_{(r^2/3)-7}^{\sqrt{49-r^2}} dr\, d\theta = \int_0^{2\pi}\int_0^{\sqrt{33}} \left(r\sqrt{49-r^2} - \frac{1}{3}r^3 + 7r\right)dr\, d\theta$$

$$= \int_0^{2\pi} \left[\frac{-1}{3}(49-r^2)^{3/2} - \frac{1}{12} r^4 + \frac{7}{2} r^2\right]\Big|_0^{\sqrt{33}} d\theta = \int_0^{2\pi} \frac{471}{4}\, d\theta$$

$$= \frac{471}{2}\pi$$

30. In cylindrical coordinates the cylinder and paraboloid are given by $r = 6\cos\theta$ and $r^2 = 4z$. In polar coordinates R is the circular region between the graphs of $r = 0$ and $r = 6\cos\theta$ on $[-\frac{\pi}{2},\frac{\pi}{2}]$. Then D is the solid region between the graphs of $z = -2$ and $z = \frac{1}{4} r^2$. Thus

$$V = \iiint_D 1\,dV = \int_{-\pi/2}^{\pi/2} \int_0^{6\cos\theta} \int_{-2}^{r^2/4} r\,dz\,dr\,d\theta$$

$$= \int_{-\pi/2}^{\pi/2} \int_0^{6\cos\theta} rz \Big|_{-2}^{r^2/4} dr\,d\theta = \int_{-\pi/2}^{\pi/2} \int_0^{6\cos\theta} (\tfrac{1}{4}r^3 + 2r)\,dr\,d\theta$$

$$= \int_{-\pi/2}^{\pi/2} (\tfrac{1}{16}r^4 + r^2)\Big|_0^{6\cos\theta} d\theta = \int_{-\pi/2}^{\pi/2} (81\cos^4\theta + 36\cos^2\theta)\,d\theta$$

$$= \int_{-\pi/2}^{\pi/2} (81\cos^4\theta + 18 + 18\cos 2\theta)\,d\theta$$

$$= [81(\tfrac{1}{4}\cos^3\theta\sin\theta + \tfrac{3}{8}\cos\theta\sin\theta + \tfrac{3}{8}\theta) + 18\theta + 9\sin 2\theta]\Big|_{-\pi/2}^{\pi/2}$$

$$= \frac{387}{8}\pi$$

with the next to last equality coming from (15) in Section 7.1.

31. Since the region D occupied by the solid is symmetric with respect to the yz plane and the xz plane, and since $\delta(x,y,z) = z$, so that $\delta(x,y,z)$ is independent of x and y, we have $\bar{x} = \bar{y} = 0$. The cone $z = \sqrt{x^2 + y^2}$ and the plane $z = 3$ intersect for (x,y,z) such that $\sqrt{x^2 + y^2} = z = 3$, and thus $r = 3$. Consequently D is the solid region between the graphs of $z = r$ and $z = 3$ on the disk $0 \le r \le 3$. Therefore

$$\mathcal{M}_{xy} = \iiint_D z\,\delta(x,y,z)\,dV = \int_0^{2\pi} \int_0^3 \int_r^3 z^2 r\,dz\,dr\,d\theta$$

$$= \int_0^{2\pi} \int_0^3 \tfrac{1}{3} z^3 r \Big|_r^3 dr\,d\theta = \int_0^{2\pi} \int_0^3 (9r - \tfrac{1}{3}r^4)\,dr\,d\theta$$

$$= \int_0^{2\pi} (\tfrac{9}{2}r^2 - \tfrac{1}{15}r^5)\Big|_0^3 d\theta = \int_0^{2\pi} \frac{243}{10}\,d\theta = \frac{243}{5}\pi$$

Since

$$m = \iiint_D \delta(x,y,z)\,dV = \int_0^{2\pi} \int_0^3 \int_r^3 zr\,dz\,dr\,d\theta$$

$$= \int_0^{2\pi} \int_0^3 \tfrac{1}{2} z^2 r \Big|_r^3 dr\,d\theta = \int_0^{2\pi} \int_0^3 (\tfrac{9}{2}r - \tfrac{1}{2}r^3)\,dr\,d\theta$$

$$= \int_0^{2\pi} (\tfrac{9}{4}r^2 - \tfrac{1}{8}r^4)\Big|_0^3 d\theta = \int_0^{2\pi} \frac{81}{8}\,d\theta = \frac{81}{4}\pi$$

we have $\bar{z} = \dfrac{\mathcal{M}_{xy}}{m} = \dfrac{243\pi/5}{81\pi/4} = \dfrac{12}{5}$. Thus $(\bar{x},\bar{y},\bar{z}) = (0,0,\frac{12}{5})$.

32. The cylinder $x^2 + y^2 = 4$ and the cone $z = \sqrt{x^2 + y^2}$ intersect for (r,θ,z) such that $z = r = 2$. Thus the body occupies the solid region D between the graphs of $z = 0$ and $z = r$ on the disk $0 \le r \le 2$. Therefore

$$m = \iiint_D \delta(x,y,z)\,dV = \int_0^{2\pi} \int_0^2 \int_0^r (z + 3)r\,dz\,dr\,d\theta$$

$$= \int_0^{2\pi} \int_0^2 (\tfrac{1}{2}z^2 + 3z)r \Big|_0^r dr\,d\theta = \int_0^{2\pi} \int_0^2 (\tfrac{1}{2}r^3 + 3r^2)\,dr\,d\theta$$

$$= \int_0^{2\pi} (\tfrac{1}{8}r^4 + r^3)\Big|_0^2 d\theta = \int_0^{2\pi} 10\,d\theta = 20\pi$$

Since D is symmetric with respect to the yz plane and the xz plane, and since $\delta(x,y,z)$ is independent of x and y, we have $\bar{x} = \bar{y} = 0$. Now

$$\mathcal{M}_{xy} = \iiint_D z\,\delta(x,y,z)\,dV = \int_0^{2\pi} \int_0^2 \int_0^r (z^2 + 3z)r\,dz\,dr\,d\theta$$

$$= \int_0^{2\pi} \int_0^2 (\tfrac{1}{3}z^3 + \tfrac{3}{2}z^2)r \Big|_0^r dr\,d\theta = \int_0^{2\pi} \int_0^2 (\tfrac{1}{3}r^4 + \tfrac{3}{2}r^3)\,dr\,d\theta$$

$$= \int_0^{2\pi} (\tfrac{1}{15}r^5 + \tfrac{3}{8}r^4)\Big|_0^2 d\theta = \int_0^{2\pi} \frac{122}{15}\,d\theta = \frac{244}{15}\pi$$

Thus $\bar{z} = \dfrac{\mathcal{M}_{xy}}{m} = \dfrac{244\pi/15}{20\pi} = \dfrac{61}{75}$, so that $(\bar{x},\bar{y},\bar{z}) = (0,0,\frac{61}{75})$.

33. By symmetry, $\bar{x} = \bar{y} = 0$. The paraboloid $z = x^2 + y^2$ and the upper nappe of the cone $z^2 = x^2 + y^2$ intersect for (r,θ,z) such that $z = r^2 = z^2$, so that $z = 0$ or $z = 1$, and thus $r = 0$ or $r = 1$. Therefore the given region D is the solid

region between the graphs of $z = r^2$ and $z = r$ on the disk $0 \le r \le 1$. Taking $\delta = 1$, we have

$$\mathcal{M}_{xy} = \iiint_D z\,dV = \int_0^{2\pi}\int_0^1\int_{r^2}^{r} zr\,dz\,dr\,d\theta$$

$$= \int_0^{2\pi}\int_0^1 \frac{1}{2} z^2 r\,\Big|_{r^2}^{r} dr\,d\theta = \int_0^{2\pi}\int_0^1 \frac{1}{2}(r^3 - r^5)\,dr\,d\theta$$

$$= \int_0^{2\pi} \frac{1}{2}\left(\frac{1}{4} r^4 - \frac{1}{6} r^6\right)\Big|_0^1 d\theta = \int_0^{2\pi} \frac{1}{24}\,d\theta = \frac{1}{12}\pi$$

Since $\delta = 1$, we have

$$m = \iiint_D 1\,dV = \int_0^{2\pi}\int_0^1\int_{r^2}^{r} r\,dz\,dr\,d\theta = \int_0^{2\pi}\int_0^1 rz\,\Big|_{r^2}^{r} dr\,d\theta$$

$$= \int_0^{2\pi}\int_0^1 (r^2 - r^3)\,dr\,d\theta = \int_0^{2\pi}\left(\frac{1}{3} r^3 - \frac{1}{4} r^4\right)\Big|_0^1 d\theta$$

$$= \int_0^{2\pi} \frac{1}{12}\,d\theta = \frac{1}{6}\pi$$

and thus $\bar{z} = \dfrac{\mathcal{M}_{xy}}{m} = \dfrac{\pi/12}{\pi/6} = \dfrac{1}{2}$. Therefore $(\bar{x},\bar{y},\bar{z}) = (0,0,\frac{1}{2})$.

34. Since $\delta(x,y,z) = a - \sqrt{x^2 + y^2 + z^2}$, the mass m of the object is given by

$$m = \iiint_D \delta(x,y,z)\,dV = \iiint_D \left(a - \sqrt{x^2 + y^2 + z^2}\right)dV$$

$$= \int_0^{2\pi}\int_0^{\pi}\int_0^{a} (a - \rho)\rho^2 \sin\phi\,d\rho\,d\phi\,d\theta$$

$$= \int_0^{2\pi}\int_0^{\pi} \left(\frac{1}{3} a\rho^3 - \frac{1}{4}\rho^4\right)\sin\phi\,\Big|_0^a d\phi\,d\theta = \int_0^{2\pi}\int_0^{\pi} \frac{1}{12} a^4 \sin\phi\,d\phi\,d\theta$$

$$= \int_0^{2\pi} -\frac{1}{12} a^4 \cos\phi\,\Big|_0^{\pi} d\theta = \int_0^{2\pi} \frac{1}{6} a^4\,d\theta = \frac{1}{3}\pi a^4$$

35. First,

$$\frac{\partial(x,y)}{\partial(u,v)} = \begin{vmatrix} \frac{\partial x}{\partial u} & \frac{\partial x}{\partial v} \\ \frac{\partial y}{\partial u} & \frac{\partial y}{\partial v} \end{vmatrix} = \begin{vmatrix} 1 & 1 \\ \frac{-v}{(u+v)^2} & \frac{u}{(u+v)^2} \end{vmatrix}$$

$$= (1)\left(\frac{u}{(u+v)^2}\right) - (1)\left(\frac{-v}{(u+v)^2}\right) = \frac{1}{u+v}$$

To find S we observe that for $xy = 1$ we have $(u+v)\left(\frac{v}{u+v}\right) = 1$, or $v = 1$; similarly, for $xy = 2$ we have $v = 2$. For $x(1-y) = 1$ we have $(u+v)\left(1 - \frac{v}{u+v}\right) = 1$, or $u + v - v = 1$, or $u = 1$; similarly, for $x(1-y) = 2$ we have $u = 2$. Thus S is the square region in the uv plane bounded by the lines $u = 1$, $u = 2$, $v = 1$, and $v = 2$. By (9) in Section 14.8,

$$\iint_R x\,dA = \iint_S (u+v)\left|\frac{\partial(x,y)}{\partial(u,v)}\right| dA = \int_1^2\int_1^2 (u+v)\,\frac{1}{u+v}\,du\,dv$$

$$= \int_1^2\int_1^2 1\,du\,dv = 1$$

36. First,

$$\frac{\partial(x,y)}{\partial(u,v)} = \begin{vmatrix} \frac{\partial x}{\partial u} & \frac{\partial x}{\partial v} \\ \frac{\partial y}{\partial u} & \frac{\partial y}{\partial v} \end{vmatrix} = \begin{vmatrix} 2 + 2(u+v) & -1 + 2(u+v) \\ 1 & 1 \end{vmatrix}$$

$$= [2 + 2(u+v)] - [-1 + 2(u+v)] = 3$$

To find S we observe that for $x = y^2 - y$ we have $2u - v + (u+v)^2 = (u+v)^2 - (u+v)$, or $u = 0$; for $x = 2y + y^2$ we have $2u - v + (u+v)^2 = 2(u+v) + (u+v)^2$, or $v = 0$; for $y = 2$ we have $u + v = 2$. Consequently S is the triangular region in the uv plane bounded by the lines $u = 0$, $v = 0$, and $u + v = 2$. By (9) in Section 14.8,

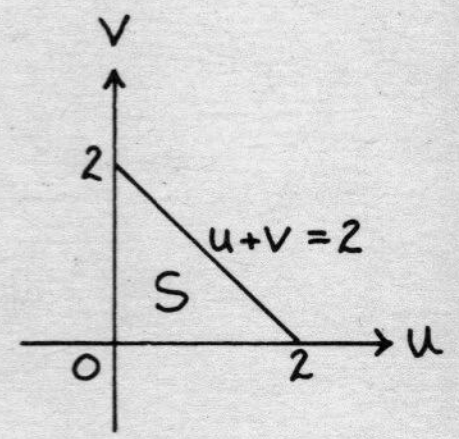

$$\iint_R (x - y^2)\, dA = \iint_S [2u - v + (u + v)^2 - (u + v)^2]\left|\frac{\partial(x,y)}{\partial(u,v)}\right| dA$$

$$= \int_0^2 \int_0^{2-u} (2u - v)\, 3\, dv\, du = \int_0^2 (6uv - \tfrac{3}{2}v^2)\Big|_0^{2-u} du$$

$$= \int_0^2 [6u(2 - u) - \tfrac{3}{2}(2 - u)^2]\, du = \int_0^2 (-\tfrac{15}{2}u^2 + 18u - 6)\, du$$

$$= (-\tfrac{5}{2}u^3 + 9u^2 - 6u)\Big|_0^2 = 4$$

37. Let T_R be defined by $u = x - y$ and $v = x + y$. To find S we observe that for $x - y = 1$ we have $u = 1$; for $x - y = 3$ we have $u = 3$; for $x + y = 2$ we have $v = 2$; for $x + y = 4$ we have $v = 4$. Consequently S is the square region in the uv plane bounded by the lines $u = 1$, $u = 3$, $v = 2$, and $v = 4$. Solving for x and y in terms of u and v, we find that $u + v = (x - y) + (x + y) = 2x$, so that $x = \frac{1}{2}(u + v)$, and $v - u = (x + y) - (x - y) = 2y$, so that $y = \frac{1}{2}(v - u)$. Then T is defined by $x = \frac{1}{2}(u + v)$ and $y = \frac{1}{2}(v - u)$. Thus

$$\frac{\partial(x,y)}{\partial(u,v)} = \begin{vmatrix} \frac{\partial x}{\partial u} & \frac{\partial x}{\partial v} \\ \frac{\partial y}{\partial u} & \frac{\partial y}{\partial v} \end{vmatrix} = \begin{vmatrix} \frac{1}{2} & \frac{1}{2} \\ -\frac{1}{2} & \frac{1}{2} \end{vmatrix} = (\tfrac{1}{2})(\tfrac{1}{2}) - (\tfrac{1}{2})(-\tfrac{1}{2}) = \tfrac{1}{2}$$

By (9) in Section 14.8,

$$\iint_R (2x - y^2)\, dA = \iint_S [(u + v) - \tfrac{1}{4}(v - u)^2]\left|\frac{\partial(x,y)}{\partial(u,v)}\right| dA$$

$$= \int_2^4 \int_1^3 (u + v - \tfrac{1}{4}v^2 + \tfrac{1}{2}uv - \tfrac{1}{4}u^2)\, \tfrac{1}{2}\, du\, dv$$

$$= \int_2^4 (\tfrac{1}{4}u^2 + \tfrac{1}{2}uv - \tfrac{1}{8}uv^2 + \tfrac{1}{8}u^2v - \tfrac{1}{24}u^3)\Big|_1^3 dv$$

$$= \int_2^4 (\tfrac{11}{12} + 2v - \tfrac{1}{4}v^2)\, dv = (\tfrac{11}{12}v + v^2 - \tfrac{1}{12}v^3)\Big|_2^4 = \tfrac{55}{6}$$

38. Let T_R be defined by $u = y - x$ and $v = y + x$. To find S we observe that for $x + y = 2$ we have $v = 2$; for $x + y = 4$ we have $v = 4$; for $x = 0$ we have $u = y$ and $v = y$, so that $u = v$; for $y = 0$ we have $u = -x$ and $v = x$, so that $u = -v$. Consequently S is the trapezoidal region in the uv plane bounded by the lines $v = 2$, $v = 4$, $u = -v$, and $u = v$ (see the figure). Next,

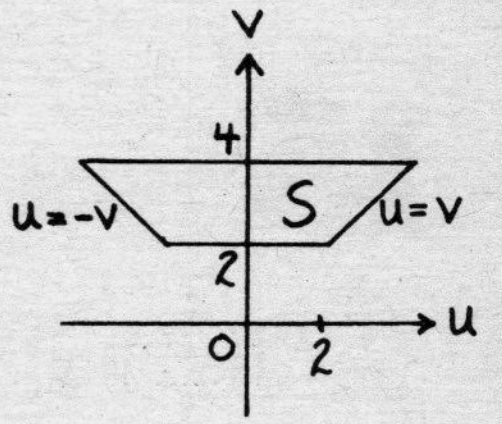

$$\frac{\partial(u,v)}{\partial(x,y)} = \begin{vmatrix} \frac{\partial u}{\partial x} & \frac{\partial u}{\partial y} \\ \frac{\partial v}{\partial x} & \frac{\partial v}{\partial y} \end{vmatrix} = \begin{vmatrix} -1 & 1 \\ 1 & 1 \end{vmatrix} = (-1)(1) - (1)(1) = -2$$

By (9) and (14) in Section 14.8,

$$\iint_R \cos\left(\frac{y - x}{y + x}\right) dA = \iint_S \cos\frac{u}{v}\left|\frac{\partial(x,y)}{\partial(u,v)}\right| dA$$

$$= \int_2^4 \int_{-v}^{v} (\cos\tfrac{u}{v})\left|-\tfrac{1}{2}\right| du\, dv = \int_2^4 \tfrac{v}{2}\sin\tfrac{u}{v}\Big|_{-v}^{v} dv$$

$$= \int_2^4 \tfrac{v}{2}(\sin 1 - \sin(-1))\, dv = \int_2^4 v \sin 1\, dv$$

$$= \tfrac{1}{2}v^2 \sin 1\Big|_2^4 = 6 \sin 1$$

15

CALCULUS OF VECTOR FIELDS

Section 15.1

1. $\text{curl } \vec{F}(x,y) = \left(\frac{\partial N}{\partial x} - \frac{\partial M}{\partial y}\right)\vec{k} = (0 - 0)\vec{k} = \vec{0}$

$\text{div } \vec{F}(x,y) = \frac{\partial M}{\partial x} + \frac{\partial N}{\partial y} = 1 + 1 = 2$

2. $\text{curl } \vec{F}(x,y) = \left(\frac{\partial N}{\partial x} - \frac{\partial M}{\partial y}\right)\vec{k} = \left(\frac{-2xy}{(x^2+y^2)^2} + \frac{2xy}{(x^2+y^2)^2}\right)\vec{k} = \vec{0}$

$\text{div } \vec{F}(x,y) = \frac{\partial M}{\partial x} + \frac{\partial N}{\partial y} = \frac{x^2+y^2-2x^2}{(x^2+y^2)^2} + \frac{x^2+y^2-2y^2}{(x^2+y^2)^2} = 0$

3. $\text{curl } \vec{F}(x,y,z) = \begin{vmatrix} \vec{i} & \vec{j} & \vec{k} \\ \frac{\partial}{\partial x} & \frac{\partial}{\partial y} & \frac{\partial}{\partial z} \\ y & z & x \end{vmatrix} = -\vec{i} - \vec{j} - \vec{k}$

$\text{div } \vec{F}(x,y,z) = \frac{\partial M}{\partial x} + \frac{\partial N}{\partial y} + \frac{\partial P}{\partial z} = 0 + 0 + 0 = 0$

4. $\text{curl } \vec{F}(x,y,z) = \begin{vmatrix} \vec{i} & \vec{j} & \vec{k} \\ \frac{\partial}{\partial x} & \frac{\partial}{\partial y} & \frac{\partial}{\partial z} \\ yz & zx & xy \end{vmatrix} = 0\vec{i} - 0\vec{j} + 0\vec{k} = \vec{0}$

$\text{div } \vec{F}(x,y,z) = \frac{\partial M}{\partial x} + \frac{\partial N}{\partial y} + \frac{\partial P}{\partial z} = 0 + 0 + 0 = 0$

5. $\text{curl } \vec{F}(x,y,z) = \begin{vmatrix} \vec{i} & \vec{j} & \vec{k} \\ \frac{\partial}{\partial x} & \frac{\partial}{\partial y} & \frac{\partial}{\partial z} \\ x^2 & y^2 & z^2 \end{vmatrix} = 0\vec{i} + 0\vec{j} + 0\vec{k} = \vec{0}$

$\text{div } \vec{F}(x,y,z) = \frac{\partial M}{\partial x} + \frac{\partial N}{\partial y} + \frac{\partial P}{\partial z} = 2x + 2y + 2z = 2(x + y + z)$

6. $\text{curl } \vec{F}(x,y,z) = \begin{vmatrix} \vec{i} & \vec{j} & \vec{k} \\ \frac{\partial}{\partial x} & \frac{\partial}{\partial y} & \frac{\partial}{\partial z} \\ \cos x & \sin y & e^{xy} \end{vmatrix} = xe^{xy}\vec{i} - ye^{xy}\vec{j} + 0\vec{k}$

$= xe^{xy}\vec{i} - ye^{xy}\vec{j}$

$\text{div } \vec{F}(x,y,z) = \frac{\partial M}{\partial x} + \frac{\partial N}{\partial y} + \frac{\partial P}{\partial z} = -\sin x + \cos y$

7. $\text{curl } \vec{F}(x,y,z) = \begin{vmatrix} \vec{i} & \vec{j} & \vec{k} \\ \frac{\partial}{\partial x} & \frac{\partial}{\partial y} & \frac{\partial}{\partial z} \\ \frac{-x}{z} & \frac{-y}{z} & \frac{1}{z} \end{vmatrix} = \frac{-y}{z^2}\vec{i} + \frac{x}{z^2}\vec{j} + 0\vec{k} = \frac{-y}{z^2}\vec{i} + \frac{x}{z^2}\vec{j}$

$\text{div } \vec{F}(x,y,z) = \frac{\partial M}{\partial x} + \frac{\partial N}{\partial y} + \frac{\partial P}{\partial z} = -\frac{1}{z} - \frac{1}{z} - \frac{1}{z^2} = -\frac{2}{z} - \frac{1}{z^2}$

8. $\text{curl } \vec{F}(x,y,z) = \begin{vmatrix} \vec{i} & \vec{j} & \vec{k} \\ \frac{\partial}{\partial x} & \frac{\partial}{\partial y} & \frac{\partial}{\partial z} \\ y+z & z+x & x+y \end{vmatrix} = 0\vec{i} + 0\vec{j} + 0\vec{k} = \vec{0}$

$\text{div } \vec{F}(x,y,z) = \frac{\partial M}{\partial x} + \frac{\partial N}{\partial y} + \frac{\partial P}{\partial z} = 0 + 0 + 0 = 0$

9. $\text{curl } \vec{F}(x,y,z) = \begin{vmatrix} \vec{i} & \vec{j} & \vec{k} \\ \frac{\partial}{\partial x} & \frac{\partial}{\partial y} & \frac{\partial}{\partial z} \\ e^x \cos y & e^x \sin y & z \end{vmatrix}$

$= 0\vec{i} + 0\vec{j} + (e^x \sin y + e^x \sin y)\vec{k} = 2\, e^x \sin y\, \vec{k}$

$\text{div } \vec{F}(x,y,z) = \frac{\partial M}{\partial x} + \frac{\partial N}{\partial y} + \frac{\partial P}{\partial z} = e^x \cos y + e^x \cos y + 1$

$= 2\, e^x \cos y + 1$

10. $\text{curl}\ \vec{F}(x,y,z) = \begin{vmatrix} \vec{i} & \vec{j} & \vec{k} \\ \frac{\partial}{\partial x} & \frac{\partial}{\partial y} & \frac{\partial}{\partial z} \\ \frac{x}{(x^2+y^2)^{3/2}} & \frac{y}{(x^2+y^2)^{3/2}} & 1 \end{vmatrix}$

$$= 0\vec{i} + 0\vec{j} + \left[\frac{-3xy}{(x^2+y^2)^{5/2}} + \frac{3xy}{(x^2+y^2)^{5/2}}\right]\vec{k} = \vec{0}$$

$$\text{div}\ \vec{F}(x,y,z) = \frac{(x^2+y^2)^{3/2} - 3x^2(x^2+y^2)^{1/2}}{(x^2+y^2)^3}$$

$$+ \frac{(x^2+y^2)^{3/2} - 3y^2(x^2+y^2)^{1/2}}{(x^2+y^2)^3} + 0$$

$$= -\frac{1}{(x^2+y^2)^{3/2}}$$

11. $\frac{\partial^2 f}{\partial x^2} + \frac{\partial^2 f}{\partial y^2} = 0 + 0 = 0$

12. $\frac{\partial^2 f}{\partial x^2} + \frac{\partial^2 f}{\partial y^2} = 2 - 2 = 0$

13. $\frac{\partial^2 f}{\partial x^2} + \frac{\partial^2 f}{\partial y^2} + \frac{\partial^2 f}{\partial z^2} = 2 + 2 - 4 = 0$

14. $\frac{\partial f}{\partial x} = \frac{-x}{(x^2+y^2+z^2)^{3/2}}$ and $\frac{\partial^2 f}{\partial x^2} = \frac{-1}{(x^2+y^2+z^2)^{3/2}}$ $+ \frac{3x^2}{(x^2+y^2+z^2)^{5/2}}$; similarly, $\frac{\partial^2 f}{\partial y^2} = \frac{-1}{(x^2+y^2+z^2)^{3/2}}$ $+ \frac{3y^2}{(x^2+y^2+z^2)^{5/2}}$ and $\frac{\partial^2 f}{\partial z^2} = \frac{-1}{(x^2+y^2+z^2)^{3/2}}$ $+ \frac{3z^2}{(x^2+y^2+z^2)^{5/2}}$. It follows that $\frac{\partial^2 f}{\partial x^2} + \frac{\partial^2 f}{\partial y^2} + \frac{\partial^2 f}{\partial z^2} = 0$.

15. $\frac{\partial N}{\partial x} = e^y = \frac{\partial M}{\partial y}$, so $\vec{F}$ is the gradient of some function f, and

$$\frac{\partial f}{\partial x} = e^y \quad \text{and} \quad \frac{\partial f}{\partial y} = xe^y + y \qquad (*)$$

Integrating both sides of the first equation in (*) with respect to x, we obtain $f(x,y) = xe^y + g(y)$. Taking partial derivatives with respect to y, we find that $\frac{\partial f}{\partial y} = xe^y + \frac{dg}{dy}$. Comparing this with the second equation in (*), we conclude that $\frac{dg}{dy} = y$, so that $g(y) = \frac{y^2}{2} + C$. Therefore $f(x,y) = xe^y + \frac{y^2}{2} + C$.

16. By Example 7, $\vec{F}$ is the gradient of some function f , and

$$\frac{\partial f}{\partial x} = y^2 e^{xy} \quad \text{and} \quad \frac{\partial f}{\partial y} = (1 + xy)e^{xy} \qquad (*)$$

Integrating both sides of the first equation in (*) with respect to x , we obtain $f(x,y) = y\, e^{xy} + g(y)$. Taking partial derivatives with respect to y , we find that $\frac{\partial f}{\partial y} = e^{xy} + xye^{xy} + \frac{dg}{dy} = (1 + xy)e^{xy} + \frac{dg}{dy}$. Comparing this with the second equation in (*), we conclude that $\frac{dg}{dy} = 0$, so that $g(y) = C$. Therefore $f(x,y) = ye^{xy} + C$.

17. Since $\frac{\partial N}{\partial x} = -y \sin xy$ and $\frac{\partial M}{\partial y} = x \cos xy$, $\vec{F}$ is not a gradient.

18. $\frac{\partial N}{\partial x} = 6x^2y + 3 = \frac{\partial M}{\partial y}$, so $\vec{F}$ is the gradient of some function f , and

$$\frac{\partial f}{\partial x} = 3x^2y^2 + 3y \quad \text{and} \quad \frac{\partial f}{\partial y} = 2x^3y + 3x \qquad (*)$$

Integrating both sides of the first equation in (*) with respect to x, we obtain $f(x,y) = x^3y^2 + 3xy + g(y)$. Taking partial derivatives with respect to y , we find that $\frac{\partial f}{\partial y} = 2x^3y + 3x + \frac{dg}{dy}$. Comparing this with the second equation in (*), we conclude that $\frac{dg}{dy} = 0$, so that $g(y) = C$. Therefore $f(x,y) = x^3y^2 + 3xy + C$.

19. By Example 6, $\vec{F}$ is the gradient of some function f , and

$$\frac{\partial f}{\partial x} = 2xyz , \quad \frac{\partial f}{\partial y} = x^2z , \text{ and } \frac{\partial f}{\partial z} = x^2y + 1 \qquad (*)$$

Integrating both sides of the first equation in (*) with respect to x, we obtain $f(x,y,z) = x^2yz + g(y,z)$. Taking partial derivatives with respect to y, we find that $\frac{\partial f}{\partial y} = x^2z + \frac{\partial g}{\partial y}$. Comparing this with the second equation in (*), we deduce that $\frac{\partial g}{\partial y} = 0$, so that g is constant with respect to y. Thus $f(x,y,z) = x^2yz + h(z)$. Taking partial derivatives with respect to z, we obtain $\frac{\partial f}{\partial z} = x^2y + \frac{dh}{dz}$. Comparing this with the third equation in (*), we conclude that $\frac{dh}{dz} = 1$, so that $h(z) = z + C$. Therefore $f(x,y,z) = x^2yz + z + C$.

20. $\frac{\partial P}{\partial y} = x = \frac{\partial N}{\partial z}$, $\frac{\partial M}{\partial z} = y = \frac{\partial P}{\partial x}$, and $\frac{\partial N}{\partial x} = z = \frac{\partial M}{\partial y}$, so F is the gradient of some function f, and

$$\frac{\partial f}{\partial x} = yz, \quad \frac{\partial f}{\partial y} = xz, \text{ and } \frac{\partial f}{\partial z} = xy \qquad (*)$$

Integrating both sides of the first equation in (*) with respect to x, we find that $f(x,y,z) = xyz + g(y,z)$. Taking partial derivatives with respect to y, we find that $\frac{\partial f}{\partial y} = xz + \frac{\partial g}{\partial y}$. Comparing this with the second equation in (*), we deduce that $\frac{\partial g}{\partial y} = 0$, so that g is constant with respect to y. Thus $f(x,y,z) = xyz + h(z)$. Taking partial derivatives with respect to z, we obtain $\frac{\partial f}{\partial z} = xy + \frac{dh}{dz}$. Comparing this with the third equation in (*), we conclude that $\frac{dh}{dz} = 0$, so that $h(z) = C$. Therefore $f(x,y,z) = xyz + C$.

21. Since $\frac{\partial P}{\partial y} = 0$ and $\frac{\partial N}{\partial z} = y$, $\vec{F}$ is not a gradient.

22. $\frac{\partial P}{\partial y} = 2y = \frac{\partial N}{\partial z}$, $\frac{\partial M}{\partial z} = 2x = \frac{\partial P}{\partial x}$, and $\frac{\partial N}{\partial x} = 0 = \frac{\partial M}{\partial y}$, so $\vec{F}$ is the gradient of some function f, and

$$\frac{\partial f}{\partial x} = 2xz + 1, \quad \frac{\partial f}{\partial y} = 2y(z+1), \text{ and } \frac{\partial f}{\partial z} = x^2 + y^2 + 3z^2 \qquad (*)$$

Integrating both sides of the first equation in (*) with respect to x, we obtain $f(x,y,z) = x^2z + x + g(y,z)$. Taking partial derivatives with respect to y, we find that $\frac{\partial f}{\partial y} = \frac{\partial g}{\partial y}$. Comparing this with the second equation in (*), we deduce that $\frac{\partial g}{\partial y} = 2y(z+1)$, so that $g(y,z) = y^2(z+1) + h(z)$. Thus $f(x,y,z) = x^2z + x + y^2(z+1) + h(z)$. Taking partial derivatives with respect to z, we obtain $\frac{\partial f}{\partial z} = x^2 + y^2 + \frac{dh}{dz}$. Comparing this with the third equation in (*), we conclude that $\frac{dh}{dz} = 3z^2$, so that $h(z) = z^3 + C$. Therefore $f(x,y,z) = x^2z + x + y^2(z+1) + z^3 + C$.

23. Since $\frac{\partial P}{\partial y} = 0$ and $\frac{\partial N}{\partial z} = 2z$, $\vec{F}$ is not a gradient.

24. $\frac{\partial P}{\partial y} = xe^{xy} = \frac{\partial N}{\partial z}$, $\frac{\partial M}{\partial z} = ye^{xy} = \frac{\partial P}{\partial x}$, and $\frac{\partial N}{\partial x} = ze^{xy} + xyze^{xy} = \frac{\partial M}{\partial y}$, so $\vec{F}$ is the gradient of some function f, and

$$\frac{\partial f}{\partial x} = yze^{xy}, \quad \frac{\partial f}{\partial y} = xze^{xy}, \text{ and } \frac{\partial f}{\partial z} = e^{xy} + \cos z \qquad (*)$$

Integrating both sides of the first equation in (*) with respect to x, we obtain $f(x,y,z) = ze^{xy} + g(y,z)$. Taking partial derivatives with respect to y, we find that $\frac{\partial f}{\partial y} = xze^{xy} + \frac{\partial g}{\partial y}$. Comparing this with the second equation in (*), we deduce that $\frac{\partial g}{\partial y} = 0$, so that g is constant with respect to y. Then $f(x,y,z) = ze^{xy} + h(z)$. Taking partial derivatives with respect to z, we obtain $\frac{\partial f}{\partial z} = e^{xy} + \frac{dh}{dz}$. Comparing this with the third equation in (*), we conclude that $\frac{dh}{dz} = \cos z$, so that $h(z) = \sin z + C$. Therefore $f(x,y,z) = ze^{xy} + \sin z + C$.

25. a. grad (fg) is a vector field.

b. grad $\vec{F}$ is meaningless.

c. curl (grad f) is a vector field.

d. grad (div $\vec{F}$) is a vector field.

e. curl (curl $\vec{F}$) is a vector field.

f. div (grad f) is a function of several variables.

g. (grad f) $\times$ (curl $\vec{F}$) is a vector field.

h. div (curl (grad f)) is a function of several variables.

i. curl (div (grad f)) is meaningless.

26. Let $\vec{F} = M_1\vec{i} + N_1\vec{j} + P_1\vec{k}$ and $G = M_2\vec{i} + N_2\vec{j} + P_2\vec{k}$.

a. By definition, $f\vec{F} = fM_1\vec{i} + fN_1\vec{j} + fP_1\vec{k}$. Since products of continuous functions are continuous, the components of $f\vec{F}$ are continuous, and thus $f\vec{F}$ is continuous by definition.

b. By definition, $\vec{F}\cdot\vec{G} = M_1M_2 + N_1N_2 + P_1P_2$. Since products of continuous functions are continuous, as well as sums, $\vec{F}\cdot\vec{G}$ is continuous.

c. By definition, $\vec{F}\times\vec{G} = (N_1P_2 - N_2P_1)\vec{i} + (M_2P_1 - M_1P_2)\vec{j} + (M_1N_2 - M_2N_1)\vec{k}$. Since products and differences of continuous functions are continuous, the components of $\vec{F}\times\vec{G}$ are continuous, and thus $\vec{F}\times\vec{G}$ is continuous.

27. Let $\vec{F} = M\vec{i} + N\vec{j} + P\vec{k}$. Then

$$\text{curl } \vec{F} = \left(\frac{\partial P}{\partial y} - \frac{\partial N}{\partial z}\right)\vec{i} + \left(\frac{\partial M}{\partial z} - \frac{\partial P}{\partial x}\right)\vec{j} + \left(\frac{\partial N}{\partial x} - \frac{\partial M}{\partial y}\right)\vec{k}$$

so that

$$\text{div (curl } \vec{F}) = \left(\frac{\partial^2 P}{\partial x\partial y} - \frac{\partial^2 N}{\partial x\partial z}\right) + \left(\frac{\partial^2 M}{\partial y\partial z} - \frac{\partial^2 P}{\partial y\partial x}\right) + \left(\frac{\partial^2 N}{\partial z\partial x} - \frac{\partial^2 M}{\partial z\partial y}\right)$$

Since all second partials are continuous by assumption,

$$\frac{\partial^2 M}{\partial y\partial z} = \frac{\partial^2 M}{\partial z\partial y}, \quad \frac{\partial^2 N}{\partial x\partial z} = \frac{\partial^2 N}{\partial z\partial x}, \quad \text{and} \quad \frac{\partial^2 P}{\partial x\partial y} = \frac{\partial^2 P}{\partial y\partial x}$$

Thus div (curl $\vec{F}$) = 0 .

28. grad $f = \frac{\partial f}{\partial x}\vec{i} + \frac{\partial f}{\partial y}\vec{j} + \frac{\partial f}{\partial z}\vec{k}$, so that

$$\text{curl (grad f)} = \begin{vmatrix} \vec{i} & \vec{j} & \vec{k} \\ \frac{\partial}{\partial x} & \frac{\partial}{\partial y} & \frac{\partial}{\partial z} \\ \frac{\partial f}{\partial x} & \frac{\partial f}{\partial y} & \frac{\partial f}{\partial z} \end{vmatrix} = \left(\frac{\partial^2 f}{\partial y\partial z} - \frac{\partial^2 f}{\partial z\partial y}\right)\vec{i}$$

$$+ \left(\frac{\partial^2 f}{\partial z\partial x} - \frac{\partial^2 f}{\partial x\partial z}\right)\vec{j} + \left(\frac{\partial^2 f}{\partial x\partial y} - \frac{\partial^2 f}{\partial y\partial x}\right)\vec{k}$$

Since all second partials are continuous by assumption, the components of curl (grad f) are 0 , and therefore curl (grad f)$=\vec{0}$.

29. Let $\vec{F} = M\vec{i} + N\vec{j} + P\vec{k}$. Then $f\vec{F} = fM\vec{i} + fN\vec{j} + fP\vec{k}$, so that

$$\text{div } (f\vec{F}) = \left(f\frac{\partial M}{\partial x} + \frac{\partial f}{\partial x}M\right) + \left(f\frac{\partial N}{\partial y} + \frac{\partial f}{\partial y}N\right) + \left(f\frac{\partial P}{\partial z} + \frac{\partial f}{\partial z}P\right)$$

$$= f\left(\frac{\partial M}{\partial x} + \frac{\partial N}{\partial y} + \frac{\partial P}{\partial z}\right) + \left(\frac{\partial f}{\partial x}M + \frac{\partial f}{\partial y}N + \frac{\partial f}{\partial z}P\right)$$

$$= f \text{ div } \vec{F} + (\text{grad } f)\cdot\vec{F}$$

30. Let $\vec{F} = M_1\vec{i} + N_1\vec{j} + P_1\vec{k}$ and $\vec{G} = M_2\vec{i} + N_2\vec{j} + P_2\vec{k}$. Then $\vec{F}\times\vec{G} = (N_1P_2 - N_2P_1)\vec{i} + (M_2P_1 - M_1P_2)\vec{j} + (M_1N_2 - M_2N_1)\vec{k}$. Thus

$$\text{div } (\vec{F}\times\vec{G}) = \left(\frac{\partial N_1}{\partial x}P_2 + N_1\frac{\partial P_2}{\partial x} - \frac{\partial N_2}{\partial x}P_1 - N_2\frac{\partial P_1}{\partial x}\right) + \left(\frac{\partial M_2}{\partial y}P_1\right.$$

$$\left. + M_2\frac{\partial P_1}{\partial y} - \frac{\partial M_1}{\partial y}P_2 - M_1\frac{\partial P_2}{\partial y}\right) + \left(\frac{\partial M_1}{\partial z}N_2 + M_1\frac{\partial N_2}{\partial z} - \frac{\partial M_2}{\partial z}N_1\right.$$

$$\left. - M_2\frac{\partial N_1}{\partial z}\right) = \left[\left(\frac{\partial P_1}{\partial y} - \frac{\partial N_1}{\partial z}\right)M_2 + \left(\frac{\partial M_1}{\partial z} - \frac{\partial P_1}{\partial x}\right)N_2 + \left(\frac{\partial N_1}{\partial x} - \frac{\partial M_1}{\partial y}\right)P_2\right]$$

$$- \left[M_1\left(\frac{\partial P_2}{\partial y} - \frac{\partial N_2}{\partial z}\right) + N_1\left(\frac{\partial M_2}{\partial z} - \frac{\partial P_2}{\partial x}\right) + P_1\left(\frac{\partial N_2}{\partial x} - \frac{\partial M_2}{\partial y}\right)\right]$$

$$= (\text{curl } \vec{F})\cdot\vec{G} - \vec{F}\cdot(\text{curl } \vec{G}).$$

31. Let $\vec{F} = M\vec{i} + N\vec{j} + P\vec{k}$. Then $f\vec{F} = fM\vec{i} + fN\vec{j} + fP\vec{k}$, so that

$$\text{curl } f\vec{F} = \begin{vmatrix} \vec{i} & \vec{j} & \vec{k} \\ \frac{\partial}{\partial x} & \frac{\partial}{\partial y} & \frac{\partial}{\partial z} \\ fM & fN & fP \end{vmatrix} = \left(\frac{\partial f}{\partial y}P + f\frac{\partial P}{\partial y} - \frac{\partial f}{\partial z}N - f\frac{\partial N}{\partial z}\right)\vec{i}$$

$$+ \left(\frac{\partial f}{\partial z}M + f\frac{\partial M}{\partial z} - \frac{\partial f}{\partial x}P - f\frac{\partial P}{\partial x}\right)\vec{j} + \left(\frac{\partial f}{\partial x}N + f\frac{\partial N}{\partial x} - \frac{\partial f}{\partial y}M\right.$$

$$\left. - f\frac{\partial M}{\partial y}\right)\vec{k} = f\left[\left(\frac{\partial P}{\partial y} - \frac{\partial N}{\partial z}\right)\vec{i} + \left(\frac{\partial M}{\partial z} - \frac{\partial P}{\partial x}\right)\vec{j} + \left(\frac{\partial N}{\partial x} - \frac{\partial M}{\partial y}\right)\vec{k}\right]$$

$$+ \left[\left(\frac{\partial f}{\partial y}P - \frac{\partial f}{\partial z}N\right)\vec{i} + \left(\frac{\partial f}{\partial z}M - \frac{\partial f}{\partial x}P\right)\vec{j} + \left(\frac{\partial f}{\partial x}N - \frac{\partial f}{\partial y}M\right)\vec{k}\right]$$

$$= f\ (\text{curl } \vec{F}) + (\text{grad } f)\times\vec{F}$$

32. a. By hypothesis, $\vec{0} = \text{grad } f(x,y) = \frac{\partial f}{\partial x}\vec{i} + \frac{\partial f}{\partial y}\vec{j}$, so that $\frac{\partial f}{\partial x} = \frac{\partial f}{\partial y} = 0$ for (x,y) in R. Since $\frac{\partial f}{\partial x} = 0$, integration yields $f(x,y) = c_1 + g(y)$ for some constant c_1 and

some function g of y. Then $\frac{dg}{dy} = \frac{\partial f}{\partial y} = 0$, so integration yields $g(y) = c_2$ for some constant c_2. Thus $f(x,y) = c_1 + c_2$, and hence f is constant.

b. By hypothesis, $\vec{0} = \text{grad } f(x,y,z) = \frac{\partial f}{\partial x}\vec{i} + \frac{\partial f}{\partial y}\vec{j} + \frac{\partial f}{\partial z}\vec{k}$, so that $\frac{\partial f}{\partial x} = \frac{\partial f}{\partial y} = \frac{\partial f}{\partial z} = 0$ for (x,y,z) in D. Since $\frac{\partial f}{\partial x} = 0$, integration yields $f(x,y,z) = c_1 + g(y,z)$ for some constant c_1 and function g of y and z. Then $\frac{\partial g}{\partial y} = \frac{\partial f}{\partial y} = 0$, so that integration yields $g(y,z) = c_2 + h(z)$ for some constant c_2 and function h of z. Since $g(y,z) = f(x,y,z) - c_1$, we find that $\frac{dh}{dz} = \frac{\partial g}{\partial z} = \frac{\partial f}{\partial z} = 0$, so that integration yields $h(z) = c_3$ for some constant c_3. Therefore $f(x,y,z) = c_1 + g(y,z) = c_1 + c_2 + h(z)$ $= c_1 + c_2 + c_3$, and hence f is constant.

33. Let $\vec{F} = a\vec{i} + b\vec{j} + c\vec{k}$, where a, b, and c are constants. Then

$$(F\times G)(x,y,z) = \begin{vmatrix} \vec{i} & \vec{j} & \vec{k} \\ a & b & c \\ x & y & z \end{vmatrix} = (bz - cy)\vec{i} + (cx - az)\vec{j} + (ay - bx)\vec{k}$$

and thus

$$[\text{curl } (\vec{F}\times\vec{G})](x,y,z) = \begin{vmatrix} \vec{i} & \vec{j} & \vec{k} \\ \frac{\partial}{\partial x} & \frac{\partial}{\partial y} & \frac{\partial}{\partial z} \\ bz-cy & cx-az & ay-bx \end{vmatrix}$$

$$= [a - (-a)]\vec{i} + [b - (-b)]\vec{j} + [c - (-c)]\vec{k} = 2\vec{F}(x,y,z)$$

34. First we will show that $\text{curl } (\vec{F} + \vec{F}_1) = \text{curl } \vec{F} + \text{curl } \vec{F}_1$ for any vector field $\vec{F}_1$ that has the required continuous partial derivatives. Let $\vec{F} = M\vec{i} + N\vec{j} + P\vec{k}$ and $\vec{F}_1 = M_1\vec{i} + N_1\vec{j} + P_1\vec{k}$. Then

$$\text{curl } (\vec{F} + \vec{F}_1) = \begin{vmatrix} \vec{i} & \vec{j} & \vec{k} \\ \frac{\partial}{\partial x} & \frac{\partial}{\partial y} & \frac{\partial}{\partial z} \\ M+M_1 & N+N_1 & P+P_1 \end{vmatrix} = \left[\frac{\partial(P+P_1)}{\partial y} - \frac{\partial(N+N_1)}{\partial z}\right]\vec{i}$$

$$+ \left[\frac{\partial(M+M_1)}{\partial z} - \frac{\partial(P+P_1)}{\partial x}\right]\vec{j} + \left[\frac{\partial(N+N_1)}{\partial x} - \frac{\partial(M+M_1)}{\partial y}\right]\vec{k}$$

$$= \left[\left(\frac{\partial P}{\partial y} - \frac{\partial N}{\partial z}\right)\vec{i} + \left(\frac{\partial M}{\partial z} - \frac{\partial P}{\partial x}\right)\vec{j} + \left(\frac{\partial N}{\partial x} - \frac{\partial M}{\partial y}\right)\vec{k}\right] + \left[\left(\frac{\partial P_1}{\partial y} - \frac{\partial N_1}{\partial z}\right)\vec{i}\right.$$

$$\left. + \left(\frac{\partial M_1}{\partial z} - \frac{\partial P_1}{\partial x}\right)\vec{j} + \left(\frac{\partial N_1}{\partial x} - \frac{\partial M_1}{\partial y}\right)\vec{k}\right] = \text{curl } \vec{F} + \text{curl } \vec{F}_1$$

In particular, if $\vec{F}_1 = \text{grad } f$, then $\text{curl } (\vec{F} + \text{grad } f) = \text{curl } \vec{F} + \text{curl (grad } f)$, so that by (5) (see Exercise 28), $\text{curl } \vec{G} = \text{curl } (\vec{F} + \text{grad } f) = \text{curl } \vec{F} + \text{curl (grad } f)$ $= \text{curl } \vec{F} + \vec{0} = \text{curl } \vec{F}$.

35. Let $\vec{F} = \text{grad } f$ and $\vec{G} = \text{grad } g$. Then

$$\vec{F} + \vec{G} = \left(\frac{\partial f}{\partial x}\vec{i} + \frac{\partial f}{\partial y}\vec{j} + \frac{\partial f}{\partial z}\vec{k}\right) + \left(\frac{\partial g}{\partial x}\vec{i} + \frac{\partial g}{\partial y}\vec{j} + \frac{\partial g}{\partial z}\vec{k}\right)$$

$$= \left(\frac{\partial f}{\partial x} + \frac{\partial g}{\partial x}\right)\vec{i} + \left(\frac{\partial f}{\partial y} + \frac{\partial g}{\partial y}\right)\vec{j} + \left(\frac{\partial f}{\partial z} + \frac{\partial g}{\partial z}\right)\vec{k}$$

$$= \frac{\partial(f+g)}{\partial x}\vec{i} + \frac{\partial(f+g)}{\partial y}\vec{j} + \frac{\partial(f+g)}{\partial z}\vec{k} = \text{grad } (f+g)$$

Thus $\vec{F} + \vec{G}$ is conservative.

36. $\text{div } \vec{F} = \frac{\partial M}{\partial x} + \frac{\partial N}{\partial y} + \frac{\partial P}{\partial z} = 0 + 0 + 0 = 0$. Thus $\vec{F}$ is solenoidal.

37. $\text{grad } f(x,y,z) = \frac{m\omega^2}{2}(2x\vec{i} + 2y\vec{j} + 2z\vec{k}) = m\omega^2(x\vec{i} + y\vec{j} + z\vec{k})$ $= \vec{F}(x,y,z)$. Therefore f is a potential function for $\vec{F}$.

38. $$\frac{\partial f}{\partial x} = \frac{a(x^2 + y^2 + z^2)^{3/2} - (ax + by + cz)\frac{3}{2}(x^2 + y^2 + z^2)^{1/2}(2x)}{(x^2 + y^2 + z^2)^3}$$

$$= \frac{a(x^2 + y^2 + z^2) - 3x(ax + by + cz)}{(x^2 + y^2 + z^2)^{5/2}}$$

Likewise

$$\frac{\partial f}{\partial y} = \frac{b(x^2+y^2+z^2) - 3y(ax+by+cz)}{(x^2+y^2+z^2)^{5/2}} \text{ and } \frac{\partial f}{\partial z} = \frac{c(x^2+y^2+z^2) - 3z(ax+by+cz)}{(x^2+y^2+z^2)^{5/2}}$$

Thus

$$\vec{E}(x,y,z) = \frac{\partial f}{\partial x}\vec{i} + \frac{\partial f}{\partial y}\vec{j} + \frac{\partial f}{\partial z}\vec{k}$$

$$= \frac{1}{(x^2+y^2+z^2)^{5/2}}[(a\vec{i}+b\vec{j}+c\vec{k})(x^2+y^2+z^2)-3(x\vec{i}+y\vec{j}+z\vec{k})(ax+by+cz)]$$

39. If $\vec{F} = \text{curl } \vec{G}$, then by (4), $\text{div } \vec{F} = \text{div } (\text{curl } \vec{G}) = 0$, so that $\vec{F}$ is solenoidal.

40. $$(\text{curl } \vec{G})(x,y,z) = \begin{vmatrix} \vec{i} & \vec{j} & \vec{k} \\ \frac{\partial}{\partial x} & \frac{\partial}{\partial y} & \frac{\partial}{\partial z} \\ 0 & 0 & \frac{-I}{2}\ln(x^2+y^2) \end{vmatrix}$$

$$= \frac{-I}{2}\frac{2y}{x^2+y^2}\vec{i} + \frac{I}{2}\frac{2x}{x^2+y^2}\vec{j} = \vec{B}(x,y,z)$$

Thus $\vec{G}$ is a vector potential for $\vec{B}$.

41. Let $\vec{G} = M\vec{i} + N\vec{j} + P\vec{k}$, and assume that $\vec{F}(x,y,z) = 8\vec{i} = \text{curl } \vec{G}(x,y,z)$. Then

$$\frac{\partial P}{\partial y} - \frac{\partial N}{\partial z} = 8, \quad \frac{\partial M}{\partial z} - \frac{\partial P}{\partial x} = 0, \quad \text{and} \quad \frac{\partial N}{\partial x} - \frac{\partial M}{\partial y} = 0$$

Notice that if $P(x,y,z) = 8y$ and $M(x,y,z) = 0 = N(x,y,z)$, then the three equations are satisfied. Consequently if we let $\vec{G}(x,y,z) = 8y\vec{k}$, then $\text{curl } \vec{G}(x,y,z) = 8\vec{i} = \vec{F}(x,y,z)$. Thus $\vec{G}$ is a vector potential of $\vec{F}$. (Other solutions are also possible.)

42. $$\text{curl } \vec{V}(x,y,z) = \begin{vmatrix} \vec{i} & \vec{j} & \vec{k} \\ \frac{\partial}{\partial x} & \frac{\partial}{\partial y} & \frac{\partial}{\partial z} \\ -\omega y & \omega x & 0 \end{vmatrix} = 0\vec{i} + 0\vec{j} + \left[\frac{\partial(\omega x)}{\partial x} - \frac{\partial(-\omega y)}{\partial y}\right]\vec{k}$$

$= [\omega - (-\omega)]\vec{k} = 2\omega\vec{k}$. Thus $\text{curl } \vec{V}(x,y,z)$ depends only on ω and not on (x,y,z).

43. a. $\text{grad } \vec{T}(x,y,z) = -4x\vec{i} - 2y\vec{j} - 8z\vec{k}$. Since each component is continuous, so is $\text{grad } \vec{T}$.

b. $\|\text{grad } \vec{T}(x,y,z)\| = \sqrt{16x^2 + 4y^2 + 64z^2}$. Then $\|\text{grad } \vec{T}(1,0,0)\| = 4$ and $\|\text{grad } \vec{T}(0,1,0)\| = 2$. Since $(1,0,0)$ and $(0,1,0)$ are the same distance from the origin, and since the magnitudes of $\text{grad } \vec{T}$ at these points are distinct, $\text{grad } \vec{T}$ is not a central force field.

Section 15.2

1. Since $x(t) = 2t^{3/2}$, $y(t) = t^2$, $z(t) = 0$, and

$\left\|\frac{d\vec{r}}{dt}\right\| = \sqrt{(3t^{1/2})^2 + (2t)^2 + 0^2} = \sqrt{9t + 4t^2}$, (4) implies that

$$\int_C (9 + 8y^{1/2})\, ds = \int_0^1 (9 + 8t)\sqrt{9t + 4t^2}\, dt = \frac{2}{3}(9t + 4t^2)^{3/2}\Big|_0^1$$

$$= \frac{26}{3}\sqrt{13}.$$

2. The circle C is parameterized by $\vec{r}(t) = 2\cos t\,\vec{i} + 2\sin t\,\vec{j}$ for $0 \le t \le 2\pi$. Since $x(t) = 2\cos t$, $y(t) = 2\sin t$, $z(t) = 0$, and $\left\|\frac{d\vec{r}}{dt}\right\| = \sqrt{(-2\sin t)^2 + (2\cos t)^2 + 0^2} = 2$, (4) implies that

$$\int_C xy\, ds = \int_0^{2\pi} (2\cos t)(2\sin t)(2)\, dt = 4\sin^2 t\Big|_0^{2\pi} = 0$$

3. Since $x(t) = t$, $y(t) = t^3$, $z(t) = 0$, and

$\left\|\frac{d\vec{r}}{dt}\right\| = \sqrt{1^2 + (3t^2)^2 + 0^2} = \sqrt{1 + 9t^4}$, (4) implies that

$$\int_C y\, ds = \int_{-1}^0 t^3\sqrt{1 + 9t^4}\, dt = \frac{1}{54}(1 + 9t^4)^{3/2}\Big|_{-1}^0$$

$$= \frac{1}{54}(1 - 10^{3/2})$$

4. Since $x(t) = \cos^3 t$, $y(t) = \sin^3 t$, $z(t) = 0$, and

$$\left\|\frac{d\vec{r}}{dt}\right\| = \sqrt{(-3\cos^2 t\sin t)^2 + (3\sin^2 t\cos t)^2 + 0^2}$$

$$= \sqrt{9\cos^2 t\sin^2 t(\cos^2 t + \sin^2 t)} = 3\cos t\sin t$$

for $0 \le t \le \frac{\pi}{2}$, (4) implies that

$$\int_C (x^3 + y^3)\, ds = \int_0^{\pi/2} (\cos^9 t + \sin^9 t)(3\cos t\sin t)\, dt$$

$$= \left(-\frac{3}{11}\cos^{11} t + \frac{3}{11}\sin^{11} t\right)\Big|_0^{\pi/2} = \frac{6}{11}$$

5. Since $x(t) = e^t$, $y(t) = e^{-t}$, $z(t) = \sqrt{2}\,t$, and $\left\|\frac{d\vec{r}}{dt}\right\|$

$= \sqrt{(e^t)^2 + (-e^{-t})^2 + (\sqrt{2})^2} = \sqrt{e^{2t} + 2 + e^{-2t}} = \sqrt{(e^t + e^{-t})^2}$

$= e^t + e^{-t}$, (4) implies that $\int_C 2xyz\, ds$

$$= \int_0^1 2(e^t)(e^{-t})(\sqrt{2}\,t)(e^t + e^{-t})\, dt = \int_0^1 2\sqrt{2}\,t(e^t + e^{-t})\, dt$$

parts

$$= 2\sqrt{2}\,t(e^t - e^{-t})\Big|_0^1 - \int_0^1 2\sqrt{2}\,(e^t - e^{-t})\, dt = 2\sqrt{2}\,(e - e^{-1})$$

$$- [2\sqrt{2}\,(e^t + e^{-t})]\Big|_0^1 = 4\sqrt{2}\,(1 - e^{-1}).$$

6. Since $x(t) = \ln t$, $y(t) = -t^2$, $z(t) = 2t$, and $\left\|\frac{d\vec{r}}{dt}\right\|$

$= \sqrt{\left(\frac{1}{t}\right)^2 + (-2t)^2 + 2^2} = \sqrt{\frac{1}{t^2} + 4 + 4t^2} = \sqrt{\left(\frac{1}{t} + 2t\right)^2} = \frac{1}{t} + 2t$

for $1 \le t \le 2$, (4) implies that $\int_C (x - z^2)\, ds$

$$= \int_1^2 (\ln t - 4t^2)\left(\frac{1}{t} + 2t\right) dt = \int_1^2 \left(\frac{1}{t}\ln t + 2t\ln t - 4t\right.$$

$$\left. - 8t^3\right) dt = \left[\frac{1}{2}(\ln t)^2 - 2t^2 - 2t^4\right]\Big|_1^2 + \int_1^2 2t\ln t\, dt$$

parts

$$= \frac{1}{2}(\ln 2)^2 - 36 + t^2\ln t\Big|_1^2 - \int_1^2 t\, dt = \frac{1}{2}(\ln 2)^2 - 36$$

$$+ 4\ln 2 - \frac{1}{2}t^2\Big|_1^2 = \frac{1}{2}(\ln 2)^2 + 4\ln 2 - \frac{75}{2}.$$

7. Since $x(t) = \cos t$, $y(t) = \sin t$, $z(t) = t^{3/2}$, and $\left\|\frac{d\vec{r}}{dt}\right\|$

$= \sqrt{(-\sin t)^2 + (\cos t)^2 + \left(\frac{3}{2}t^{1/2}\right)^2} = \sqrt{1 + \frac{9}{4}t}$, (4) implies that

$$\int_C \left(1 + \frac{9}{4}z^{2/3}\right)^{1/4} ds = \int_0^{20/3} \left(1 + \frac{9}{4}t\right)^{1/4}\sqrt{1 + \frac{9}{4}t}\, dt$$

$$= \int_0^{20/3} \left(1 + \frac{9}{4}t\right)^{3/4} dt = \frac{16}{63}\left(1 + \frac{9}{4}t\right)^{7/4}\Big|_0^{20/3} = \frac{2032}{63}.$$

8. The line segment is parameterized by $\vec{r}(t) = (1 - t)\vec{i} + 3t\,\vec{j} + (1 + t)\vec{k}$ for $0 \le t \le 1$. Since $x(t) = 1 - t$, $y(t) = 3t$,

$z(t) = 1 + t$, and $\left\|\frac{d\vec{r}}{dt}\right\| = \sqrt{(-1)^2 + 3^2 + 1^2} = \sqrt{11}$, (4) implies

that $\int_C (2xy - 5yz)\,ds = \int_0^1 [2(1-t)(3t) - 5(3t)(1+t)]\sqrt{11}\,dt$

$= \sqrt{11}\int_0^1 (-9t - 21t^2)\,dt = \sqrt{11}(-\frac{9}{2}t^2 - 7t^3)\Big|_0^1 = -\frac{23}{2}\sqrt{11}$.

9. The triangular path is composed of the three line segments C_1, C_2, and C_3 parameterized respectively by $\vec{r}_1(t) = (-1+t)\vec{i} + t\vec{j}$ for $0 \le t \le 1$, $\vec{r}_2(t) = (1-t)\vec{j} + t\vec{k}$ for $0 \le t \le 1$, and $\vec{r}_3(t) = -t\vec{i} + (1-t)\vec{k}$ for $0 \le t \le 1$. Since $x(t) = -1 + t$, $y(t) = t$, $z(t) = 0$, and

$\left\|\frac{d\vec{r}_1}{dt}\right\| = \sqrt{1^2 + 1^2 + 0^2} = \sqrt{2}$ for C_1, (4) implies that

$\int_{C_1} (y + 2z)\,ds = \int_0^1 [t + 2(0)]\sqrt{2}\,dt = \int_0^1 \sqrt{2}\,t\,dt = \frac{\sqrt{2}}{2}t^2\Big|_0^1 = \frac{\sqrt{2}}{2}$.

Since $x(t) = 0$, $y(t) = 1 - t$, $z(t) = t$, and

$\left\|\frac{d\vec{r}_2}{dt}\right\| = \sqrt{0^2 + (-1)^2 + 1^2} = \sqrt{2}$ for C_2, (4) implies that

$\int_{C_2} (y + 2z)\,ds = \int_0^1 (1 - t + 2t)\sqrt{2}\,dt = \int_0^1 \sqrt{2}(1 + t)\,dt$

$= \sqrt{2}(t + \frac{1}{2}t^2)\Big|_0^1 = \frac{3}{2}\sqrt{2}$. Since $x(t) = -t$, $y(t) = 0$,

$z(t) = 1 - t$, and $\left\|\frac{d\vec{r}_3}{dt}\right\| = \sqrt{(-1)^2 + 0^2 + (-1)^2} = \sqrt{2}$ for

C_3, (4) implies that

$\int_{C_3} (y + 2z)\,ds = \int_0^1 [0 + 2(1-t)]\sqrt{2}\,dt = \int_0^1 2\sqrt{2}(1 - t)\,dt$

$= 2\sqrt{2}(t - \frac{1}{2}t^2)\Big|_0^1 = \sqrt{2}$. It follows that

$\int_C (y + 2z)\,ds = \int_{C_1} (y + 2z)\,ds + \int_{C_2} (y + 2z)\,ds + \int_{C_3} (y + 2z)\,ds$

$= \frac{\sqrt{2}}{2} + \frac{3}{2}\sqrt{2} + \sqrt{2} = 3\sqrt{2}$

10. The curve C is composed of the curves C_1 and C_2 parameterized respectively by $\vec{r}_1(t) = 3(1-t)\vec{i} + \vec{j}$ for $0 \le t \le 1$, and $\vec{r}_2(t) = \cos t\,\vec{j} + \sin t\,\vec{k}$ for $0 \le t \le \frac{\pi}{2}$.

Since $x(t) = 3(1 - t)$, $y(t) = 1$, $z(t) = 0$, and

$\left\|\frac{d\vec{r}_1}{dt}\right\| = \sqrt{(-3)^2 + 0^2 + 0^2} = 3$ for C_1, (4) implies that

$\int_{C_1} (3x - 2y + z)\,ds = \int_0^1 [9(1-t) - 2 + 0]\,3\,dt$

$= \int_0^1 3(7 - 9t)\,dt = 3(7t - \frac{9}{2}t^2)\Big|_0^1 = \frac{15}{2}$

Since $x(t) = 0$, $y(t) = \cos t$, $z(t) = \sin t$, and

$\left\|\frac{d\vec{r}_2}{dt}\right\| = \sqrt{0^2 + (-\sin t)^2 + (\cos t)^2} = 1$ for C_2, (4) implies that

$\int_{C_2} (3x - 2y + z)\,ds = \int_0^{\pi/2} [3(0) - 2\cos t + \sin t](1)\,dt$

$= (-2\sin t - \cos t)\Big|_0^{\pi/2} = -1$

Thus

$\int_C (3x - 2y + z)ds = \int_{C_1} (3x - 2y + z)ds + \int_{C_2} (3x - 2y + z)ds = \frac{15}{2} - 1 = \frac{13}{2}$

11. Since $x(t) = 5$, $y(t) = -\sin t$, $z(t) = -\cos t$, and

$\frac{d\vec{r}}{dt} = -\cos t\,\vec{j} + \sin t\,\vec{k}$, (7) implies that

$\int_C \vec{F}\cdot d\vec{r} = \int_0^{\pi/4} (-\cos t\,\vec{i} + \sin t\,\vec{j} - 5\vec{k})\cdot(-\cos t\,\vec{j} + \sin t\,\vec{k})\,dt$

$= \int_0^{\pi/4} (-\sin t\cos t - 5\sin t)dt = (-\frac{1}{2}\sin^2 t + 5\cos t)\Big|_0^{\pi/4}$

$= \frac{5}{2}\sqrt{2} - \frac{21}{4}$

12. Since $x(t) = 1 - t$, $y(t) = t$, $z(t) = \pi t$, and

$\frac{d\vec{r}}{dt} = -\vec{i} + \vec{j} + \pi\vec{k}$, (7) implies that

$\int_C \vec{F}\cdot d\vec{r} = \int_0^1 [t\vec{i} + (1-t)\vec{j} + \pi^3 t^3\vec{k}]\cdot(-\vec{i} + \vec{j} + \pi\vec{k})\,dt$

$= \int_0^1 (-t + 1 - t + \pi^4 t^3)\,dt = (t - t^2 + \frac{1}{4}\pi^4 t^4)\Big|_0^1 = \frac{1}{4}\pi^4$

13. Since $x(t) = \cos t$, $y(t) = \sin t$, $z(t) = 2t$, and

$\frac{d\vec{r}}{dt} = -\sin t\,\vec{i} + \cos t\,\vec{j} + 2\vec{k}$, (7) implies that

$\int_C \vec{F}\cdot d\vec{r} = \int_0^{\pi/2} (\sin t\,\vec{i} + \cos t\sin t\,\vec{j} + 8t^3\vec{k})\cdot(-\sin t\,\vec{i}$

$+ \cos t\,\vec{j} + 2\vec{k})\,dt = \int_0^{\pi/2} (-\sin^2 t + \cos^2 t \sin t + 16t^3)\,dt$

$= \int_0^{\pi/2} (-\frac{1}{2} + \frac{1}{2}\cos 2t + \cos^2 t \sin t + 16t^3)\,dt$

$= (-\frac{1}{2}t + \frac{1}{4}\sin 2t - \frac{1}{3}\cos^3 t + 4t^4)\Big|_0^{\pi/2} = -\frac{1}{4}\pi + \frac{1}{4}\pi^4 + \frac{1}{3}$

14. Since $x(t) = \cos t$, $y(t) = 0$, $z(t) = \sin t$, and $\frac{d\vec{r}}{dt} = -\sin t\,\vec{i} + \cos t\,\vec{k}$, (7) implies that

$\int_C \vec{F}\cdot d\vec{r} = \int_0^{\pi} (-\sin t\,\vec{i} + \cos t\,\vec{k})\cdot(-\sin t\,\vec{i} + \cos t\,\vec{k})\,dt$

$= \int_0^{\pi} (\sin^2 t + \cos^2 t)\,dt = \int_0^{\pi} 1\,dt = \pi$

15. $\int_{-C} \vec{F}\cdot d\vec{r} = -\int_C \vec{F}\cdot d\vec{r} = -\pi$, where C is the curve in Exercise 14.

16. Since $x(t) = e^t$, $y(t) = e^t$, $z(t) = 3$, and $\frac{d\vec{r}}{dt} = e^t\vec{i} + e^t\vec{j}$, (7) implies that

$\int_C \vec{F}\cdot d\vec{r} = \int_0^1 [e^t e^{(e^{2t})}\vec{i} + e^t e^{(e^{2t})}\vec{j} + \cosh e^{4t}\,\vec{k}]\cdot(e^t\vec{i} + e^t\vec{j})\,dt$

$= \int_0^1 2e^{2t}e^{(e^{2t})}\,dt = \int_1^{e^2} e^u\,du = e^u\Big|_1^{e^2} = e^{(e^2)} - e$

17. Since $x(t) = \frac{1}{2}$, $y(t) = 2$, $z(t) = -\ln(\cosh t)$, and $\frac{d\vec{r}}{dt} = -\frac{\sinh t}{\cosh t}\vec{k}$, we have $\vec{F}(x(t),y(t),z(t))\cdot\frac{d\vec{r}}{dt} = 0$, so that by (7), $\int_C \vec{F}\cdot d\vec{r} = \int_0^{\pi/6} 0\,dt = 0$.

18. a. The curve C is composed of the line segments C_1 and C_2 parameterized respectively by $\vec{r}_1(t) = -t\vec{j}$ for $0 \le t \le 1$, and $\vec{r}_2(t) = t\vec{i} + (-1 + 2t)\vec{j} + 2t\vec{k}$ for $0 \le t \le 1$. Since $x(t) = 0$, $y(t) = -t$, $z(t) = 0$, and $\frac{d\vec{r}_1}{dt} = -\vec{j}$ for C_1, (7) implies that

$\int_{C_1} \vec{F}\cdot d\vec{r} = \int_0^1 (0\vec{i} + 0\vec{j} - t\vec{k})\cdot(-\vec{j})\,dt = \int_0^1 0\,dt = 0$

Since $x(t) = t$, $y(t) = -1 + 2t$, $z(t) = 2t$, and $\frac{d\vec{r}_2}{dt} = \vec{i} + 2\vec{j} + 2\vec{k}$ for C_2, (7) implies that

$\int_{C_2} \vec{F}\cdot d\vec{r} = \int_0^1 [t(-1 + 2t)\vec{i} + 4t\vec{j} + (-1 + 4t)\vec{k}]\cdot(\vec{i}+2\vec{j}+2\vec{k})\,dt$

$= \int_0^1 [t(-1 + 2t) + 8t + 2(-1 + 4t)]\,dt = \int_0^1 (2t^2+15t-2)\,dt$

$= (\frac{2}{3}t^3 + \frac{15}{2}t^2 - 2t)\Big|_0^1 = \frac{37}{6}$. We conclude that

$\int_C \vec{F}\cdot d\vec{r} = \int_{C_1} \vec{F}\cdot d\vec{r} + \int_{C_2} \vec{F}\cdot d\vec{r} = 0 + \frac{37}{6} = \frac{37}{6}$.

b. The curve C is composed of the line segments C_1 and C_2 parameterized respectively by $\vec{r}_1(t) = t\vec{j} + t\vec{k}$ for $0 \le t \le 1$, and $\vec{r}_2(t) = t\vec{i} + \vec{j} + (1 + t)\vec{k}$ for $0 \le t \le 1$. Since $x(t) = 0$, $y(t) = t$, $z(t) = t$, and $\frac{d\vec{r}_1}{dt} = \vec{j} + \vec{k}$, (7) implies that

$\int_{C_1} \vec{F}\cdot d\vec{r} = \int_0^1 (0\vec{i} + 2t\vec{j} + 2t\vec{k})\cdot(\vec{j} + \vec{k})\,dt = \int_0^1 (2t + 2t)\,dt$

$= 2t^2\Big|_0^1 = 2$. Since $x(t) = t$, $y(t) = 1$, $z(t) = 1 + t$, and $\frac{d\vec{r}_2}{dt} = \vec{i} + \vec{k}$ for C_2, (7) implies that

$\int_{C_2} \vec{F}\cdot d\vec{r} = \int_0^1 [t\vec{i} + 2(1 + t)\vec{j} + (2 + t)\vec{k}]\cdot(\vec{i} + \vec{k})\,dt$

$= \int_0^1 (t + 2 + t)\,dt = (2t + t^2)\Big|_0^1 = 3$. We conclude that

$\int_C \vec{F}\cdot d\vec{r} = \int_{C_1} \vec{F}\cdot d\vec{r} + \int_{C_2} \vec{F}\cdot d\vec{r} = 2 + 3 = 5.$

c. Since $x(t) = t$, $y(t) = t$, $z(t) = 2t^2$, and $\frac{d\vec{r}}{dt} = \vec{i} + \vec{j} + 4t\vec{k}$, (7) implies that

$\int_C \vec{F}\cdot d\vec{r} = \int_0^1 [t^2\vec{i} + 4t^2\vec{j} + (t + 2t^2)\vec{k}]\cdot(\vec{i} + \vec{j} + 4t\vec{k})\,dt$

$$= \int_0^1 [t^2 + 4t^2 + (t + 2t^2)4t]\, dt = \int_0^1 (9t^2 + 8t^3)\, dt$$

$$= (3t^3 + 2t^4)\Big|_0^1 = 5$$

19. Since $x(t) = e^{-t}$, $y(t) = e^t$, $z(t) = t$, $\frac{dx}{dt} = -e^{-t}$, $\frac{dy}{dt} = e^t$, and $\frac{dz}{dt} = 1$, (9) implies that

$$\int_C y\, dx - x\, dy + xyz^2\, dz = \int_0^1 [(e^t)(-e^{-t}) - (e^{-t})(e^t)$$

$$+ (e^{-t}e^t t^2)(1)]\, dt = \int_0^1 (-2 + t^2)\, dt = (-2t + \tfrac{1}{3}t^3)\Big|_0^1 = -\tfrac{5}{3}$$

20. Since $x(t) = t$, $y(t) = t$, $z(t) = 2t$, $\frac{dx}{dt} = 1$, $\frac{dy}{dt} = 1$, and $\frac{dz}{dt} = 2$, (9) implies that

$$\int_C e^x\, dx + xy\, dy + xyz\, dz = \int_{-1}^1 [(e^t)(1) + (t\cdot t)(1)$$

$$+ (t\cdot t\cdot 2t)(2)]\, dt = \int_{-1}^1 (e^t + t^2 + 4t^3)\, dt$$

$$= (e^t + \tfrac{1}{3}t^3 + t^4)\Big|_{-1}^1 = e - e^{-1} + \tfrac{2}{3}$$

21. $\int_C e^x\, dx + xy\, dy + xyz\, dz = -\int_{-C} e^x\, dx + xy\, dy + xyz\, dz$

$= e^{-1} - e - \frac{2}{3}$ by Exercise 20.

22. Since $x(t) = \cos t$, $y(t) = \sin t$, $z(t) = t$, $\frac{dx}{dt} = -\sin t$, $\frac{dy}{dt} = \cos t$, and $\frac{dz}{dt} = 1$, (9) implies that

$$\int_C y(x^2 + y^2)\, dx - x(x^2 + y^2)dy + xy\, dz$$

$$= \int_{-\pi}^{\pi} [\sin t(\cos^2 t + \sin^2 t)(-\sin t) - \cos t\ (\cos^2 t + \sin^2 t)(\cos t)$$

$$+ (\cos t \sin t)(1)]\, dt = \int_{-\pi}^{\pi} (-\sin^2 t - \cos^2 t + \cos t \sin t)\, dt$$

$$= \int_{-\pi}^{\pi} (-1 + \cos t \sin t)\, dt = (-t + \tfrac{1}{2}\sin^2 t)\Big|_{-\pi}^{\pi} = -2\pi$$

23. Since $x(t) = t + 1$, $y(t) = t - 1$, $z(t) = t^2$, $\frac{dx}{dt} = 1$, $\frac{dy}{dt} = 1$, and $\frac{dz}{dt} = 2t$, (9) implies that

$$\int_C xy\, dx + (x + z)\, dy + z^2\, dz = \int_{-1}^2 [(t + 1)(t - 1)(1)$$

$$+ (t + 1 + t^2)(1) + (t^4)(2t)]\, dt = \int_{-1}^2 (2t^5 + 2t^2 + t)\, dt$$

$$= (\tfrac{1}{3}t^6 + \tfrac{2}{3}t^3 + \tfrac{1}{2}t^2)\Big|_{-1}^2 = \tfrac{57}{2}$$

24. Since $x(t) = \cos t$, $y(t) = \sin t$, $z(t) = \cos t$, $\frac{dx}{dt} = -\sin t$, $\frac{dy}{dt} = \cos t$, and $\frac{dz}{dt} = -\sin t$, (9) implies that

$$\int_C x\, dx + y\, dy + xy\, dz = \int_{-\pi/2}^0 [(\cos t)(-\sin t) + (\sin t)(\cos t)$$

$$+ (\cos t \sin t)(-\sin t)]\, dt = \int_{-\pi/2}^0 -\cos t \sin^2 t\, dt$$

$$= -\tfrac{1}{3}\sin^3 t\Big|_{-\pi/2}^0 = -\tfrac{1}{3}$$

25. Since C is parameterized by $\vec{r}(t) = \cos t\, \vec{i} + \sin t\, \vec{j}$ for $0 \le t \le \frac{\pi}{2}$, and since $x(t) = \cos t$, $y(t) = \sin t$, $\frac{dx}{dt} = -\sin t$, and $\frac{dy}{dt} = \cos t$, the two-dimensional version of (9) implies that

$$\int_C \frac{1}{1 + x^2}\, dx + \frac{2}{1 + y^2}\, dy = \int_0^{\pi/2} \left[\frac{1}{1 + \cos^2 t}(-\sin t)\right.$$

$$\left. + \frac{2}{1 + \sin^2 t}(\cos t)\right] dt = [\arctan(\cos t) + 2\arctan(\sin t)]\Big|_0^{\pi/2}$$

$$= \frac{\pi}{4}$$

26. Since C is parameterized by $\vec{r}(t) = (-1 + 3t)\vec{i} + \vec{j}$ for $0 \le t \le 1$, and since $x(t) = -1 + 3t$, $y(t) = 1$, $z(t) = 0$, $\frac{dx}{dt} = 3$, $\frac{dy}{dt} = 0$, and $\frac{dz}{dt} = 0$, (9) implies that

$$\int_C z\, dx + xy\, dy = \int_0^1 [(0)(3) + (-1 + 3t)(0)]\, dt = \int_0^1 0\, dt = 0$$

27. Since $x(t) = t$, $y(t) = t^2$, $z(t) = t^3$, $\frac{dx}{dt} = 1$, $\frac{dy}{dt} = 2t$, and $\frac{dz}{dt} = 3t^2$, (9) implies that

$$\int_C x \ln\left(\frac{xz}{y}\right) dx + \cos\left(\frac{\pi xy}{z}\right) dy = \int_1^2 [(t \ln t^2)(1) + (\cos \pi)(2t)]\, dt = \int_1^2 (2t \ln t - 2t)\, dt = t^2 \ln t\Big|_1^2 - \int_1^2 t\, dt - t^2\Big|_1^2 = 4 \ln 2 - 3 - \frac{1}{2}t^2\Big|_1^2 = 4 \ln 2 - \frac{9}{2}$$

28. The curve C is composed of the line segments C_1 and C_2 parameterized respectively by $\vec{r}_1(t) = t\vec{i} + t\vec{j} + t\vec{k}$ for $1 \le t \le 2$, and $\vec{r}_2(t) = t\vec{i} + 2\vec{j} + 2\vec{k}$ for $2 \le t \le 4$. By (9),

$$\int_C x \ln\left(\frac{xz}{y}\right) dx + \cos\left(\frac{\pi xy}{z}\right) dy = \int_{C_1} x \ln\left(\frac{xz}{y}\right) dx + \cos\left(\frac{\pi xy}{z}\right) dy + \int_{C_2} x \ln\left(\frac{xz}{y}\right) dx + \cos\left(\frac{\pi xy}{z}\right) dy = \int_1^2 [(t \ln t)(1) + (\cos \pi t)(1)]\, dt + \int_2^4 [(t \ln t)(1) + (\cos \pi t)(0)]\, dt$$

$$= \int_1^4 t \ln t\, dt + \int_1^2 \cos \pi t\, dt = \frac{1}{2}t^2 \ln t\Big|_1^4 - \int_1^4 \frac{1}{2}t\, dt + \frac{1}{\pi}\sin \pi t\Big|_1^2 = 8 \ln 4 - \frac{1}{4}t^2\Big|_1^4 = 8 \ln 4 - \frac{15}{4}$$

29. a. The curve C is composed of the line segments C_1 and C_2 parameterized respectively by $\vec{r}_1(t) = -5t\vec{j}$ for $0 \le t \le 1$, and $\vec{r}_2(t) = (-5 + 6t)\vec{j} + t\vec{k}$ for $0 \le t \le 1$. By (9),

$$\int_C y\, dx + z\, dy + x\, dz = \int_{C_1} y\, dx + z\, dy + x\, dz + \int_{C_2} y\, dx + z\, dy + x\, dz = \int_0^1 [(-5t)(0) + (0)(-5) + (0)(0)]\, dt + \int_0^1 [(-5 + 6t)(0) + (t)(6) + (0)(1)]\, dt$$

$$= \int_0^1 0\, dt + \int_0^1 6t\, dt = 3t^2\Big|_0^1 = 3$$

b. The curve C is composed of the line segments C_1 and C_2 parameterized respectively by $\vec{r}_1(t) = t\vec{i}$ for $0 \le t \le 1$, and $\vec{r}_2(t) = (1 - t)\vec{i} + t\vec{j} + t\vec{k}$ for $0 \le t \le 1$. By (9),

$$\int_C y\, dx + z\, dy + x\, dz = \int_{C_1} y\, dx + z\, dy + x\, dz + \int_{C_2} y\, dx + z\, dy + x\, dz = \int_0^1 [(0)(1) + (0)(0) + (t)(0)]\, dt + \int_0^1 [(t)(-1) + (t)(1) + (1 - t)(1)]\, dt = \int_0^1 0\, dt + \int_0^1 (1 - t)\, dt = \left(t - \frac{1}{2}t^2\right)\Big|_0^1 = \frac{1}{2}$$

30. Since $x(t) = t$, $y(t) = t$, $z(t) = t$, and $\left\|\frac{d\vec{r}_1}{dt}\right\| = \sqrt{1^2 + 1^2 + 1^2} = \sqrt{3}$ for C_1, (4) implies that

$$\int_{C_1} (xy + z)\, ds = \int_0^{1/2} (t^2 + t)\sqrt{3}\, dt = \sqrt{3}\left(\frac{1}{3}t^3 + \frac{1}{2}t^2\right)\Big|_0^{1/2} = \frac{1}{6}\sqrt{3}$$

Since $x(t) = \sin t$, $y(t) = \sin t$, $z(t) = \sin t$, and $\left\|\frac{d\vec{r}_2}{dt}\right\| = \sqrt{\cos^2 t + \cos^2 t + \cos^2 t} = \sqrt{3} \cos t$ for C_2, (4) implies that

$$\int_{C_2} (xy + z)\, ds = \int_0^{\pi/6} (\sin^2 t + \sin t)\sqrt{3} \cos t\, dt = \sqrt{3}\left(\frac{1}{3}\sin^3 t + \frac{1}{2}\sin^2 t\right)\Big|_0^{\pi/6} = \frac{1}{6}\sqrt{3}$$

The answers are the same because C_1 and C_2 are the same curve.

31. If the first component of a parameterization is constant, then $\frac{dx}{dt} = 0$, so that by the first formula in (10),

$$\int_C M(x,y,z)\, dx = \int_a^b M(x(t),y(t),z(t))\,\frac{dx}{dt}\, dt = \int_a^b 0\, dt = 0$$

32. Since the density at (x,y,z) is given by $f(x,y,z) = y^2 + z^2$,

(3) implies that $m = \int_C (y^2 + z^2)\,ds$. Since $x(t) = \sin t$, $y(t) = -\cos t$, $z(t) = 4t$, and $\left\|\frac{d\vec{r}}{dt}\right\| = \sqrt{\cos^2 t + \sin^2 t + 4^2} = \sqrt{17}$, (4) implies that

$$m = \int_C (y^2 + z^2)\,ds = \int_\pi^{2\pi} [(-\cos t)^2 + (4t)^2]\sqrt{17}\,dt$$

$$= \sqrt{17}\int_\pi^{2\pi} \left(\frac{1}{2} + \frac{1}{2}\cos 2t + 16t^2\right) dt$$

$$= \sqrt{17}\left(\frac{1}{2}t + \frac{1}{4}\sin 2t + \frac{16}{3}t^3\right)\Big|_\pi^{2\pi} = \sqrt{17}\left(\frac{\pi}{2} + \frac{112}{3}\pi^3\right)$$

33. Since the density at (x,y,z) is given by $f(x,y,z) = x^2+y^2+z^2$,

$$m = \int_C (x^2 + y^2 + z^2)\,ds = \int_\pi^{2\pi} (\sin^2 t + \cos^2 t + 16t^2)\sqrt{17}\,dt$$

$$= \sqrt{17}\int_\pi^{2\pi} (1 + 16t^2)\,dt = \sqrt{17}\left(t + \frac{16}{3}t^3\right)\Big|_\pi^{2\pi} = \sqrt{17}\left(\pi + \frac{112}{3}\pi^3\right)$$

34. By (6), $W = \int_C \vec{F}\cdot d\vec{r}$. Since $x(t) = t$, $y(t) = t^2$, $z(t) = t^4$, and $\frac{d\vec{r}}{dt} = \vec{i} + 2t\vec{j} + 4t^3\vec{k}$, (7) implies that

$$W = \int_C \vec{F}\cdot d\vec{r} = \int_0^1 (t^3\vec{i} + t^6\vec{j} + t^5\vec{k})\cdot(\vec{i} + 2t\vec{j} + 4t^3\vec{k})\,dt$$

$$= \int_0^1 (t^3 + 2t^7 + 4t^8)\,dt = \left(\frac{1}{4}t^4 + \frac{1}{4}t^8 + \frac{4}{9}t^9\right)\Big|_0^1 = \frac{17}{18}$$

35. a. The line segment C from $(0,0,0)$ to $(1,1,1)$ is parameterized by $\vec{r}(t) = t\vec{i} + t\vec{j} + t\vec{k}$ for $0 \le t \le 1$. By (6), $W = \int_C \vec{F}\cdot d\vec{r}$. Since $x(t) = t$, $y(t) = t$, $z(t) = t$, and $\frac{d\vec{r}}{dt} = \vec{i} + \vec{j} + \vec{k}$, (7) implies that

$$W = \int_C \vec{F}\cdot d\vec{r} = \int_0^1 (t\vec{i} + 2t\vec{j} + 0\vec{k})\cdot(\vec{i} + \vec{j} + \vec{k})\,dt$$

$$= \int_0^1 (t + 2t)\,dt = \frac{3}{2}t^2\Big|_0^1 = \frac{3}{2}$$

b. Let C be the curve parameterized by $\vec{r}$. By (6), $W = \int_C \vec{F}\cdot d\vec{r}$. Since $x(t) = \sin\frac{\pi t}{2}$, $y(t) = \sin\frac{\pi t}{2}$, $z(t) = t$, and $\frac{d\vec{r}}{dt} = \frac{\pi}{2}\cos\frac{\pi t}{2}\vec{i} + \frac{\pi}{2}\cos\frac{\pi t}{2}\vec{j} + \vec{k}$, (7) implies that

$$W = \int_C \vec{F}\cdot d\vec{r} = \int_0^1 \left[\sin\frac{\pi t}{2}\vec{i} + 2t\vec{j} + \left(\sin\frac{\pi t}{2} - t\right)\vec{k}\right]\cdot$$

$$\cdot\left[\frac{\pi}{2}\cos\frac{\pi t}{2}\vec{i} + \frac{\pi}{2}\cos\frac{\pi t}{2}\vec{j} + \vec{k}\right] dt = \int_0^1 \left(\frac{\pi}{2}\sin\frac{\pi t}{2}\cos\frac{\pi t}{2} + \pi t\cos\frac{\pi t}{2} + \sin\frac{\pi t}{2} - t\right) dt$$

$$= \left[\frac{1}{2}\sin^2\left(\frac{\pi t}{2}\right) - \frac{2}{\pi}\cos\frac{\pi t}{2} - \frac{1}{2}t^2\right]\Big|_0^1 + \int_0^1 \pi t\cos\frac{\pi t}{2}\,dt$$

(parts)
$$= \frac{2}{\pi} + 2t\sin\frac{\pi t}{2}\Big|_0^1 - \int_0^1 2\sin\frac{\pi t}{2}\,dt = \frac{2}{\pi} + 2 + \frac{4}{\pi}\cos\frac{\pi t}{2}\Big|_0^1$$

$$= 2 - \frac{2}{\pi}$$

36. The staircase determines a curve C parameterized by $\vec{r}(t) = 50\cos t\,\vec{i} + 50\sin t\,\vec{j} + \frac{25}{\pi}t\,\vec{k}$ for $0 \le t \le 8\pi$. The force is given by $\vec{F}(x,y,z) = -150\vec{k}$. By (6), $W = \int_C \vec{F}\cdot d\vec{r}$. Since $\frac{d\vec{r}}{dt} = -50\sin t\,\vec{i} + 50\cos t\,\vec{j} + \frac{25}{\pi}\vec{k}$, (7) implies that

$$W = \int_C \vec{F}\cdot d\vec{r} = \int_0^{8\pi} (-150\vec{k})\cdot\left(-50\sin t\,\vec{i} + 50\cos t\,\vec{j} + \frac{25}{\pi}\vec{k}\right) dt$$

$$= \int_0^{8\pi} -\frac{3750}{\pi}\,dt = -30{,}000 \text{ (foot-pounds)}$$

37. When the height of the painter is z, the weight of the painter and pail is $120 + (30 - \frac{1}{10}z) = 150 - \frac{1}{10}z$. Thus $\vec{F}(x,y,z) = -(150 - \frac{1}{10}z)\vec{k} = (\frac{1}{10}z - 150)\vec{k}$. By (6) and (7),

$$W = \int_C \vec{F}\cdot d\vec{r} = \int_0^{8\pi} \left[\frac{1}{10}\left(\frac{25t}{\pi}\right) - 150\right]\vec{k}\cdot\left[-50\sin t\,\vec{i} + 50\cos t\,\vec{j}\right.$$

$$\left. + \frac{25}{\pi}\vec{k}\right] dt = \int_0^{8\pi} \frac{25}{\pi}\left[\frac{1}{10}\left(\frac{25t}{\pi}\right) - 150\right] dt$$

$$= \frac{25}{\pi}\left(\frac{5}{4\pi}t^2 - 150t\right)\Big|_0^{8\pi} = -28{,}000 \text{ (foot-pounds)}$$

38. a. Set up a coordinate system with the origin at the center of the earth, and so that the curve C traced out during

half a revolution is parameterized by $\vec{r}(t) = 4400 \cos t \, \vec{i} + 4400 \sin t \, \vec{j}$ for $0 \le t \le \pi$. The magnitude of the force is 6000, and the force is directed toward the center of the earth (at the origin). Thus

$$\vec{F}(x,y) = -6000 \left(\frac{x}{4400} \vec{i} + \frac{y}{4400} \vec{j}\right) = -\frac{15}{11} (x\vec{i} + y\vec{j})$$

By (6), $W = \int_C \vec{F} \cdot d\vec{r}$. Since $x(t) = 4400 \cos t$, $y(t) = 4400 \sin t$, $z(t) = 0$, and $\frac{d\vec{r}}{dt} = -4400 \sin t \, \vec{i} + 4400 \cos t \, \vec{j}$, (7) implies that

$$W = \int_C \vec{F} \cdot d\vec{r} = \int_0^{\pi} -\frac{15}{11} (4400 \cos t \, \vec{i} + 4400 \sin t \, \vec{j}) \cdot$$

$$\cdot \, (-4400 \sin t \, \vec{i} + 4400 \cos t \, \vec{j}) \, dt = \int_0^{\pi} 0 \, dt = 0$$

b. The curve C traced out during one complete revolution is parameterized by $\vec{r}(t) = 4400 \cos t \, \vec{i} + 4400 \sin t \, \vec{j}$ for $0 \le t \le 2\pi$. Using the same type of argument as in part (a), we find that $W = \int_0^{2\pi} 0 \, dt = 0$.

39. a. If the force acts in a direction normal to the path, then $\vec{F}(x,y,z) = f(x,y,z) \, \vec{N}(x,y,z)$, where $\vec{N}$ is the normal vector at (x,y,z) and f is a function of three variables. Then by (5),

$$W = \int_C \vec{F}(x,y,z) \cdot \vec{T}(x,y,z) \, ds = \int_C f(x,y,z) \, \vec{N}(x,y,z) \cdot \vec{T}(x,y,z) \, ds$$

$$= \int_C 0 \, ds = 0$$

b. Since the gravitational field of the earth is a central force field and since the normal vector at any point on the circular orbit also points toward the origin, it follows that the gravitational force acts in a direction normal to the path of the object. Consequently by part (a), the work done by the force is 0 .

Section 15.3

Note: In Exercises 1-8 of this section, the curve C lies in a region without holes, so conditions 1-4 are equivalent. In particular, if $\text{curl } \vec{F} = \vec{0}$, then $\int_C \vec{F} \cdot d\vec{r}$ is independent of path.

1. Let $\vec{F}(x,y) = (e^x + y)\vec{i} + (x + 2y)\vec{j} = M(x,y)i + N(x,y)j$. Since $\frac{\partial N}{\partial x} = 1 = \frac{\partial M}{\partial y}$, so $\text{curl } \vec{F} = \vec{0}$, the line integral is independent of path. Let $\text{grad } f(x,y) = \vec{F}(x,y)$. Then

$$\frac{\partial f}{\partial x} = e^x + y \quad \text{and} \quad \frac{\partial f}{\partial y} = x + 2y \qquad (*)$$

Integrating both sides of the first equation in (*) with respect to x, we obtain $f(x,y) = e^x + xy + g(y)$. Taking partial derivatives with respect to y, we find that $\frac{\partial f}{\partial y} = x + \frac{dg}{dy}$. Comparing this with the second equation in (*), we conclude that $\frac{dg}{dy} = 2y$, so that $g(y) = y^2 + C$. If $C = 0$, then $f(x,y) = e^x + xy + y^2$. Thus

$$\int_C (e^x + y) \, dx + (x + 2y) \, dy = f(2,3) - f(0,1) = (e^2 + 15) - 2$$

$$= e^2 + 13$$

2. Let $\vec{F}(x,y) = (2xy^2 + 1)\vec{i} + 2x^2y \, \vec{j} = M(x,y)\vec{i} + N(x,y)\vec{j}$. Since $\frac{\partial N}{\partial x} = 4xy = \frac{\partial M}{\partial y}$, so $\text{curl } \vec{F} = \vec{0}$, the line integral is independent of path. Let $\text{grad } f(x,y) = \vec{F}(x,y)$. Then

$$\frac{\partial f}{\partial x} = 2xy^2 + 1 \quad \text{and} \quad \frac{\partial f}{\partial y} = 2x^2y \qquad (*)$$

Integrating both sides of the first equation in (*) with respect to x, we obtain $f(x,y) = x^2y^2 + x + g(y)$. Taking partial derivatives with respect to y, we find that $\frac{\partial f}{\partial y} = 2x^2y + \frac{dg}{dy}$. Comparing this with the second equation in (*), we conclude that $\frac{dg}{dy} = 0$, so that $g(y) = C$. If $C = 0$, then $f(x,y) = x^2y^2 + x$. Thus

$$\int_C (2xy^2 + 1)\,dx + 2x^2y\,dy = f(2,3) - f(-1,2) = 38 - 3 = 35$$

3. Let $\vec{F}(x,y,z) = y\vec{i} + (x+z)\vec{j} + y\vec{k} = M(x,y,z)\vec{i} + N(x,y,z)\vec{j} + P(x,y,z)\vec{k}$. Since $\frac{\partial P}{\partial y} = 1 = \frac{\partial N}{\partial z}$, $\frac{\partial M}{\partial z} = 0 = \frac{\partial P}{\partial x}$, and $\frac{\partial N}{\partial x} = 1 = \frac{\partial M}{\partial y}$, so $\text{curl}\,\vec{F} = \vec{0}$, the line integral is independent of path. Let $\text{grad}\, f(x,y,z) = \vec{F}(x,y,z)$. Then

$$\frac{\partial f}{\partial x} = y, \quad \frac{\partial f}{\partial y} = x + z, \quad \text{and} \quad \frac{\partial f}{\partial z} = y \qquad (*)$$

Integrating both sides of the first equation in (*) with respect to x, we obtain $f(x,y,z) = xy + g(y,z)$. Taking partial derivatives with respect to y, we find that $\frac{\partial f}{\partial y} = x + \frac{\partial g}{\partial y}$. Comparing this with the second equation in (*), we deduce that $\frac{\partial g}{\partial y} = z$, so that by integrating with respect to y we obtain $g(y,z) = yz + h(z)$. Thus $f(x,y,z) = xy + yz + h(z)$. Taking partial derivatives with respect to z, we find that $\frac{\partial f}{\partial z} = y + \frac{dh}{dz}$. Comparing this with the third equation in (*), we conclude that $\frac{dh}{dz} = 0$, so that $h(z) = C$. If $C = 0$, then $f(x,y,z) = xy + yz$. Since $\vec{r}(0) = -\vec{i} + \vec{j}$ and $\vec{r}(\frac{1}{2}) = -\frac{5}{3}\vec{i} + \vec{k}$, it follows that the initial point of C is $(-1,1,0)$ and the terminal point is $(-\frac{5}{3},0,1)$. Thus

$$\int_C y\,dx + (x+z)\,dy + y\,dz = f(-\tfrac{5}{3},0,1) - f(-1,1,0) = 0-(-1) = 1$$

4. Let $\vec{F}(x,y,z) = (\cos x + 2yz)\vec{i} + (\sin y + 2xz)\vec{j} + (z + 2xy)\vec{k} = M(x,y,z)\vec{i} + N(x,y,z)\vec{j} + P(x,y,z)\vec{k}$. Since $\frac{\partial P}{\partial y} = 2x = \frac{\partial N}{\partial z}$, $\frac{\partial M}{\partial z} = 2y = \frac{\partial P}{\partial x}$, and $\frac{\partial N}{\partial x} = 2z = \frac{\partial M}{\partial y}$, so $\text{curl}\,\vec{F} = \vec{0}$, the line integral is independent of path. Let $\text{grad}\, f(x,y,z) = \vec{F}(x,y,z)$. Then

$$\frac{\partial f}{\partial x} = \cos x + 2yz, \quad \frac{\partial f}{\partial y} = \sin y + 2xz, \quad \text{and} \quad \frac{\partial f}{\partial z} = z + 2xy \qquad (*)$$

Integrating both sides of the first equation in (*) with respect to x, we obtain $f(x,y,z) = \sin x + 2xyz + g(y,z)$. Taking partial derivatives with respect to y, we find that $\frac{\partial f}{\partial y} = 2xz + \frac{\partial g}{\partial y}$. Comparing this with the second equation in (*), we deduce that $\frac{\partial g}{\partial y} = \sin y$, so that by integrating with respect to y we obtain $g(y,z) = -\cos y + h(z)$. Thus $f(x,y,z) = \sin x + 2xyz - \cos y + h(z)$. Taking partial derivatives with respect to z, we find that $\frac{\partial f}{\partial z} = 2xy + \frac{dh}{dz}$. Comparing this with the third equation in (*), we conclude that $\frac{dh}{dz} = z$, so that integration yields $h(z) = \frac{1}{2}z^2 + C$. If $C = 0$, then $f(x,y,z) = \sin x + 2xyz - \cos y + \frac{1}{2}z^2$. Then

$$\int_C (\cos x + 2yz)\,dx + (\sin y + 2xz)\,dy + (z + 2xy)\,dz = f(\pi,\pi,\tfrac{1}{\pi}) - f(0,0,0) = 2\pi + 1 + \frac{1}{2\pi^2} - (-1) = 2\pi + 2 + \frac{1}{2\pi^2}$$

5. Let $\vec{F}(x,y,z) = \frac{x}{1+x^2+y^2+z^2}\vec{i} + \frac{y}{1+x^2+y^2+z^2}\vec{j} + \frac{z}{1+x^2+y^2+z^2}\vec{k} = M(x,y,z)\vec{i} + N(x,y,z)\vec{j} + P(x,y,z)\vec{k}$. Since

$$\frac{\partial P}{\partial y} = \frac{-2yz}{(1+x^2+y^2+z^2)^2} = \frac{\partial N}{\partial z}, \quad \frac{\partial M}{\partial z} = \frac{-2xz}{(1+x^2+y^2+z^2)^2} = \frac{\partial P}{\partial x},$$

and $\frac{\partial N}{\partial x} = \frac{-2xy}{(1+x^2+y^2+z^2)^2} = \frac{\partial M}{\partial y}$, so $\text{curl}\,\vec{F} = \vec{0}$, the line integral is independent of path. Let $\text{grad}\, f(x,y,z) = \vec{F}(x,y,z)$. Then

$$\frac{\partial f}{\partial x} = \frac{x}{1+x^2+y^2+z^2}, \quad \frac{\partial f}{\partial y} = \frac{y}{1+x^2+y^2+z^2}, \quad \text{and} \quad \frac{\partial f}{\partial z} = \frac{z}{1+x^2+y^2+z^2} \qquad (*)$$

Integrating both sides of the first equation in (*) with respect to x, we obtain $f(x,y,z) = \frac{1}{2}\ln(1 + x^2 + y^2 + z^2) + g(y,z)$. Taking partial derivatives with respect to y, we find that $\frac{\partial f}{\partial y} = \frac{y}{1+x^2+y^2+z^2} + \frac{\partial g}{\partial y}$. Comparing this with the second equation in (*), we deduce that $\frac{\partial g}{\partial y} = 0$, so that integrating with respect to y yields $g(y,z) = h(z)$. Thus $f(x,y,z) = \frac{1}{2}\ln(1 + x^2 + y^2 + z^2) + h(z)$. Taking partial derivatives with respect to z, we find that

$\frac{\partial f}{\partial z} = \frac{z}{1 + x^2 + y^2 + z^2} + \frac{dh}{dz}$. Comparing this with the third equation in (*), we conclude that $\frac{dh}{dz} = 0$, so that integration yields $h(z) = C$. If $C = 0$, then $f(x,y,z)$ $= \frac{1}{2}\ln(1 + x^2 + y^2 + z^2)$. Since $\vec{r}(0) = \vec{0}$ and $\vec{r}(1) = \vec{i} + \vec{j} + \vec{k}$, it follows that the initial and terminal points of C are $(0,0,0)$ and $(1,1,1)$, respectively. Then

$$\int_C \frac{x}{1 + x^2 + y^2 + z^2}\,dx + \frac{y}{1 + x^2 + y^2 + z^2}\,dy + \frac{z}{1 + x^2 + y^2 + z^2}\,dz$$

$$= f(1,1,1) - f(0,0,0) = \frac{1}{2}\ln 4 - 0 = \ln 2$$

6. Let $\vec{F}(x,y,z) = (y + 2xe^y)\vec{i} + (x + x^2e^y)\vec{j} = M(x,y,z)\vec{i} + N(x,y,z)\vec{j}$ $+ P(x,y,z)\vec{k}$. Since $\frac{\partial P}{\partial y} = 0 = \frac{\partial N}{\partial z}$, $\frac{\partial M}{\partial z} = 0 = \frac{\partial P}{\partial x}$, and $\frac{\partial N}{\partial x} = 1 + 2xe^y = \frac{\partial M}{\partial y}$, so curl $\vec{F} = \vec{0}$, the line integral is independent of path. Let grad $f(x,y,z) = \vec{F}(x,y,z)$. Then

$$\frac{\partial f}{\partial x} = y + 2xe^y, \quad \frac{\partial f}{\partial y} = x + x^2e^y, \quad \text{and} \quad \frac{\partial f}{\partial z} = 0 \qquad (*)$$

Integrating both sides of the first equation in (*) with respect to x, we obtain $f(x,y,z) = xy + x^2e^y + g(y,z)$. Taking partial derivatives with respect to y, we find that $\frac{\partial f}{\partial y} = x + x^2e^y + \frac{\partial g}{\partial y}$. Comparing this with the second equation in (*), we deduce that $\frac{\partial g}{\partial y} = 0$, so integration yields $g(y,z) = h(z)$. Thus $f(x,y,z) = xy + x^2e^y + h(z)$. Taking partial derivatives with respect to z, we find that $\frac{\partial f}{\partial z} = \frac{dh}{dz}$. Comparing this with the third equation in (*), we conclude that $\frac{dh}{dz} = 0$, so that integration yields $h(z) = C$. If $C = 0$, then $f(x,y,z) = xy + x^2e^y$. Since $\vec{r}(1) = \vec{i} + \vec{k}$ and $\vec{r}(4) = 2\vec{i} + \ln 4\,\vec{j} + 4\vec{k}$, it follows that the initial and terminal points of C are $(1,0,1)$ and $(2, \ln 4, 4)$, respectively. Then

$$\int_C (y + 2xe^y)\,dx + (x + x^2e^y)\,dy = f(2, \ln 4, 4) - f(1,0,1)$$

$$= (2\ln 4 + 16) - 1 = 4\ln 2 + 15$$

7. Let $\vec{F}(x,y,z) = e^{-x}\ln y\,\vec{i} - \frac{e^{-x}}{y}\vec{j} + z\vec{k} = M(x,y,z)\vec{i} + N(x,y,z)\vec{j}$ $+ P(x,y,z)\vec{k}$. Since $\frac{\partial P}{\partial y} = 0 = \frac{\partial N}{\partial z}$, $\frac{\partial M}{\partial z} = 0 = \frac{\partial P}{\partial x}$, and $\frac{\partial N}{\partial x} = \frac{e^{-x}}{y} = \frac{\partial M}{\partial y}$, so curl $\vec{F} = \vec{0}$, the line integral is independent of path. Let grad $f(x,y,z) = \vec{F}(x,y,z)$. Then

$$\frac{\partial f}{\partial x} = e^{-x}\ln y, \quad \frac{\partial f}{\partial y} = \frac{-e^{-x}}{y}, \quad \text{and} \quad \frac{\partial f}{\partial z} = z \qquad (*)$$

Integrating both sides of the first equation in (*) with respect to x, we obtain $f(x,y,z) = -e^{-x}\ln y + g(y,z)$. Taking partial derivatives with respect to y, we find that $\frac{\partial f}{\partial y} = \frac{-e^{-x}}{y} + \frac{\partial g}{\partial y}$. Comparing this with the second equation in (*), we deduce that $\frac{\partial g}{\partial y} = 0$, so integration yields $g(y,z) = h(z)$. Then $f(x,y,z) = -e^{-x}\ln y + h(z)$. Taking partial derivatives with respect to z, we find that $\frac{\partial f}{\partial z} = \frac{dh}{dz}$. Comparing this with the third equation in (*), we conclude that $\frac{dh}{dz} = z$, so integration yields $h(z) = \frac{1}{2}z^2 + C$. If $C = 0$, then we find that $f(x,y,z) = -e^{-x}\ln y + \frac{1}{2}z^2$. Since $\vec{r}(0) = -\vec{i} + \vec{j} + \vec{k}$ and $\vec{r}(1) = e\vec{j} + 2\vec{k}$, it follows that the initial and terminal points of C are $(-1,1,1)$ and $(0,e,2)$, respectively. Then

$$\int_C e^{-x}\ln y\,dx - \frac{e^{-x}}{y}\,dy + z\,dz = f(0,e,2) - f(-1,1,1) = 1 - \frac{1}{2} = \frac{1}{2}$$

8. Let $\vec{F}(x,y,z) = (x + \cos\pi y)\vec{i} - \pi x\sin\pi y\,\vec{j} = M(x,y,z)\vec{i}$ $+ N(x,y,z)\vec{j} + P(x,y,z)\vec{k}$. Since $\frac{\partial P}{\partial y} = 0 = \frac{\partial N}{\partial z}$, $\frac{\partial M}{\partial z} = 0 = \frac{\partial P}{\partial x}$, and $\frac{\partial N}{\partial x} = -\pi\sin\pi y = \frac{\partial M}{\partial y}$, so curl $\vec{F} = \vec{0}$, the line integral is independent of path. Let grad $f(x,y,z) = \vec{F}(x,y,z)$. Then

$$\frac{\partial f}{\partial x} = x + \cos \pi y, \quad \frac{\partial f}{\partial y} = -\pi x \sin \pi y, \quad \text{and} \quad \frac{\partial f}{\partial z} = 0 \qquad (*)$$

Integrating both sides of the first equation in (*) with respect to x, we obtain $f(x,y,z) = \frac{1}{2}x^2 + x \cos \pi y + g(y,z)$. Taking partial derivatives with respect to y, we find that $\frac{\partial f}{\partial y} = -\pi x \sin \pi y + \frac{\partial g}{\partial y}$. Comparing this with the second equation in (*), we deduce that $\frac{\partial g}{\partial y} = 0$, so integration yields $g(y,z) = h(z)$. Then $f(x,y,z) = \frac{1}{2}x^2 + x\cos \pi y + h(z)$. Taking partial derivatives with respect to z, we find that $\frac{\partial f}{\partial z} = \frac{dh}{dz}$. Comparing this with the third equation in (*), we conclude that $\frac{dh}{dz} = 0$, so integration yields $h(z) = C$. If $C = 0$, then $f(x,y,z) = \frac{1}{2}x^2 + x \cos \pi y$. Since $\vec{r}(0) = \vec{i}$ and $\vec{r}(1) = e\vec{i} + \vec{j} + \vec{k}$, it follows that the initial and terminal points of C are $(1,0,0)$ and $(e,1,1)$, respectively. Then

$$\int_C (x + \cos \pi y)\, dx - \pi x \sin \pi y\, dy = f(e,1,1) - f(1,0,0)$$

$$= \left(\frac{1}{2}e^2 - e\right) - \left(-\frac{1}{2}\right) = \frac{1}{2}e^2 - e + \frac{1}{2}$$

9. Let $\vec{F}(x,y,z) = f(x)\vec{i} + g(y)\vec{j} + h(z)\vec{k} = M(x,y,z)\vec{i} + N(x,y,z)\vec{j} + P(x,y,z)k$. Since $\frac{\partial P}{\partial y} = 0 = \frac{\partial N}{\partial z}$, $\frac{\partial M}{\partial z} = 0 = \frac{\partial P}{\partial x}$, and $\frac{\partial N}{\partial x} = 0 = \frac{\partial M}{\partial y}$, it follows that $\text{curl}\, \vec{F} = \vec{0}$, so that

$\int_C \vec{F}\cdot d\vec{r} = \int_C f(x)\, dx + g(y)\, dy + h(z)\, dz$ is independent of path.

10. Let $\vec{F}(x,y) = \frac{y}{x^2+y^2}\vec{i} - \frac{x}{x^2+y^2}\vec{j} = M(x,y)\vec{i} + N(x,y)\vec{j}$.

a. Since $\frac{\partial N}{\partial x} = \frac{x^2 - y^2}{(x^2+y^2)^2} = \frac{\partial M}{\partial y}$, it follows that $\text{curl}\, \vec{F} = \vec{0}$.

b. If C_1 is parameterized by $\vec{r}_1(t) = \cos t\, \vec{i} + \sin t\, \vec{j}$, so that $x = \cos t$ and $y = \sin t$ for $0 \le t \le \pi$, then

$$\int_{C_1} \vec{F}\cdot d\vec{r} = \int_0^\pi \left(M\frac{dx}{dt} + N\frac{dy}{dt}\right) dt = \int_0^\pi \left[\frac{\sin t}{\cos^2 t + \sin^2 t}(-\sin t) - \frac{\cos t}{\cos^2 t + \sin^2 t}(\cos t)\right] dt = \int_0^\pi -1\, dt = -\pi$$

If C_2 is parameterized by $\vec{r}_2(t) = \cos t\, \vec{i} - \sin t\, \vec{j}$, so that $x = \cos t$ and $y = -\sin t$ for $0 \le t \le \pi$, then

$$\int_{C_2} \vec{F}\cdot d\vec{r} = \int_0^\pi \left(M\frac{dx}{dt} + N\frac{dy}{dt}\right) dt = \int_0^\pi \left[\frac{-\sin t}{\cos^2 t + \sin^2 t}(-\sin t) - \frac{\cos t}{\cos^2 t + \sin^2 t}(-\cos t)\right] dt = \int_0^\pi 1\, dt = \pi$$

Since C_1 and C_2 have the same initial and terminal points, and since the corresponding integrals have distinct values, $\int_C \vec{F}\cdot d\vec{r}$ is not independent of path in R.

11. a. Let $h(u) = \int g(u)\, du$ and $f(x,y,z) = \frac{1}{2}h(x^2 + y^2 + z^2)$. If $u = x^2 + y^2 + z^2$, then

$$\text{grad } f = \frac{\partial f}{\partial x}\vec{i} + \frac{\partial f}{\partial y}\vec{j} + \frac{\partial f}{\partial z}\vec{k} = \frac{1}{2}\frac{dh}{du}\frac{\partial u}{\partial x}\vec{i} + \frac{1}{2}\frac{dh}{du}\frac{\partial u}{\partial y}\vec{j} + \frac{1}{2}\frac{dh}{du}\frac{\partial u}{\partial z}\vec{k}$$

$$= \frac{1}{2}g(x^2+y^2+z^2)(2x)\vec{i} + \frac{1}{2}g(x^2+y^2+z^2)(2y)\vec{j} + \frac{1}{2}g(x^2+y^2+z^2)(2z)\vec{k}$$

$$= g(x^2+y^2+z^2)(x\vec{i} + y\vec{j} + z\vec{k}) = \vec{F}(x,y,z)$$

Thus $\vec{F}$ is conservative.

b. Since $\text{curl}\, \vec{F} = \text{curl (grad } f)$ from (a), and since $\text{curl (grad } f) = \vec{0}$ from (5) in Section 15.1, it follows that $\text{curl}\, \vec{F} = \vec{0}$, so $\vec{F}$ is irrotational.

12. Since the gravitational field $\vec{F}$ is conservative, the work is independent of path. Thus we may assume that the rocket descends along a straight line. We set up a coordinate system so that the center of the earth is the origin and the rocket descends along a path C on the z axis from $(0,0,7460)$ to $(0,0,3960)$. Notice that $\vec{F}(x,y,z) = \frac{c}{(x^2+y^2+z^2)^{3/2}}(x\vec{i} + y\vec{j} + z\vec{k})$, for an appropriate negative constant c. But the hypothesis implies that if $x^2 + y^2 + z^2 = (3960)^2$, then $5000 = \|\vec{F}(x,y,z)\| = \left|\frac{c}{(3960)^2}\right|$, so that $c = -(3960)^2 5000$, and

therefore $\vec{F}(x,y,z) = -\dfrac{(3960)^2 5000}{(x^2+y^2+z^2)^{3/2}}(x\vec{i} + y\vec{j} + z\vec{k})$.

If $f(x,y,z) = \dfrac{(3960)^2 5000}{(x^2+y^2+z^2)^{1/2}}$, then from (3) in Section 15.1 we deduce that grad $f(x,y,z) = \vec{F}(x,y,z)$, and then we conclude that

$$W = \int_C \vec{F}\cdot d\vec{r} = f(0,0,3960) - f(0,0,7460)$$

$$= (3960)^2 5000\left(\frac{1}{3960} - \frac{1}{7460}\right) \approx 9{,}289{,}544 \text{ (mile-pounds)}$$

13. Since the electric field $\vec{E}$ is conservative, the work is independent of path. Thus we may assume that the charge moves in a straight line. We set up a coordinate system so that the electron is at the origin and the charge moves from $(0,0,10^{-11})$ to $(0,0,10^{-12})$. At this time we recall from Section 15.1 that $\vec{E}(x,y,z) = \dfrac{(-1.6)\times 10^{-19}}{4\pi\varepsilon_0(x^2+y^2+z^2)^{3/2}}(x\vec{i} + y\vec{j} + z\vec{k})$. Now if $f(x,y,z) = \dfrac{(1.6)\times 10^{-19}}{(x^2+y^2+z^2)^{1/2}}$, then grad $f(x,y,z) = \vec{E}(x,y,z)$, so

$$W = \int_C \vec{E}\cdot d\vec{r} = f(0,0,10^{-12}) - f(0,0,10^{-11})$$

$$= \frac{(1.6)\times 10^{-19}}{4\pi\varepsilon_0}(10^{12} - 10^{11}) \approx 1293.8 \text{ (joules)}$$

14. If $\vec{F}(x,y) = M(x,y)\vec{i} + N(x,y)\vec{j}$, then $\dfrac{\partial N}{\partial x} = 0 = \dfrac{\partial M}{\partial y}$, so the work is independent of path, and there is a function f such that grad $f = \vec{F}$. Then

$$\frac{\partial f}{\partial x} = -ax \quad \text{and} \quad \frac{\partial f}{\partial y} = -ay \qquad (*)$$

Integrating both sides of the first equation in (*) with respect to x, we obtain $f(x,y) = -\frac{a}{2}x^2 + g(y)$. Taking partial derivatives with respect to y, we find that $\dfrac{\partial f}{\partial y} = \dfrac{dg}{dy}$. Comparing this with the second equation of (*), we deduce that $\dfrac{dg}{dy} = -ay$, so integration yields $g(y) = -\frac{a}{2}y^2 + C$. If $C = 0$, then $f(x,y) = -\frac{a}{2}x^2 - \frac{a}{2}y^2$, and consequently

$$\int_C \vec{F}\cdot d\vec{r} = f(1,-2) - f(3,-6) = -\frac{5}{2}a + \frac{45}{2}a = 20a$$

15. Let $t = a$ when the speed of the object is 50 meters per second, and $t = b$ when the speed of the object is 10 meters per second. The change in kinetic energy (in joules) is

$$\frac{m}{2}\|\vec{r}\,'(b)\|^2 - \frac{m}{2}\|\vec{r}\,'(a)\|^2 = \frac{5}{2}(10)^2 - \frac{5}{2}(50)^2 = -6000$$

It follows from the Law of Conservation of Energy that the change in kinetic energy is the negative of the change in potential energy, so this latter change is 6000 joules.

Section 15.4

In Exercises 1-18, R denotes the region enclosed by C.

1. By Green's Theorem, $\int_C M(x,y)\,dx + N(x,y)\,dy = \iint_R \left(\frac{\partial N}{\partial x} - \frac{\partial M}{\partial y}\right) dA$

$= \iint_R (0 - 1)\,dA = -(\text{area of } R) = -\pi.$

2. By Green's Theorem, $\int_C M(x,y)\,dx + N(x,y)\,dy = \iint_R \left(\frac{\partial N}{\partial x} - \frac{\partial M}{\partial y}\right) dA$

$= \iint_R (1 - 0)\,dA = \text{area of } R = 9\pi.$

3. By Green's Theorem, $\int_C M(x,y)\,dx + N(x,y)\,dy = \iint_R \left(\frac{\partial N}{\partial x} - \frac{\partial M}{\partial y}\right) dA$

$= \iint_R \left(\frac{3}{2}x^{1/2} - x\right) dA = \int_0^1\int_0^1 \left(\frac{3}{2}x^{1/2} - x\right) dx\,dy$

$= \int_0^1 \left(x^{3/2} - \frac{1}{2}x^2\right)\Big|_0^1 dy = \int_0^1 \frac{1}{2}\,dy = \frac{1}{2}.$

4. By Green's Theorem, $\int_C M(x,y)\,dx + N(x,y)\,dy = \iint_R \left(\frac{\partial N}{\partial x} - \frac{\partial M}{\partial y}\right) dA$

$= \iint_R (\sin y - \cos x)\,dA = \int_0^{\pi/2}\int_0^{\pi/2-x} (\sin y - \cos x)\,dy\,dx$

$= \int_0^{\pi/2} (-\cos y - y\cos x)\Big|_0^{\pi/2-x} dx = \int_0^{\pi/2} \left[-\cos\left(\frac{\pi}{2} - x\right)\right.$

$\left. - \left(\frac{\pi}{2} - x\right)\cos x + 1\right] dx = \int_0^{\pi/2} \left[-\cos\left(\frac{\pi}{2} - x\right) - \frac{\pi}{2}\cos x + 1\right] dx$

$+ \int_0^{\pi/2} x\cos x\,dx = \left[\sin\left(\frac{\pi}{2} - x\right) - \frac{\pi}{2}\sin x + x\right]\Big|_0^{\pi/2}$

$+ x\sin x\Big|_0^{\pi/2} - \int_0^{\pi/2} \sin x\,dx = -1 + \frac{\pi}{2} + \cos x\Big|_0^{\pi/2} = \frac{\pi}{2} - 2.$

5. By Green's Theorem, $\int_C M(x,y)\,dx + N(x,y)\,dy = \iint_R \left(\frac{\partial N}{\partial x} - \frac{\partial M}{\partial y}\right) dA$

$= \iint_R [3x(x^2 + y^2)^{1/2} - 3y(x^2 + y^2)^{1/2}]\,dA$

$= \int_0^{2\pi}\int_0^1 3r^3(\cos\theta - \sin\theta)\,dr\,d\theta = \int_0^{2\pi} \frac{3}{4}r^4(\cos\theta - \sin\theta)\Big|_0^1 d\theta$

$= \int_0^{2\pi} \frac{3}{4}(\cos\theta - \sin\theta)\,d\theta = \frac{3}{4}(\sin\theta + \cos\theta)\Big|_0^{2\pi} = 0.$

6. By Green's Theorem, $\int_C (y^3 + y)\,dx + 3y^2x\,dy$

$= \iint_R \left[\frac{\partial}{\partial x}(3y^2x) - \frac{\partial}{\partial y}(y^3 + y)\right] dA = \iint_R [3y^2 - (3y^2 + 1)]\,dA$

$= \iint_R -1\,dA = -(\text{area of } R) = -100\pi.$

7. By Green's Theorem, $\int_C y\,dx - x\,dy = \iint_R \left[\frac{\partial}{\partial x}(-x) - \frac{\partial y}{\partial y}\right] dA$

$= \iint_R -2\,dA = \int_0^{2\pi}\int_0^{1-\cos\theta} -2r\,dr\,d\theta = \int_0^{2\pi} -r^2\Big|_0^{1-\cos\theta} d\theta$

$= \int_0^{2\pi} (-1 + 2\cos\theta - \cos^2\theta)\,d\theta = \int_0^{2\pi} \left(-1 + 2\cos\theta - \frac{1}{2} - \cos 2\theta\right) d\theta$

$= \left(-\frac{3}{2}\theta + 2\sin\theta - \frac{1}{2}\sin 2\theta\right)\Big|_0^{2\pi} = -3\pi.$

8. By Green's Theorem, $\int_C (2xy^3 + \cos x)\,dx + (3x^2y^2 + 5x)\,dy$

$= \iint_R \left[\frac{\partial}{\partial x}(3x^2y^2 + 5x) - \frac{\partial}{\partial y}(2xy^3 + \cos x)\right] dA$

$= \iint_R [(6xy^2 + 5) - (6xy^2)]\,dA = \iint_R 5\,dA = 5\,(\text{area of } R) = 320\pi.$

9. By Green's Theorem, $\int_C e^x \sin y\,dx + e^x \cos y\,dy$

$= \iint_R \left[\frac{\partial}{\partial x}(e^x \cos y) - \frac{\partial}{\partial y}(e^x \sin y)\right] dA$

$= \iint_R (e^x \cos y - e^x \cos y)\,dA = \iint_R 0\,dA = 0.$

10. By Green's Theorem, $\int_C (x\cos^2 x - y)\,dx + (x - e^y)\,dy$

$= \iint_R [\frac{\partial}{\partial x}(x - e^y) - \frac{\partial}{\partial y}(x\cos^2 x - y)]\,dA = \iint_R [1 - (-1)]\,dA$

$= 2(\text{area of } R) = 2.$

11. By Green's Theorem, $\int_C xy\,dx + (\frac{1}{2}x^2 + xy)\,dy$

$= \iint_R [\frac{\partial}{\partial x}(\frac{1}{2}x^2 + xy) - \frac{\partial}{\partial y}(xy)]\,dA = \iint_R (x + y - x)\,dA$

$= \iint_R y\,dA = \int_{-1}^{1}\int_0^{\frac{1}{2}\sqrt{1-x^2}} y\,dy\,dx = \int_{-1}^{1} \frac{1}{2}y^2\Big|_0^{\frac{1}{2}\sqrt{1-x^2}} dx$

$= \int_{-1}^{1} \frac{1}{8}(1 - x^2)\,dx = \frac{1}{8}(x - \frac{1}{3}x^3)\Big|_{-1}^{1} = \frac{1}{6}\,.$

12. By Green's Theorem, $\int_C xy^2\,dx + (x^4 + x^2y)\,dy$

$= \iint_R [\frac{\partial}{\partial x}(x^4 + x^2y) - \frac{\partial}{\partial y}(xy^2)]\,dA = \iint_R (4x^3 + 2xy - 2xy)\,dA$

$= \iint_R 4x^3\,dA = \int_{-1}^{1}\int_{-(1-x^4)^{1/4}}^{(1-x^4)^{1/4}} 4x^3\,dy\,dx = \int_{-1}^{1} 4x^3y\Big|_{-(1-x^4)^{1/4}}^{(1-x^4)^{1/4}} dx$

$= \int_{-1}^{1} 8x^3(1 - x^4)^{1/4}\,dx = -\frac{8}{5}(1 - x^4)^{5/4}\Big|_{-1}^{1} = 0.$

13. By Green's Theorem, $\int_C (\cos^3 x + e^x)\,dx + e^y\,dy$

$= \iint_R [\frac{\partial}{\partial x}(e^y) - \frac{\partial}{\partial y}(\cos^3 x + e^x)]\,dA = \iint_R 0\,dA = 0.$

14. By Green's Theorem, $\int_C \ln(x^2 + y^2)\,dx + \ln(x^2 + y^2)\,dy$

$= \iint_R [\frac{\partial}{\partial x}\ln(x^2 + y^2) - \frac{\partial}{\partial y}\ln(x^2 + y^2)]\,dA$

$= \iint_R \frac{2(x - y)}{x^2 + y^2}\,dA = \int_0^{\pi}\int_1^2 2(\cos\theta - \sin\theta)\,dr\,d\theta$

$= \int_0^{\pi} 2(\cos\theta - \sin\theta)\,r\Big|_1^2 d\theta = \int_0^{\pi} 2(\cos\theta - \sin\theta)\,d\theta$

$= 2(\sin\theta + \cos\theta)\Big|_0^{\pi} = -4.$

15. By Green's Theorem, $\int_C \vec{F}\cdot d\vec{r} = \int_C y\,dx + 3x\,dy$

$= \iint_R [\frac{\partial}{\partial x}(3x) - \frac{\partial y}{\partial y}]\,dA = \iint_R (3 - 1)\,dA = 2\,(\text{area of } R) = 8\pi.$

16. By Green's Theorem, $\int_C \vec{F}\cdot d\vec{r} = \int_C y^4\,dx + x^3\,dy$

$= \iint_R [\frac{\partial}{\partial x}(x^3) - \frac{\partial}{\partial y}(y^4)]\,dA = \iint_R (3x^2 - 4y^3)\,dA$

$= \int_{-2}^{2}\int_{-2}^{2} (3x^2 - 4y^3)\,dy\,dx = \int_{-2}^{2} (3x^2y - y^4)\Big|_{-2}^{2} dx$

$= \int_{-2}^{2} 12x^2\,dx = 4x^3\Big|_{-2}^{2} = 64.$

17. By Green's Theorem, $\int_C \vec{F}\cdot d\vec{r} = \int_C y\sin x\,dx - \cos x\,dy$

$= \iint_R [\frac{\partial}{\partial x}(-\cos x) - \frac{\partial}{\partial y}(y\sin x)]\,dA = \iint_R (\sin x - \sin x)\,dA$

$= \iint_R 0\,dA = 0.$

18. By Green's Theorem, $\int_C \vec{F}\cdot d\vec{r} = \int_C y(x^2 + y^2)\,dx - x(x^2 + y^2)\,dy$

$= \iint_R [\frac{\partial}{\partial x}(-x(x^2 + y^2)) - \frac{\partial}{\partial y}(y(x^2 + y^2))]\,dA$

$= \iint_R [-(x^2 + y^2 + 2x^2) - (x^2 + y^2 + 2y^2)]\,dA = \iint_R -4(x^2 + y^2)\,dA$

$= \int_0^{2\pi}\int_0^1 -4r^3\,dr\,d\theta = \int_0^{2\pi} -r^4\Big|_0^1 d\theta = \int_0^{2\pi} -1\,d\theta = -2\pi.$

19. Let C be the boundary of the given region R, with C oriented counterclockwise. Then C is composed of C_1 and $-C_2$, where C_1 is the interval $[0,2\pi]$, parameterized by

$\vec{r}_1(t) = t\vec{i}$ for $0 \le t \le 2\pi$, and C_2 is the cycloid parameterized by the given vector-valued function $\vec{r}$. Thus by (4),

$$A = \frac{1}{2}\int_C x\,dy - y\,dx = \frac{1}{2}\int_{C_1} x\,dy - y\,dx - \frac{1}{2}\int_{C_2} x\,dy - y\,dx$$

$$= \frac{1}{2}\int_0^{2\pi} [(t)(0) - (0)(1)]\,dt - \frac{1}{2}\int_0^{2\pi} [(t - \sin t)(\sin t)$$

$$- (1 - \cos t)(1 - \cos t)]\,dt = -\frac{1}{2}\int_0^{2\pi} (t \sin t - \sin^2 t$$

$$- 1 + 2\cos t - \cos^2 t)\,dt = -\frac{1}{2}\int_0^{2\pi} (-2 + 2\cos t)\,dt$$

$$- \frac{1}{2}\int_0^{2\pi} t \sin t\,dt = -\frac{1}{2}(-2t + 2\sin t)\Big|_0^{2\pi} + \frac{1}{2} t \cos t\Big|_0^{2\pi}$$

$$- \frac{1}{2}\int_0^{2\pi} \cos t\,dt = 2\pi + \pi - \frac{1}{2}\sin t\Big|_0^{2\pi} = 3\pi$$

20. The given hypocycloid is parameterized in the counterclockwise direction by $\vec{r}$. Thus by (4),

$$A = \int_C x\,dy = \int_0^{2\pi} (\cos^3 t)(3\sin^2 t \cos t)\,dt$$

$$= 3\int_0^{2\pi} \cos^4 t\,(1 - \cos^2 t)\,dt = 3\int_0^{2\pi} (\cos^4 t - \cos^6 t)\,dt$$

By (11) in Section 7.1,

$$\int_0^{2\pi} \cos^6 t\,dt = \frac{1}{6}\cos^5 t \sin t\Big|_0^{2\pi} + \frac{5}{6}\int_0^{2\pi} \cos^4 t\,dt = \frac{5}{6}\int_0^{2\pi} \cos^4 t\,dt.$$

Then

$$A = 3\int_0^{2\pi} (\cos^4 t - \cos^6 t)\,dt = 3\int_0^{2\pi} \frac{1}{6}\cos^4 t\,dt$$

$$= \frac{1}{2}\left(\frac{1}{4}\cos^3 t \sin t + \frac{3}{8}\cos t \sin t + \frac{3}{8}t\right)\Big|_0^{2\pi} = \frac{3}{8}\pi$$

with the next to last equality coming from (15) in Section 7.1.

21. Let C be the boundary of the given region, with C oriented in the counterclockwise direction. Then C consists of C_1, C_2, and C_3, where C_1 is the curve parameterized by the given vector-valued function $\vec{r}$, C_2 is the curve parameterized by $\vec{r}_2(t) = (1 - t)\vec{i} + \frac{1}{4}\vec{j}$ for $0 \le t \le 1$, and C_3 is the curve parameterized by $\vec{r}_3(t) = (\frac{1}{4} - t)\vec{j}$ for $0 \le t \le \frac{1}{4}$. Thus by (4),

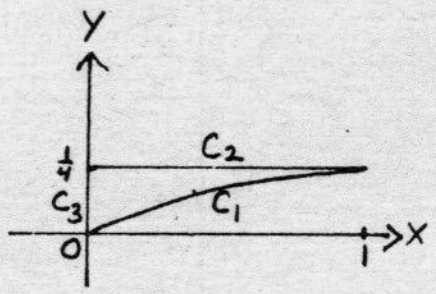

$$A = \int_C x\,dy = \int_{C_1} x\,dy + \int_{C_2} x\,dy + \int_{C_3} x\,dy$$

$$= \int_0^{1/2} (\sin \pi t)(1 - 2t)\,dt + \int_0^1 (1 - t)(0)\,dt + \int_0^{1/4} (0)(-1)\,dt$$

$$= \int_0^{1/2} \sin \pi t\,dt - 2\int_0^{1/2} t \sin \pi t\,dt = -\frac{1}{\pi}\cos \pi t\Big|_0^{1/2}$$

$$+ \frac{2}{\pi} t \cos \pi t\Big|_0^{1/2} - 2\int_0^{1/2} \frac{1}{\pi}\cos \pi t\,dt = \frac{1}{\pi} - \frac{2}{\pi^2}\sin \pi t\Big|_0^{1/2}$$

$$= \frac{1}{\pi} - \frac{2}{\pi^2}$$

22. a. Let C_1 be the circle of radius 2 parameterized by $\vec{r}_1(t) = 2\cos t\,\vec{i} + 2\sin t\,\vec{j}$, for $0 \le t \le 2\pi$, and C_2 the circle of radius 1 parameterized by $\vec{r}_2(t) = \cos t\,\vec{i} - \sin t\,\vec{j}$ for $0 \le t \le 2\pi$. Then

$$\int_C M(x,y)\,dx + N(x,y)\,dy = \int_{C_1} \frac{-y}{x^2 + y^2}\,dx + \frac{x}{x^2 + y^2}\,dy$$

$$+ \int_{C_2} \frac{-y}{x^2 + y^2}\,dx + \frac{x}{x^2 + y^2}\,dy$$

$$= \int_0^{2\pi} \left[\left(\frac{-2\sin t}{4\cos^2 t + 4\sin^2 t}\right)(-2\sin t)\right.$$

$$\left. + \left(\frac{2\cos t}{4\cos^2 t + 4\sin^2 t}\right)(2\cos t)\right] dt$$

$$+ \int_0^{2\pi} \left[\left(\frac{\sin t}{\cos^2 t + \sin^2 t}\right)(-\sin t) + \left(\frac{\cos t}{\cos^2 t + \sin^2 t}\right)(-\cos t)\right] dt$$

$$= \int_0^{2\pi} 1\,dt + \int_0^{2\pi} (-1)\,dt = 2\pi - 2\pi = 0$$

Also

$$\iint_R \left(\frac{\partial N}{\partial x} - \frac{\partial M}{\partial y}\right) dA = \iint_R \left[\frac{y^2 - x^2}{(x^2 + y^2)^2} - \frac{y^2 - x^2}{(x^2 + y^2)^2}\right] dA$$

$$= \iint_R 0\, dA = 0$$

Thus

$$\int_C M(x,y)\, dx + N(x,y)\, dy = \iint_R \left(\frac{\partial N}{\partial x} - \frac{\partial M}{\partial y}\right) dA$$

b. The circle C is parameterized in the counterclockwise direction by $\vec{r}(t) = \cos t\, \vec{i} + \sin t\, \vec{j}$ for $0 \le t \le 2\pi$, so that

$$\int_C M(x,y)\, dx + N(x,y)\, dy = \int_C \frac{-y}{x^2 + y^2}\, dx + \frac{x}{x^2 + y^2}\, dy$$

$$= \int_0^{2\pi} \left[\left(\frac{-\sin t}{\cos^2 t + \sin^2 t}\right)(-\sin t) + \left(\frac{\cos t}{\cos^2 t + \sin^2 t}\right)(\cos t)\right] dt$$

$$= \int_0^{2\pi} 1\, dt = 2\pi$$

Since

$$\iint_R \left(\frac{\partial N}{\partial x} - \frac{\partial M}{\partial y}\right) dA = \iint_R \left[\frac{y^2 - x^2}{(x^2 + y^2)^2} - \frac{y^2 - x^2}{(x^2 + y^2)^2}\right] dA$$

$$= \iint_R 0\, dA = 0$$

we have

$$\int_C M(x,y)\, dx + N(x,y)\, dy \ne \iint_R \left(\frac{\partial N}{\partial x} - \frac{\partial M}{\partial y}\right) dA$$

c. One of the hypotheses of Green's Theorem is that M and N must be defined at every point of R. In the present case, M and N are not defined at $(0,0)$, and

$\iint_R \left(\frac{\partial N}{\partial x} - \frac{\partial M}{\partial y}\right) dA$ exists only as an improper integral.

Thus Green's Theorem is not contradicted.

23. Let R_1 and R_2 be the regions enclosed by C_1 and C_2, respectively. Then by Green's Theorem,

$$\int_{C_1} M(x,y)\, dx + N(x,y)\, dy = \iint_{R_1} \left(\frac{\partial N}{\partial x} - \frac{\partial M}{\partial y}\right) dA = \iint_{R_1} 0\, dA = 0$$

and

$$\int_{C_2} M(x,y)\, dx + N(x,y)\, dy = \iint_{R_2} \left(\frac{\partial N}{\partial x} - \frac{\partial M}{\partial y}\right) dA = \iint_{R_2} 0\, dA = 0$$

Thus

$$\int_{C_1} M(x,y)\, dx + N(x,y)\, dy = \int_{C_2} M(x,y)\, dx + N(x,y)\, dy$$

24. Assume that R is the horizontally simple region between the graphs of h_1 and h_2 on an interval $[c,d]$ on the y axis. Then

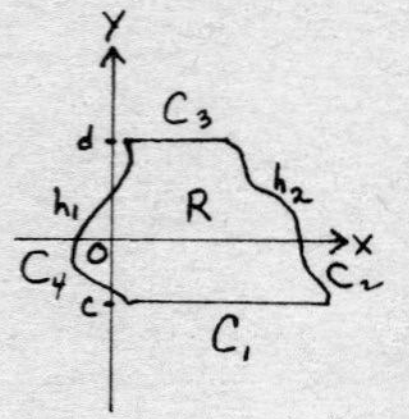

$$\iint_R \frac{\partial N}{\partial x}\, dA = \int_c^d \int_{h_1(y)}^{h_2(y)} \frac{\partial N}{\partial x}\, dx\, dy$$

$$= \int_c^d N(x,y)\Big|_{h_1(y)}^{h_2(y)} dy$$

$$= \int_c^d [N(h_2(y),y) - N(h_1(y),y)]\, dy$$

But the boundary C of R is composed of the curves C_1, C_2, C_3, and C_4, parameterized as follows:

C_1: $\vec{r}_1(t) = t\vec{i} + c\vec{j}$ for $h_1(c) \le t \le h_2(c)$

C_2: $\vec{r}_2(t) = h_2(t)\vec{i} + t\vec{j}$ for $c \le t \le d$

C_3: $\vec{r}_3(t) = [h_1(d) + h_2(d) - t]\vec{i} + d\vec{j}$ for $h_1(d) \le t \le h_2(d)$

C_4: $\vec{r}_4(t) = h_1(c+d-t)\vec{i} + (c+d-t)\vec{j}$ for $c \le t \le d$

Because C_1 and C_3 have constant y values, we have $\int_{C_1} N(x,y)\, dy = \int_{C_3} N(x,y)\, dy = 0$. Therefore

$$\int_C N(x,y)\, dy = \int_{C_1} N(x,y)\, dy + \int_{C_2} N(x,y)\, dy + \int_{C_3} N(x,y)\, dy$$

$$+ \int_{C_4} N(x,y)\, dy = \int_{C_2} N(x,y)\, dy + \int_{C_4} N(x,y)\, dy$$

$$= \int_c^d N(h_2(t),t)\,(1)\, dt + \int_c^d N(h_1(c+d-t),c+d-t)\,(-1)\, dt$$

$u = c+d-t$

$$= \int_c^d N(h_2(t),t)\, dt + \int_d^c N(h_1(u),u)\, du$$

$$= \int_c^d [N(h_2(y),y) - N(h_1(y),y)]\, dy$$

Notice that the last integral appears at the end of our calculation of the double integral above. It follows that

$$\int_C N(x,y)\, dy = \iint_R \frac{\partial N}{\partial x}\, dA .$$

25. a. Applying (6) with $\vec{F}$ replaced by $g\vec{F}$, we obtain

$$\int_C g\vec{F}\cdot\vec{n}\, ds = \iint_R \text{div}\,(g\vec{F})\, dA = \iint_R (g\,\text{div}\,\vec{F} + (\text{grad}\, g)\cdot\vec{F})\, dA$$

b. Applying part (a) with $\vec{F}$ replaced by grad f , and using the fact that div (grad f) = $\nabla^2 f$, we obtain

$$\int_C g\,(\text{grad}\, f)\cdot\vec{n}\, ds = \iint_R [g\,\text{div}\,(\text{grad}\, f) + (\text{grad}\, g)\cdot(\text{grad}\, f)]\, dA$$

$$= \iint_R [g\nabla^2 f + (\text{grad}\, g)\cdot(\text{grad}\, f)]\, dA$$

c. From (8) we obtain

$$\int_C (g\,\text{grad}\, f - f\,\text{grad}\, g)\cdot\vec{n}\, ds = \int_C g\,(\text{grad}\, f)\cdot\vec{n}\, ds$$

$$- \int_C f\,(\text{grad}\, g)\cdot\vec{n}\, ds = \iint_R [g\nabla^2 f + (\text{grad}\, g)\cdot(\text{grad}\, f)]\, dA$$

$$- \iint_R [f\nabla^2 g + (\text{grad}\, f)\cdot(\text{grad}\, g)]\, dA = \iint_R (g\nabla^2 f - f\nabla^2 g)\, dA$$

26. a. Taking f = g in (8) and using the facts that $f(x,y) = 0$ for (x,y) on C and $\nabla^2 f(x,y) = 0$ for (x,y) in R, we obtain

$$0 = \int_C f\,(\text{grad}\, f)\cdot\vec{n}\, ds = \iint_R [f\nabla^2 f + (\text{grad}\, f)\cdot(\text{grad}\, f)]\, dA$$

$$= \iint_R [\text{grad}\, f \cdot \text{grad}\, f]\, dA = \iint_R \|\text{grad}\, f\|^2\, dA$$

Thus if R_0 is a rectangle contained in R, then

$$0 \le \iint_{R_0} \|\text{grad}\, f\|^2\, dA \le \iint_R \|\text{grad}\, f\|^2\, dA = 0$$

so that $\iint_{R_0} \|\text{grad}\, f\|^2\, dA = 0$.

b. From (a) and Exercise 66 of Section 14.1 with f replaced by $\|\text{grad}\, f\|^2$, it follows that $\|\text{grad}\, f(x,y)\|^2 = 0$ for every (x,y) in R. Thus $\text{grad}\, f(x,y) = \vec{0}$ for all (x,y) in R.

c. From part (b) and Exercise 32(a) of Section 15.1, we conclude that f is constant on R.

27. a. The line segment C is parameterized by $\vec{r}(t) = [x_1 + (x_2 - x_1)t]\vec{i} + [y_1 + (y_2 - y_1)t]\vec{j}$ for $0 \le t \le 1$. Thus

$$\frac{1}{2}\int_C x\, dy - y\, dx = \frac{1}{2}\int_0^1 \{[x_1 + (x_2 - x_1)t](y_2 - y_1)$$

$$- [y_1 + (y_2 - y_1)t](x_2 - x_1)\}\, dt$$

$$= \frac{1}{2}\int_0^1 [x_1(y_2 - y_1) - y_1(x_2 - x_1)]\, dt = \frac{1}{2}(x_1y_2 - x_2y_1)$$

b. Let C be the polygon oriented counterclockwise. Then we have $C = C_1 + C_2 + \ldots + C_n$, where for $1 \le k \le n-1$, C_k is the line segment joining (x_k, y_k) to (x_{k+1}, y_{k+1}) and C_n is the line segment joining (x_n, y_n) to (x_1, y_1). Then by (4) and part (a),

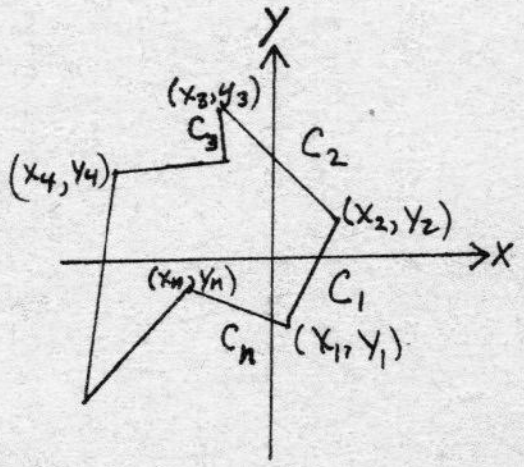

$$A = \frac{1}{2}\int_C x\, dy - y\, dx = \frac{1}{2}\int_{C_1} x\, dy - y\, dx + \frac{1}{2}\int_{C_2} x\, dy - y\, dx$$

$$+ \ldots + \int_{C_n} x\, dy - y\, dx = \frac{1}{2}(x_1y_2 - x_2y_1)$$

$$+ \frac{1}{2}(x_2y_3 - x_3y_2) + \ldots + \frac{1}{2}(x_{n-1}y_n - x_ny_{n-1})$$

$$+ \frac{1}{2}(x_ny_1 - x_1y_n)$$

c. Taking $(x_1,y_1) = (0,0)$, $(x_2,y_2) = (1,0)$, $(x_3,y_3) = (2,3)$, and $(x_4,y_4) = (-1,1)$ in part (b), we obtain

$$A = \frac{1}{2}(0) + \frac{1}{2}(3) + \frac{1}{2}(5) + \frac{1}{2}(0) = 4$$

28. If we apply Green's Theorem to a closed curve C that is the boundary of a region R, and then use the fact that f

is harmonic, we find that $\int_C -f_y\,dx + f_x\,dy =$ $\iint_R [f_{xx} - (-f_{yy})]\,dA = \iint_R (f_{xx} + f_{yy})\,dA = \iint_R 0\,dA = 0$. By the results of Section 15.3, the given line integral is independent of path.

29. a. Since $\vec{r} = x\vec{i} + y\vec{j}$, we have $\frac{dr}{d\tau} = \frac{dx}{d\tau}\vec{i} + \frac{dy}{d\tau}\vec{j}$, so that $\vec{r}\times\frac{d\vec{r}}{d\tau} = (x\frac{dy}{d\tau} - y\frac{dx}{d\tau})\vec{k}$. Thus (4) of Section 12.6, with τ replacing t, implies that $x\frac{dy}{d\tau} - y\frac{dx}{d\tau} = p$.

b. Since C_1 is the line segment joining (x,y) to $(0,0)$, and C_2 is the line segment joining $(0,0)$ to (x_0,y_0), Exercise 27(a) implies that

$$\frac{1}{2}\int_{C_1} x\,dy - y\,dx = \frac{1}{2}[(x)(0) - (0)(y)] = 0$$

and

$$\frac{1}{2}\int_{C_2} x\,dy - y\,dx = \frac{1}{2}[(0)(y_0) - (x_0)(0)] = 0$$

Since C_3 is parameterized by $\vec{r}(\tau) = x(\tau)\vec{i} + y(\tau)\vec{j}$ for $t_0 \le \tau \le t$, we have

$$\frac{1}{2}\int_{C_3} x\,dy - y\,dx = \frac{1}{2}\int_{t_0}^{t} (x\frac{dy}{d\tau} - y\frac{dx}{d\tau})\,d\tau$$

Therefore (4) (in the present section) implies that

$$A(t) = \frac{1}{2}\int_C x\,dy - y\,dx = \frac{1}{2}\int_{C_1} x\,dy - y\,dx + \frac{1}{2}\int_{C_2} x\,dy - y\,dx$$

$$+ \frac{1}{2}\int_{C_3} x\,dy - y\,dx = \frac{1}{2}\int_{t_0}^{t} (x\frac{dy}{d\tau} - y\frac{dx}{d\tau})\,d\tau$$

c. From (a) and (b) we have

$$A(t) = \frac{1}{2}\int_{t_0}^{t} (x\frac{dy}{d\tau} - y\frac{dx}{d\tau})\,d\tau = \frac{1}{2}\int_{t_0}^{t} p\,d\tau = \frac{p}{2}\tau\Big|_{t_0}^{t}$$

$$= \frac{p}{2}(t - t_0)$$

Thus $\frac{dA}{dt} = \frac{p}{2}$.

Section 15.5

1. Let R be the region in the xy plane between the graphs of $y = 0$ and $y = \frac{6 - 2x}{3}$ on $[0,3]$. If $f(x,y) = 6 - 2x - 3y$ for (x,y) in R, then Σ is the graph of f on R. Since

$$\sqrt{f_x^2(x,y) + f_y^2(x,y) + 1} = \sqrt{(-2)^2 + (-3)^2 + 1} = \sqrt{14}$$

it follows from (3) that

$$\iint_\Sigma x\,dS = \iint_R x\sqrt{14}\,dA = \sqrt{14}\int_0^3\int_0^{\frac{6-2x}{3}} x\,dy\,dx = \sqrt{14}\int_0^3 xy\Big|_0^{\frac{6-2x}{3}} dx$$

$$= \sqrt{14}\int_0^3 (2x - \frac{2}{3}x^2)\,dx = \sqrt{14}(x^2 - \frac{2}{9}x^3)\Big|_0^3 = 3\sqrt{14}$$

2. Let R be the region in the xy plane bounded by the circles $r = 1$ and $r = 3$ in polar coordinates. If $f(x,y) = \sqrt{x^2 + y^2}$ for (x,y) in R, then Σ is the graph of f on R. Since

$$\sqrt{f_x^2(x,y) + f_y^2(x,y) + 1} = \sqrt{\left(\frac{x}{\sqrt{x^2 + y^2}}\right)^2 + \left(\frac{y}{\sqrt{x^2 + y^2}}\right)^2 + 1} = \sqrt{2}$$

it follows from (3) that

$$\iint_\Sigma z^2\,dS = \iint_R (x^2 + y^2)\sqrt{2}\,dA = \int_0^{2\pi}\int_1^3 r^3\sqrt{2}\,dr\,d\theta = \int_0^{2\pi} \frac{r^4}{4}\sqrt{2}\Big|_1^3 d\theta$$

$$= \int_0^{2\pi} 20\sqrt{2}\,d\theta = 40\pi\sqrt{2}$$

3. Let R be the circular region in the xy plane bounded by the circle $r = 2$ in polar coordinates. If $f(x,y) = 3x - 2$ for (x,y) in R, then Σ is the graph of f on R. Since

$$\sqrt{f_x^2(x,y) + f_y^2(x,y) + 1} = \sqrt{3^2 + 1} = \sqrt{10}$$

it follows from (3) that

$$\iint_\Sigma (2x^2+1)\,dS = \iint_R (2x^2+1)\sqrt{10}\,dA$$

$$= \int_0^{2\pi}\int_0^2 (2r^2\cos^2\theta + 1)\sqrt{10}\,r\,dr\,d\theta$$

$$= \sqrt{10}\int_0^{2\pi} \left(\tfrac{1}{2}r^4\cos^2\theta + \tfrac{1}{2}r^2\right)\Big|_0^2 d\theta = \sqrt{10}\int_0^{2\pi}(8\cos^2\theta + 2)\,d\theta$$

$$= \sqrt{10}\int_0^{2\pi}(4 + 4\cos 2\theta + 2)\,d\theta = \sqrt{10}\,(6\theta + 2\sin 2\theta)\Big|_0^{2\pi}$$

$$= 12\pi\sqrt{10}$$

4. Let R be the region in the xy plane bounded by $r = 0$ and $r = 3$ on $[0,\frac{\pi}{2}]$ in polar coordinates, and let R_b be the region bounded by $r = 0$ and $r = b$ on $[0,\frac{\pi}{2}]$ for $0 < b < 3$. If $f(x,y) = \sqrt{9 - x^2 - y^2}$ for (x,y) in R, then Σ is the graph of f on R. Since

$$\sqrt{f_x^2(x,y) + f_y^2(x,y) + 1} = \sqrt{\left(\frac{-x}{\sqrt{9-x^2-y^2}}\right)^2 + \left(\frac{-y}{\sqrt{9-x^2-y^2}}\right)^2 + 1}$$

$$= \frac{3}{\sqrt{9-x^2-y^2}} \quad \text{for } (x,y) \text{ in } R_b$$

it follows from (3) and the solution of Example 3 that

$$\iint_\Sigma z^2\,dS = \lim_{b\to 3^-}\iint_{R_b} (9 - x^2 - y^2)\frac{3}{\sqrt{9-x^2-y^2}}\,dA$$

$$= \lim_{b\to 3^-}\int_0^{\pi/2}\int_0^b \sqrt{9-r^2}\,3r\,dr\,d\theta = \lim_{b\to 3^-}\int_0^{\pi/2} -(9-r^2)^{3/2}\Big|_0^b d\theta$$

$$= \lim_{b\to 3^-}\int_0^{\pi/2} [27 - (9-b^2)^{3/2}]\,d\theta$$

$$= \lim_{b\to 3^-} [27 - (9-b^2)^{3/2}]\,\theta\Big|_0^{\pi/2} = \frac{27}{2}\pi$$

5. The paraboloid and plane intersect for (x,y,z) such that $x^2 + y^2 = z = y$, which in polar coordinates means that $r^2 = r\sin\theta$, so that $r = \sin\theta$ for $0 \le \theta \le \pi$. Let R be the region in the xy plane bounded by $r = \sin\theta$ on $[0,\pi]$ in polar coordinates. If $f(x,y) = x^2 + y^2$ for (x,y) in R, then Σ is the graph of f on R. Since

$$\sqrt{f_x^2(x,y) + f_y^2(x,y) + 1} = \sqrt{(2x)^2 + (2y)^2 + 1} = \sqrt{4x^2 + 4y^2 + 1}$$

it follows from (3) that

$$\iint_\Sigma \sqrt{4x^2+4y^2+1}\,dS = \iint_R \sqrt{4x^2+4y^2+1}\sqrt{4x^2+4y^2+1}\,dA$$

$$= \int_0^\pi\int_0^{\sin\theta} (4r^2+1)\,r\,dr\,d\theta = \int_0^\pi \left(r^4 + \tfrac{1}{2}r^2\right)\Big|_0^{\sin\theta} d\theta$$

$$= \int_0^\pi \left(\sin^4\theta + \tfrac{1}{2}\sin^2\theta\right)d\theta = \int_0^\pi \left(\sin^4\theta + \tfrac{1}{4} - \tfrac{1}{4}\cos 2\theta\right)d\theta$$

$$= \left(-\tfrac{1}{4}\sin^3\theta\cos\theta - \tfrac{3}{8}\sin\theta\cos\theta + \tfrac{3}{8}\theta + \tfrac{1}{4}\theta - \tfrac{1}{8}\sin 2\theta\right)\Big|_0^\pi = \frac{5}{8}\pi$$

with the next to last equality coming from (14) in Section 7.1.

6. Let R be the region in the xy plane between the graphs of $y = -\sqrt{4-x^2}$ and $y = \sqrt{4-x^2}$ on $[-2,2]$. If $f(x,y) = 4 - x^2 - y^2$ for (x,y) in R, then Σ is the graph of f on R. Since

$$\sqrt{f_x^2(x,y) + f_y^2(x,y) + 1} = \sqrt{(-2x)^2 + (-2y)^2 + 1} = \sqrt{4x^2 + 4y^2 + 1}$$

it follows from (3) that

$$\iint_\Sigma xy\,dS = \iint_R xy\sqrt{4x^2+4y^2+1}\,dA = \int_{-2}^2\int_{-\sqrt{4-x^2}}^{\sqrt{4-x^2}} xy\sqrt{4x^2+4y^2+1}\,dy\,dx$$

$$= \int_{-2}^2 \frac{x}{12}(4x^2+4y^2+1)^{3/2}\Big|_{-\sqrt{4-x^2}}^{\sqrt{4-x^2}} dx = \int_{-2}^2 0\,dx = 0$$

7. Let R be the region in the xy plane between the graphs of $y = 0$ and $y = 2$ on $[0,3]$. If $f(x,y) = 4 - y^2$ for (x,y) in R, then Σ is the graph of f on R. Since

$$\sqrt{f_x^2(x,y) + f_y^2(x,y) + 1} = \sqrt{(-2y)^2 + 1} = \sqrt{4y^2+1}\ .$$

it follows from (3) that

$$\iint_\Sigma y\,dS = \iint_R y\sqrt{4y^2+1}\,dA = \int_0^3\int_0^2 y\sqrt{4y^2+1}\,dy\,dx$$

$$= \int_0^3 \frac{1}{12}(4y^2+1)^{3/2}\Big|_0^2 dx = \int_0^3 \frac{1}{12}(17^{3/2}-1)\,dx$$

$$= \frac{1}{4}(17^{3/2}-1)$$

8. Let R be the region in the xy plane between the graphs of $y = -1$ and $y = 2$ on $[-1,1]$, and let R_b be the region between the graphs of $y = -1$ and $y = 2$ on $[-b,b]$ for $0 < b < 1$. If $f(x,y) = \sqrt{1-x^2}$ for (x,y) in R, then Σ is the graph of f on R. Since

$$\sqrt{f_x^2(x,y) + f_y^2(x,y) + 1} = \sqrt{\left(\frac{-x}{\sqrt{1-x^2}}\right)^2 + 1} = \frac{1}{\sqrt{1-x^2}} \text{ for } (x,y) \text{ in } R_b$$

it follows from (3) that

$$\iint_\Sigma x^2 z\,dS = \lim_{b\to 1^-} \iint_{R_b} (x^2\sqrt{1-x^2}) \frac{1}{\sqrt{1-x^2}}\,dA = \lim_{b\to 1^-} \int_{-b}^{b}\int_{-1}^{2} x^2\,dy\,dx$$

$$= \lim_{b\to 1^-} \int_{-b}^{b} x^2 y\Big|_{-1}^{2} dx = \lim_{b\to 1^-} \int_{-b}^{b} 3x^2\,dx$$

$$= \lim_{b\to 1^-} x^3\Big|_{-b}^{b} = \lim_{b\to 1^-} 2b^3 = 2$$

9. Let R be the region in the xy plane bounded by the circle $r = 2$ in polar coordinates, and for $0 < b < 2$, let R_b be the region bounded by $r = b$. If $f(x,y) = \sqrt{4-x^2-y^2}$ for (x,y) in R, then Σ is the graph of f on R. Since

$$\sqrt{f_x^2(x,y) + f_y^2(x,y) + 1} = \sqrt{\left(\frac{-x}{\sqrt{4-x^2-y^2}}\right)^2 + \left(\frac{-y}{\sqrt{4-x^2-y^2}}\right)^2 + 1}$$

$$= \frac{2}{\sqrt{4-x^2-y^2}} \quad \text{for } (x,y) \text{ in } R_b$$

it follows from (3) and the solution of Example 3 that

$$\iint_\Sigma z(x^2+y^2)\,dS = \lim_{b\to 2^-} \iint_{R_b} [(x^2+y^2)\sqrt{4-x^2-y^2}] \frac{2}{\sqrt{4-x^2-y^2}}\,dA$$

$$= \lim_{b\to 2^-} \int_0^{2\pi}\int_0^{b} 2r^3\,dr\,d\theta = \lim_{b\to 2^-} \int_0^{2\pi} \frac{1}{2} r^4\Big|_0^b d\theta$$

$$= \lim_{b\to 2^-} \int_0^{2\pi} \frac{1}{2} b^4\,d\theta = \lim_{b\to 2^-} \pi b^4 = 16\pi$$

10. Let Σ_1 be the portion of Σ that lies inside the circle $x^2 + y^2 = 1$ in the xy plane. If $R_1 = \Sigma_1$ and $f(x,y) = 0$ for (x,y) in R_1, then Σ_1 is the graph of f on R, so

$$\iint_{\Sigma_1} (x^2+y^2)\,dS = \iint_{R_1} (x^2+y^2)\,dA = \int_0^{2\pi}\int_0^1 r^3\,dr\,d\theta$$

$$= \int_0^{2\pi} \frac{1}{4} r^4\Big|_0^1 d\theta = \int_0^{2\pi} \frac{1}{4}\,d\theta = \frac{1}{2}\pi$$

Let Σ_2 be the portion of Σ that lies above the xy plane, and let R_2 be the region in the xy plane bounded by $r = 1$ in polar coordinates. If $f(x,y) = 1 - x^2 - y^2$ for (x,y) in R_2, then Σ_2 is the graph of f on R_2. Since

$$\sqrt{f_x^2(x,y) + f_y^2(x,y) + 1} = \sqrt{(-2x)^2 + (-2y)^2 + 1} = \sqrt{4x^2 + 4y^2 + 1}$$

it follows from (3) that

$$\iint_{\Sigma_2} (x^2+y^2)\,dS = \iint_{R_2} (x^2+y^2)\sqrt{4x^2+4y^2+1}\,dA$$

$$= \int_0^{2\pi}\int_0^1 r^3\sqrt{4r^2+1}\,dr\,d\theta$$

Making the substitution $u = 4r^2 + 1$, we find that

$$\int_0^1 r^3\sqrt{4r^2+1}\,dr = \int_1^5 \frac{u-1}{4} u^{1/2} \frac{1}{8}\,du = \frac{1}{32}\int_1^5 (u^{3/2} - u^{1/2})\,du$$

$$= \frac{1}{32}\left(\frac{2}{5}u^{5/2} - \frac{2}{3}u^{3/2}\right)\Big|_1^5 = \frac{1}{120}(25\sqrt{5}+1)$$

Thus

$$\iint_{\Sigma_2} (x^2+y^2)\,dS = \int_0^{2\pi}\int_0^1 r^3\sqrt{4r^2+1}\,dr\,d\theta = \int_0^{2\pi} \frac{1}{120}(25\sqrt{5}+1)\,d\theta$$

$$= \frac{\pi}{60}(25\sqrt{5}+1)$$

11. Let Σ be composed of the six surfaces Σ_1, Σ_2, Σ_3, Σ_4, Σ_5, and Σ_6, as in the figure. For Σ_1 and Σ_2 we use the region R_1 in the xy plane bounded by $y = 0$ and $y = 1$ on $[0,1]$. If $f(x,y) = 0$, then $\sqrt{f_x^2(x,y) + f_y^2(x,y) + 1} = 1$,

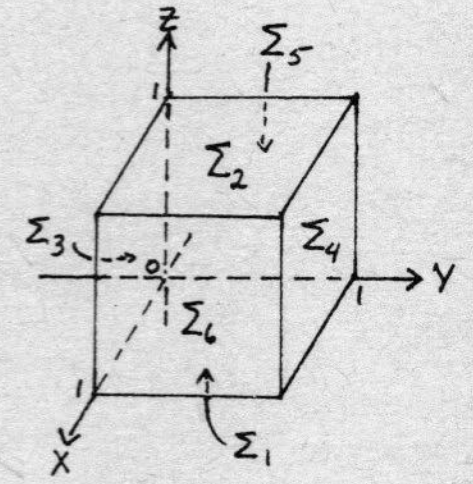

and

$$\iint_{\Sigma_1} (x + y)\, dS = \iint_{R_1} (x + y)\, dA = \int_0^1\int_0^1 (x + y)\, dy\, dx$$

$$= \int_0^1 \left(xy + \frac{y^2}{2}\right)\Big|_0^1 dx = \int_0^1 \left(x + \frac{1}{2}\right) dx = \left(\frac{1}{2}x^2 + \frac{1}{2}x\right)\Big|_0^1 = 1$$

If $f(x,y) = 1$, then $\sqrt{f_x^2(x,y) + f_y^2(x,y) + 1} = 1$, and as above,

$$\iint_{\Sigma_2} (x + y)\, dS = \iint_{R_1} (x + y)\, dA = 1$$

For Σ_3 and Σ_4 we use the region R_3 in the xz plane bounded by $z = 0$ and $z = 1$ on $[0,1]$. If $f(x,z) = 0$, then $\sqrt{f_x^2(x,z) + f_z^2(x,z) + 1} = 1$, and

$$\iint_{\Sigma_3} (x + y)\, dS = \iint_{R_3} x\, dA = \int_0^1\int_0^1 x\, dz\, dx = \int_0^1 xz\Big|_0^1 dx = \int_0^1 x\, dx$$

$$= \frac{1}{2}x^2\Big|_0^1 = \frac{1}{2}$$

If $f(x,z) = 1$, then $\sqrt{f_x^2(x,z) + f_z^2(x,z) + 1} = 1$, and

$$\iint_{\Sigma_4} (x + y)\, dS = \iint_{R_3} (x + 1)\, dA = \int_0^1\int_0^1 (x + 1)\, dz\, dx$$

$$= \int_0^1 (xz + z)\Big|_0^1 dx = \int_0^1 (x + 1)\, dx = \left(\frac{1}{2}x^2 + x\right)\Big|_0^1 = \frac{3}{2}$$

For Σ_5 and Σ_6 we use the region R_5 in the yz plane bounded by $z = 0$ and $z = 1$ on $[0,1]$. If $f(y,z) = 0$, then $\sqrt{f_y^2(y,z) + f_z^2(y,z) + 1} = 1$, and

$$\iint_{\Sigma_5} (x + y)\, dS = \iint_{R_5} y\, dA = \int_0^1\int_0^1 y\, dz\, dy = \int_0^1 yz\Big|_0^1 dy = \int_0^1 y\, dy$$

$$= \frac{1}{2}y^2\Big|_0^1 = \frac{1}{2}$$

Finally, if $f(y,z) = 1$, then $\sqrt{f_y^2(y,z) + f_z^2(y,z) + 1} = 1$, and

$$\iint_{\Sigma_6} (x + y)\, dS = \iint_{R_5} (1 + y)\, dA = \int_0^1\int_0^1 (1 + y)\, dz\, dy$$

$$= \int_0^1 (z + yz)\Big|_0^1 dy = \int_0^1 (1 + y)\, dy = \left(y + \frac{1}{2}y^2\right)\Big|_0^1 = \frac{3}{2}$$

Consequently

$$\iint_{\Sigma} (x + y)\, dS = \sum_{k=1}^{6} \iint_{\Sigma_k} (x + y)\, dS = 1 + 1 + \frac{1}{2} + \frac{3}{2} + \frac{1}{2} + \frac{3}{2} = 6$$

12. Let Σ be composed of the four surfaces Σ_1, Σ_2, Σ_3, and Σ_4, as in the figure. For Σ_1 we use the region R_1 in the xy plane between the graphs of $y = 0$ and $y = 1 - x$ on $[0,1]$. If $f(x,y) = 0$, then $\sqrt{f_x^2(x,y) + f_y^2(x,y) + 1} = 1$, and

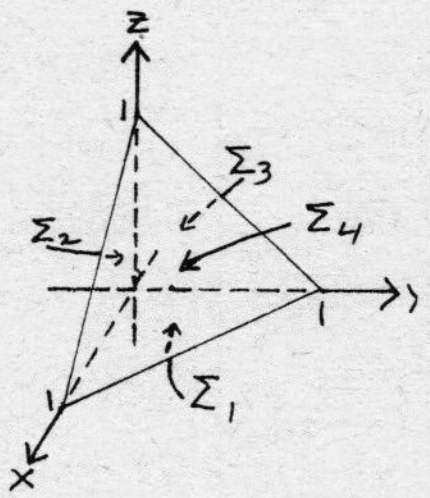

$$\iint_{\Sigma_1} (x + 1)\, dS = \iint_{R_1} (x + 1)\, dA = \int_0^1\int_0^{1-x} (x + 1)\, dy\, dx$$

$$= \int_0^1 (x + 1)y\Big|_0^{1-x} dx = \int_0^1 (1 - x^2)\, dx = \left(x - \frac{1}{3}x^3\right)\Big|_0^1 = \frac{2}{3}$$

For Σ_2 we use the region R_2 in the xz plane between the graphs of $z = 0$ and $z = 1 - x$ on $[0,1]$. If $f(x,z) = 0$, then $\sqrt{f_x^2(x,z) + f_z^2(x,z) + 1} = 1$, and

$$\iint_{\Sigma_2} (x + 1)\, dS = \iint_{R_2} (x + 1)\, dA = \int_0^1\int_0^{1-x} (x + 1)\, dz\, dx = \frac{2}{3}$$

as above. For Σ_3 we use the region R_3 in the yz plane between the graphs of $z = 0$ and $z = 1 - y$ on $[0,1]$. If $f(y,z) = 0$, $\sqrt{f_y^2(y,z) + f_z^2(y,z) + 1} = 1$, and

$$\iint_{\Sigma_3} (x + 1)\, dS = \iint_{R_3} 1\, dA = \int_0^1\int_0^{1-y} 1\, dz\, dy = \int_0^1 z\Big|_0^{1-y} dy$$

$$= \int_0^1 (1 - y)\, dy = \left(y - \frac{1}{2}y^2\right)\Big|_0^1 = \frac{1}{2}$$

Finally, for Σ_4 we use the region R_1. If $f(x,y) = 1 - x - y$, then $\sqrt{f_x^2(x,y) + f_y^2(x,y) + 1} = \sqrt{(-1)^2 + (-1)^2 + 1} = \sqrt{3}$, and

$$\iint_{\Sigma_4} (x + 1)\,dS = \iint_{R_1} (x + 1)\sqrt{3}\,dA = \sqrt{3}\int_0^1\int_0^{1-x} (x + 1)\,dy\,dx = \frac{2}{3}\sqrt{3}$$

by the first calculation above. Consequently

$$\iint_{\Sigma} (x + 1)\,dS = \sum_{k=1}^{4} \iint_{\Sigma_k} (x + 1)\,dS = \frac{2}{3} + \frac{2}{3} + \frac{1}{2} + \frac{2}{3}\sqrt{3} = \frac{11}{6} + \frac{2}{3}\sqrt{3}$$

13. Let R be the region in the xy plane bounded by $r = \frac{1}{4}$ and $r = 2$ in polar coordinates, and let $f(x,y) = 2\sqrt{x^2 + y^2}$ for (x,y) in R. Then the funnel occupies the region Σ which is the graph of f on R. The mass of the funnel is given by

$$m = \iint_{\Sigma} \delta(x,y,z)\,dS = \iint_{\Sigma} (6 - z)\,dS$$

$$= \iint_R \left(6 - 2\sqrt{x^2 + y^2}\right)\sqrt{\left(\frac{2x}{\sqrt{x^2 + y^2}}\right)^2 + \left(\frac{2y}{\sqrt{x^2 + y^2}}\right)^2 + 1}\,dA$$

$$= \iint_R \left(6 - 2\sqrt{x^2 + y^2}\right)\sqrt{5}\,dA = \int_0^{2\pi}\int_{1/4}^{2} (6 - 2r)\sqrt{5}\,r\,dr\,d\theta$$

$$= \sqrt{5}\int_0^{2\pi} \left(3r^2 - \frac{2}{3}r^3\right)\Big|_{1/4}^{2} d\theta = \sqrt{5}\int_0^{2\pi} \frac{623}{96}\,d\theta = \frac{623}{48}\sqrt{5}\,\pi$$

14. The mass m_1 of the top half, Σ_1, equals the mass m_2 of the bottom half, Σ_2. Let R be the region in the xy plane bounded by $r = 5$, and for $0 < b < 5$ let R_b be the region bounded by $r = b$. Let $f(x,y) = \sqrt{25 - x^2 - y^2}$ for (x,y) in R. Then Σ_1 is the graph of f on R, and

$$m_1 = \iint_{\Sigma_1} \delta(x,y,z)\,dS = \iint_{\Sigma_1} (1 + z^2)\,dS$$

$$= \lim_{b\to 5^-} \iint_{R_b} [1 + (25 - x^2 - y^2)]\sqrt{\left(\frac{-x}{\sqrt{25 - x^2 - y^2}}\right)^2 + \left(\frac{-y}{\sqrt{25 - x^2 - y^2}}\right)^2 + 1}\,dA$$

$$= \lim_{b\to 5^-} \iint_{R_b} \left(\frac{5}{\sqrt{25 - x^2 - y^2}} + 5\sqrt{25 - x^2 - y^2}\right) dA$$

$$= \lim_{b\to 5^-} \int_0^{2\pi}\int_0^b \left(\frac{5r}{\sqrt{25 - r^2}} + 5r\sqrt{25 - r^2}\right) dr\,d\theta$$

$$= \lim_{b\to 5^-} \int_0^{2\pi} \left[-5\sqrt{25 - r^2} - \frac{5}{3}(25 - r^2)^{3/2}\right]\Big|_0^b d\theta$$

$$= \lim_{b\to 5^-} \int_0^{2\pi} \left[-5\sqrt{25 - b^2} - \frac{5}{3}(25 - b^2)^{3/2} + 25 + \frac{625}{3}\right] d\theta$$

$$= \lim_{b\to 5^-} 2\pi\left[-5\sqrt{25 - b^2} - \frac{5}{3}(25 - b^2)^{3/2} + 25 + \frac{625}{3}\right] = \frac{1400}{3}\pi$$

Thus the total mass $m = \frac{2800}{3}\pi$

15. The surface Σ of the tank consists of the top part, Σ_1, and the bottom part, Σ_2, as in the figure. Let R be the region in the xy plane bounded by the circle $r = 10$, and for $0 < b < 10$ let R_b be the region in the xy plane bounded by the circle $r = b$. If $f(x,y) = \sqrt{100 - x^2 - y^2}$, then Σ_1 is the graph of f on R, and $\Sigma_2 = R$. Moreover, $z_0 = 10$. By the formula for the force F on Σ and by (3),

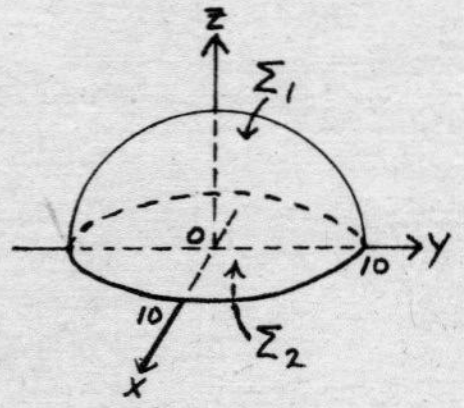

$$F = \iint_{\Sigma} (62.5)(z_0 - z)\,dS = \iint_{\Sigma_1} (62.5)(10 - z)\,dS + \iint_{\Sigma_2} (62.5)(10 - z)\,dS$$

$$= (62.5)\lim_{b\to 10^-} \iint_{R_b} \left(10 - \sqrt{100 - x^2 - y^2}\right)\sqrt{\left(\frac{-x}{\sqrt{100 - x^2 - y^2}}\right)^2 + \left(\frac{-y}{\sqrt{100 - x^2 - y^2}}\right)^2 + 1}\,dA$$

$$+ (62.5)\iint_R (10 - 0)\,dA = (62.5)\lim_{b\to 10^-}\left[\iint_{R_b} \frac{100}{\sqrt{100 - x^2 - y^2}}\,dA - \iint_{R_b} 10\,dA\right]$$

$$+ (62.5)\iint_R 10\,dA = (62.5)\lim_{b\to 10^-} \iint_{R_b} \frac{100}{\sqrt{100 - x^2 - y^2}}\,dA$$

$$= (62.5)\lim_{b\to 10^-} \int_0^{2\pi}\int_0^b \frac{100}{\sqrt{100 - r^2}}\,r\,dr\,d\theta$$

$$= (62.5)\lim_{b\to 10^-} \int_0^{2\pi} -100\sqrt{100 - r^2}\,\Big|_0^b d\theta$$

$$= (62.5) \lim_{b\to 10^-} \int_0^{2\pi} (-100\sqrt{100 - b^2} + 1000)\, d\theta$$

$$= (62.5)(2\pi) \lim_{b\to 10^-} (-100\sqrt{100 - b^2} + 1000) = 125{,}000\pi \text{ (pounds)}$$

16. The surface Σ of the tank consists of the bottom Σ_1, the sides Σ_2 and Σ_3, and the top Σ_4, as in the figure. Since $z_0 = 0$, the force F on Σ is given by

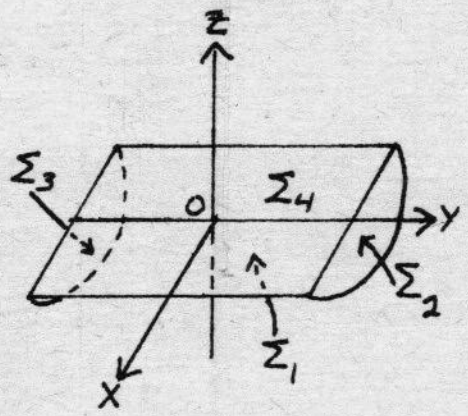

$$F = \iint_\Sigma (62.5)(z_0 - z)\, dS = \sum_{k=1}^{4} \iint_{\Sigma_k} -(62.5)z\, dS$$

For Σ_1, let R be the region in the xy plane between the graphs of $y = 0$ and $y = 12$ on $[-4,4]$, and for $0 < b < 4$, let R_b be the region in the xy plane between the graphs of $y = 0$ and $y = 12$ on $[-b,b]$. If $f(x,y) = -\sqrt{16 - x^2}$, then Σ_1 is the graph of f on R. Thus by (3),

$$\iint_{\Sigma_1} -(62.5)z\, dS = \lim_{b\to 4^-} \iint_{R_b} 62.5\sqrt{16 - x^2}\sqrt{\left(\frac{x}{\sqrt{16 - x^2}}\right)^2 + 0^2 + 1}\, dA$$

$$= 62.5 \lim_{b\to 4^-} \iint_{R_b} 4\, dA = 250 \lim_{b\to 4^-} (\text{area of } R_b) = 250 \lim_{b\to 4^-} 24b$$

$$= (250)(96) = 24{,}000$$

For Σ_2 and Σ_3, let R be the region in the xz plane between the graphs of $z = -\sqrt{16 - x^2}$ and $z = 0$ on $[-4,4]$. Then by (3), with the roles of y and z interchanged,

$$\iint_{\Sigma_2} -(62.5)z\, dS = \iint_R -(62.5)z\, dA = \int_{-4}^{4} \int_{-\sqrt{16-x^2}}^{0} -(62.5)z\, dz\, dx$$

$$= -62.5 \int_{-4}^{4} \frac{1}{2} z^2 \Big|_{-\sqrt{16-x^2}}^{0} dx = 62.5 \int_{-4}^{4} \frac{1}{2} (16 - x^2)\, dx$$

$$= 62.5(8x - \frac{1}{6} x^3)\Big|_{-4}^{4} = \frac{8000}{3}$$

Similarly,

$$\iint_{\Sigma_3} -(62.5)z\, dS = \frac{8000}{3}$$

Since Σ_4 lies in the plane $z = 0$,

$$\iint_{\Sigma_4} -(62.5)z\, dS = \iint_{\Sigma_4} 0\, dS = 0$$

Thus

$$F = 24{,}000 + \frac{8000}{3} + \frac{8000}{3} + 0 = \frac{88{,}000}{3} \text{ (pounds)}$$

17. The surface Σ of the tank consists of the top hemisphere, Σ_1 and the bottom hemisphere, Σ_2. Let R be the region in the xy plane bounded by the circle $r = 10$, and for $0 < b < 10$ let R_b be the region in the xy plane bounded by the circle $r = b$. If $f(x,y) = \sqrt{100 - x^2 - y^2}$, then Σ_1 is the graph of f on R, and Σ_2 is the graph of $-f$ on R. Moreover, $z_0 = 10$. Thus by (3),

$$F = \iint_\Sigma (62.5)(z_0 - z)\, dS = \iint_{\Sigma_1} (62.5)(10-z)dS + \iint_{\Sigma_2} (62.5)(10-z)dS$$

$$= 62.5 \iint_R (10-\sqrt{100-x^2-y^2})\sqrt{\left(\frac{-x}{\sqrt{100-x^2-y^2}}\right)^2 + \left(\frac{-y}{\sqrt{100-x^2-y^2}}\right)^2 + 1}\, dA$$

$$+ 62.5 \iint_R (10+\sqrt{100-x^2-y^2})\sqrt{\left(\frac{x}{\sqrt{100-x^2-y^2}}\right)^2 + \left(\frac{y}{\sqrt{100-x^2-y^2}}\right)^2 + 1}\, dA$$

$$= 62.5 \iint_R 20\sqrt{\frac{x^2}{100 - x^2 - y^2} + \frac{y^2}{100 - x^2 - y^2} + 1}\, dA$$

$$= 12{,}500 \iint_R \frac{1}{\sqrt{100 - x^2 - y^2}}\, dA = 12{,}500 \lim_{b\to 10^-} \int_0^{2\pi}\int_0^b \frac{r}{\sqrt{100-r^2}}\, dr\, d\theta$$

$$= 12{,}500 \lim_{b\to 10^-} \int_0^{2\pi} -\sqrt{100 - r^2}\Big|_0^b\, d\theta$$

$$= 12{,}500 \lim_{b\to 10^-} \int_0^{2\pi} (-\sqrt{100 - b^2} + 10)\, d\theta$$

$$= 25{,}000\pi \lim_{b\to 10^-} (-\sqrt{100 - b^2} + 10)$$

$$= 250{,}000\pi \text{ (pounds)}$$

Section 15.6

1.

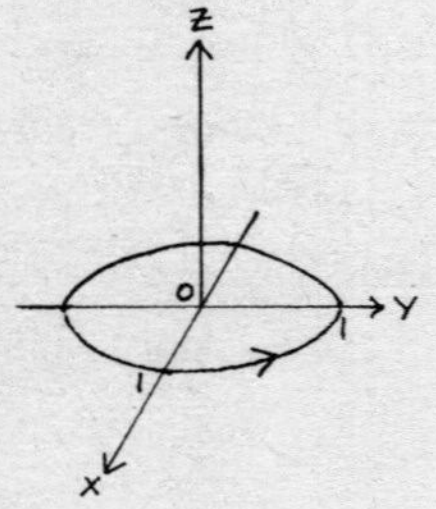

2.

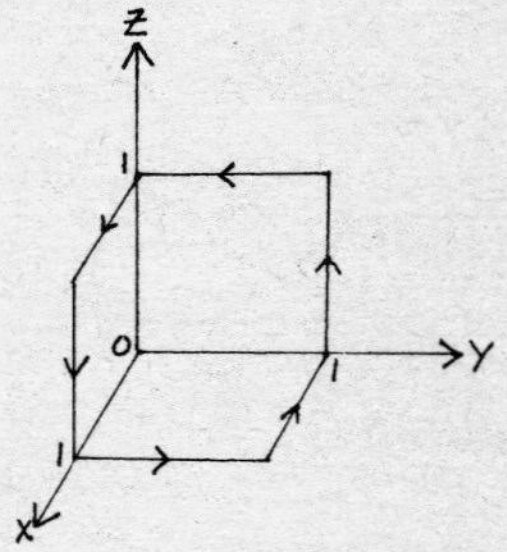

3.

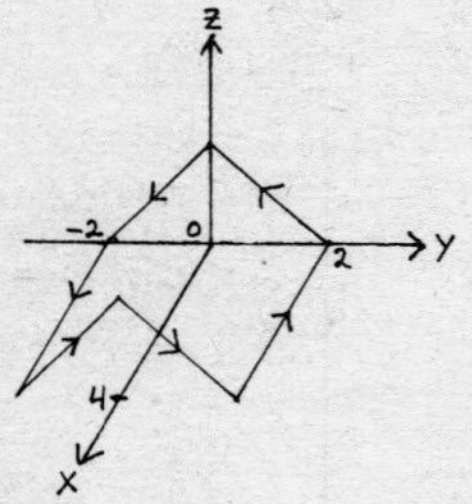

4.

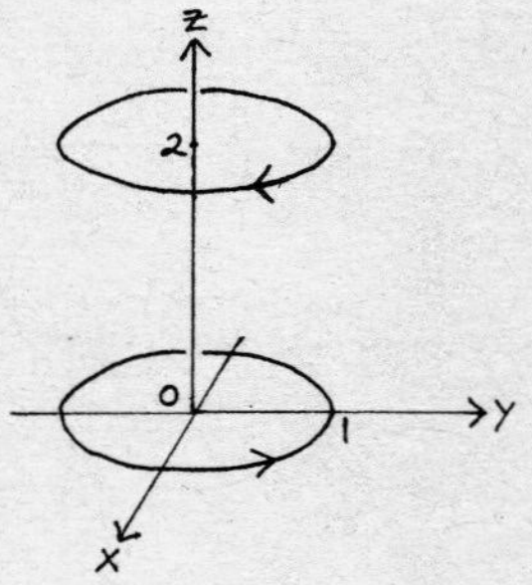

5. Let R be the region in the xy plane bounded by the circle $r = 3$ in polar coordinates, and let $f(x,y) = 9 - x^2 - y^2$ for (x,y) in R. We use (5) with $f_x(x,y) = -2x$, $f_y(x,y) = -2y$, $M(x,y,f(x,y)) = y$, $N(x,y,f(x,y)) = -x$, and $P(x,y,f(x,y)) = 8$, and find that

$$\iint_\Sigma \vec{F}\cdot\vec{n}\, dS = \iint_R [-y(-2x) + x(-2y) + 8]\, dA = \iint_R 8\, dA$$
$$= 8\ (\text{area of } R) = 72\pi$$

6. Let R be the region in the xy plane between the graphs of $y = 0$ and $y = 1$ on $[0,1]$, and let R_b be the region in the xy plane between the graphs of $y = 0$ and $y = 1$ on $[b,1]$ for $0 < b < 1$. Let $f(x,y) = \sqrt{x^2 + y^2}$ for (x,y) in R. We use (5) with $f_x(x,y) = \dfrac{x}{\sqrt{x^2 + y^2}}$, $f_y(x,y) = \dfrac{y}{\sqrt{x^2 + y^2}}$, $M(x,y,f(x,y)) = y$, $N(x,y,f(x,y)) = -x$, and $P(x,y,f(x,y)) = x^2 + y^2$, and find that

$$\iint_\Sigma \vec{F}\cdot\vec{n}\, dS = \lim_{b\to 0^+} \iint_{R_b} \left[-y\left(\frac{x}{\sqrt{x^2 + y^2}}\right) + x\left(\frac{y}{\sqrt{x^2 + y^2}}\right) + (x^2 + y^2)\right] dA$$

$$= \lim_{b\to 0^+} \int_b^1\int_0^1 (x^2 + y^2)\, dy\, dx = \lim_{b\to 0^+} \int_b^1 \left(x^2 y + \frac{1}{3} y^3\right)\Big|_0^1 dx$$

$$= \lim_{b\to 0^+} \int_b^1 \left(x^2 + \frac{1}{3}\right) dx = \lim_{b\to 0^+} \left(\frac{1}{3} x^3 + \frac{1}{3} x\right)\Big|_b^1$$

$$= \lim_{b\to 0^+} \left(\frac{2}{3} - \frac{1}{3} b^3 - \frac{1}{3} b\right) = \frac{2}{3}$$

7. Let R be the region in the xy plane between the graphs of $y = -\sqrt{1 - x^2}$ and $y = \sqrt{1 - x^2}$ on $[-1,1]$, and R_b the region between the graphs of $y = -\sqrt{b^2 - x^2}$ and $y = \sqrt{b^2 - x^2}$ on $[-b,b]$ for $0 < b < 1$. Let $f(x,y) = -\sqrt{1 - x^2 - y^2}$ for (x,y) in R. We use (5) with $f_x(x,y) = \dfrac{x}{\sqrt{1 - x^2 - y^2}}$, $f_y(x,y) = \dfrac{y}{\sqrt{1 - x^2 - y^2}}$, $M(x,y,f(x,y)) = 1$, $N(x,y,f(x,y)) = 1$, and $P(x,y,f(x,y)) = 2$, and find that

$$\iint_\Sigma \vec{F}\cdot\vec{n}\, dS = \lim_{b\to 1^-} \iint_{R_b} \left[\frac{-x}{\sqrt{1 - x^2 - y^2}} - \frac{y}{\sqrt{1 - x^2 - y^2}} + 2\right] dA$$

Notice that

$$\lim_{b\to 1^-} \iint_{R_b} \frac{-y}{\sqrt{1 - x^2 - y^2}}\, dA = \lim_{b\to 1^-} \int_{-b}^{b} \int_{-\sqrt{b^2-x^2}}^{\sqrt{b^2-x^2}} \frac{-y}{\sqrt{1 - x^2 - y^2}}\, dy\, dx$$

$$= \lim_{b\to1^-} \int_{-b}^{b} \sqrt{1 - x^2 - y^2}\,\Big|_{-\sqrt{b^2-x^2}}^{\sqrt{b^2-x^2}}\, dx = 0$$

Similarly,

$$\lim_{b\to1^-} \iint_{R_b} \frac{-x}{\sqrt{1 - x^2 - y^2}}\, dA = 0$$

Finally,

$$\lim_{b\to1^-} \iint_{R_b} 2\, dA = \lim_{b\to1^-} \int_0^{2\pi}\int_0^{b} 2r\, dr\, d\theta = \lim_{b\to1^-} \int_0^{2\pi} r^2\Big|_0^b\, d\theta$$

$$= \lim_{b\to1^-} \int_0^{2\pi} b^2\, d\theta = \lim_{b\to1^-} 2\pi b^2 = 2\pi$$

Thus

$$\iint_\Sigma \vec{F}\cdot\vec{n}\, dS = 0 + 0 + 2\pi = 2\pi$$

8. The parabolas $x = 1 - y^2$ and $x = y^2 - 1$ intersect for (x,y) such that $y = -1$ or $y = 1$. Let R be the region in the xy plane between the graphs of $x = y^2 - 1$ and $x = 1 - y^2$ on $[-1,1]$, and let $f(x,y) = x^2 + y^2$ for (x,y) in R. We use (6) with $f_x(x,y) = 2x$, $f_y(x,y) = 2y$, $M(x,y,f(x,y)) = x$, $N(x,y,f(x,y)) = -1$, and $P(x,y,f(x,y)) = 2x^2$, and find that

$$\iint_\Sigma \vec{F}\cdot\vec{n}\, dS = \iint_R [x(2x) - 2y - 2x^2]\, dA = \int_{-1}^{1}\int_{y^2-1}^{1-y^2} (-2y)\, dx\, dy$$

$$= \int_{-1}^{1} (-2yx)\Big|_{y^2-1}^{1-y^2} dy = \int_{-1}^{1} -2y(2 - 2y^2)\, dy = 4\int_{-1}^{1} (y^3 - y)\, dy$$

$$= 4\left(\frac{1}{4}y^4 - \frac{1}{2}y^2\right)\Big|_{-1}^{1} = 0$$

9. Let Σ be composed of the six surfaces Σ_1, Σ_2, Σ_3, Σ_4, Σ_5, and Σ_6, as in the figure. Using (6) with $f(x,y) = 0$, $M(x,y,f(x,y)) = x$, $N(x,y,f(x,y)) = y$, and $P(x,y,f(x,y)) = 0$, we have

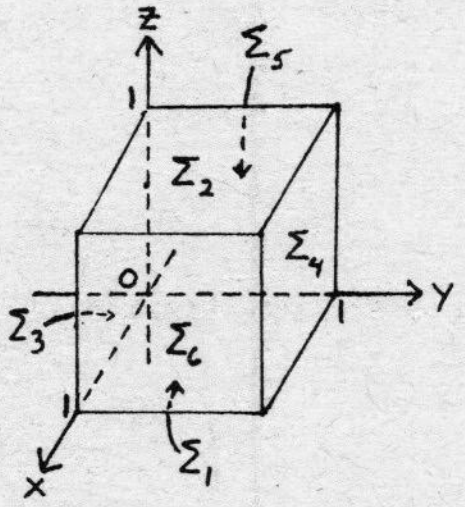

$$\iint_{\Sigma_1} \vec{F}\cdot\vec{n}\, dS = \int_0^1\int_0^1 (x\cdot 0 + y\cdot 0 - 0)\, dy\, dx = 0$$

Using (5) with $f(x,y) = 1$, $M(x,y,f(x,y)) = x$, $N(x,y,f(x,y)) = y$, and $P(x,y,f(x,y)) = 1$, we have

$$\iint_{\Sigma_2} \vec{F}\cdot\vec{n}\, dS = \int_0^1\int_0^1 (-x\cdot 0 - y\cdot 0 + 1)\, dy\, dx = \int_0^1 y\Big|_0^1 dx$$

$$= \int_0^1 1\, dx = 1$$

Since $\vec{F}$ and the cube Σ are symmetric in x, y, and z, it follows that

$$\iint_{\Sigma_1} \vec{F}\cdot\vec{n}\, dS = \iint_{\Sigma_3} \vec{F}\cdot\vec{n}\, dS = \iint_{\Sigma_5} \vec{F}\cdot\vec{n}\, dS = 0$$

and

$$\iint_{\Sigma_2} \vec{F}\cdot\vec{n}\, dS = \iint_{\Sigma_4} \vec{F}\cdot\vec{n}\, dS = \iint_{\Sigma_6} \vec{F}\cdot\vec{n}\, dS = 1$$

Thus

$$\iint_\Sigma \vec{F}\cdot\vec{n}\, dS = \sum_{k=1}^{6} \iint_{\Sigma_k} \vec{F}\cdot\vec{n}\, dS = 0 + 1 + 0 + 1 + 0 + 1 = 3$$

10. Let Σ be composed of the top half, Σ_1, and the bottom half, Σ_2. Let R be the region in the xy plane between the graphs of $y = -2$ and $y = 1$ on $[-1,1]$, and let R_b be the region between the graphs of $y = -2$ and $y = 1$ on $[-b,b]$ for $0 < b < 1$. Let $f(x,y) = \sqrt{1 - x^2}$ for (x,y) in R. Using (5) with $f_x(x,y) = \dfrac{-x}{\sqrt{1 - x^2}}$, $f_y(x,y) = 0$, $M(x,y,f(x,y)) = x$, $N(x,y,f(x,y)) = y$, and $P(x,y,f(x,y)) = \sqrt{1 - x^2}$, we have

$$\iint_{\Sigma_1} \vec{F}\cdot\vec{n}\, dS = \lim_{b\to1^-} \iint_{R_b} \left[-x\left(\frac{-x}{\sqrt{1 - x^2}}\right) - y\cdot 0 + \sqrt{1 - x^2}\,\right] dA$$

$$= \lim_{b\to1^-} \int_{-b}^{b}\int_{-2}^{1} \frac{1}{\sqrt{1 - x^2}}\, dy\, dx = \lim_{b\to1^-} \int_{-b}^{b} \frac{y}{\sqrt{1 - x^2}}\Big|_{-2}^{1} dx$$

$$= 3\lim_{b\to1^-} \int_{-b}^{b} \frac{1}{\sqrt{1 - x^2}}\, dx = 3\lim_{b\to1^-} \arcsin x\Big|_{-b}^{b}$$

$$= 3 \lim_{b\to 1^-} [\arcsin b - \arcsin(-b)] = 3\pi$$

For Σ_2 let $f(x,y) = -\sqrt{1-x^2}$ for (x,y) in R. Using (6) with $f_x(x,y) = \dfrac{x}{\sqrt{1-x^2}}$, $f_y(x,y) = 0$, M and N as above, and $P(x,y,f(x,y)) = -\sqrt{1-x^2}$, we have

$$\iint_{\Sigma_2} \vec{F}\cdot\vec{n}\, dS = \lim_{b\to 1^-} \iint_{R_b} [x(\frac{x}{\sqrt{1-x^2}}) + y\cdot 0 + \sqrt{1-x^2}\,]\, dA$$

$$= \lim_{b\to 1^-} \int_{-b}^{b}\int_{-2}^{1} \frac{1}{\sqrt{1-x^2}}\, dy\, dx = 3\pi$$

as in the first set of calculations. Thus

$$\iint_{\Sigma} \vec{F}\cdot\vec{n}\, dS = \iint_{\Sigma_1} \vec{F}\cdot\vec{n}\, dS + \iint_{\Sigma_2} \vec{F}\cdot\vec{n}\, dS = 3\pi + 3\pi = 6\pi$$

11. Let Σ be composed of the top half, Σ_1, and the bottom half, Σ_2. Let R be the region in the xy plane bounded by the circle $r = 2$ in polar coordinates, and let R_b be the region bounded by the circle $r = b$ for $0 < b < 2$. For Σ_1, let $f(x,y) = \sqrt{4-x^2-y^2}$ for (x,y) in R. Using (5) with $f_x(x,y) = \dfrac{-x}{\sqrt{4-x^2-y^2}}$, $f_y(x,y) = \dfrac{-y}{\sqrt{4-x^2-y^2}}$, $M(x,y,f(x,y)) = -y$, $N(x,y,f(x,y)) = x$, and $P(x,y,f(x,y)) = (\sqrt{4-x^2-y^2}\,)^4$, we have

$$\iint_{\Sigma_1} \vec{F}\cdot\vec{n}\, dS = \lim_{b\to 2^-} \iint_{R_b} [y\left(\frac{-x}{\sqrt{4-x^2-y^2}}\right) - x\left(\frac{-y}{\sqrt{4-x^2-y^2}}\right)$$

$$+ (\sqrt{4-x^2-y^2}\,)^4]\, dA = \lim_{b\to 2^-} \iint_{R_b} (4-x^2-y^2)^2\, dA$$

$$= \lim_{b\to 2^-} \int_0^{2\pi}\int_0^b (4-r^2)^2\, r\, dr\, d\theta = \lim_{b\to 2^-} \int_0^{2\pi} \frac{-1}{6}(4-r^2)^3 \Big|_0^b d\theta$$

$$= \lim_{b\to 2^-} \int_0^{2\pi} \frac{-1}{6}[(4-b^2)^3 - 64]\, d\theta = \lim_{b\to 2^-} \frac{\pi}{3}[64 - (4-b^2)^3]$$

$$= \frac{64}{3}\pi$$

For Σ_2 let $f(x,y) = -\sqrt{4-x^2-y^2}$ for (x,y) in R. Using (6) with $f_x(x,y) = \dfrac{x}{\sqrt{4-x^2-y^2}}$, $f_y(x,y) = \dfrac{y}{\sqrt{4-x^2-y^2}}$, M and N as above, and $P(x,y,f(x,y)) = (-\sqrt{4-x^2-y^2}\,)^4$, we have

$$\iint_{\Sigma_2} \vec{F}\cdot\vec{n}\, dS = \lim_{b\to 2^-} \iint_{R_b} [-y\left(\frac{x}{\sqrt{4-x^2-y^2}}\right) + x\left(\frac{y}{\sqrt{4-x^2-y^2}}\right)$$

$$- (-\sqrt{4-x^2-y^2}\,)^4]\, dA = -\lim_{b\to 2^-} \iint_{R_b} (4-x^2-y^2)^2\, dA = -\frac{64}{3}\pi$$

calculated as above. Thus

$$\iint_{\Sigma} \vec{F}\cdot\vec{n}\, dS = \iint_{\Sigma_1} \vec{F}\cdot\vec{n}\, dS + \iint_{\Sigma_2} \vec{F}\cdot\vec{n}\, dS = \frac{64}{3}\pi - \frac{64}{3}\pi = 0$$

12. Let Σ be composed of the bottom, Σ_1, the top, Σ_2, the part of the side for which the y coordinates are positive, Σ_3, and the rest of the side, Σ_4. For Σ_1 let R_1 be the region in the xy plane bounded by the circle $r = \sqrt{\frac{\pi}{2}}$, and let $f(x,y) = 0$. Using (6) with $f_x(x,y) = f_y(x,y) = 0$, $M(x,y,f(x,y)) = \sin(x^2+y^2)$, $N(x,y,f(x,y)) = y\sin(x^2+y^2)$, and $P(x,y,f(x,y)) = 0$, we have

$$\iint_{\Sigma_1} \vec{F}\cdot\vec{n}\, dS = \iint_{R_1} [(\sin(x^2+y^2))\cdot 0 + (y\sin(x^2+y^2))\cdot 0 - 0]\, dA = 0$$

For Σ_2 we use $R_2 = R_1$ and we let $f(x,y) = 1$. Then as above, $\iint_{\Sigma_2} \vec{F}\cdot\vec{n}\, dS = 0$. For Σ_3 we let R_3 be the region in the xz plane between the graphs of $z = 0$ and $z = 1$ on $[-\sqrt{\frac{\pi}{2}}, \sqrt{\frac{\pi}{2}}]$, and R_b the region in the xz plane between $z = 0$ and $z = 1$ on $[-b,b]$ for $0 < b < \sqrt{\frac{\pi}{2}}$. Let $f(x,z) = \sqrt{\frac{\pi}{2} - x^2}$ for (x,z) in R_3. By a formula analogous to (5), with $f_x(x,z) = \dfrac{-x}{\sqrt{\frac{\pi}{2} - x^2}}$, $f_z(x,z) = 0$, $M(x,f(x,z),z) = \sin\frac{\pi}{2} = 1$,

$N(x,f(x,z),z) = (\sin\frac{\pi}{2})\sqrt{\frac{\pi}{2} - x^2} = \sqrt{\frac{\pi}{2} - x^2}$, and $P(x,f(x,z),z) = 0$, we have

$$\iint_{\Sigma_3} \vec{F}\cdot\vec{n}\, dS = \iint_{R_3} [-M(x,f(x,z),z)f_x(x,z) - P(x,f(x,z),z)f_z(x,z)$$

$$+ N(x,f(x,z),z)]\, dA = \lim_{b\to\sqrt{\frac{\pi}{2}}^-} \iint_{R_b} [-\left(\frac{-x}{\sqrt{\frac{\pi}{2} - x^2}}\right) - 0 + \sqrt{\frac{\pi}{2} - x^2}]dA$$

$$= \lim_{b\to\sqrt{\frac{\pi}{2}}^-} \int_{-b}^{b}\int_0^1 \left(\frac{x}{\sqrt{\frac{\pi}{2} - x^2}} + \sqrt{\frac{\pi}{2} - x^2}\right) dz\, dx$$

$$= \lim_{b\to\sqrt{\frac{\pi}{2}}^-} \int_{-b}^{b} \left(\frac{x}{\sqrt{\frac{\pi}{2} - x^2}} + \sqrt{\frac{\pi}{2} - x^2}\right) z \Big|_0^1 dx$$

$$= \lim_{b\to\sqrt{\frac{\pi}{2}}^-} \int_{-b}^{b} \left(\frac{x}{\sqrt{\frac{\pi}{2} - x^2}} + \sqrt{\frac{\pi}{2} - x^2}\right) dx$$

$$= \lim_{b\to\sqrt{\frac{\pi}{2}}^-} \int_{-b}^{b} \frac{x}{\sqrt{\frac{\pi}{2} - x^2}}\, dx + \lim_{b\to\sqrt{\frac{\pi}{2}}^-} \int_{-b}^{b} \sqrt{\frac{\pi}{2} - x^2}\, dx$$

$$= \lim_{b\to\sqrt{\frac{\pi}{2}}^-} -\sqrt{\frac{\pi}{2} - x^2}\Big|_{-b}^{b} + \int_{-\sqrt{\pi/2}}^{\sqrt{\pi/2}} \sqrt{\frac{\pi}{2} - x^2}\, dx$$

$$= 0 + \frac{1}{2}\,(\text{area of circle of radius } \sqrt{\tfrac{\pi}{2}}\,)$$

$$= 0 + \frac{1}{2}\pi\left(\frac{\pi}{2}\right) = \frac{\pi^2}{4}$$

For Σ_4 we use $R_4 = R_3$, let R_b be as before, and let $f(x,z) = -\sqrt{\frac{\pi}{2} - x^2}$ for (x,z) in R_3. By a formula analogous to (6), with $f_x(x,z) = \dfrac{x}{\sqrt{\frac{\pi}{2} - x^2}}$, $f_z(x,z) = 0$, M and P as above, and $N(x,f(x,z),z) = -\sqrt{\frac{\pi}{2} - x^2}$, we have

$$\iint_{\Sigma_4} \vec{F}\cdot\vec{n}\, dS = \iint_{R_4} [M(x,f(x,z),z)f_x(x,z) + P(x,f(x,z),z)f_z(x,z)$$

$$- N(x,f(x,z),z)]dA = \lim_{b\to\sqrt{\frac{\pi}{2}}^-}\left[\iint_{R_b} \frac{x}{\sqrt{\frac{\pi}{2} - x^2}} + 0 + \sqrt{\frac{\pi}{2} - x^2}\right] dA$$

$$= \frac{\pi^2}{4}$$

as in the first set of calculations. Thus

$$\iint_{\Sigma} \vec{F}\cdot\vec{n}\, dS = \sum_{k=1}^{4} \iint_{\Sigma_k} \vec{F}\cdot\vec{n}\, dS = 0 + 0 + \frac{\pi^2}{4} + \frac{\pi^2}{4} = \frac{\pi^2}{2}$$

13. The sphere Σ is composed of its top, Σ_1, and its bottom, Σ_2. Let R be the region in the xy plane bounded by the circle $r = \sqrt{10}$, and for $0 < b < \sqrt{10}$ let R_b be the region bounded by the circle $r = b$. If $f(x,y) = \sqrt{10 - x^2 - y^2}$ for (x,y) in R, then Σ_1 is the graph of f on R. By (1) and (5) the rate of mass flow through Σ_1 is given by

$$\iint_{\Sigma_1} \delta\vec{v}\cdot\vec{n}\, dS = \lim_{b\to\sqrt{10}^-} \iint_{R_b} 50\, [-x\left(\frac{-x}{\sqrt{10 - x^2 - y^2}}\right) - y\left(\frac{-y}{\sqrt{10 - x^2 - y^2}}\right)$$

$$+ \sqrt{10 - x^2 - y^2}\,]\, dA = \lim_{b\to\sqrt{10}^-} \int_0^{2\pi}\int_0^b \frac{500}{\sqrt{10 - r^2}}\, r\, dr\, d\theta$$

$$= \lim_{b\to\sqrt{10}^-} \int_0^{2\pi} -500\sqrt{10 - r^2}\Big|_0^b d\theta$$

$$= \lim_{b\to\sqrt{10}^-} \int_0^{2\pi} (-500\sqrt{10 - b^2} + 500\sqrt{10})\, d\theta$$

$$= \lim_{b\to\sqrt{10}^-} 2\pi(-500\sqrt{10 - b^2} + 500\sqrt{10}) = 1000\pi\sqrt{10}$$

By (1) and (6) with $f(x,y) = -\sqrt{10 - x^2 - y^2}$ for (x,y) in R we find that the rate of mass flow through Σ_2 is given by

$$\iint_{\Sigma_2} \delta\vec{v}\cdot\vec{n}\, dS = \iint_{\Sigma_1} \delta\vec{v}\cdot\vec{n}\, dS = 1000\pi\sqrt{10}$$

Thus the total mass flow through the sphere Σ is

$$\iint_{\Sigma_1} \delta\vec{v}\cdot\vec{n}\, dS + \iint_{\Sigma_2} \delta\vec{v}\cdot\vec{n}\, dS = 2000\pi\sqrt{10}$$

14. Let $\Sigma = R$ be the region in the xz plane between the graphs of $z = 0$ and $z = 10$ on $[-20,20]$, and assume that the normal points in the direction of the positive y axis. Taking $\delta = 1.95$, we have $\delta\vec{v}\cdot\vec{n} = (1.95)[z(400 - x^2)\vec{j}]\cdot\vec{j}$ $= (1.95)z(400 - x^2)$ for (x,z) in R. By (1) the rate of flow of mass through Σ is given by

$$\iint_\Sigma \delta\vec{v}\cdot\vec{n}\,dS = \iint_R (1.95)z(400 - x^2)\,dz\,dx$$

$$= 1.95\int_{-20}^{20}\int_0^{10} z(400 - x^2)\,dz\,dx = 1.95\int_{-20}^{20} \frac{z^2}{2}(400 - x^2)\Big|_0^{10}dx$$

$$= 97.5\int_{-20}^{20} (400 - x^2)\,dx = (97.5)\left(400x - \frac{x^3}{3}\right)\Big|_{-20}^{20}$$

$= 1{,}040{,}000$ (slugs per minute)

15. Let R be the region in the xy plane between the graphs of $x = -y$ and $x = y$ on $[0,1]$, and let R_b be the region between the graphs of $x = -y$ and $x = y$ on $[b,1]$ for $0 < b < 1$. If $f(x,y) = \sqrt{y^2 - x^2}$, then Σ is the graph of f on R. By (5),

$$\iint_\Sigma \vec{E}\cdot\vec{n}\,dS = \lim_{b\to 0^+}\iint_{R_b}\left[-x\left(\frac{-x}{\sqrt{y^2 - x^2}}\right) - y\left(\frac{y}{\sqrt{y^2 - x^2}}\right) + 0\right]dA$$

$$= \lim_{b\to 0^+}\int_b^1\int_{-y}^{y} -\sqrt{y^2 - x^2}\,dx\,dy$$

(x = y sin u)

$$= \lim_{b\to 0^+}\int_b^1\int_{-\pi/2}^{\pi/2} -(y\cos u)(y\cos u)\,du\,dy$$

$$= \lim_{b\to 0^+}\int_b^1\int_{-\pi/2}^{\pi/2} -y^2\left(\frac{1}{2} + \frac{1}{2}\cos 2u\right)du\,dy$$

$$= \lim_{b\to 0^+}\int_b^1 -y^2\left(\frac{1}{2}u + \frac{1}{4}\sin 2u\right)\Big|_{-\pi/2}^{\pi/2}dy$$

$$= \lim_{b\to 0^+}\int_b^1 -\frac{1}{2}\pi y^2\,dy = \lim_{b\to 0^+}\left(-\frac{1}{6}\pi y^3\right)\Big|_b^1$$

$$= \lim_{b\to 0^+}\frac{1}{6}\pi(b^3 - 1) = -\frac{\pi}{6}$$

16. Let the surface of the cube be Σ, composed of the six faces Σ_1, Σ_2, Σ_3, Σ_4, Σ_5, and Σ_6, as in the figure. By (8), the total charge in the cube is given by

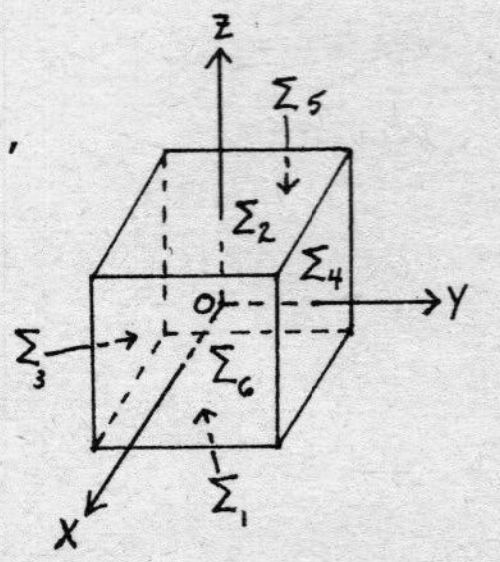

$$q = \varepsilon_0\iint_\Sigma \vec{E}\cdot\vec{n}\,dS = \sum_{k=1}^{6}\varepsilon_0\iint_{\Sigma_k}\vec{E}\cdot\vec{n}\,dS$$

For Σ_1, let R_1 be the square region in the xy plane between the graphs of $y = -1$ and $y = 1$ on $[-1,1]$, and let $f(x,y) = -1$ for (x,y) in R_1. Then (6) implies that

$$\varepsilon_0\iint_{\Sigma_1}\vec{E}\cdot\vec{n}\,dS = \varepsilon_0\iint_{R_1}[(2x)(0) + (2y)(0) - (4)(-1)]\,dA$$

$$= \varepsilon_0\int_{-1}^{1}\int_{-1}^{1} 4\,dy\,dx = 4\varepsilon_0(\text{area of R}) = 16\varepsilon_0$$

For Σ_2, let $f(x,y) = 1$ for (x,y) in $R_2 = R_1$, and use (5) to conclude that

$$\varepsilon_0\iint_{\Sigma_2}\vec{E}\cdot\vec{n}\,dS = \varepsilon_0\iint_{\Sigma_1}\vec{E}\cdot\vec{n}\,dS = 16\varepsilon_0$$

For Σ_3, let R_3 be the square region in the xz plane between the graphs of $z = -1$ and $z = 1$ on $[-1,1]$, and let $f(x,z) = -1$ for (x,z) in R_3. Interchanging the roles of y and z in (6), we find that

$$\varepsilon_0\iint_{\Sigma_3}\vec{E}\cdot\vec{n}\,dS = \varepsilon_0\iint_{R_3}[(2x)(0) - (2)(-1) + (4z)(0)]\,dA$$

$$= \varepsilon_0\int_{-1}^{1}\int_{-1}^{1} 2\,dz\,dx = 8\varepsilon_0$$

For Σ_4, let $f(x,z) = 1$ for (x,z) in $R_4 = R_3$, and use (5) with the roles of y and z interchanged. It follows that

$$\varepsilon_0\iint_{\Sigma_4}\vec{E}\cdot\vec{n}\,dS = \varepsilon_0\iint_{\Sigma_3}\vec{E}\cdot\vec{n}\,dS = 8\varepsilon_0$$

Because of the symmetry between x and y in the problem,

$$\varepsilon_0 \iint_{\Sigma_5} \vec{E}\cdot\vec{n}\, dS = \varepsilon_0 \iint_{\Sigma_6} \vec{E}\cdot\vec{n}\, dS = \varepsilon_0 \iint_{\Sigma_3} \vec{E}\cdot\vec{n}\, dS = 8\varepsilon_0$$

Consequently

$$q = \varepsilon_0 \iint_{\Sigma} \vec{E}\cdot\vec{n}\, dS = \sum_{k=1}^{6} \varepsilon_0 \iint_{\Sigma_k} \vec{E}\cdot\vec{n}\, dS = 16\varepsilon_0 + 16\varepsilon_0 + 8\varepsilon_0 + 8\varepsilon_0$$
$$+ 8\varepsilon_0 + 8\varepsilon_0 = 64\varepsilon_0$$

17. Let (x_0, y_0, z_0) be a point in space with $z_0 > 0$, and consider a rectangular parallelepiped Σ centered at $(x_0, y_0, 0)$, with height $2z_0$ and base area 1, with top Σ_t, bottom Σ_b, and sides Σ_s. Let R be the region in the xy plane inside the parallelepiped. By symmetry there is a function f of a single variable such that $\vec{E}(x,y,z) = f(z)\vec{k}$ and such that $f(-z) = -f(z)$ for $z \neq 0$. Since the area of R is 1, the total charge inside the parallelepiped is σ, so Gauss's Law implies that

$$\frac{\sigma}{\varepsilon_0} = \frac{q}{\varepsilon_0} = \iint_{\Sigma} \vec{E}\cdot\vec{n}\, dS = \iint_{\Sigma_t} \vec{E}\cdot\vec{n}\, dS + \iint_{\Sigma_b} \vec{E}\cdot\vec{n}\, dS + \iint_{\Sigma_s} \vec{E}\cdot\vec{n}\, dS$$

Now

$$\iint_{\Sigma_t} \vec{E}\cdot\vec{n}\, dS = \iint_{\Sigma_t} \{[f(z_0)\vec{k}]\cdot\vec{k}\}\, dS = \iint_{\Sigma_t} f(z_0)\, dS = f(z_0) \iint_R 1\, dA$$
$$= f(z_0)$$

and

$$\iint_{\Sigma_b} \vec{E}\cdot\vec{n}\, dS = \iint_{\Sigma_b} \{[-f(z_0)\vec{k}]\cdot(-\vec{k})\}\, dS = f(z_0) \iint_R 1\, dA = f(z_0)$$

On Σ_s the normal $\vec{n}$ is $\pm\vec{i}$ or $\pm\vec{j}$, and thus $\iint_{\Sigma_s} \vec{E}\cdot\vec{n}\, dS = 0$.

Consequently $\frac{\sigma}{\varepsilon_0} = f(z_0) + f(z_0) + 0$, so $f(z_0) = \frac{\sigma}{2\varepsilon_0}$ if $z_0 > 0$.

By symmetry, $f(z_0) = \frac{-\sigma}{2\varepsilon_0}$ if $z_0 < 0$. Therefore the electric field is given by

$$\vec{E}(x,y,z) = \begin{cases} \frac{\sigma}{2\varepsilon_0}\vec{k} & \text{for } z > 0 \\ \frac{-\sigma}{2\varepsilon_0}\vec{k} & \text{for } z < 0 \end{cases}$$

18. By symmetry $\vec{E}$ is constant on spheres centered at the origin and is normal to the spheres, so there is a function f of a single variable such that

$$\vec{E}(x,y,z) = f(\sqrt{x^2+y^2+z^2})\frac{x\vec{i}+y\vec{j}+z\vec{k}}{\sqrt{x^2+y^2+z^2}} \quad \text{for } x^2+y^2+z^2 > 0$$

Since no charge is contained in any such sphere with radius less than a, $f(\sqrt{x^2+y^2+z^2}) = 0$ if $0 \le x^2+y^2+z^2 < a^2$. If $x_0^2 + y_0^2 + z_0^2 \ge a^2$, then let Σ be the sphere centered at the origin and passing through (x_0, y_0, z_0). Then

$$\iint_{\Sigma} \vec{E}\cdot\vec{n}\, dS = \iint_{\Sigma} f(\sqrt{x_0^2+y_0^2+z_0^2})\, dS = f(\sqrt{x_0^2+y_0^2+z_0^2}) \iint_{\Sigma} 1\, dS$$
$$= f(\sqrt{x_0^2+y_0^2+z_0^2})\, 4\pi(x_0^2+y_0^2+z_0^2)$$

The total charge q inside the sphere is $4\pi a^2\sigma$, so by Gauss's Law this means that

$$\frac{4\pi a^2\sigma}{\varepsilon_0} = \frac{q}{\varepsilon_0} = \iint_{\Sigma} \vec{E}\cdot\vec{n}\, dS = f(\sqrt{x_0^2+y_0^2+z_0^2})\, 4\pi(x_0^2+y_0^2+z_0^2)$$

Thus

$$f(\sqrt{x_0^2+y_0^2+z_0^2}) = \frac{a^2\sigma}{\varepsilon_0(x_0^2+y_0^2+z_0^2)}$$

Consequently the electric field is given by

$$\vec{E}(x,y,z) = \begin{cases} \vec{0} & \text{for } 0 \le x^2+y^2+z^2 < a^2 \\ \frac{a^2\sigma}{\varepsilon_0(x_0^2+y_0^2+z_0^2)^{3/2}}(x\vec{i}+y\vec{j}+z\vec{k}) & \text{for } x^2+y^2+z^2 \ge a^2 \end{cases}$$

19. Assume that the center of the sphere is the origin. By symmetry $\vec{E}$ is constant on spheres centered at the origin, and is normal to the spheres, so there is a function f of a single variable such that

$$\vec{E}(x,y,z) = f(\sqrt{x^2+y^2+z^2})\frac{x\vec{i}+y\vec{j}+z\vec{k}}{\sqrt{x^2+y^2+z^2}} \quad \text{for } x^2+y^2+z^2 > 0$$

If (x_0, y_0, z_0) is not the origin, let Σ be the sphere centered at the origin with radius $\sqrt{x_0^2+y_0^2+z_0^2}$. Then

$$\iint_\Sigma \vec{E}\cdot\vec{n}\,dS = \iint_\Sigma f(\sqrt{x_0^2+y_0^2+z_0^2})\,dS = f(\sqrt{x_0^2+y_0^2+z_0^2})\iint_\Sigma 1\,dS$$
$$= f(\sqrt{x_0^2+y_0^2+z_0^2})\,4\pi(x_0^2+y_0^2+z_0^2)$$

Let $x_0^2+y_0^2+z_0^2 \le a^2$, and let D be the interior of Σ. By hypothesis the total charge inside Σ is given by

$$q = \iiint_D \rho_0\,dV = \rho_0[\tfrac{4}{3}\pi(x_0^2+y_0^2+z_0^2)^{3/2}]$$

By Gauss's Law this means that

$$\frac{\rho_0}{\varepsilon_0}[\tfrac{4}{3}\pi(x_0^2+y_0^2+z_0^2)^{3/2}] = \frac{q}{\varepsilon_0} = \iint_\Sigma \vec{E}\cdot\vec{n}\,dS$$
$$= f(\sqrt{x_0^2+y_0^2+z_0^2})\,4\pi(x_0^2+y_0^2+z_0^2)$$

so that

$$f(\sqrt{x_0^2+y_0^2+z_0^2}) = \frac{\rho_0}{3\varepsilon_0}(x_0^2+y_0^2+z_0^2)^{1/2}$$

Now let $x_0^2+y_0^2+z_0^2 > a^2$, and again let D be the interior of Σ. By hypothesis the total charge inside Σ is given by $q = \frac{4}{3}\pi a^3\rho_0$. By Gauss's Law this means that

$$\frac{4}{3}\pi a^3\frac{\rho_0}{\varepsilon_0} = \frac{q}{\varepsilon_0} = \iint_\Sigma \vec{E}\cdot\vec{n}\,dS = f(\sqrt{x_0^2+y_0^2+z_0^2})\,4\pi(x_0^2+y_0^2+z_0^2)$$

so that

$$f(\sqrt{x_0^2+y_0^2+z_0^2}) = \frac{\rho_0}{3\varepsilon_0}\frac{a^3}{x_0^2+y_0^2+z_0^2}$$

Consequently the electric field is given by

$$\vec{E}(x,y,z) = \begin{cases} \dfrac{\rho_0}{3\varepsilon_0}(x\vec{i}+y\vec{j}+z\vec{k}) & \text{for } 0 \le x^2+y^2+z^2 \le a^2 \\[2ex] \dfrac{\rho_0}{3\varepsilon_0}\dfrac{a^3}{(x^2+y^2+z^2)^{3/2}}(x\vec{i}+y\vec{j}+z\vec{k}) & \text{for } x^2+y^2+z^2 > a^2 \end{cases}$$

Section 15.7

1. $$\operatorname{curl}\vec{F}(x,y,z) = \begin{vmatrix} \vec{i} & \vec{j} & \vec{k} \\ \frac{\partial}{\partial x} & \frac{\partial}{\partial y} & \frac{\partial}{\partial z} \\ z & x & y \end{vmatrix} = \vec{i}+\vec{j}+\vec{k}$$

Let $f(x,y) = 1 - x^2 - y^2$, and let R be the region in the first quadrant of the xy plane bounded by the lines $x = 0$, $y = 0$, and the circle $x^2 + y^2 = 1$. Then Σ is the graph of f on R. Thus by Stokes's Theorem and (6) of Section 15.6,

$$\int_C \vec{F}\cdot d\vec{r} = \iint_\Sigma (\operatorname{curl}\vec{F})\cdot\vec{n}\,dS = \iint_R [(1)(-2x) + (1)(-2y) - 1]\,dA$$
$$= \int_0^{\pi/2}\int_0^1 (-2r\sin\theta - 2r\cos\theta - 1)\,r\,dr\,d\theta$$
$$= \int_0^{\pi/2} \left(-\frac{2}{3}r^3\sin\theta - \frac{2}{3}r^3\cos\theta - \frac{1}{2}r^2\right)\Big|_0^1 d\theta$$
$$= \int_0^{\pi/2}\left(-\frac{2}{3}\sin\theta - \frac{2}{3}\cos\theta - \frac{1}{2}\right)d\theta$$
$$= \left(\frac{2}{3}\cos\theta - \frac{2}{3}\sin\theta - \frac{1}{2}\theta\right)\Big|_0^{\pi/2} = -\frac{4}{3} - \frac{\pi}{4}$$

2. $$\operatorname{curl}\vec{F}(x,y,z) = \begin{vmatrix} \vec{i} & \vec{j} & \vec{k} \\ \frac{\partial}{\partial x} & \frac{\partial}{\partial y} & \frac{\partial}{\partial z} \\ z^2 & -y^2 & 0 \end{vmatrix} = 2z\vec{j}$$

Let Σ_1 be the square in the xy plane, Σ_2 the square in the yz plane, and Σ_3 the square in the xz plane. Then the normal to Σ_1 is $\vec{k}$, the normal to Σ_2 is $\vec{i}$, and the normal to Σ_3 is $\vec{j}$. Thus by Stokes's Theorem,

$$\int_C \vec{F}\cdot d\vec{r} = \iint_\Sigma (\operatorname{curl}\vec{F})\cdot\vec{n}\,dS = \iint_\Sigma (2z\vec{j})\cdot\vec{n}\,dS = \iint_{\Sigma_1}(2z\vec{j})\cdot\vec{k}\,dS$$
$$+ \iint_{\Sigma_2}(2z\vec{j})\cdot\vec{i}\,dS + \iint_{\Sigma_3}(2z\vec{j})\cdot\vec{j}\,dS = 0 + 0 + \int_0^1\int_0^1 2z\,dz\,dx$$

$$= \int_0^1 z^2 \Big|_0^1 dx = \int_0^1 1\,dx = 1$$

3. $$\text{curl}\,\vec{F}(x,y,z) = \begin{vmatrix} \vec{i} & \vec{j} & \vec{k} \\ \frac{\partial}{\partial x} & \frac{\partial}{\partial y} & \frac{\partial}{\partial z} \\ 2y & 3z & -2x \end{vmatrix} = -3\vec{i} + 2\vec{j} - 2\vec{k}$$

Let $f(x,y) = \sqrt{1 - x^2 - y^2}$ and let R be the region in the first quadrant of the xy plane bounded by the lines $x = 0$, $y = 0$, and the circle $x^2 + y^2 = 1$. Then Σ is the graph of f on R. For $0 \le b < 1$, let R_b be the part of R inside the circle $x^2 + y^2 = b^2$. Then by Stokes's Theorem and (5) of Section 15.6,

$$\int_C \vec{F}\cdot d\vec{r} = \iint_\Sigma (\text{curl}\,\vec{F})\cdot\vec{n}\,dS = \lim_{b\to1^-} \iint_{R_b} \left[-(-3)\frac{-x}{\sqrt{1 - x^2 - y^2}} - (2)\frac{-y}{\sqrt{1 - x^2 - y^2}} - 2\right] dA$$

$$= \lim_{b\to1^-} \left[\int_0^b \int_0^{\sqrt{b^2-x^2}} \left(\frac{-3x}{\sqrt{1-x^2-y^2}} + \frac{2y}{\sqrt{1-x^2-y^2}}\right) dy\,dx - 2(\text{area of } R_b)\right]$$

$$= \lim_{b\to1^-} \left[\int_0^b \left(3\sqrt{1-x^2-y^2} - 2\sqrt{1-x^2-y^2}\right)\Big|_0^{\sqrt{b^2-x^2}} dx - \tfrac{1}{2}\pi b^2\right]$$

$$= \lim_{b\to1^-} \int_0^b \left(\sqrt{1 - b^2} - \sqrt{1 - x^2}\right) dx - \frac{\pi}{2}$$

$$= \lim_{b\to1^-} x\sqrt{1 - b^2}\Big|_0^b - \lim_{b\to1^-} \int_0^{\arcsin b} \cos^2 u\,du - \frac{\pi}{2}$$

$$= \lim_{b\to1^-} b\sqrt{1 - b^2} - \lim_{b\to1^-} \int_0^{\arcsin b} \left(\tfrac{1}{2} + \tfrac{1}{2}\cos 2u\right) du - \frac{\pi}{2}$$

$$= 0 - \lim_{b\to1^-} \left(\tfrac{1}{2}u + \tfrac{1}{4}\sin 2u\right)\Big|_0^{\arcsin b} - \frac{\pi}{2}$$

$$= -\lim_{b\to1^-} \left(\tfrac{1}{2}u + \tfrac{1}{2}\sin u \cos u\right)\Big|_0^{\arcsin b} - \frac{\pi}{2}$$

$$= -\lim_{b\to1^-} \left(\tfrac{1}{2}\arcsin b + \tfrac{1}{2} b\sqrt{1 - b^2}\right) - \frac{\pi}{2}$$

$$= -\frac{\pi}{4} - \frac{\pi}{2} = -\frac{3}{4}\pi$$

4. $$\text{curl}\,\vec{F}(x,y,z) = \begin{vmatrix} \vec{i} & \vec{j} & \vec{k} \\ \frac{\partial}{\partial x} & \frac{\partial}{\partial y} & \frac{\partial}{\partial z} \\ y^2 & xy & -2xz \end{vmatrix} = 2z\vec{j} - y\vec{k}$$

Let $f(x,y) = \sqrt{4 - x^2 - y^2}$, and let R be the region in the xy plane bounded by the circle $x^2 + y^2 = 4$. Then Σ is the graph of f on R. For $0 \le b < 2$, let R_b be the part of R inside the circle $x^2 + y^2 = b^2$. Thus by Stokes's Theorem and (5) of Section 15.6,

$$\int_C \vec{F}\cdot d\vec{r} = \iint_\Sigma (\text{curl}\,\vec{F})\cdot\vec{n}\,dS = \lim_{b\to2^-} \iint_{R_b} \left[-(0)\left(\frac{-x}{\sqrt{4 - x^2 - y^2}}\right) - \left(2\sqrt{4 - x^2 - y^2}\right)\left(\frac{-y}{\sqrt{4 - x^2 - y^2}}\right) - y\right] dA$$

$$= \lim_{b\to2^-} \iint_{R_b} y\,dA = \lim_{b\to2^-} \int_0^{2\pi}\int_0^b r^2 \sin\theta\,dr\,d\theta$$

$$= \lim_{b\to2^-} \int_0^{2\pi} \tfrac{1}{3} r^3 \sin\theta \Big|_0^b d\theta = \lim_{b\to2^-} \int_0^{2\pi} \tfrac{1}{3} b^3 \sin\theta\,d\theta$$

$$= \lim_{b\to2^-} \left(-\tfrac{1}{3} b^3 \cos\theta\right)\Big|_0^{2\pi} = \lim_{b\to2^-} 0 = 0$$

5. $$\text{curl}\,\vec{F}(x,y,z) = \begin{vmatrix} \vec{i} & \vec{j} & \vec{k} \\ \frac{\partial}{\partial x} & \frac{\partial}{\partial y} & \frac{\partial}{\partial z} \\ y & -x & z \end{vmatrix} = -2\vec{k}$$

Let Σ_1 be the part of Σ on the plane $z = 1$, and Σ_2 the part of Σ on the cylinder $x^2 + y^2 = 1$. On Σ_1, $\vec{n} = \vec{k}$, so that $(\text{curl}\,\vec{F})\cdot\vec{n} = (-2\vec{k})\cdot\vec{k} = -2$. On Σ_2, $\vec{n}$ is perpendicular to the z axis, so that $(\text{curl}\,\vec{F})\cdot\vec{n} = 0$. Thus by Stokes's Theorem,

$$\int_C \vec{F}\cdot d\vec{r} = \iint_\Sigma (\text{curl}\,\vec{F})\cdot\vec{n}\,dS = \iint_{\Sigma_1} (\text{curl}\,\vec{F})\cdot\vec{n}\,dS + \iint_{\Sigma_2} (\text{curl}\,\vec{F})\cdot\vec{n}\,dS$$

$$= \iint_{\Sigma_1} -2\,dS + 0 = -2(\text{area of } \Sigma_1) = -2\pi$$

6. $\operatorname{curl} \vec{F}(x,y,z) = \begin{vmatrix} \vec{i} & \vec{j} & \vec{k} \\ \frac{\partial}{\partial x} & \frac{\partial}{\partial y} & \frac{\partial}{\partial z} \\ \frac{x}{\sqrt{x^2+y^2+z^2+1}} & \frac{y}{\sqrt{x^2+y^2+z^2+1}} & \frac{z}{\sqrt{x^2+y^2+z^2+1}} \end{vmatrix} = \vec{0}$

Let Σ be the part of the paraboloid $2z = x^2 + y^2$ that is bounded by C, and let Σ be oriented with normal $\vec{n}$ directed upward. Thus by Stokes's Theorem,

$$\int_C \vec{F}\cdot d\vec{r} = \iint_\Sigma (\operatorname{curl} \vec{F})\cdot\vec{n}\, dS = \iint_\Sigma \vec{0}\cdot\vec{n}\, dS = \iint_\Sigma 0\, dS = 0$$

7. $\operatorname{curl} \vec{F}(x,y,z) = \begin{vmatrix} \vec{i} & \vec{j} & \vec{k} \\ \frac{\partial}{\partial x} & \frac{\partial}{\partial y} & \frac{\partial}{\partial z} \\ xz & y^2 & x^2 \end{vmatrix} = -x\vec{j}$

Let Σ be the part of the plane $x + y + z = 5$ that lies inside the cylinder $x^2 + \frac{1}{4}y^2 = 1$, and let Σ be oriented with normal $\vec{n}$ directed upward. If $f(x,y) = 5 - x - y$, then Σ is the graph of f on the region R in the xy plane bounded by the ellipse $x^2 + \frac{1}{4}y^2 = 1$. Thus by Stokes's Theorem and (5) of Section 15.6,

$$\int_C \vec{F}\cdot d\vec{r} = \iint_\Sigma (\operatorname{curl} \vec{F})\cdot\vec{n}\, dS = \iint_R [-(0)(-1) - (-x)(-1) + 0]\, dA$$

$$= \int_{-2}^{2}\int_{-\sqrt{1-\frac{1}{4}y^2}}^{\sqrt{1-\frac{1}{4}y^2}} -x\, dx\, dy = \int_{-2}^{2} -\frac{1}{2}x^2 \Big|_{-\sqrt{1-\frac{1}{4}y^2}}^{\sqrt{1-\frac{1}{4}y^2}} dy$$

$$= \int_{-2}^{2} 0\, dy = 0$$

8. $\operatorname{curl} \vec{F}(x,y,z) = \begin{vmatrix} \vec{i} & \vec{j} & \vec{k} \\ \frac{\partial}{\partial x} & \frac{\partial}{\partial y} & \frac{\partial}{\partial z} \\ 3y & 2z & -x \end{vmatrix} = -2\vec{i} + \vec{j} - 3\vec{k}$

Let Σ be the part of the plane $x + y + z = 1$ that is bounded by C, and let Σ be oriented with normal $\vec{n}$ directed upward. If $f(x,y) = 1 - x - y$, then Σ is the graph of f on the region R in the first quadrant of the xy plane bounded by the lines $x = 0$, $y = 0$, and $x + y = 1$. Thus by Stokes's Theorem and (5) of Section 15.6,

$$\int_C \vec{F}\cdot d\vec{r} = \iint_\Sigma (\operatorname{curl} \vec{F})\cdot\vec{n}\, dS = \iint_R [-(-2)(-1) - (1)(-1) - 3]\, dA$$

$$= \int_0^1\int_0^{1-x} -4\, dy\, dx = \int_0^1 -4y\Big|_0^{1-x} dx = \int_0^1 (4x - 4)\, dx$$

$$= (2x^2 - 4x)\Big|_0^1 = -2$$

9. $\operatorname{curl} \vec{F}(x,y,z) = \begin{vmatrix} \vec{i} & \vec{j} & \vec{k} \\ \frac{\partial}{\partial x} & \frac{\partial}{\partial y} & \frac{\partial}{\partial z} \\ y(x^2+y^2) & -x(x^2+y^2) & 0 \end{vmatrix} = -4(x^2 + y^2)\vec{k}$

Let Σ be the part of the plane $z = y$ that is bounded by C, and let Σ be oriented with normal $\vec{n}$ directed upward. If $f(x,y) = y$, then Σ is the graph of f on the region R in the xy plane bounded by the rectangle with vertices $(0,0)$, $(1,0)$, $(1,1)$, and $(0,1)$. Thus by Stokes's Theorem and (5) in Section 15.6,

$$\int_C \vec{F}\cdot d\vec{r} = \iint_\Sigma (\operatorname{curl} \vec{F})\cdot\vec{n}\, dS = \iint_R [-(0)(0) - (0)(1) - 4(x^2+y^2)]\, dA$$

$$= \int_0^1\int_0^1 -4(x^2 + y^2)\, dy\, dx = \int_0^1 -4(x^2y + \tfrac{1}{3}y^3)\Big|_0^1 dx$$

$$= \int_0^1 -4(x^2 + \tfrac{1}{3})\, dx = -4(\tfrac{1}{3}x^3 + \tfrac{1}{3}x)\Big|_0^1 = -\frac{8}{3}$$

10. $\operatorname{curl} \vec{F}(x,y,z) = \begin{vmatrix} \vec{i} & \vec{j} & \vec{k} \\ \frac{\partial}{\partial x} & \frac{\partial}{\partial y} & \frac{\partial}{\partial z} \\ \ln(y^2+1) & x & x+y \end{vmatrix} = \vec{i} - \vec{j} + \left(1 - \frac{2y}{y^2+1}\right)\vec{k}$

Let $\Sigma = R$ be the part of the xy plane bounded by C, and let Σ be oriented with normal $\vec{n} = \vec{k}$. If $f(x,y) = 0$, then Σ is the graph of f on the region R in the xy plane. Thus by Stokes's Theorem and (5) of Section 15.6,

$$\int_C \vec{F}\cdot d\vec{r} = \iint_\Sigma (\operatorname{curl} \vec{F})\cdot\vec{n}\, dS = \iint_R \left[-(1)(0) - (-1)(0) + \left(1 - \frac{2y}{y^2+1}\right)\right] dA$$

$$= \int_0^3 \int_0^1 \left(1 - \frac{2y}{y^2+1}\right) dy\, dx = \int_0^3 [y - \ln(y^2+1)]\Big|_0^1 dx$$

$$= \int_0^3 (1 - \ln 2)\, dx = 3(1 - \ln 2)$$

11. $$\text{curl } \vec{F}(x,y,z) = \begin{vmatrix} \vec{i} & \vec{j} & \vec{k} \\ \frac{\partial}{\partial x} & \frac{\partial}{\partial y} & \frac{\partial}{\partial z} \\ z-y & y & x \end{vmatrix} = \vec{k}$$

Let Σ be the part of the sphere $x^2 + y^2 + z^2 = 1$ that is contained in the cylinder $r = \cos\theta$ and lies above the xy plane, and let Σ be oriented with normal $\vec{n}$ directed upward. If $f(x,y) = \sqrt{1 - x^2 - y^2}$, then Σ is the graph of f on the region in the xy plane bounded by the circle $r = \cos\theta$. Thus by Stokes's Theorem and (5) of Section 15.6,

$$\int_C \vec{F}\cdot d\vec{r} = \iint_\Sigma (\text{curl } \vec{F})\cdot\vec{n}\, dS = \iint_R \left[-(0)\frac{-x}{\sqrt{1-x^2-y^2}} - (0)\frac{-y}{\sqrt{1-x^2-y^2}} + 1\right] dA$$

$$= \iint_R 1\, dA = \text{area of } R = \frac{\pi}{4}$$

12. $$\text{curl } \vec{F}(x,y,z) = \begin{vmatrix} \vec{i} & \vec{j} & \vec{k} \\ \frac{\partial}{\partial x} & \frac{\partial}{\partial y} & \frac{\partial}{\partial z} \\ 0 & 0 & yz \end{vmatrix} = z\vec{i}$$

Let Σ be the part of the cone $z = \sqrt{x^2 + y^2}$ in the first octant between the planes $z = 2$ and $z = 3$, and let Σ be oriented with normal $\vec{n}$ directed downward. If $f(x,y) = \sqrt{x^2 + y^2}$, then Σ is the graph of f on the part of the ring R in the first quadrant of the xy plane bounded by the circles $r = 2$ and $r = 3$ and the lines $\theta = 0$ and $\theta = \frac{\pi}{2}$. Thus by Stokes's Theorem and (5) of Section 15.6,

$$\int_C \vec{F}\cdot d\vec{r} = \iint_\Sigma (\text{curl } \vec{F})\cdot\vec{n}\, dS = \iint_R \left[\sqrt{x^2+y^2}\left(\frac{x}{\sqrt{x^2+y^2}}\right) + (0)\frac{y}{\sqrt{x^2+y^2}}\right.$$

$$\left. - 0\right] dA = \iint_R x\, dA = \int_0^{\pi/2}\int_2^3 r^2\cos\theta\, dr\, d\theta$$

$$= \int_0^{\pi/2} \frac{1}{3} r^3 \cos\theta \Big|_2^3 d\theta = \int_0^{\pi/2} \frac{19}{3}\cos\theta\, d\theta = \frac{19}{3}\sin\theta\Big|_0^{\pi/2} = \frac{19}{3}$$

13. $$\text{curl } \vec{F}(x,y,z) = \begin{vmatrix} \vec{i} & \vec{j} & \vec{k} \\ \frac{\partial}{\partial x} & \frac{\partial}{\partial y} & \frac{\partial}{\partial z} \\ x^2+z & y^2+x & z^2+y \end{vmatrix} = \vec{i} + \vec{j} + \vec{k}$$

The sphere $x^2 + y^2 + z^2 = 1$ and the cone $z = \sqrt{x^2 + y^2}$ intersect at (x,y,z) such that $z \geq 0$ and $1 - x^2 - y^2 = z^2 = x^2 + y^2$, so that $x^2 + y^2 = \frac{1}{2}$ and thus $z = \frac{\sqrt{2}}{2}$. Making use of (1), we let Σ be the part of the plane $z = \frac{\sqrt{2}}{2}$ that lies inside the cone $z = \sqrt{x^2 + y^2}$, and let Σ be oriented with normal $\vec{n}$ directed upward. If $f(x,y) = \frac{\sqrt{2}}{2}$, then Σ is the graph of f on the region R in the xy plane bounded by the circle $x^2 + y^2 = \frac{1}{2}$. Thus by Stokes's Theorem and (5) of Section 15.6,

$$\int_C \vec{F}\cdot d\vec{r} = \iint_\Sigma (\text{curl } \vec{F})\cdot\vec{n}\, dS = \iint_R [-(1)(0) - (1)(0) + 1]\, dA$$

$$= \text{area of } R = \frac{\pi}{2}$$

14. $$\text{curl } \vec{F}(x,y,z) = \begin{vmatrix} \vec{i} & \vec{j} & \vec{k} \\ \frac{\partial}{\partial x} & \frac{\partial}{\partial y} & \frac{\partial}{\partial z} \\ xz & y^2+2x & x \end{vmatrix} = (x-1)\vec{j} + 2\vec{k}$$

Notice that Σ is bounded by the circle $x^2 + y^2 = 9$. Let Σ_1 be the disk in the xy plane bounded by the circle $x^2 + y^2 = 9$, and let Σ_1 be oriented with normal $\vec{n} = \vec{k}$. Then Σ and Σ_1 induce the same orientation on the circle. Thus by (9),

$$\iint_\Sigma (\text{curl } \vec{F})\cdot\vec{n}\, dS = \iint_{\Sigma_1} (\text{curl } \vec{F})\cdot\vec{n}\, dS = \iint_{\Sigma_1} [(x-1)\vec{j} + 2\vec{k}]\cdot\vec{k}\, dS$$

$$= \iint_{\Sigma_1} 2\, dS = 2\,(\text{area of } \Sigma_1) = 18\pi$$

15. $$\operatorname{curl} \vec{F}(x,y,z) = \begin{vmatrix} \vec{i} & \vec{j} & \vec{k} \\ \frac{\partial}{\partial x} & \frac{\partial}{\partial y} & \frac{\partial}{\partial z} \\ x & x^2+y^2+z^2 & z(y^4-1) \end{vmatrix} = (4zy^3 - 2z)\vec{i} + 2x\vec{k}$$

Let Σ_1 be the rectangular region in the xy plane bounded by the lines $x = -1$, $x = 1$, $y = -1$, and $y = 1$, and orient Σ_1 with normal $\vec{n} = \vec{k}$. Then Σ and Σ_1 induce the same orientation on their common boundary. Thus by (9),

$$\iint_{\Sigma} (\operatorname{curl} \vec{F}) \cdot \vec{n}\, dS = \iint_{\Sigma_1} (\operatorname{curl} \vec{F}) \cdot \vec{n}\, dS = \iint_{\Sigma_1} [(4zy^3-2z)\vec{j} + 2x\vec{k}] \cdot \vec{k}\, dS$$

$$= \iint_{\Sigma_1} 2x\, dS = \int_{-1}^{1}\int_{-1}^{1} 2x\, dy\, dx = \int_{-1}^{1} 2xy\Big|_{-1}^{1} dx = \int_{-1}^{1} 4x\, dx$$

$$= 2x^2\Big|_{-1}^{1} = 0$$

16. The boundary C of Σ is composed of two circles C_1 and C_2 of radius $\sqrt{15}$ in the planes $z = -1$ and $z = 2$, respectively. The orientation of Σ induces the counterclockwise orientation on C_1 and the clockwise orientation on C_2. Thus Stokes's Theorem implies that

$$\iint_{\Sigma} (\operatorname{curl} \vec{F}) \cdot \vec{n}\, dS = \int_C \vec{F} \cdot d\vec{r} = \int_{C_1} \vec{F} \cdot d\vec{r} + \int_{C_2} \vec{F} \cdot d\vec{r}$$

Now let Σ_1 be the part of the plane $z = -1$ inside C_1 and Σ_2 the part of the plane $z = 2$ inside C_2. Orient Σ_1 by using normal $\vec{n} = \vec{k}$ and orient Σ_2 with normal $\vec{n} = -\vec{k}$. Then Σ and Σ_1 induce the same orientation on C_1 and Σ and Σ_2 induce the same orientation on C_2. If R is the disk in the xy plane bounded by the circle $x^2 + y^2 = 15$, then by Stokes's Theorem we have

$$\int_{C_1} \vec{F} \cdot d\vec{r} = \iint_{\Sigma_1} (\operatorname{curl} \vec{F}) \cdot \vec{n}\, dS = \iint_{\Sigma_1} (\operatorname{curl} \vec{F}) \cdot \vec{k}\, dS$$

$$= \iint_{\Sigma_1} \left\{\left[\frac{\partial}{\partial x}(-x) - \frac{\partial}{\partial y}(z^2 y)\right]\vec{k}\right\} \cdot \vec{k}\, dS = \iint_{\Sigma_1} (-1 - z^2)\, dS$$

$$= \iint_R [-1 - (-1)^2]\, dA = -2\,(\text{area of } R) = -30\pi$$

Analogously,

$$\int_{C_2} \vec{F} \cdot d\vec{r} = \iint_{\Sigma_2} (\operatorname{curl} \vec{F}) \cdot \vec{n}\, dS = \iint_{\Sigma_2} (\operatorname{curl} \vec{F}) \cdot (-\vec{k})\, dS$$

$$= \iint_{\Sigma_2} (1 + z^2)\, dS = \iint_R (1 + 4)\, dA = 5\,(\text{area of } R) = 75\pi$$

Thus

$$\iint_{\Sigma} (\operatorname{curl} \vec{F}) \cdot \vec{n}\, dS = \int_C \vec{F} \cdot d\vec{r} = \int_{C_1} \vec{F} \cdot d\vec{r} + \int_{C_2} \vec{F} \cdot d\vec{r}$$

$$= -30\pi + 75\pi = 45\pi$$

17. $$\operatorname{curl} \vec{F}(x,y,z) = \begin{vmatrix} \vec{i} & \vec{j} & \vec{k} \\ \frac{\partial}{\partial x} & \frac{\partial}{\partial y} & \frac{\partial}{\partial z} \\ x \sin z & xy & yz \end{vmatrix} = z\vec{i} + x \cos z\, \vec{j} + y\vec{k}$$

Let Σ_1 be the face of the cube in the plane $z = 1$, and let Σ_1 be oriented with normal $\vec{n} = -\vec{k}$. Then Σ and Σ_1 induce the same orientation on their common boundary. Thus by (9),

$$\iint_{\Sigma} (\operatorname{curl} \vec{F}) \cdot \vec{n}\, dS = \iint_{\Sigma_1} (\operatorname{curl} \vec{F}) \cdot \vec{n}\, dS$$

$$= \iint_{\Sigma_1} [(z\vec{i} + x \cos z\, \vec{j} + y\, \vec{k}) \cdot (-\vec{k})]\, dS = \iint_{\Sigma_1} -y\, dS$$

$$= \int_0^1\int_0^1 -y\, dy\, dx = \int_0^1 -\frac{1}{2}y^2\Big|_0^1 dx = \int_0^1 -\frac{1}{2}\, dx = -\frac{1}{2}$$

18. $$\operatorname{curl} \vec{F}(x,y,z) = \begin{vmatrix} \vec{i} & \vec{j} & \vec{k} \\ \frac{\partial}{\partial x} & \frac{\partial}{\partial y} & \frac{\partial}{\partial z} \\ 3y^2 z + y & y & 3xy^2 \end{vmatrix} = 6xy\vec{i} - (6yz + 1)\vec{k}$$

The boundary C of Σ consists of the two circles C_1 and C_2

shown in the figure. Then Stokes's Theorem implies that

$$\iint_{\Sigma} (\text{curl } \vec{F})\cdot\vec{n}\, dS = \int_C \vec{F}\cdot d\vec{r} = \int_{C_1} \vec{F}\cdot d\vec{r} + \int_{C_2} \vec{F}\cdot d\vec{r}$$

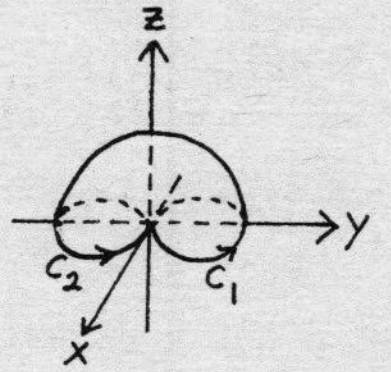

Now let Σ_1 be the region in the xy plane bounded by C_1, let Σ_2 be the region in the xy plane bounded by C_2, and let both Σ_1 and Σ_2 be oriented with normal $\vec{n} = \vec{k}$. Then the orientations of Σ_1 and Σ_2 induce the counterclockwise orientations on C_1 and C_2, respectively. Thus by Stokes's Theorem,

$$\int_{C_1} \vec{F}\cdot d\vec{r} = \iint_{\Sigma_1} (\text{curl } \vec{F})\cdot\vec{n}\, dS = \iint_{\Sigma_1} [6xy\vec{i} - (6yz+1)\vec{k}]\cdot\vec{k}\, dS$$

$$= \iint_{\Sigma_1} -(6yz+1)\, dS = \iint_{\Sigma_1} -1\, dS = -(\text{area of } \Sigma_1) = -\frac{\pi}{4}$$

and

$$\int_{C_2} \vec{F}\cdot d\vec{r} = \iint_{\Sigma_2} (\text{curl } \vec{F})\cdot\vec{n}\, dS = \iint_{\Sigma_2} [6xy\vec{i} - (6yz+1)\vec{k}]\cdot\vec{k}\, dS$$

$$= \iint_{\Sigma_2} -(6yz+1)\, dS = \iint_{\Sigma_2} -1\, dS = -(\text{area of } \Sigma_2) = -\frac{\pi}{4}$$

Thus

$$\iint_{\Sigma} (\text{curl } \vec{F})\cdot\vec{n}\, dS = \int_{C_1} \vec{F}\cdot d\vec{r} + \int_{C_2} \vec{F}\cdot d\vec{r} = -\frac{\pi}{4} - \frac{\pi}{4} = -\frac{\pi}{2}$$

19. $$\text{curl } \vec{F}(x,y,z) = \begin{vmatrix} \vec{i} & \vec{j} & \vec{k} \\ \frac{\partial}{\partial x} & \frac{\partial}{\partial y} & \frac{\partial}{\partial z} \\ xz^2 & x^3 & \cos xz \end{vmatrix} = (2xz + z\sin xz)\vec{j} + 3x^2\vec{k}$$

Let Σ_1 be the disk in the xy plane bounded by the circle $x^2 + y^2 = 1$, and let Σ_1 be oriented with normal $\vec{n} = -\vec{k}$. Then Σ and Σ_1 induce the same orientation on their common boundary. Thus by (9),

$$\iint_{\Sigma} (\text{curl } \vec{F})\cdot\vec{n}\, dS = \iint_{\Sigma_1} (\text{curl } \vec{F})\cdot\vec{n}\, dS$$

$$= \iint_{\Sigma_1} [(2xz + z\sin xz)\vec{j} + 3x^2\vec{k}]\cdot(-\vec{k})\, dS = \iint_{\Sigma_1} -3x^2\, dS$$

$$= \int_0^{2\pi}\int_0^1 -3r^3\cos^2\theta\, dr\, d\theta = \int_0^{2\pi} -\frac{3}{4}r^4\cos^2\theta\Big|_0^1 d\theta$$

$$= \int_0^{2\pi} -\frac{3}{4}\cos^2\theta\, d\theta = \int_0^{2\pi} -\left(\frac{3}{8} + \frac{3}{8}\cos 2\theta\right) d\theta$$

$$= -\left(\frac{3}{8}\theta + \frac{3}{16}\sin 2\theta\right)\Big|_0^{2\pi} = -\frac{3}{4}\pi$$

20. Let $\Sigma_1 = R$ be the disk in the xy plane bounded by the circle $x^2 + y^2 = 1$, and let Σ_1 be oriented with normal $\vec{n} = \vec{k}$. Then Σ and Σ_1 induce the same orientation on their common boundary. Thus by (9),

$$\iint_{\Sigma} (\text{curl } \vec{F})\cdot\vec{n}\, dS = \iint_{\Sigma_1} (\text{curl } \vec{F})\cdot\vec{n}\, dS$$

$$= \iint_{\Sigma_1} \left\{\left[\frac{\partial}{\partial x}(-(z+1)xy) - \frac{\partial}{\partial y}((z+1)y^3)\right]\vec{k}\right\}\cdot\vec{k}\, dS$$

$$= \iint_{\Sigma_1} (-zy - y - 3zy^2 - 3y^2)\, dS = \iint_R (-y - 3y^2)\, dA$$

$$= \int_0^{2\pi}\int_0^1 (-r\sin\theta - 3r^2\sin^2\theta)\, r\, dr\, d\theta$$

$$= \int_0^{2\pi} \left(-\frac{1}{3}r^3\sin\theta - \frac{3}{4}r^4\sin^2\theta\right)\Big|_0^1 d\theta$$

$$= \int_0^{2\pi} \left(-\frac{1}{3}\sin\theta - \frac{3}{4}\sin^2\theta\right) d\theta$$

$$= \int_0^{2\pi} \left(-\frac{1}{3}\sin\theta - \frac{3}{8} + \frac{3}{8}\cos 2\theta\right) d\theta$$

$$= \left(\frac{1}{3}\cos\theta - \frac{3}{8}\theta + \frac{3}{16}\sin 2\theta\right)\Big|_0^{2\pi} = -\frac{3}{4}\pi$$

21. Since F is a constant vector field, $\text{curl } \vec{F}(x,y,z) = \vec{0}$. Thus by Stokes's Theorem,

$$\int_C \vec{F}\cdot d\vec{r} = \iint_\Sigma (\text{curl } \vec{F})\cdot\vec{n}\, dS = \iint_\Sigma \vec{0}\cdot\vec{n}\, dS = \iint_\Sigma 0\, dS = 0$$

22. Let Σ_1 be the part of Σ that lies above the xy plane, let Σ_2 be the part of Σ that lies on or below the xy plane, and let Σ_1 and Σ_2 have the normals they receive from Σ. Then Σ_1 and Σ_2 induce opposite orientations on their common boundary. Thus by (10),

$$\iint_\Sigma (\text{curl } \vec{F})\cdot\vec{n}\, dS = \iint_{\Sigma_1} (\text{curl } \vec{F})\cdot\vec{n}\, dS + \iint_{\Sigma_2} (\text{curl } \vec{F})\cdot\vec{n}\, dS = 0$$

23. $$\text{curl } \vec{v}(x,y,z) = \begin{vmatrix} \vec{i} & \vec{j} & \vec{k} \\ \frac{\partial}{\partial x} & \frac{\partial}{\partial y} & \frac{\partial}{\partial z} \\ x^3 & -zy & x \end{vmatrix} = y\vec{i} - \vec{j}$$

The sphere $x^2 + y^2 + z^2 = 1$ and the plane $z = y$ intersect at (x,y,z) such that $1 = x^2 + y^2 + z^2 = x^2 + 2y^2$. Let Σ_1 be the part of the plane $z = y$ that is enclosed by the boundary C of Σ, and orient Σ_1 with normal n directed upward. Then Σ and Σ_1 induce the same orientation on C. Let $f(x,y) = y$, and let R be the region in the xy plane bounded by the ellipse $x^2 + 2y^2 = 1$. Then Σ_1 is the graph of f on R. By the definition of circulation, by Stokes's Theorem, and by (5) in Section 15.6, the circulation of the fluid is given by

$$\int_C \vec{v}\cdot d\vec{r} = \iint_{\Sigma_1} (\text{curl } \vec{v})\cdot\vec{n}\, dS = \iint_R [-(y)(0) - (-1)(1) + 0]\, dA$$

$$= \iint_R 1\, dA = \text{area of } R = \frac{\pi}{\sqrt{2}}$$

24. $$\text{curl } \vec{v}(x,y,z) = \begin{vmatrix} \vec{i} & \vec{j} & \vec{k} \\ \frac{\partial}{\partial x} & \frac{\partial}{\partial y} & \frac{\partial}{\partial z} \\ \sin xz + 2yz & \cosh y + 2xz & e^{x^2z^2} + 5y \end{vmatrix}$$

$$= (5 - 2x)\vec{i} + (x \cos xz + 2y - 2xz^2e^{x^2z^2})\vec{j}$$

The paraboloid $2z = x^2 + y^2$ and the plane $z = x$ intersect at (x,y,z) such that $x^2 + y^2 = 2z = 2x$. Let Σ_1 be the part of the plane $z = x$ that lies inside the cylinder $x^2 + y^2 = 2x$, and let Σ_1 be oriented with normal $\vec{n}$ directed downward. If $f(x,y) = x$, then Σ_1 is the graph of f on the region R in the xy plane bounded by the circle $x^2 + y^2 = 2x$, whose equation in polar coordinates is $r = 2\cos\theta$. Since Σ and Σ_1 induce the same orientation on their common boundary, Stokes's Theorem and (6) in Section 15.6 imply that the circulation of fluid around the boundary C of Σ is given by

$$\int_C \vec{v}\cdot d\vec{r} = \iint_{\Sigma_1} (\text{curl } \vec{v})\cdot\vec{n}\, dS = \iint_R [(5 - 2x)(1) + (x \cos x^2 + 2y - 2x^3e^{x^4})(0) - 0]\, dA = \iint_R (5 - 2x)\, dA$$

$$= \int_{-\pi/2}^{\pi/2}\int_0^{2\cos\theta} (5 - 2r\cos\theta)r\, dr\, d\theta$$

$$= \int_{-\pi/2}^{\pi/2} \left(\frac{5}{2}r^2 - \frac{2}{3}r^3\cos\theta\right)\Big|_0^{2\cos\theta} d\theta$$

$$= \int_{-\pi/2}^{\pi/2} \left(10\cos^2\theta - \frac{16}{3}\cos^4\theta\right) d\theta$$

$$= \int_{-\pi/2}^{\pi/2} \left(5 + 5\cos 2\theta - \frac{16}{3}\cos^4\theta\right) d\theta$$

$$= \left[5\theta + \frac{5}{2}\sin\theta - \frac{16}{3}\left(\frac{1}{4}\cos^3\theta\sin\theta + \frac{3}{8}\cos\theta\sin\theta + \frac{3}{8}\theta\right)\right]\Big|_{-\pi/2}^{\pi/2} = 3\pi + 5$$

with the next to last equality coming from (15) in Section 7.1.

Section 15.8

1. Yes 2. Yes 3. Yes 4. Yes

5. No 6. Yes 7. No 8. No

9. $\operatorname{div} \vec{F}(x,y,z) = 2x + x - 2x = x$

$$\iint_\Sigma \vec{F}\cdot\vec{n}\, dS = \iiint_D \operatorname{div} \vec{F}(x,y,z)\, dV = \iiint_D x\, dV$$

$$= \int_0^1\int_0^{1-x}\int_0^{1-x-y} x\, dz\, dy\, dx = \int_0^1\int_0^{1-x} xz\Big|_0^{1-x-y} dy\, dx$$

$$= \int_0^1\int_0^{1-x} (x - x^2 - xy)\, dy\, dx = \int_0^1 [(x-x^2)y - \tfrac{1}{2}xy^2]\Big|_0^{1-x} dx$$

$$= \int_0^1 [x(1-x)^2 - \tfrac{1}{2}x(1-x)^2]\, dx$$

$$= \frac{1}{2}\int_0^1 (x - 2x^2 + x^3)\, dx = \frac{1}{2}\left(\tfrac{1}{2}x^2 - \tfrac{2}{3}x^3 + \tfrac{1}{4}x^4\right)\Big|_0^1 = \frac{1}{24}$$

10. $\operatorname{div} \vec{F}(x,y,z) = 2x + 2y + 2z$

$$\iint_\Sigma \vec{F}\cdot\vec{n}\, dS = \iiint_D \operatorname{div} \vec{F}(x,y,z)\, dV = \iiint_D (2x + 2y + 2z)\, dV$$

$$= 2\int_0^1\int_0^2\int_0^3 (x + y + z)\, dz\, dy\, dx$$

$$= 2\int_0^1\int_0^2 [(x+y)z + \tfrac{1}{2}z^2]\Big|_0^3 dy\, dx$$

$$= 6\int_0^1\int_0^2 (x + y + \tfrac{3}{2})\, dy\, dx = 6\int_0^1 (xy + \tfrac{1}{2}y^2 + \tfrac{3}{2}y)\Big|_0^2 dx$$

$$= 6\int_0^1 (2x + 5)\, dx = 6(x^2 + 5x)\Big|_0^1 = 36$$

11. $\operatorname{div} \vec{F}(x,y,z) = 1 + 1 + 1 = 3$

$$\iint_\Sigma \vec{F}\cdot\vec{n}\, dS = \iiint_D \operatorname{div} \vec{F}(x,y,z)\, dV = \iiint_D 3\, dV = 3\ (\text{volume of } D)$$

$$= 3\pi/4$$

12. $\operatorname{div} \vec{F}(x,y,z) = 2 + x + x = 2 + 2x$

$$\iint_\Sigma \vec{F}\cdot\vec{n}\, dS = \iiint_D \operatorname{div} \vec{F}(x,y,z)\, dV = \iiint_D (2 + 2x)\, dV$$

$$= \iiint_D 2\, dV + \int_{-1}^1\int_{-\sqrt{1-z^2}}^{\sqrt{1-z^2}}\int_{-\sqrt{1-z^2-y^2}}^{\sqrt{1-z^2-y^2}} 2x\, dx\, dy\, dz$$

$$= 2\ (\text{volume of } D) + \int_{-1}^1\int_{-\sqrt{1-z^2}}^{\sqrt{1-z^2}} x^2\Big|_{-\sqrt{1-z^2-y^2}}^{\sqrt{1-z^2-y^2}} dy\, dz$$

$$= \frac{8}{3}\pi + \int_{-1}^1\int_{-\sqrt{1-z^2}}^{\sqrt{1-z^2}} 0\, dy\, dz = \frac{8}{3}\pi$$

13. $\operatorname{div} \vec{F}(x,y,z) = 1 + 1 + 1 = 3$

$$\iint_\Sigma \vec{F}\cdot\vec{n}\, dS = \iiint_D \operatorname{div} \vec{F}(x,y,z)\, dV = \iiint_D 3\, dV = 3(\text{volume of } D) = 2\pi$$

14. $\operatorname{div} \vec{F}(x,y,z) = (1 + \sin x) + (1 - \sin x) + 2 = 4$

$$\iint_\Sigma \vec{F}\cdot\vec{n}\, dS = \iiint_D \operatorname{div} \vec{F}(x,y,z)\, dV = \int_0^1\int_0^{1-x}\int_0^{1-x-y} 4\, dz\, dy\, dx$$

$$= \int_0^1\int_0^{1-x} 4z\Big|_0^{1-x-y} dy\, dx = 4\int_0^1\int_0^{1-x} (1 - x - y)\, dy\, dx$$

$$= 4\int_0^1 [(1-x)y - \tfrac{1}{2}y^2]\Big|_0^{1-x} dx$$

$$= 4\int_0^1 [(1-x)^2 - \tfrac{1}{2}(1-x)^2]\, dx = 2\int_0^1 (1-x)^2\, dx$$

$$= -\frac{2}{3}(1-x)^3\Big|_0^1 = \frac{2}{3}$$

15. $\operatorname{div} \vec{F}(x,y,z) = 2x + 2y + 2z$

$$\iint_\Sigma \vec{F}\cdot\vec{n}\, dS = \iiint_D \operatorname{div} \vec{F}(x,y,z)\, dV = \iiint_D (2x + 2y + 2z)\, dV$$

$$= 2\int_0^{2\pi}\int_0^2\int_0^2 [r^2(\cos\theta + \sin\theta) + zr]\, dz\, dr\, d\theta$$

$$= 2\int_0^{2\pi}\int_0^2 [r^2 z(\cos\theta + \sin\theta) + \tfrac{1}{2}z^2 r]\Big|_0^2 dr\, d\theta$$

$$= 4\int_0^{2\pi}\int_0^2 [r^2(\cos\theta + \sin\theta) + r]\, dr\, d\theta$$

$$= 4\int_0^{2\pi} [\tfrac{1}{3} r^3(\cos\theta + \sin\theta) + \tfrac{1}{2} r^2]\Big|_0^2 \, d\theta$$

$$= 8\int_0^{2\pi} [\tfrac{4}{3}(\cos\theta + \sin\theta) + 1]\, d\theta$$

$$= [\tfrac{32}{3}(\sin\theta - \cos\theta) + 8\theta]\Big|_0^{2\pi} = 16\pi$$

16. $\operatorname{div} \vec{F}(x,y,z) = 3 - 2 + 1 = 2$

$$\iint_\Sigma \vec{F}\cdot\vec{n}\, dS = \iiint_D \operatorname{div} \vec{F}(x,y,z)\, dV = \iiint_D 2\, dV = 2 \text{ (volume of D)}$$

$$= \tfrac{64}{3}\pi$$

17. At any point (x,y,z) of intersection of the plane $z = 2x$ and the paraboloid $z = x^2 + y^2$, x, y, and z must satisfy $2x = z = x^2 + y^2$, or in polar coordinates, $2r\cos\theta = r^2$, or $r = 2\cos\theta$. Thus the given region D is the solid region between the graphs of $z = r^2$ and $z = 2r\cos\theta$ on the region in the xy plane bounded by $r = 2\cos\theta$ for $\frac{-\pi}{2} \le \theta \le \frac{\pi}{2}$. Since $\operatorname{div} \vec{F}(x,y,z) = 3xy(x^2+y^2)^{1/2} - 3xy(x^2+y^2)^{1/2} + 1 = 1$, we have

$$\iint_\Sigma \vec{F}\cdot\vec{n}\, dS = \iiint_D \operatorname{div} \vec{F}(x,y,z)\, dV = \iiint_D 1\, dV$$

$$= \int_{-\pi/2}^{\pi/2}\int_0^{2\cos\theta}\int_{r^2}^{2r\cos\theta} r\, dz\, dr\, d\theta$$

$$= \int_{-\pi/2}^{\pi/2}\int_0^{2\cos\theta} rz\Big|_{r^2}^{2r\cos\theta} dr\, d\theta$$

$$= \int_{-\pi/2}^{\pi/2}\int_0^{2\cos\theta} (2r^2\cos\theta - r^3)\, dr\, d\theta$$

$$= \int_{-\pi/2}^{\pi/2} (\tfrac{2}{3} r^3\cos\theta - \tfrac{1}{4} r^4)\Big|_0^{2\cos\theta} d\theta$$

$$= \int_{-\pi/2}^{\pi/2} (\tfrac{16}{3}\cos^4\theta - 4\cos^4\theta)\, d\theta = \int_{-\pi/2}^{\pi/2} \tfrac{4}{3}\cos^4\theta\, d\theta$$

$$= \tfrac{4}{3}(\tfrac{1}{4}\cos^3\theta\sin\theta + \tfrac{3}{8}\cos\theta\sin\theta + \tfrac{3}{8}\theta)\Big|_{-\pi/2}^{\pi/2} = \tfrac{1}{2}\pi$$

18. $\operatorname{div} \vec{F}(x,y,z) = 0 + x + x = 2x$

Using polar coordinates in the xz plane, we find that

$$\iint_\Sigma \vec{F}\cdot\vec{n}\, dS = \iiint_D \operatorname{div} \vec{F}(x,y,z)\, dV = \iiint_D 2x\, dV$$

$$= \int_0^{2\pi}\int_0^1\int_{-1}^1 (2r\cos\theta)\, r\, dy\, dr\, d\theta$$

$$= \int_0^{2\pi}\int_0^1 2r^2 y\cos\theta\Big|_{-1}^1 dr\, d\theta = \int_0^{2\pi}\int_0^1 4r^2\cos\theta\, dr\, d\theta$$

$$= \int_0^{2\pi} \tfrac{4}{3} r^3\cos\theta\Big|_0^1 d\theta = \int_0^{2\pi} \tfrac{4}{3}\cos\theta\, d\theta = \tfrac{4}{3}\sin\theta\Big|_0^{2\pi}$$

$$= 0$$

19. $\operatorname{div} \vec{F}(x,y,z) = -2 + 4 - 7 = -5$

$$\iint_\Sigma \vec{F}\cdot\vec{n}\, dS = \iiint_D \operatorname{div} \vec{F}(x,y,z)\, dV = \iiint_D -5\, dV$$

$$= \int_0^{2\pi}\int_1^2\int_{-\sqrt{4-r^2}}^{\sqrt{4-r^2}} -5r\, dz\, dr\, d\theta$$

$$= \int_0^{2\pi}\int_1^2 -5rz\Big|_{-\sqrt{4-r^2}}^{\sqrt{4-r^2}} dr\, d\theta = \int_0^{2\pi}\int_1^2 -10r\sqrt{4-r^2}\, dr\, d\theta$$

$$= \int_0^{2\pi} \tfrac{10}{3} r(4-r^2)^{3/2}\Big|_1^2 d\theta = \int_0^{2\pi} -\tfrac{10}{3}\, 3^{3/2}\, d\theta = -20\pi\sqrt{3}$$

20. $\operatorname{div} \vec{F}(x,y,z) = 0 + 0 + 0 = 0$

$$\iint_\Sigma \vec{F}\cdot\vec{n}\, dS = \iiint_D \operatorname{div} \vec{F}(x,y,z)\, dV = \iiint_D 0\, dV = 0$$

21. $\operatorname{div} \vec{F}(x,y,z) = 2x + 1 - 4z$

$$\iint_\Sigma \vec{F}\cdot\vec{n}\, dS = \iiint_D \operatorname{div} \vec{F}(x,y,z)\, dV = \iiint_D (2x + 1 - 4z)\, dV$$

$$= \int_{-\sqrt{2}}^{\sqrt{2}}\int_0^{2-y^2}\int_0^x (2x + 1 - 4z)\, dz\, dx\, dy$$

$$= \int_{-\sqrt{2}}^{\sqrt{2}}\int_0^{2-y^2} [(2x+1)z - 2z^2]\Big|_0^x dx\, dy$$

$$= \int_{-\sqrt{2}}^{\sqrt{2}}\int_0^{2-y^2} [(2x+1)x - 2x^2]\, dx\, dy$$

$$= \int_{-\sqrt{2}}^{\sqrt{2}} \int_0^{2-y^2} x\,dx\,dy = \int_{-\sqrt{2}}^{\sqrt{2}} \frac{1}{2} x^2 \Big|_0^{2-y^2} dy = \int_{-\sqrt{2}}^{\sqrt{2}} \frac{1}{2}(4 - 4y^2 + y^4)\,dy$$

$$= \frac{1}{2}(4y - \frac{4}{3}y^3 + \frac{1}{5}y^5)\Big|_{-\sqrt{2}}^{\sqrt{2}} = \frac{32}{15}\sqrt{2}$$

22. $\operatorname{div} \vec{F}(x,y,z) = 2xy + z + 2z = 2xy + 3z$

$$\iint_\Sigma \vec{F}\cdot\vec{n}\,dS = \iiint_D \operatorname{div} \vec{F}(x,y,z)\,dV = \iiint_D (2xy + 3z)\,dV$$

$$= \int_0^1 \int_0^{1-x} \int_0^1 (2xy + 3z)\,dz\,dy\,dx$$

$$= \int_0^1 \int_0^{1-x} (2xyz + \frac{3}{2}z^2)\Big|_0^1 dy\,dx = \int_0^1 \int_0^{1-x} (2xy + \frac{3}{2})\,dy\,dx$$

$$= \int_0^1 (xy^2 + \frac{3}{2}y)\Big|_0^{1-x} dx = \int_0^1 [x(1-x)^2 + \frac{3}{2}(1-x)]\,dx$$

$$= \int_0^1 (x^3 - 2x^2 - \frac{1}{2}x + \frac{3}{2})dx$$

$$= (\frac{1}{4}x^4 - \frac{2}{3}x^3 - \frac{1}{4}x^2 + \frac{3}{2}x)\Big|_0^1 = \frac{5}{6}$$

23. $\operatorname{div} \vec{F}(x,y,z) = (3x^2 + y^2 + z^2) + (x^2 + 3y^2 + z^2) + 0$

$$= 4x^2 + 4y^2 + 2z^2$$

$$\iint_\Sigma \vec{F}\cdot\vec{n}\,dS = \iiint_D \operatorname{div} \vec{F}(x,y,z)\,dV = \iiint_D (4x^2 + 4y^2 + 2z^2)\,dV$$

$$= \int_0^{2\pi} \int_0^{\pi} \int_0^3 (2\rho^2 + 2\rho^2\sin^2\phi)\rho^2 \sin\phi\,d\rho\,d\phi\,d\theta$$

$$= \int_0^{2\pi} \int_0^{\pi} \frac{2}{5}\rho^5(\sin\phi + \sin^3\phi)\Big|_0^3 d\phi\,d\theta$$

$$= \frac{486}{5} \int_0^{2\pi} \int_0^{\pi} (\sin\phi + \sin^3\phi)\,d\phi\,d\theta$$

$$= \frac{486}{5} \int_0^{2\pi} \int_0^{\pi} [\sin\phi + \sin\phi(1 - \cos^2\phi)]\,d\phi\,d\theta$$

$$= \frac{486}{5} \int_0^{2\pi} (-2\cos\phi + \frac{1}{3}\cos^3\phi)\Big|_0^{\pi} d\theta = \frac{486}{5} \int_0^{2\pi} \frac{10}{3}\,d\theta$$

$$= 648\pi$$

24. By the Divergence Theorem, $\iiint_D \operatorname{div} \vec{F}(x,y,z)\,dV = \iint_\Sigma \vec{F}\cdot\vec{n}\,dS$, where Σ is the sphere $x^2 + y^2 + z^2 = 1$. Now Σ is composed of the top half, Σ_1, and the bottom half, Σ_2. Let R be the region in the xy plane bounded by the circle $r = 1$, and let R_b be the region bounded by $r = b$ for $0 < b < 1$. For Σ_1 let $f(x,y) = \sqrt{1 - x^2 - y^2}$ for (x,y) in R. Since on Σ_1 we have $\vec{F}(x,y,z) = x^3y^2z^2\vec{i} - x^4yz^2\vec{j}$, when we use (5) in Section 15.6, we find that $M(x,y,f(x,y)) = x^3y^2(1 - x^2 - y^2)$, $N(x,y,f(x,y)) = -x^4y(1 - x^2 - y^2)$, and $P(x,y,f(x,y)) = 0$, so that

$$\iint_{\Sigma_1} \vec{F}\cdot\vec{n}\,dS = \lim_{b\to 1^-} \iint_{R_b} [-x^3y^2(1 - x^2 - y^2)\frac{-x}{\sqrt{1 - x^2 - y^2}}$$

$$+ x^4y(1 - x^2 - y^2)\frac{-y}{\sqrt{1 - x^2 - y^2}} + 0]\,dA$$

$$= \lim_{b\to 1^-} \iint_{R_b} 0\,dA = 0$$

On Σ_2, $\vec{F}(x,y,z)$ is as above, $f(x,y) = -\sqrt{1 - x^2 - y^2}$, and the normal points downward, so we use (6) in Section 15.6 to conclude that

$$\iint_{\Sigma_2} \vec{F}\cdot\vec{n}\,dS = \iint_{\Sigma_1} \vec{F}\cdot\vec{n}\,dS = 0$$

Thus

$$\iiint_D \operatorname{div} \vec{F}(x,y,z)\,dV = \iint_\Sigma \vec{F}\cdot\vec{n}\,dS = \iint_{\Sigma_1} \vec{F}\cdot\vec{n}\,dS + \iint_{\Sigma_2} \vec{F}\cdot\vec{n}\,dS$$

$$= 0 + 0 = 0$$

25. $\iint_{\Sigma} \vec{F}\cdot\vec{n}\, dS = \iiint_D \text{div } \vec{F}(x,y,z)\, dV = \iiint_D \text{div (curl } \vec{G})(x,y,z)\, dV$

$$= \iiint_D 0\, dV = 0$$

by (4) in Section 15.1.

26. $\text{div } \vec{F}(x,y,z) = 1 + 1 + 1 = 3$

$\frac{1}{3}\iint_{\Sigma} \vec{F}\cdot\vec{n}\, dS = \frac{1}{3}\iiint_D \text{div } \vec{F}(x,y,z)\, dV = \frac{1}{3}\iiint_D 3\, dV = V$

27. Let R be the region in the xy plane bounded by the circle $r = a$. Let Σ_1 denote the graph of $z = \frac{h}{a}\sqrt{x^2 + y^2}$ for (x,y) in R, and Σ_2 the graph of $z = h$ on R. Let Σ consist of Σ_1 and Σ_2. By Exercise 26, the volume of the conical region is given by

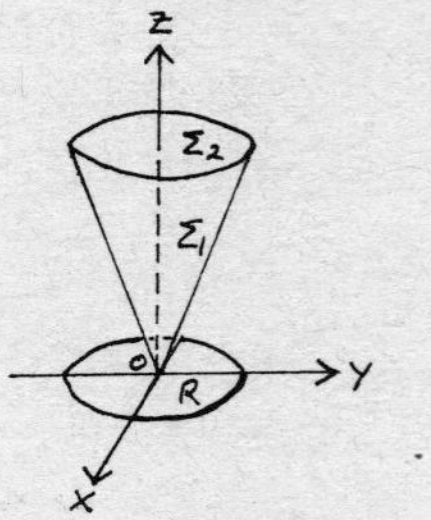

$V = \frac{1}{3}\iint_{\Sigma} \vec{F}\cdot\vec{n}\, dS = \frac{1}{3}\iint_{\Sigma_1} \vec{F}\cdot\vec{n}\, dS + \frac{1}{3}\iint_{\Sigma_2} \vec{F}\cdot\vec{n}\, dS$

with $\vec{F}(x,y,z) = x\vec{i} + y\vec{j} + z\vec{k}$. To evaluate $\iint_{\Sigma_1} \vec{F}\cdot\vec{n}\, dS$ we let $f(x,y) = \frac{h}{a}\sqrt{x^2 + y^2}$, and for $0 < b < a$, we let R_b be the region in the xy plane bounded by the circle $r = b$. We use (6) in Section 15.6 with $f_x(x,y) = \frac{h}{a}\frac{x}{\sqrt{x^2 + y^2}}$, $f_y(x,y) = \frac{h}{a}\frac{y}{\sqrt{x^2 + y^2}}$, $M(x,y,f(x,y)) = x$, $N(x,y,f(x,y)) = y$, and $P(x,y,f(x,y)) = \frac{h}{a}\sqrt{x^2 + y^2}$, and conclude that

$$\iint_{\Sigma_1} \vec{F}\cdot\vec{n}\, dS = \lim_{b\to a^-}\iint_{R_b} \left[x\left(\frac{h}{a}\frac{x}{\sqrt{x^2 + y^2}}\right) + y\left(\frac{h}{a}\frac{y}{\sqrt{x^2 + y^2}}\right) - \frac{h}{a}\sqrt{x^2 + y^2}\right] dA$$

$$= \lim_{b\to a^-}\iint_{R_b} 0\, dA = 0$$

Next,

$$\iint_{\Sigma_2} \vec{F}\cdot\vec{n}\, dS = \iint_{\Sigma_2} (x\vec{i} + y\vec{j} + h\vec{k})\cdot\vec{k}\, dS = \iint_R h\, dA = \pi a^2 h$$

Therefore

$$V = \frac{1}{3}\iint_{\Sigma} \vec{F}\cdot\vec{n}\, dS = \frac{1}{3}\iint_{\Sigma_1} \vec{F}\cdot\vec{n}\, dS + \frac{1}{3}\iint_{\Sigma_2} \vec{F}\cdot\vec{n}\, dS = 0 + \frac{1}{3}\pi a^2 h = \frac{1}{3}\pi a^2 h$$

28. a. Using the Divergence Theorem and the hint (with $\vec{F} = \text{grad } f$), we find that

$$\iint_{\Sigma} (g \text{ grad } f)\cdot\vec{n}\, dS = \iiint_D \text{div } (g \text{ grad } f)\, dV$$

$$= \iiint_D [g \text{ div (grad } f) + (\text{grad } g)\cdot(\text{grad } f)]\, dV$$

$$= \iiint_D [g\nabla^2 f + (\text{grad } g)\cdot(\text{grad } f)]\, dV$$

b. By (a),

$$\iint_{\Sigma} (g \text{ grad } f - f \text{ grad } g)\cdot\vec{n}\, dS$$

$$= \iint_{\Sigma} (g \text{ grad } f)\cdot\vec{n}\, dS - \iint_{\Sigma} (f \text{ grad } g)\cdot\vec{n}\, dS$$

$$= \iiint_D [g\nabla^2 f + (\text{grad } g)\cdot(\text{grad } f)]\, dV - \iiint_D [f\nabla^2 g + (\text{grad } f)\cdot(\text{grad } g)]\, dV = \iiint_D [g\nabla^2 f + (\text{grad } g)\cdot(\text{grad } f) - f\nabla^2 g - (\text{grad } f)\cdot(\text{grad } g)]\, dV$$

$$= \iiint_D (g\nabla^2 f - f\nabla^2 g)\, dV$$

29. If $\vec{F}$ is constant, then $\text{div } \vec{F} = 0$, so that by the Divergence Theorem,

$$\iint_{\Sigma} \vec{F}\cdot\vec{n}\, dS = \iiint_D \text{div } \vec{F}(x,y,z)\, dV = \iiint_D 0\, dV = 0$$

30. In order to apply Stokes's Theorem in step (3), we must have C be the boundary of Σ. But Σ is the boundary of a simple solid region D, and hence Σ has no boundary of its own.

Chapter 15 - Review

1. Let $\vec{a} = a_1\vec{i} + a_2\vec{j} + a_3\vec{k}$ and $\vec{b} = b_1\vec{i} + b_2\vec{j} + b_3\vec{k}$. Then

$$\vec{b}\times\vec{r} = \begin{vmatrix} \vec{i} & \vec{j} & \vec{k} \\ b_1 & b_2 & b_3 \\ x & y & z \end{vmatrix} = (b_2z - b_3y)\vec{i} + (b_3x - b_1z)\vec{j} + (b_1y - b_2x)\vec{k}$$

so that $\vec{a}\cdot(\vec{b}\times\vec{r}) = a_1(b_2z - b_3y) + a_2(b_3x - b_1z) + a_3(b_1y - b_2x)$.

Thus $\text{grad}\,[\vec{a}\cdot(\vec{b}\times\vec{r})] = (a_2b_3 - a_3b_2)\vec{i} + (a_3b_1 - a_1b_3)\vec{j}$

$+ (a_1b_2 - a_2b_1)\vec{k} = \vec{a}\times\vec{b}$.

2. Applying first Exercise 31 and then Exercise 28 of Section 15.1, we have $\text{curl}\,(f\,\text{grad}\,f) = f\,\text{curl}\,(\text{grad}\,f) + (\text{grad}\,f)\times(\text{grad}\,f)$

$= f\vec{0} + \vec{0} = \vec{0}$.

3. To begin with,

$$\frac{\partial f}{\partial x} = y^2 - y\sin xy \quad\text{and}\quad \frac{\partial f}{\partial y} = 2xy - x\sin xy \qquad (*)$$

Integrating both sides of the first equation in (*) with respect to x, we obtain $f(x,y) = xy^2 + \cos xy + g(y)$. Taking partial derivatives with respect to y, we find that

$\frac{\partial f}{\partial y} = 2xy - x\sin xy + \frac{dg}{dy}$. Comparing this with the second equation in (*), we conclude that $\frac{dg}{dy} = 0$, so that $g(y) = C$.

Therefore $f(x,y) = xy^2 + \cos xy + C$.

4. To begin with,

$$\frac{\partial f}{\partial x} = ye^z, \quad \frac{\partial f}{\partial y} = xe^z + e^y, \quad\text{and}\quad \frac{\partial f}{\partial z} = (xy + 1)e^z \qquad (*)$$

Integrating both sides of the first equation of (*) with respect to x, we obtain $f(x,y,z) = xye^z + g(y,z)$. Taking partial derivatives with respect to y, we find that

$\frac{\partial f}{\partial y} = xe^z + \frac{\partial g}{\partial y}$. Comparing this with the second equation in (*), we deduce that $\frac{\partial g}{\partial y} = e^y$, so that $g(y,z) = e^y + h(z)$. Thus $f(x,y,z) = xye^z + e^y + h(z)$. Taking partial derivatives with respect to z, we obtain $\frac{\partial f}{\partial z} = xye^z + \frac{dh}{dz}$. Comparing this with the third equation in (*), we conclude that $\frac{dh}{dz} = e^z$, so that $h(z) = e^z + C$. Therefore $f(x,y,z) = xye^z + e^y + e^z + C$.

5. Since $x(t) = \cos t$, $y(t) = \sin t$, $z(t) = t$, and $\left\|\frac{d\vec{r}}{dt}\right\| = \sqrt{(-\sin t)^2 + \cos^2 t + 1^2} = \sqrt{2}$, (4) in Section 15.2 implies that

$$\int_C (xy + z^2)\,ds = \int_{\pi/4}^{3\pi/4} (\cos t\sin t + t^2)\sqrt{2}\,dt$$

$$= \left(\tfrac{1}{2}\sin^2 t + \tfrac{1}{3}t^3\right)\sqrt{2}\,\Big|_{\pi/4}^{3\pi/4} = \frac{13\sqrt{2}}{96}\pi^3$$

6. The curve C is composed of the line segments C_1 and C_2 parameterized respectively by $\vec{r}_1(t) = (1 - t)\vec{i} + 3t\vec{j} + (4 - 2t)\vec{k}$ for $0 \le t \le 1$, and $\vec{r}_2(t) = 3(1 - t)\vec{j} + 2(1 - t)\vec{k}$ for $0 \le t \le 1$. Since $x(t) = 1 - t$, $y(t) = 3t$, $z(t) = 4 - 2t$, and $\left\|\frac{d\vec{r}_1}{dt}\right\| = \sqrt{(-1)^2 + 3^2 + (-2)^2} = \sqrt{14}$ for the segment C_1, it follows from (4) in Section 15.2 that

$$\int_{C_1} (2xy - 3yz)\,ds = \int_0^1 [2(1 - t)(3t) - 3(3t)(4 - 2t)]\sqrt{14}\,dt$$

$$= \int_0^1 (12t^2 - 30t)\sqrt{14}\,dt = \sqrt{14}\,(4t^3 - 15t^2)\Big|_0^1 = -11\sqrt{14}$$

Since $x(t) = 0$, $y(t) = 3(1 - t)$, $z(t) = 2(1 - t)$, and $\left\|\frac{d\vec{r}_2}{dt}\right\| = \sqrt{0^2 + (-3)^2 + (-2)^2} = \sqrt{13}$ for the segment C_2, it follows from (4) in Section 15.2 that

$$\int_{C_2} (2xy - 3yz)\,ds = \int_0^1 \{2(0)[3(1 - t)] - 3[3(1 - t)][2(1 - t)]\}\sqrt{13}\,dt$$

$$= \int_0^1 -18\sqrt{13}\,(1 - t)^2\,dt = 6\sqrt{13}\,(1 - t)^3\Big|_0^1 = -6\sqrt{13}$$

Thus

$$\int_C (2xy - 3yz)\,ds = \int_{C_1} (2xy - 3yz)\,ds + \int_{C_2} (2xy - 3yz)\,ds$$

$$= -11\sqrt{14} - 6\sqrt{13}$$

7. Since $x(t) = t$, $y(t) = \cos t$, $z(t) = \sin t$, $\frac{dx}{dt} = 1$, $\frac{dy}{dt} = -\sin t$, and $\frac{dz}{dt} = \cos t$, (9) of Section 15.2 implies that

$$\int_C xy\,dx + z\cos x\,dy + z\,dz = \int_0^{\pi/2} [(t\cos t)(1) + (\sin t\cos t)(-\sin t) + (\sin t)(\cos t)]\,dt$$

$$= \int_0^{\pi/2} t\cos t\,dt + \int_0^{\pi/2} (-\sin^2 t\cos t + \sin t\cos t)\,dt$$

$$\overset{\text{parts}}{=} t\sin t\Big|_0^{\pi/2} - \int_0^{\pi/2} \sin t\,dt + \left(-\frac{1}{3}\sin^3 t + \frac{1}{2}\sin^2 t\right)\Big|_0^{\pi/2}$$

$$= \frac{\pi}{2} + \cos t\Big|_0^{\pi/2} + \frac{1}{6} = \frac{\pi}{2} - \frac{5}{6}$$

8. Since $x(t) = t$, $y(t) = \sin t$, $z(t) = 0$, $\frac{dx}{dt} = 1$, $\frac{dy}{dt} = \cos t$, and $\frac{dz}{dt} = 0$, (9) of Section 15.2 implies that

$$\int_C y\sin 2x\,dx + \sin^2 x\,dy = \int_0^{\pi/3} (\sin t\sin 2t + \sin^2 t\cos t)\,dt$$

$$= \int_0^{\pi/3} (2\sin^2 t\cos t + \sin^2 t\cos t)\,dt = \int_0^{\pi/3} 3\sin^2 t\cos t\,dt$$

$$= \sin^3 t\Big|_0^{\pi/3} = \frac{3}{8}\sqrt{3}$$

(Notice that the integral is independent of path, and therefore could be solved by the Fundamental Theorem of Line Integrals if we wished to.)

9. The curve C is parameterized by $\vec{r}(t) = t\vec{i} + t^2\vec{j}$ for $0 \le t \le 1$. Since $x(t) = t$, $y(t) = 2t$, and $\left\|\frac{d\vec{r}}{dt}\right\| = \sqrt{1^2 + (2t)^2} = \sqrt{1 + 4t^2}$, it follows from (4) in Section 15.2 that

$$\int_C x\,ds = \int_0^1 t\sqrt{1 + 4t^2}\,dt = \frac{1}{12}(1 + 4t^2)^{3/2}\Big|_0^1 = \frac{1}{12}(5^{3/2} - 1)$$

10. Let $\vec{F}(x,y,z) = (1 + y\sin z)\vec{i} + (1 + x\sin z)\vec{j} + xy\cos z\vec{k} = M(x,y,z)\vec{i} + N(x,y,z)\vec{j} + P(x,y,z)\vec{k}$. Since $\frac{\partial P}{\partial y} = x\cos z = \frac{\partial N}{\partial z}$, $\frac{\partial M}{\partial z} = y\cos z = \frac{\partial P}{\partial x}$, and $\frac{\partial N}{\partial x} = \sin z = \frac{\partial M}{\partial y}$, the line integral is independent of path. Let grad $f(x,y,z) = \vec{F}(x,y,z)$. Then

$$\frac{\partial f}{\partial x} = 1 + y\sin z, \quad \frac{\partial f}{\partial y} = 1 + x\sin z, \quad \text{and} \quad \frac{\partial f}{\partial z} = xy\cos z \qquad (*)$$

Integrating both sides of the first equation in (*) with respect to x, we obtain $f(x,y,z) = x + xy\sin z + g(y,z)$. Taking partial derivatives with respect to y, we find that $\frac{\partial f}{\partial y} = x\sin z + \frac{\partial g}{\partial y}$. Comparing this with the second equation in (*), we deduce that $\frac{\partial g}{\partial y} = 1$, so that $g(y,z) = y + h(z)$. Thus $f(x,y,z) = x + xy\sin z + y + h(z)$. Taking partial derivatives with respect to z, we find that $\frac{\partial f}{\partial z} = xy\cos z + \frac{dh}{dz}$. Comparing this with the third equation in (*), we conclude that $\frac{dh}{dz} = 0$, so that $h(z) = C$. If $C = 0$, then $f(x,y,z) = x + xy\sin z + y$. Since $\vec{r}(0) = \vec{j}$ and $\vec{r}(\frac{\pi}{4}) = \vec{i} + \frac{1}{4}\vec{j} + \frac{\pi}{4}\vec{k}$, it follows that the initial and terminal points of C are (0,1,0) and $(1,\frac{1}{4},\frac{\pi}{4})$, respectively. Then

$$\int_C (1 + y\sin z)\,dx + (1 + x\sin z)\,dy + xy\cos z\,dz = f(1,\tfrac{1}{4},\tfrac{\pi}{4}) - f(0,1,0) = \left(\frac{5}{4} + \frac{1}{8}\sqrt{2}\right) - 1 = \frac{1}{4} + \frac{1}{8}\sqrt{2}$$

11. Let $\vec{F}(x,y,z) = e^x\cos z\,\vec{i} + y\vec{j} - e^x\sin z\,\vec{k} = M(x,y,z)\vec{i} + N(x,y,z)\vec{j} + P(x,y,z)\vec{k}$. Since $\frac{\partial P}{\partial y} = 0 = \frac{\partial N}{\partial z}$, $\frac{\partial M}{\partial z} = -e^x\sin z = \frac{\partial P}{\partial x}$, and $\frac{\partial N}{\partial x} = 0 = \frac{\partial M}{\partial y}$, the line integral is independent of path. Let grad $f(x,y,z) = \vec{F}(x,y,z)$. Then

$$\frac{\partial f}{\partial x} = e^x\cos z, \quad \frac{\partial f}{\partial y} = y, \quad \text{and} \quad \frac{\partial f}{\partial z} = -e^x\sin z \qquad (*)$$

Integrating both sides of the first equation in (*) with respect to x, we obtain $f(x,y,z) = e^x\cos z + g(y,z)$. Taking partial derivatives with respect to y, we find that $\frac{\partial f}{\partial y} = \frac{\partial g}{\partial y}$. Comparing this with the second equation in (*), we deduce that $\frac{\partial g}{\partial y} = y$, so that $g(y,z) = \frac{1}{2}y^2 + h(z)$. Thus $f(x,y,z) = e^x\cos z + \frac{1}{2}y^2 + h(z)$. Taking partial derivatives with respect to z, we find that $\frac{\partial f}{\partial z} = -e^x\sin z + \frac{dh}{dz}$. Comparing this with the third equation in (*), we conclude that $\frac{dh}{dz} = 0$, so that $h(z) = C$. If $C = 0$, then $f(x,y,z) = e^x\cos z + \frac{1}{2}y^2$. Since $\vec{r}(0) = \vec{i}$ and $\vec{r}(1) = \vec{i} + \vec{j} + \vec{k}$, it follows that the initial and terminal points of C are $(1,0,0)$ and $(1,1,1)$, respectively. Thus

$$\int_C e^x\cos z\,dx + y\,dy - e^x\sin z\,dz = f(1,1,1) - f(1,0,0)$$

$$= (e\cos 1 + \tfrac{1}{2}) - e = \tfrac{1}{2} + e(\cos 1 - 1)$$

12. Since $\text{div}\,\vec{F}(x,y,z) = \left(\sqrt{x^2+y^2+z^2} + \frac{x^2}{\sqrt{x^2+y^2+z^2}}\right)$

$$+\left(\sqrt{x^2+y^2+z^2} + \frac{y^2}{\sqrt{x^2+y^2+z^2}}\right) + \left(\sqrt{x^2+y^2+z^2} + \frac{z^2}{\sqrt{x^2+y^2+z^2}}\right)$$

$= 4\sqrt{x^2+y^2+z^2}$, the Divergence Theorem implies that

$$\iint_\Sigma \vec{F}\cdot\vec{n}\,dS = \iiint_D \text{div}\,\vec{F}(x,y,z)\,dV = \iiint_D 4\sqrt{x^2+y^2+z^2}\,dV$$

$$= \int_0^{2\pi}\int_0^{\pi}\int_0^{\sin\phi} 4\rho\,(\rho^2\sin\phi)\,d\rho\,d\phi\,d\theta$$

$$= \int_0^{2\pi}\int_0^{\pi} (\rho^4\sin\phi)\Big|_0^{\sin\phi} d\phi\,d\theta = \int_0^{2\pi}\int_0^{\pi} \sin^5\phi\,d\phi\,d\theta$$

$$= \int_0^{2\pi}\int_0^{\pi} (1-\cos^2\phi)^2\sin\phi\,d\phi\,d\theta$$

$$= \int_0^{2\pi}\int_0^{\pi} (1 - 2\cos^2\phi + \cos^4\phi)\sin\phi\,d\phi\,d\theta$$

$$= \int_0^{2\pi} (-\cos\phi + \tfrac{2}{3}\cos^3\phi - \tfrac{1}{5}\cos^5\phi)\Big|_0^{\pi} d\theta = \int_0^{2\pi} \tfrac{16}{15}\,d\theta$$

$$= \tfrac{32}{15}\pi$$

13. Since $\text{div}\,\vec{F}(x,y,z) = 1 + x + 1 = x + 2$, the Divergence Theorem implies that

$$\iint_\Sigma \vec{F}\cdot\vec{n}\,dS = \iiint_D \text{div}\,\vec{F}(x,y,z)\,dV = \iiint_D (x+2)\,dV$$

$$= \int_0^1\int_0^{1-y^2}\int_0^{1+x} (x+2)\,dz\,dx\,dy$$

$$= \int_0^1\int_0^{1-y^2} (x+2)z\Big|_0^{1+x} dx\,dy = \int_0^1\int_0^{1-y^2} (x^2+3x+2)\,dx\,dy$$

$$= \int_0^1 (\tfrac{1}{3}x^3 + \tfrac{3}{2}x^2 + 2x)\Big|_0^{1-y^2} dy$$

$$= \int_0^1 [\tfrac{1}{3}(1-y^2)^3 + \tfrac{3}{2}(1-y^2)^2 + 2(1-y^2)]\,dy$$

$$= \int_0^1 (-\tfrac{1}{3}y^6 + \tfrac{5}{2}y^4 - 6y^2 + \tfrac{23}{6})\,dy$$

$$= (-\tfrac{1}{21}y^7 + \tfrac{1}{2}y^5 - 2y^3 + \tfrac{23}{6}y)\Big|_0^1 = \tfrac{16}{7}$$

14. By Green's Theorem,

$$\int_C (e^x - 4y\sin^2 x)\,dx + (2x + \sin 2x)\,dy$$

$$= \iint_R [\tfrac{\partial}{\partial x}(2x+\sin 2x) - \tfrac{\partial}{\partial y}(e^x - 4y\sin^2 x)]\,dA$$

$$= \iint_R (2 + 2\cos 2x + 4\sin^2 x)\,dA$$

$$= \int_{-2}^{2}\int_{-2}^{2} (2 + 2\cos 2x + 2 - 2\cos 2x)\,dy\,dx$$

$$= \int_{-2}^{2}\int_{-2}^{2} 4\,dy\,dx = \int_{-2}^{2} 4y\Big|_{-2}^{2} dx = \int_{-2}^{2} 16\,dx = 64$$

15. Since $\text{div}\,\vec{F}(x,y,z) = yz + 2z$, the Divergence Theorem implies that

$$\iint_\Sigma \vec{F}\cdot\vec{n}\,dS = \iiint_D \text{div}\,\vec{F}(x,y,z)\,dV = \iiint_D (yz+2z)\,dV$$

$$= \int_0^{2\pi}\int_0^{2}\int_{-2}^{3} (r\sin\theta + 2)zr\,dz\,dr\,d\theta$$

$$= \int_0^{2\pi}\int_0^{2} (r^2\sin\theta + 2r)\,\frac{z^2}{2}\Big|_{-2}^{3} dr\,d\theta$$

$$= \int_0^{2\pi}\int_0^{2} \tfrac{5}{2}(r^2\sin\theta + 2r)\,dr\,d\theta$$

$$= \int_0^{2\pi} (\tfrac{5}{6}r^3\sin\theta + \tfrac{5}{2}r^2)\Big|_0^2 d\theta = \int_0^{2\pi} (\tfrac{20}{3}\sin\theta + 10)\,d\theta$$

$$= (-\tfrac{20}{3}\cos\theta + 10\theta)\Big|_0^{2\pi} = 20\pi$$

16. By Green's Theorem,

$$\int_C x(x^2 + y^2)^{1/2}\,dx + y(x^2 + y^2)^{1/2}\,dy$$

$$= \iint_R \left\{\frac{\partial}{\partial x}[y(x^2 + y^2)^{1/2}] - \frac{\partial}{\partial y}[x(x^2 + y^2)^{1/2}]\right\} dA$$

$$= \iint_R [xy(x^2 + y^2)^{-1/2} - xy(x^2 + y^2)^{-1/2}]\,dA = \iint_R 0\,dA = 0$$

17. The paraboloid $z = -1 + x^2 + y^2$ and the plane $z = 1$ intersect at (x,y,z) such that $-1 + x^2 + y^2 = z = 1$, which means that $x^2 + y^2 = 2$, or in polar coordinates, $r = \sqrt{2}$. Let R be the region in the xy plane bounded by $r = \sqrt{2}$, and let $f(x,y) = -1 + x^2 + y^2$ for (x,y) in R. We use (6) in Section 15.6, with $f_x(x,y) = 2x$, $f_y(x,y) = 2y$, $M(x,y,f(x,y)) = y$, $N(x,y,f(x,y)) = -x$, and $P(x,y,f(x,y)) = -1 + x^2 + y^2$, and find that

$$\iint_\Sigma \vec{F}\cdot\vec{n}\,dS = \iint_R [(y)(2x) + (-x)(2y) - (-1 + x^2 + y^2)]\,dA$$

$$= \iint_R (1 - x^2 - y^2)\,dA = \int_0^{2\pi}\int_0^{\sqrt{2}} (1 - r^2)r\,dr\,d\theta$$

$$= \int_0^{2\pi} \left(\frac{1}{2}r^2 - \frac{1}{4}r^4\right)\Big|_0^{\sqrt{2}} d\theta = \int_0^{2\pi} 0\,d\theta = 0$$

18. $$\text{curl}\,\vec{F}(x,y,z) = \begin{vmatrix} \vec{i} & \vec{j} & \vec{k} \\ \frac{\partial}{\partial x} & \frac{\partial}{\partial y} & \frac{\partial}{\partial z} \\ xyz & 2x^2z & y^6 \end{vmatrix} = (6y^5 - 2x^2)\vec{i} + xy\vec{j} + 3xz\vec{k}$$

Let Σ be the given rectangle in the plane $z = y$ with normal $\vec{n}$ directed upward. If $f(x,y) = y$, then Σ is the graph of f on the region R in the xy plane bounded by the lines $x = -1$, $x = 1$, $y = 0$, and $y = 2$. Thus by Stokes's Theorem and (5) in Section 15.6,

$$\int_C \vec{F}\cdot d\vec{r} = \iint_\Sigma (\text{curl}\,\vec{F})\cdot\vec{n}\,dS = \iint_R [-(6y^2 - 2x^2)(0) - xy(1) + 3xy]\,dA$$

$$= \int_{-1}^{1}\int_0^2 2xy\,dy\,dx = \int_{-1}^{1} xy^2\Big|_0^2 dx = \int_{-1}^{1} 4x\,dx = 2x^2\Big|_{-1}^{1} = 0$$

19. Let Σ_1 be the part of the plane $z = 1$ inside the sphere $x^2 + y^2 + z^2 = 2$, and let Σ_1 be oriented with normal $\vec{n} = -\vec{k}$. Let R be the region in the xy plane bounded by the circle $x^2 + y^2 = 1$, or in polar coordinates $r = 1$. Since Σ and Σ_1 induce the same orientation on their common boundary, (9) in Section 15.7 implies that

$$\iint_\Sigma (\text{curl}\,\vec{F})\cdot\vec{n}\,dS = \iint_{\Sigma_1} (\text{curl}\,\vec{F})\cdot\vec{n}\,dS$$

$$= \iint_{\Sigma_1} \left\{\left[\frac{\partial}{\partial x}(-y^3) - \frac{\partial}{\partial y}(x^3y)\right]\vec{k}\right\}\cdot -\vec{k}\,dS = \iint_{\Sigma_1} x^3\,dS = \iint_R x^3\,dA$$

$$= \int_0^{2\pi}\int_0^1 r^4\cos^3\theta\,dr\,d\theta = \int_0^{2\pi} \frac{1}{5}r^5\cos^3\theta\Big|_0^1 d\theta$$

$$= \int_0^{2\pi} \frac{1}{5}\cos^3\theta\,d\theta = \int_0^{2\pi} \frac{1}{5}(1 - \sin^2\theta)\cos\theta\,d\theta$$

$$= \frac{1}{5}\left(\sin\theta - \frac{1}{3}\sin^3\theta\right)\Big|_0^{2\pi} = 0$$

20. If $C_1 = -C$, then C_1 is oriented counterclockwise, so by Green's Theorem,

$$\int_C \sin x\sin y\,dx - \cos x\cos y\,dy$$

$$= -\int_{C_1} \sin x\sin y\,dx - \cos x\cos y\,dy$$

$$= -\iint_R \left[\frac{\partial}{\partial x}(-\cos x\cos y) - \frac{\partial}{\partial y}(\sin x\sin y)\right] dA$$

$$= -\iint_R (\sin x\cos y - \sin x\cos y)\,dA = \iint_R 0\,dA = 0$$

21. Since $\text{div}\,\vec{F}(x,y,z) = \sec^2 x - (1 + \tan^2 x) - 6 = -6$, the Divergence Theorem implies that

$$\iint_\Sigma \vec{F}\cdot\vec{n}\,dS = \iiint_D \text{div}\,\vec{F}(x,y,z)\,dV = \iiint_D -6\,dV$$

$$= -6\,(\text{volume of the hemisphere}) = -6\left(\frac{2}{3}\pi 2^3\right) = -32\pi$$

22. By Green's Theorem,

$$\int_C (y^4 + x^3y^2)\,dx + x^2y^3\,dy = \iint_R \left[\frac{\partial}{\partial x}(x^2y^3) - \frac{\partial}{\partial y}(y^4 + x^3y^2)\right] dA$$

$$= \iint_R (2xy^3 - 4y^3 - 2x^3y)\,dA$$

$$= \int_{-1}^{1}\int_{x^2}^{1} (2xy^3 - 4y^3 - 2x^3y)\,dy\,dx$$

$$= \int_{-1}^{1} \left(\frac{1}{2}xy^4 - y^4 - x^3y^2\right)\Big|_{x^2}^{1} dx$$

$$= \int_{-1}^{1} \left(\frac{1}{2}x - 1 - x^3 - \frac{1}{2}x^9 + x^8 + x^7\right) dx$$

$$= \left(\frac{1}{4}x^2 - x - \frac{1}{4}x^4 - \frac{1}{20}x^{10} + \frac{1}{9}x^9 + \frac{1}{8}x^8\right)\Big|_{-1}^{1} = -\frac{16}{9}$$

23. Let $\vec{F}(x,y,z) = y\vec{i} + y\vec{j} + x^2\vec{k}$. Then

$$\text{curl } \vec{F}(x,y,z) = \begin{vmatrix} \vec{i} & \vec{j} & \vec{k} \\ \frac{\partial}{\partial x} & \frac{\partial}{\partial y} & \frac{\partial}{\partial z} \\ y & y & x^2 \end{vmatrix} = -2x\vec{j} - \vec{k}$$

The surfaces $z = x^2 + y^2$ and $z = 1 - y^2$ intersect at (x,y,z) such that $x^2 + y^2 = z = 1 - y^2$, so that $x^2 + 2y^2 = 1$. Let $f(x,y) = 1 - y^2$, let Σ be the graph of f on the region R in the xy plane bounded by the ellipse $x^2 + 2y^2 = 1$, and let Σ be oriented with normal $\vec{n}$ directed upward. Then by Stokes's Theorem and (5) of Section 15.6,

$$\int_C y\,dx + y\,dy + x^2\,dz = \int_C \vec{F}\cdot d\vec{r} = \iint_\Sigma (\text{curl } \vec{F})\cdot\vec{n}\,dS$$

$$= \iint_R [-(-2x)(-2y) - 1]\,dA = \int_{-1}^{1}\int_{-\sqrt{(1-x^2)/2}}^{\sqrt{(1-x^2)/2}} (-4xy - 1)\,dy\,dx$$

$$= \int_{-1}^{1} (-2xy^2 - y)\Big|_{-\sqrt{(1-x^2)/2}}^{\sqrt{(1-x^2)/2}} dx = -\sqrt{2}\int_{-1}^{1}\sqrt{1 - x^2}\,dx$$

$$= -\sqrt{2}\ (\text{area of semicircle of radius } 1) = -\frac{\sqrt{2}}{2}\pi$$

24. Since $\text{div } \vec{F}(x,y,z) = 2x + 2z - 2z = 2x$, the Divergence Theorem implies that

$$\iint_\Sigma \vec{F}\cdot\vec{n}\,dS = \iiint_D \text{div } \vec{F}(x,y,z)\,dV = \iiint_D 2x\,dV$$

$$= \int_0^{\pi/2}\int_0^{\sin\theta}\int_0^{r^2\sin^2\theta} (2r\cos\theta)r\,dz\,dr\,d\theta$$

$$= \int_0^{\pi/2}\int_0^{\sin\theta} (2r^2\cos\theta)z\Big|_0^{r^2\sin^2\theta} dr\,d\theta$$

$$= \int_0^{\pi/2}\int_0^{\sin\theta} 2r^4\sin^2\theta\cos\theta\,dr\,d\theta$$

$$= \int_0^{\pi/2} \frac{2}{5}r^5\sin^2\theta\cos\theta\Big|_0^{\sin\theta} d\theta$$

$$= \int_0^{\pi/2} \frac{2}{5}\sin^7\theta\cos\theta\,d\theta = \frac{1}{20}\sin^8\theta\Big|_0^{\pi/2} = \frac{1}{20}$$

25. Since $x(t) = t$, $y(t) = 0$, $z(t) = -t^3$, and $\frac{d\vec{r}}{dt} = \vec{i} - 3t^2\vec{k}$, (7) in Section 15.2 implies that

$$\int_C \vec{F}\cdot d\vec{r} = \int_{-1}^{1} (t^4\vec{i} - t^3\vec{k})\cdot(\vec{i} - 3t^2\vec{k})\,dt = \int_{-1}^{1} (t^4 - 3t^5)\,dt$$

$$= \left(\frac{1}{5}t^5 - \frac{1}{2}t^6\right)\Big|_{-1}^{1} = \frac{2}{5}$$

26. Let R_1 be the portion of the disk $0 \le r \le 2$ in the first quadrant of the xy plane, and R_2 the portion of the ring $2 \le r \le 3$ in the first quadrant of the xy plane. The given solid region D is composed of two parts, D_1 and D_2, where D_1 lies between the graphs of $z = 2$ and $z = 3$ on R_1, and where D_2 lies between the graphs of $z = r$ and $z = 3$ on R_2. Since $\text{div } \vec{F}(x,y,z) = y$, the Divergence Theorem implies that

$$\iint_\Sigma \vec{F}\cdot\vec{n}\,dS = \iiint_D \text{div } \vec{F}(x,y,z)\,dV = \iiint_{D_1} y\,dV + \iiint_{D_2} y\,dV$$

$$= \int_0^{\pi/2}\int_0^2\int_2^3 (r\sin\theta)r\,dz\,dr\,d\theta + \int_0^{\pi/2}\int_2^3\int_r^3 (r\sin\theta)r\,dz\,dr\,d\theta$$

$$= \int_0^{\pi/2}\int_0^2 (r^2\sin\theta)z\Big|_2^3 dr\,d\theta + \int_0^{\pi/2}\int_2^3 (r^2\sin\theta)z\Big|_r^3 dr\,d\theta$$

$$= \int_0^{\pi/2}\int_0^2 r^2 \sin\theta \, dr \, d\theta + \int_0^{\pi/2}\int_2^3 (3r^2 - r^3) \sin\theta \, dr \, d\theta$$

$$= \int_0^{\pi/2} \frac{1}{3} r^3 \sin\theta \Big|_0^2 d\theta + \int_0^{\pi/2} (r^3 - \frac{1}{4} r^4) \sin\theta \Big|_2^3 d\theta$$

$$= \int_0^{\pi/2} \frac{8}{3} \sin\theta \, d\theta + \int_0^{\pi/2} \frac{11}{4} \sin\theta \, d\theta = \int_0^{\pi/2} \frac{65}{12} \sin\theta \, d\theta$$

$$= -\frac{65}{12} \cos\theta \Big|_0^{\pi/2} = \frac{65}{12}$$

27. Let $\vec{F}(x,y,z) = y\vec{i} + x\vec{j} + z^3\vec{k} = M(x,y,z)\vec{i} + N(x,y,z)\vec{j} + P(x,y,z)\vec{k}$. Since $\frac{\partial P}{\partial y} = 0 = \frac{\partial N}{\partial z}$, $\frac{\partial M}{\partial z} = 0 = \frac{\partial P}{\partial x}$, and $\frac{\partial N}{\partial x} = 1 = \frac{\partial M}{\partial y}$, the line integral $\int_C \vec{F}\cdot d\vec{r}$ is independent of path. Let grad $f(x,y,z) = \vec{F}(x,y,z)$. Then

$$\frac{\partial f}{\partial x} = y, \quad \frac{\partial f}{\partial y} = x, \quad \text{and} \quad \frac{\partial f}{\partial z} = z^3 \qquad (*)$$

Integrating both sides of the first equation in (*) with respect to x, we obtain $f(x,y,z) = xy + g(y,z)$. Taking partial derivatives with respect to y, we find that $\frac{\partial f}{\partial y} = x + \frac{\partial g}{\partial y}$. Comparing this with the second equation in (*), we deduce that $\frac{\partial g}{\partial y} = 0$, so that $g(y,z) = h(z)$. Thus $f(x,y,z) = xy + h(z)$. Taking partial derivatives with respect to z, we find that $\frac{\partial f}{\partial z} = \frac{dh}{dz}$. Comparing this with the third equation in (*), we conclude that $\frac{dh}{dz} = z^3$, so that $h(z) = \frac{1}{4} z^4 + C$. If $C = 0$, then $f(x,y,z) = xy + \frac{1}{4} z^4$.

a. Let C denote the line segment from $(1,0,0)$ to $(0,1,\pi)$. By the definition of work and the Fundamental Theorem of Line Integrals,

$$W = \int_C \vec{F}\cdot d\vec{r} = f(0,1,\pi) - f(1,0,0) = \frac{1}{4}\pi^4 - 0 = \frac{1}{4}\pi^4$$

b. Let C_1 denote the given curve. Since the integral is independent of path, it follows from part (a) and the definition of work that

$$W = \int_{C_1} \vec{F}\cdot d\vec{r} = \int_C \vec{F}\cdot d\vec{r} = \frac{1}{4}\pi^4$$

28. Since $x(t) = \cos t$, $y(t) = \sin 2t$, $\frac{dx}{dt} = -\sin t$, and $\frac{dy}{dt} = 2\cos 2t$, (4) in Section 15.4 implies that

$$A = \frac{1}{2}\int_C x\,dy - y\,dx = \frac{1}{2}\int_{-\pi/2}^{\pi/2} [(\cos t)(2\cos 2t)$$

$$- (\sin 2t)(-\sin t)]\,dt = \frac{1}{2}\int_{-\pi/2}^{\pi/2} [2\cos t\,(1 - 2\sin^2 t)$$

$$+ (2\sin t \cos t)\sin t]\,dt = \int_{-\pi/2}^{\pi/2} (\cos t - \sin^2 t \cos t)\,dt$$

$$= (\sin t - \frac{1}{3}\sin^3 t)\Big|_{-\pi/2}^{\pi/2} = \frac{4}{3}$$

16

DIFFERENTIAL EQUATIONS

Section 16.1

1. If $y = \frac{1}{3} e^{3x}$, then $\frac{dy}{dx} = 3(\frac{1}{3} e^{3x}) = e^{3x}$, so that $\frac{dy}{dx} = e^{3x}$.

2. If $y = 5e^{3x} - \frac{2}{3} x - \frac{2}{9}$, then $\frac{dy}{dx} = 15e^{3x} - \frac{2}{3}$; since $2x + 3y = 2x + 3(5e^{3x} - \frac{2}{3} x - \frac{2}{9}) = 15e^{3x} - \frac{2}{3}$, we have $\frac{dy}{dx} = 2x + 3y$.

3. If $y = \tan x + \sec x$ for $0 < x < \pi/2$, then $\frac{dy}{dx} = \sec^2 x + \sec x \tan x$, so that $2 \frac{dy}{dx} - y^2 = 2(\sec^2 x + \sec x \tan x) - (\tan x + \sec x)^2 = 2 \sec^2 x + 2 \sec x \tan x - (\tan^2 x + 2 \sec x \tan x + \sec^2 x) = \sec^2 x - \tan^2 x = 1$. Thus $2 \frac{dy}{dx} - y^2 = 1$.

4. If $y = 3 + \frac{x}{3}$ then $\frac{dy}{dx} = \frac{1}{3}$, so that $x(\frac{dy}{dx})^2 - y \frac{dy}{dx} + 1 = x(\frac{1}{9}) - (3 + \frac{x}{3})(\frac{1}{3}) + 1 = 0$. Thus $x(\frac{dy}{dx})^2 - y \frac{dy}{dx} + 1 = 0$.

5. If $y = \sinh x$, then $\frac{dy}{dx} = \cosh x$, and $\frac{d^2y}{dx^2} = \sinh x$. Thus $\frac{d^2y}{dx^2} = y$.

6. If $y = \sin 2x - \cos 2x$, then $\frac{dy}{dx} = 2 \cos 2x + 2 \sin 2x$, and $\frac{d^2y}{dx^2} = -4 \sin 2x + 4 \cos 2x$. Thus $\frac{d^2y}{dx^2} + 4y = -4 \sin 2x + 4 \cos 2x + 4(\sin 2x - \cos 2x) = 0$, so that $\frac{d^2y}{dx^2} + 4y = 0$.

7. If $y = e^{-x} + \sin x$, then $\frac{dy}{dx} = -e^{-x} + \cos x$ and $\frac{d^2y}{dx^2} = e^{-x} - \sin x$. Thus $\frac{d^2y}{dx^2} + y = (e^{-x} - \sin x) + (e^{-x} + \sin x) = 2e^{-x}$, so that $\frac{d^2y}{dx^2} + y = 2e^{-x}$.

3. If $y = xe^{-2x}$, then $\frac{dy}{dx} = e^{-2x} - 2xe^{-2x}$, and $\frac{d^2y}{dx^2} = -2e^{-2x} - 2e^{-2x} + 4xe^{-2x}$. Thus $\frac{d^2y}{dx^2} + 4 \frac{dy}{dx} + 4y = (-2e^{-2x} - 2e^{-2x} + 4xe^{-2x}) + 4(e^{-2x} - 2xe^{-2x}) + 4xe^{-2x} = 0$, so that $\frac{d^2y}{dx^2} + 4 \frac{dy}{dx} + 4y = 0$.

9. If $y = e^{ax} \sin bx$, then $\frac{dy}{dx} = ae^{ax} \sin bx + be^{ax} \cos bx$, and $\frac{d^2y}{dx^2} = a^2 e^{ax} \sin bx + 2abe^{ax} \cos bx - b^2 e^{ax} \sin bx$. Thus $\frac{d^2y}{dx^2} - 2a \frac{dy}{dx} + (a^2 + b^2)y = (a^2 e^{ax} \sin bx + 2abe^{ax} \cos bx - b^2 e^{ax} \sin bx) - 2a(ae^{ax} \sin bx + be^{ax} \cos bx) + (a^2 + b^2)e^{ax} \sin bx = 0$, so that $\frac{d^2y}{dx^2} - 2a \frac{dy}{dx} + (a^2 + b^2)y = 0$.

10. If $y = \sin(\ln x) + \cos(\ln x)$, then $\frac{dy}{dx} = \frac{\cos(\ln x)}{x} - \frac{\sin(\ln x)}{x}$, and $\frac{d^2y}{dx^2} = \frac{x(-\frac{\sin(\ln x)}{x}) - \cos(\ln x)}{x^2} - \frac{x(\frac{\cos(\ln x)}{x}) - \sin(\ln x)}{x^2} = \frac{-2 \cos(\ln x)}{x^2}$. Thus $x^2 \frac{d^2y}{dx^2} + x \frac{dy}{dx} + y = x^2(\frac{-2 \cos(\ln x)}{x^2}) + x(\frac{\cos(\ln x)}{x} - \frac{\sin(\ln x)}{x}) + \sin(\ln x) + \cos(\ln x) = 0$, so that $x^2 \frac{d^2y}{dx^2} + x \frac{dy}{dx} + y = 0$.

11. If $y = e^{-4t}$, then $\frac{dy}{dt} = -4e^{-4t}$, $\frac{d^2y}{dt^2} = 16e^{-4t}$, and $\frac{d^3y}{dt^3} = -64e^{-4t}$. Thus $\frac{d^3y}{dt^3} + 64y = -64e^{-4t} + 64e^{-4t} = 0$, so that $\frac{d^3y}{dt^3} + 64y = 0$.

12. If $y = \cos 3t$, then $\frac{dy}{dt} = -3 \sin 3t$, $\frac{d^2y}{dt^2} = 9 \cos 3t$, $\frac{d^3y}{dt^3} = -27 \sin 3t$, and $\frac{d^4t}{dt^4} = 81 \cos 3t$. Thus $\frac{d^4y}{dt^4} - 81y = 81 \cos 3t - 81 \cos 3t = 0$, so that $\frac{d^4y}{dt^4} - 81y = 0$.

13. If $y = -2e^{-3x}$, then $\frac{dy}{dx} = 6e^{-3x}$, so that $\frac{dy}{dx} + 5y = 6e^{-3x} + 5(-2e^{-3x}) = -4e^{-3x}$. Thus y satisfies the differential equation. Since $y(0) = -2e^{-3(0)} = -2$, y also satisfies the

initial condition.

14. If $y = e^x \sin x$, then $\frac{dy}{dx} = e^x \sin x + e^x \cos x$, and $\frac{d^2y}{dx^2} =$ $e^x \sin x + 2e^x \cos x - e^x \sin x = 2e^x \cos x$. Thus $\frac{d^2y}{dx^2} - 2\frac{dy}{dx} +$ $2y = 2e^x \cos x - 2(e^x \sin x + e^x \cos x) + 2e^x \sin x = 0$, so that y satisfies the differential equation. Since $y(0) = e^0 \sin 0 =$ 0 and $y'(0) = e^0 \sin 0 + e^0 \cos 0 = 1$, y also satisfies the initial conditions.

15. If $y = \frac{1}{x} - 1$, then $\frac{dy}{dx} = -\frac{1}{x^2}$, and $\frac{d^2y}{dx^2} = \frac{2}{x^3}$. Thus $x^3 \frac{d^2y}{dx^2} + x^2 \frac{dy}{dx} - xy = x^3(\frac{2}{x^3}) + x^2(-\frac{1}{x^2}) - x(\frac{1}{x} - 1) = x$, so that y satisfies the differential equation. Since $y(1) =$ $\frac{1}{1} - 1 = 0$ and $y'(1) = -\frac{1}{1} = -1$, y also satisfies the initial conditions.

16. If $y = x^2 - 2x$, then $\frac{dy}{dx} = 2x - 2$. Thus $(\frac{dy}{dx})^2 = (2x - 2)^2 =$ $4x^2 - 8x + 4$ and $4(y + 1) = 4(x^2-2x + 1) = 4x^2 - 8x + 4$, so that $(\frac{dy}{dx})^2 = 4(y + 1)$. Thus y satisfies the differential equation. Since $y(0) = 0^2 - 2\cdot 0 = 0$ and $y(2) = 2^2 - 2\cdot 2 = 0$, y also satisfies the initial conditions.

17. If $y = x\int_0^x \sqrt{1 + t^4}\,dt$, then $\frac{dy}{dx} = \int_0^x \sqrt{1 + t^4}\,dt + x\sqrt{1 + x^4}$. Thus $x\frac{dy}{dx} - y = x(\int_0^x \sqrt{1 + t^4}\,dt + x\sqrt{1 + x^4}) - x\int_0^x \sqrt{1 + t^4}\,dt =$ $x^2\sqrt{1 + x^4}$, so that y satisfies the differential equation. Since $y(0) = 0\int_0^0 \sqrt{1 + t^4}\,dt = 0$ and $y'(0) = \int_0^0 \sqrt{1 + t^4}\,dt +$ $0\sqrt{1 + 0^4} = 0$, y also satisfies the initial conditions.

18. If $y = \sqrt{r^2 - x^2}$, then $\frac{dy}{dx} = \frac{-x}{\sqrt{r^2 - x^2}} = \frac{-x}{y}$, so that $y\frac{dy}{dx} +$ $x = y(\frac{-x}{y}) + x = 0$. Thus y satisfies the differential equation.

19. If $y^2 = 8x + 16$, then $2y\frac{dy}{dx} = 8$, so that $\frac{dy}{dx} = \frac{8}{2y} = \frac{4}{y}$, and thus $2x\frac{dy}{dx} + y(\frac{dy}{dx})^2 = 2x(\frac{4}{y}) + y(\frac{4}{y})^2 = \frac{8x}{y} + \frac{16}{y} = \frac{8x + 16}{y} =$ $\frac{y^2}{y} = y$. Consequently y satisfies the differential equation.

20. If $y = c\cosh x/c$, then $\frac{dy}{dx} = \sinh x/c$, and $\frac{d^2y}{dx^2} = \frac{1}{c}\cosh x/c$. Thus $\frac{1}{c}\sqrt{1 + (\frac{dy}{dx})^2} = \frac{1}{c}\sqrt{1 + (\sinh x/c)^2} = \frac{1}{c}\cosh x/c = \frac{d^2y}{dx^2}$, so that y satisfies the differential equation.

21. If $N = N_0e^{kt} + \frac{c}{k}(e^{kt} - 1)$, then $\frac{dN}{dt} = kN_0e^{kt} + ce^{kt}$. Thus $kN + c = (kN_0e^{kt} + ce^{kt} - c) + c = kN_0e^{kt} + ce^{kt} = \frac{dN}{dt}$, so that N is a solution of the differential equation.

Section 16.2

1. $\frac{dy}{dx} = \frac{x}{y}$, so $y\,dy = x\,dx$; thus $\frac{1}{2}y^2 = \frac{1}{2}x^2 + C_1$, or $y^2 - x^2 = C$.

2. $\frac{dy}{dx} = \frac{y}{x}$, so $\frac{1}{y}\,dy = \frac{1}{x}\,dx$; thus $\ln|y| = \ln x + C_1$, so that $|y| = xe^{C_1}$, which means that $y = Cx$.

3. $\frac{2y}{y^2+1}\frac{dy}{dx} = \frac{1}{x^2}$, so $\frac{2y}{y^2+1}\,dy = \frac{1}{x^2}\,dx$; thus $\ln(y^2+1) = -\frac{1}{x} + C_1$, so that $y^2 + 1 = e^{-(1/x)+C_1}$, which means that $y^2 = -1 + Ce^{-1/x}$, with $C > 0$.

4. $\frac{dy}{dx} = \frac{\sin x - \cos x}{y^4 + y}$, so $(y^4 + y)dy = (\sin x - \cos x)dx$; thus $\frac{1}{5}y^5 + \frac{1}{2}y^2 = -\cos x - \sin x + C$.

5. $(y^2 - 3)\frac{dy}{dt} = 1$, so $(y^2 - 3)dy = dt$; thus $\frac{1}{3}y^3 - 3y = t + C$.

6. $t^3\frac{dy}{dt} = \sqrt{t^2 - y^2t^2}$ for $t > 0$, so $t^3\frac{dy}{dt} = t\sqrt{1 - y^2}$, or $\frac{1}{\sqrt{1-y^2}}\,dy = \frac{1}{t^2}\,dt$; thus $\arcsin y = -\frac{1}{t} + C$, so $y = \sin(-\frac{1}{t} + C)$.

7. $(1 + x^2)dy = (1 + y^2)dx$, so $\frac{1}{1+y^2}\,dy = \frac{1}{1+x^2}\,dx$; thus $\arctan y = \arctan x + C$.

8. $dy = (y + y^2)dx$, so $\frac{1}{y+y^2}\,dy = dx$. Since $\frac{1}{y+y^2} = \frac{1}{y(y+1)} = \frac{1}{y} - \frac{1}{y+1}$, it follows that $(\frac{1}{y} - \frac{1}{y+1})dy = dx$. Thus $\ln|y| - \ln|y+1| = x + C_1$, so that $\ln\left|\frac{y}{y+1}\right| = x + C_1$, and therefore $\left|\frac{y}{y+1}\right| = e^{x+C_1} = Ce^x$, with $C > 0$. Thus $\frac{1}{y+1} = Ce^x$.

9. $\frac{1+e^x}{1-e^{-y}}\,dy + e^{x+y}dx = 0$, so $\frac{e^{-y}}{1-e^{-y}}\,dy + \frac{e^x}{1+e^x}\,dx = 0$; thus $\ln|1 - e^{-y}| + \ln(1 + e^x) = C_1$, so that if $C_1 = \ln C$, then $\ln|1 - e^{-y}| + \ln(1 + e^x) = \ln C$, or $\ln[|1 - e^{-y}|(1 + e^x)] = \ln C$. Therefore $|1 - e^{-y}|(1 + e^x) = C$, or $|1 - e^{-y}| = \frac{C}{1 + e^x}$.

10. $e^{x+y^2}dy = \frac{x}{y}\,dx$, so $ye^{y^2}dy = xe^{-x}dx$. Since $\int xe^{-x}dx \overset{\text{parts}}{=} -xe^{-x} + \int e^{-x}dx = -xe^{-x} - e^{-x} + C$, we conclude that $\frac{1}{2}e^{y^2} = -xe^{-x} - e^{-x} + C$.

11. $y^2x\frac{dy}{dx} - x + 1 = 0$, so $y^2\,dy = \frac{1}{x}(x - 1)dx = (1 - \frac{1}{x})dx$; thus $\frac{1}{3}y^3 = x - \ln|x| + C$. If $y(1) = 3$, then $\frac{1}{3}(3)^3 = 1 - \ln 1 + C$, so that $C = 8$. Therefore the particular solution with $y(1) = 3$ is $\frac{1}{3}y^3 = x - \ln|x| + 8$.

12. $(\ln y)^2\frac{dy}{dx} = x^2y$, so $\frac{1}{y}(\ln y)^2dy = x^2dx$; thus $\frac{1}{3}(\ln y)^3 = \frac{1}{3}x^3 + C_1$, or $y = e^{(x^3+C)^{1/3}}$. If $y(2) = 1$, then $1 = e^{(2^3+C)^{1/3}}$, so that $0 = 2^3 + C$ and thus $C = -8$. Therefore the particular solution with $y(2) = 1$ is $y = e^{(x^3-8)^{1/3}}$.

13. $\sqrt{x^2+1}\,\frac{dy}{dx} = \frac{x}{y}$, so $y\,dy = \frac{x}{\sqrt{x^2+1}}\,dx$; thus $\frac{1}{2}y^2 = \sqrt{x^2+1} + C$. If $y(\sqrt{3}) = 2$, then $\frac{1}{2}(2)^2 = \sqrt{(\sqrt{3})^2 + 1} + C$, so that $C = 0$. Therefore the particular solution with $y(\sqrt{3}) = 2$ is $\frac{1}{2}y^2 = \sqrt{x^2+1}$, or $y = \sqrt{2\sqrt{x^2+1}}$.

14. $\frac{dy}{dx} = x\sin x$, so $dy = x\sin x\,dx$; thus $y = \int x\sin x\,dx \overset{\text{parts}}{=} -x\cos x + \int\cos x\,dx = -x\cos x + \sin x + C$. If $y(\frac{\pi}{2}) = 0$, then $0 = -\frac{\pi}{2}\cos\frac{\pi}{2} + \sin\frac{\pi}{2} + C = 1 + C$, so that $C = -1$. Therefore the particular solution with $y(\frac{\pi}{2}) = 0$ is

$y = -x \cos x + \sin x - 1.$

15. $e^{-2y}dy = (x - 2)dx$, and thus $-\frac{1}{2} e^{-2y} = \frac{1}{2} x^2 - 2x + C$. If $y(0) = 0$, then $-\frac{1}{2} e^0 = 0 - 0 + C$, so that $C = -\frac{1}{2}$. Therefore the particular solution with $y(0) = 0$ is $-\frac{1}{2} e^{-2y} = \frac{1}{2} x^2 - 2x - \frac{1}{2}$, or $y = -\frac{1}{2} \ln(-x^2 + 4x + 1)$.

16. $\frac{1}{9}\, dy = \frac{e^x}{ey^2 + y^2e^2}\, dx$, so $(e + e^2)y^2\, dy = 9e^x\, dx$. Thus $\frac{1}{3}(e + e^2)y^3 = 9e^x + C$. If $y(1) = 3$, then $\frac{1}{3}(e + e^2)3^3 = 9e + C$, so that $9e^2 = C$. Therefore the particular solution with $y(1) = 3$ is $\frac{1}{3}(e + e^2)y^3 = 9e^x + 9e^2$, or $(e + e^2)y^3 = 27(e^x + e^2)$.

17. a. Since $v = y/x$, we have $y = xv$, so that $\frac{dy}{dx} = x\frac{dv}{dx} + v$.

b. Using the definition of g and part (a), we have $g(v) = g(y/x) = f(x,y) = \frac{dy}{dx} = x\frac{dv}{dx} + v$, so that $g(v) - v = x\frac{dv}{dx}$, and thus $\frac{1}{g(v) - v}\, dv = \frac{1}{x}\, dx$.

18. $f(x,y) = \frac{y^2 + 2xy}{x^2} = (\frac{y}{x})^2 + 2(\frac{y}{x}) = g(y/x)$, where $g(v) = v^2 + 2v$. By (8), $\frac{1}{(v^2 + 2v) - v}\, dv = \frac{1}{x}\, dx$, so that $\frac{1}{v^2 + v}\, dv = \frac{1}{x}\, dx$. Since $\frac{1}{v^2 + v} = \frac{1}{v(v + 1)} = \frac{1}{v} - \frac{1}{v + 1}$, it follows that $(\frac{1}{v} - \frac{1}{v + 1})dv = \frac{1}{x}\, dx$. Thus $\ln|v| - \ln|v + 1| = \ln|x| + C_1$. If $C_1 = \ln C$, then this yields $\ln\left|\frac{v}{v + 1}\right| = \ln|x| + \ln C = \ln C|x|$, so that $\left|\frac{v}{v + 1}\right| = C|x|$. Since $v = y/x$, we conclude that $\left|\frac{y/x}{(y/x) + 1}\right| = C|x|$, or $\left|\frac{y}{y + x}\right| = C|x|$, with $C > 0$.

19. $f(x,y) = \frac{x + y}{x} = 1 + \frac{y}{x} = g(y/x)$, where $g(v) = 1 + v$. By (8), $\frac{1}{(1 + v) - v}\, dv = \frac{1}{x}\, dx$, so that $dv = \frac{1}{x}\, dx$, and thus $v = \ln|x| + C_1$. If $\ln C = C_1$, then since $v = y/x$, we conclude that $\frac{y}{x} = \ln|x| + \ln C = \ln C|x|$, so that $y = x \ln C|x|$, with $C > 0$.

Section 16.3

1. Since $\frac{\partial}{\partial x}(-3xy^2) = -3y^2 = \frac{\partial}{\partial y}(2x - y^3)$, the differential equation is exact. Thus there is a function f such that $\frac{\partial f}{\partial x} = 2x - y^3$ and $\frac{\partial f}{\partial y} = -3xy^2$. Then $f(x,y) = x^2 - xy^3 + g(y)$ for a suitable function g, so that $\frac{\partial f}{\partial y} = -3xy^2 + \frac{dg}{dy}$. Since $\frac{\partial f}{\partial y} = -3xy^2$, it follows that $\frac{dg}{dy} = 0$, and thus $g(y) = C_1$. Consequently the general solution is $x^2 - xy^3 = C$.

2. Since $\frac{\partial}{\partial x}(-y + x \cos y) = \cos y = \frac{\partial}{\partial y}(\sin y)$, the differential equation is exact. Thus there is a function f such that $\frac{\partial f}{\partial x} = \sin y$ and $\frac{\partial f}{\partial y} = -y + x \cos y$. Then $f(x,y) = x \sin y + g(y)$, for a suitable function g, so that $\frac{\partial f}{\partial y} = x \cos y + \frac{dg}{dy}$. Since $\frac{\partial f}{\partial y} = -y + x \cos y$, it follows that $\frac{dg}{dy} = -y$, and thus $g(y) = -\frac{1}{2} y^2 + C_1$. Consequently the general solution is $x \sin y - \frac{1}{2} y^2 = C$.

3. Since $\frac{\partial}{\partial x}(3x^2y^2 + e^{-x} - 4) = 6xy^2 - e^{-x} = \frac{\partial}{\partial y}(2xy^3 - ye^{-x})$, the differential equation is exact. Thus there is a function f such that $\frac{\partial f}{\partial x} = 2xy^3 - ye^{-x}$ and $\frac{\partial f}{\partial y} = 3x^2y^2 + e^{-x} - 4$. Then $f(x,y) = x^2y^3 + ye^{-x} + g(y)$, for a suitable function g, so that $\frac{\partial f}{\partial y} = 3x^2y^2 + e^{-x} + \frac{dg}{dy}$. Since $\frac{\partial f}{\partial y} = 3x^2y^2 + e^{-x} - 4$, it follows that $\frac{dg}{dy} = -4$, so that $g(y) = -4y + C_1$. Consequently the general solution is $x^2y^3 + ye^{-x} - 4y = C$.

4. The differential equation is equivalent to $2xy \cos x^2y + (x^2 \cos x^2y) \frac{dy}{dx} = 0$. Since $\frac{\partial}{\partial x}(x^2 \cos x^2y) = 2x \cos x^2y - 2x^3y \sin x^2y = \frac{\partial}{\partial y}(2xy \cos x^2y)$, this differential equation is exact. Thus there is a function f such that $\frac{\partial f}{\partial x} = 2xy \cos x^2y$ and $\frac{\partial f}{\partial y} = x^2 \cos x^2y$. Then $f(x,y) = \sin x^2y + g(y)$, for a suitable function g, so that $\frac{\partial f}{\partial y} = x^2 \cos x^2y + \frac{dg}{dy}$. Since $\frac{\partial f}{\partial y} = x^2 \cos x^2y$, it follows that $\frac{dg}{dy} = 0$, so that $g(y) = C_1$. Consequently the general solution is $\sin x^2y = C$.

5. The differential equation is equivalent to $2x - \frac{y}{x^2} + (\frac{1}{x} + \cos 2y) \frac{dy}{dx} = 0$. Since $\frac{\partial}{\partial x}(\frac{1}{x} + \cos 2y) = -\frac{1}{x^2} = \frac{\partial}{\partial y}(2x - \frac{y}{x^2})$, this differential equation is exact. Thus there is a function f such that $\frac{\partial f}{\partial x} = 2x - \frac{y}{x^2}$ and $\frac{\partial f}{\partial y} = \frac{1}{x} + \cos 2y$. Then $f(x,y) = x^2 + \frac{y}{x} + g(y)$, for a suitable function g, so that $\frac{\partial f}{\partial y} = \frac{1}{x} + \frac{dg}{dy}$. Since $\frac{\partial f}{\partial y} = \frac{1}{x} + \cos 2y$, it follows that $\frac{dg}{dy} = \cos 2y$, so that $g(y) = \frac{1}{2} \sin 2y + C_1$. Consequently the general solution is $x^2 + \frac{y}{x} + \frac{1}{2} \sin 2y = C$.

6. The differential equation is equivalent to $(6x - 2y) + (5y - 2x) \frac{dy}{dx} = 0$. Since $\frac{\partial}{\partial x}(5y - 2x) = -2 = \frac{\partial}{\partial y}(6x - 2y)$, the differential equation is exact. Thus there is a function f such that $\frac{\partial f}{\partial x} = 6x - 2y$ and $\frac{\partial f}{\partial y} = 5y - 2x$. Then $f(x,y) = 3x^2 - 2xy + g(y)$, for a suitable function g, so that $\frac{\partial f}{\partial y} = -2x + \frac{dg}{dy}$. Since $\frac{\partial f}{\partial y} = 5y - 2x$, it follows that $\frac{dg}{dy} = 5y$, so that $g(y) = \frac{5}{2} y^2 + C_1$. Consequently the general solution is $3x^2 - 2xy + \frac{5}{2} y^2 = C$.

7. The differential equation is equivalent to $(\pi y - \sin x) + (\pi x + \arcsin y) \frac{dy}{dx} = 0$. Since $\frac{\partial}{\partial x}(\pi x + \arcsin y) = \pi = \frac{\partial}{\partial y}(\pi y - \sin x)$, this differential equation is exact. Thus there is a function f such that $\frac{\partial f}{\partial x} = \pi y - \sin x$ and $\frac{\partial f}{\partial y} = \pi x + \arcsin y$. Then $f(x,y) = \pi xy + \cos x + g(y)$, for a suitable function g, so that $\frac{\partial f}{\partial y} = \pi x + \frac{dg}{dy}$. Since $\frac{\partial f}{\partial y} = \pi x + \arcsin y$, it follows that $\frac{dg}{dy} = \arcsin y$, so that by integration by parts, $g(y) = \int \arcsin y\,dy = y \arcsin y - \int \frac{y}{\sqrt{1 - y^2}}\,dy = y \arcsin y + \sqrt{1 - y^2} + C_1$. Consequently the general solution is $\pi xy + \cos x + y \arcsin y + \sqrt{1 - y^2} = C$.

8. Since $\frac{\partial}{\partial x}(-3y^2 - 3x) = -3 = \frac{\partial}{\partial y}(3x^2 - 3y)$, the differential equation is exact. Thus there is a function f such that $\frac{\partial f}{\partial x} = 3x^2 - 3y$ and $\frac{\partial f}{\partial y} = -3y^2 - 3x$. Then $f(x,y) = x^3 - 3xy + g(y)$,

for a suitable function g, so that $\frac{\partial f}{\partial y} = -3x + \frac{dg}{dy}$. Since $\frac{\partial f}{\partial y} = -3y^2 - 3x$, it follows that $\frac{dg}{dy} = -3y^2$, and thus $g(y) = -y^3 + C_1$. Consequently the general solution is $x^3 - 3xy - y^3 = C$.

9. Since $\frac{\partial}{\partial x}(\frac{\ln x}{y} + \sin y) = \frac{1}{xy} = \frac{\partial}{\partial y}(\frac{\ln y}{x})$, the differential equation is exact. Thus there is a function f such that $\frac{\partial f}{\partial x} = \frac{\ln y}{x}$ and $\frac{\partial f}{\partial y} = \frac{\ln x}{y} + \sin y$. Then $f(x,y) = \ln x \ln y + g(y)$, for a suitable function g, so that $\frac{\partial f}{\partial y} = \frac{\ln x}{y} + \frac{dg}{dy}$. Since $\frac{\partial f}{\partial y} = \frac{\ln x}{y} + \sin y$, it follows that $\frac{dg}{dy} = \sin y$, and thus $g(y) = -\cos y + C_1$. Consequently the general solution is $\ln x \ln y - \cos y = C$.

10. Since $\frac{\partial}{\partial x}[(1 + xy)e^{xy}] = ye^{xy} + (1 + xy)ye^{xy} = 2ye^{xy} + xy^2e^{xy} = \frac{\partial}{\partial y}(y^2e^{xy} - \pi)$, the differential equation is exact. Thus there is a function f such that $\frac{\partial f}{\partial x} = y^2e^{xy} - \pi$ and $\frac{\partial f}{\partial y} = (1 + xy)e^{xy}$. Then $f(x,y) = ye^{xy} - \pi x + g(y)$, for a suitable function g, so that $\frac{\partial f}{\partial y} = e^{xy} + xye^{xy} + \frac{dg}{dy} = (1 + xy)e^{xy} + \frac{dg}{dy}$. Since $\frac{\partial f}{\partial y} = (1 + xy)e^{xy}$, it follows that $\frac{dg}{dy} = 0$, so that $g(y) = C_1$. Consequently the general solution is given by $ye^{xy} - \pi x = C$.

11. Since $\frac{\partial}{\partial x}(1 + \tan x \sec y \tan y) = \sec^2 x \sec y \tan y = \frac{\partial}{\partial y}(\sec^2 x \sec y)$, the differential equation is exact. Thus there is a function f such that $\frac{\partial f}{\partial x} = \sec^2 x \sec y$ and $\frac{\partial f}{\partial y} = 1 + \tan x \sec y \tan y$. Then $f(x,y) = \tan x \sec y + g(y)$, for a suitable function g, so that $\frac{\partial f}{\partial y} = \tan x \sec y \tan y + \frac{dg}{dy}$. Since $\frac{\partial f}{\partial y} = 1 + \tan x \sec y \tan y$, it follows that $\frac{dg}{dy} = 1$, and thus $g(y) = y + C_1$. Consequently the general solution is $\tan x \sec y + y = C$.

12. Since $\frac{\partial}{\partial x}(\sin xy + xy \cos xy) = y \cos xy + y \cos xy - xy^2 \sin xy = 2y \cos xy - xy^2 \sin xy = \frac{\partial}{\partial y}(y^2 \cos xy)$, the differential equation is exact. Thus there is a function f such that $\frac{\partial f}{\partial x} = y^2 \cos xy$ and $\frac{\partial f}{\partial y} = \sin xy + xy \cos xy$. Then $f(x,y) = y \sin xy + g(y)$, for a suitable function g, so that $\frac{\partial f}{\partial y} = \sin xy + xy \cos xy + \frac{dg}{dy}$. Since $\frac{\partial f}{\partial y} = \sin xy + xy \cos xy$, it follows that $\frac{dg}{dy} = 0$, so that $g(y) = C_1$. Consequently the general solution is $y \sin xy = C$.

13. Since $\frac{\partial}{\partial x}(e^x \sin y + \frac{1}{4}x^4 + \sec^2 y) = e^x \sin y + x^3 = \frac{\partial}{\partial y}(x^3 y - e^x \cos y)$, the differential equation is exact. Thus there is a function f such that $\frac{\partial f}{\partial x} = x^3 y - e^x \cos y$ and $\frac{\partial f}{\partial y} = e^x \sin y + \frac{1}{4}x^4 + \sec^2 y$. Then $f(x,y) = \frac{1}{4}x^4 y - e^x \cos y + g(y)$, for a suitable function g, so that $\frac{\partial f}{\partial y} = \frac{1}{4}x^4 + e^x \sin y + \frac{dg}{dy}$. Since $\frac{\partial f}{\partial y} = e^x \sin y + \frac{1}{4}x^4 + \sec^2 y$, it follows that $\frac{dg}{dy} = \sec^2 y$, so that $g(y) = \tan y + C_1$. Consequently the general solution is $\frac{1}{4}x^4 y - e^x \cos y + \tan y = C$.

14. Since $\frac{\partial}{\partial x}(x^2 e^{x^2 y} + x \cos y - y) = 2xe^{x^2 y} + 2x^3 ye^{x^2 y} + \cos y = \frac{\partial}{\partial y}(2xy\, e^{x^2 y} + \sin y)$, the differential equation is exact. Thus there is a function f such that $\frac{\partial f}{\partial x} = 2xy\, e^{x^2 y} + \sin y$ and $\frac{\partial f}{\partial y} = x^2 e^{x^2 y} + x \cos y - y$. Then $f(x,y) = e^{x^2 y} + x \sin y + g(y)$, for a suitable function g, so that $\frac{\partial f}{\partial y} = x^2\, e^{x^2 y} + x \cos y + \frac{dg}{dy}$. Since $\frac{\partial f}{\partial y} = x^2 e^{x^2 y} + x \cos y - y$, it follows that $\frac{dg}{dy} = -y$, so that $g(y) = -\frac{1}{2}y^2 + C_1$. Thus the general solution is given by $e^{x^2 y} + x \sin y - \frac{1}{2}y^2 = C$.

15. Since $\frac{\partial}{\partial x}(8xy) = 8y = \frac{\partial}{\partial y}(4y^2)$, the differential equation is exact. Thus there is a function f such that $\frac{\partial f}{\partial x} = 4y^2$ and $\frac{\partial f}{\partial y} = 8xy$. Then $f(x,y) = 4xy^2 + g(y)$, for a suitable function g, so that $\frac{\partial f}{\partial y} = 8xy + \frac{dg}{dy}$. Since $\frac{\partial f}{\partial y} = 8xy$, it follows that $\frac{dg}{dy} = 0$, and thus $g(y) = C_1$. Consequently the general solution is $4xy^2 = C$. If $y(3) = \frac{\sqrt{2}}{2}$, then $4(3)(\frac{\sqrt{2}}{2})^2 = C$, so that $C = 6$. Therefore the particular solution with $y(3) = \frac{\sqrt{2}}{2}$ is $4xy^2 = 6$, or $xy^2 = \frac{3}{2}$, so $y = \sqrt{3/(2x)}$.

16. Since $\frac{\partial}{\partial x}(e^x + xe^y) = e^x + e^y = \frac{\partial}{\partial y}(e^y + ye^x)$, the differential equation is exact. Thus there is a function f such that $\frac{\partial f}{\partial x} = e^y + ye^x$ and $\frac{\partial f}{\partial y} = e^x + xe^y$. Then $f(x,y) = xe^y + ye^x + g(y)$ for a suitable function g, so that $\frac{\partial f}{\partial y} = xe^y + e^x + \frac{dg}{dy}$. Since $\frac{\partial f}{\partial y} = e^x + xe^y$, it follows that $\frac{dg}{dy} = 0$, and thus $g(y) = C_1$. Consequently the general solution is $xe^y + ye^x = C$. If $y(1) = 0$, then $1 \cdot e^0 + 0 \cdot e^1 = C$, so that $C = 1$. Therefore the particular solution with $y(1) = 0$ is $xe^y + ye^x = 1$.

17. Since $\frac{\partial}{\partial x}\left(\frac{2xy}{1+y^2}\right) = \frac{2y}{1+y^2} = \frac{\partial}{\partial y}[\ln(1+y^2)]$, the differential equation is exact. Thus there is a function f such that $\frac{\partial f}{\partial x} = \ln(1+y^2)$ and $\frac{\partial f}{\partial y} = \frac{2xy}{1+y^2}$. Then $f(x,y) = x\ln(1+y^2) + g(y)$, for a suitable function g, so that $\frac{\partial f}{\partial y} = \frac{2xy}{1+y^2} + \frac{dg}{dy}$. Since $\frac{\partial f}{\partial y} = \frac{2xy}{1+y^2}$, it follows that $\frac{dg}{dy} = 0$, and thus $g(y) = C_1$. Consequently the general solution is $x\ln(1+y^2) = C$. If $y(2) = \sqrt{e-1}$, then $2\ln[1 + (\sqrt{e-1})^2] = C$, so that $C = 2$. Therefore the particular solution with $y(2) = \sqrt{e-1}$ is $x\ln(1+y^2) = 2$, so that $1 + y^2 = e^{2/x}$, and thus $y = \sqrt{e^{2/x} - 1}$.

18. Since $\frac{\partial}{\partial x}(x\cosh xy - y) = \cosh xy + xy\sinh xy = \frac{\partial}{\partial y}(y\cosh xy)$, the differential equation is exact. Thus there is a function f such that $\frac{\partial f}{\partial x} = y\cosh xy$ and $\frac{\partial f}{\partial y} = x\cosh xy - y$. Then $f(x,y) = \sinh xy + g(y)$, for a suitable function g, so that $\frac{\partial f}{\partial y} = x\cosh xy + \frac{dg}{dy}$. Since $\frac{\partial f}{\partial y} = x\cosh xy - y$, it follows that $\frac{dg}{dy} = -y$, and thus $g(y) = -\frac{1}{2}y^2 + C_1$. Consequently the general solution is $\sinh xy - \frac{1}{2}y^2 = C$. If $y(0) = \sqrt{5}$, then $\sinh(0\cdot\sqrt{5}) - \frac{1}{2}(\sqrt{5})^2 = C$, so that $C = -\frac{5}{2}$. Therefore the particular solution with $y(0) = \sqrt{5}$ is $\sinh xy - \frac{1}{2}y^2 = -\frac{5}{2}$.

19. Since $\frac{\partial}{\partial x}(\frac{1}{4}e^{x^2}\cos 3y) = \frac{1}{2}xe^{x^2}\cos 3y$ and $\frac{\partial}{\partial y}(axe^{x^2}\sin 3y) = 3axe^{x^2}\cos 3y$, it follows that $\frac{\partial}{\partial x}(\frac{1}{4}e^{x^2}\cos 3y) = \frac{\partial}{\partial y}(axe^{x^2}\sin 3y)$ if $\frac{1}{2}xe^{x^2}\cos 3y = 3axe^{x^2}\cos 3y$, that is, if $a = \frac{1}{6}$. The exact differential equation is $\frac{1}{6}xe^{x^2}\sin 3y + \frac{1}{4}e^{x^2}\cos 3y\,\frac{dy}{dx} = 0$. Thus there is a function f such that $\frac{\partial f}{\partial x} = \frac{1}{6}xe^{x^2}\sin 3y$ and $\frac{\partial f}{\partial y} = \frac{1}{4}e^{x^2}\cos 3y$. Then $f(x,y) = \frac{1}{12}e^{x^2}\sin 3y + g(y)$, for a suitable function g, so that $\frac{\partial f}{\partial y} = \frac{1}{4}e^{x^2}\cos 3y + \frac{dg}{dy}$. Since $\frac{\partial f}{\partial y} = \frac{1}{4}e^{x^2}\cos 3y$, it follows that $\frac{dg}{dy} = 0$, so that $g(y) = C_1$. Consequently the general solution is $\frac{1}{12}e^{x^2}\sin 3y = C$.

20. Since $\frac{\partial}{\partial x}(2x^6y^a) = 12x^5y^a$ and $\frac{\partial}{\partial y}(ax^5y^{a+1}) = a(a+1)x^5y^a$, it follows that $\frac{\partial}{\partial x}(2x^6y^a) = \frac{\partial}{\partial y}(ax^5y^{a+1})$ if $12x^5y^a = a(a+1)x^5y^a$. For the equation to hold for all x and y, we must have $12 = a(a+1)$, so that $a^2 + a - 12 = 0$, or $(a+4)(a-3) = 0$. Since $a > 0$ by hypothesis, we conclude that $a = 3$, so the exact differential equation is $3x^5y^4dx + 2x^6y^3dy = 0$. Thus there is a function f such that $\frac{\partial f}{\partial x} = 3x^5y^4$ and $\frac{\partial f}{\partial y} = 2x^6y^3$. Then $f(x,y) = \frac{1}{2}x^6y^4 + g(y)$, for a suitable function g, so that $\frac{\partial f}{\partial y} = 2x^6y^3 + \frac{dg}{dy}$. Since $\frac{\partial f}{\partial y} = 2x^6y^3$, it follows that $\frac{dg}{dy} = 0$, so that $g(y) = C_1$. Consequently the general solution is $\frac{1}{2}x^6y^4 = C$.

21. If we multiply both sides of the differential equation by $x^2 + y^2$, then it becomes $y^2 + 2xy\frac{dy}{dx} = 0$, or $y^2dx + 2xy\,dy = 0$. Since $\frac{\partial}{\partial x}(2xy) = 2y = \frac{\partial}{\partial y}(y^2)$, the new differential equation is exact. Thus there is a function f such that $\frac{\partial f}{\partial x} = y^2$ and $\frac{\partial f}{\partial y} = 2xy$. Then $f(x,y) = xy^2 + g(y)$, for a suitable function g, so that $\frac{\partial f}{\partial y} = 2xy + \frac{dg}{dy}$. Since $\frac{\partial f}{\partial y} = 2xy$, it follows that $\frac{dg}{dy} = 0$, and thus $g(y) = C_1$. Consequently

the general solution of the differential equation $y^2 dx + 2xy\, dy = 0$, and hence of $\frac{y^2}{x^2 + y^2} + \frac{2xy}{x^2 + y^2}\frac{dy}{dx} = 0$, is $xy^2 = C$.

Section 16.4

1. $P(x) = 1/x^2$ and $Q(x) = 0$. Since $-1/x$ is an antiderivative of P, $S(x) = -1/x$, so (3) implies that $y = e^{1/x}\int e^{-1/x}\, 0\, dx = e^{1/x}(C) = Ce^{1/x}$.

2. $P(x) = -\sinh x$ and $Q(x) = 0$. Since $-\cosh x$ is an antiderivative of P, $S(x) = -\cosh x$, so (3) implies that $y = e^{\cosh x}\int e^{-\cosh x}\, 0\, dx = e^{\cosh x}(C) = Ce^{\cosh x}$.

3. $P(x) = 2$ and $Q(x) = 4$. Since $2x$ is an antiderivative of P, $S(x) = 2x$, so (3) implies that $y = e^{-2x}\int e^{2x}\, 4dx = 4e^{-2x}\int e^{2x}\, dx = 4e^{-2x}(\frac{1}{2}e^{2x} + C_1) = 2 + Ce^{-2x}$.

4. $P(x) = -2$ and $Q(x) = x$. Since $-2x$ is an antiderivative of P, $S(x) = -2x$, so (3) implies that $y = e^{2x}\int e^{-2x}(x)\, dx = e^{2x}\int xe^{-2x}\, dx \overset{\text{parts}}{=} e^{2x}(-\frac{1}{2}xe^{-2x} + \int \frac{1}{2}e^{-2x}\, dx) = e^{2x}(-\frac{1}{2}xe^{-2x} - \frac{1}{4}e^{-2x} + C) = -\frac{1}{2}x - \frac{1}{4} + Ce^{2x}$.

5. $P(x) = -a$ and $Q(x) = f(x)$. Since $-ax$ is an antiderivative of P, $S(x) = -ax$, so (3) implies that $y = e^{ax}\int e^{-ax}f(x)\, dx$.

6. $P(x) = 2x$ and $Q(x) = 4x$. Since x^2 is an antiderivative of P, $S(x) = x^2$, so (3) implies that $y = e^{-x^2}\int e^{x^2}(4x)\, dx = 4e^{-x^2}\int xe^{x^2}\, dx = 4e^{-x^2}(\frac{1}{2}e^{x^2} + C_1) = 2 + Ce^{-x^2}$.

7. $P(x) = 6x^5$ and $Q(x) = x^5$. Since x^6 is an antiderivative of P, $S(x) = x^6$, so (3) implies that $y = e^{-x^6}\int e^{x^6}(x^5)\, dx = \frac{1}{6}e^{-x^6}\int (6x^5)e^{x^6}\, dx = \frac{1}{6}e^{-x^6}(e^{x^6} + C_1) = \frac{1}{6} + Ce^{-x^6}$.

8. The equation is equivalent to $y' - \frac{1}{x}y = \frac{1}{x^2}$, for which $P(x) = -\frac{1}{x}$ and $Q(x) = \frac{1}{x^2}$. Since $-\ln x$ is an antiderivative of P for $x > 0$, $S(x) = -\ln x$, so that (3) implies that $y = e^{\ln x}\int e^{-\ln x}\frac{1}{x^2}\, dx = x\int \frac{1}{x^3}\, dx = x(-\frac{1}{2x^2} + C) = -\frac{1}{2x} + Cx$.

9. $P(x) = -1$ and $Q(x) = \frac{1}{1 - e^{-x}}$. Since $-x$ is an antiderivative of P, $S(x) = -x$, so (3) implies that $y = e^x \int e^{-x} \frac{1}{1 - e^{-x}}\,dx = e^x(\ln|1 - e^{-x}| + C)$.

10. $P(x) = \cos x$ and $Q(x) = \cos x$. Since $\sin x$ is an antiderivative of P, $S(x) = \sin x$, so (3) implies that $y = e^{-\sin x} \int e^{\sin x} \cos x\,dx = e^{-\sin x}(e^{\sin x} + C) = 1 + Ce^{-\sin x}$.

11. $P(x) = \tan x$ and $Q(x) = \tan x$. Since $-\ln \cos x$ is an antiderivative of P for $-\pi/2 < x < \pi/2$ (since $\cos x > 0$ for such x), we have $S(x) = -\ln \cos x$. Then (3) implies that $y = e^{\ln \cos x} \int e^{-\ln \cos x} \tan x\,dx = \cos x \int \sec x \tan x\,dx$ $= \cos x(\sec x + C) = 1 + C \cos x$.

12. $P(x) = -\tan x$ and $Q(x) = e^{\sin x}$. Since $\ln \cos x$ is an antiderivative of P for $-\pi/2 < x < \pi/2$ (since $\cos x > 0$ for such x), we have $S(x) = \ln \cos x$. Then (3) implies that $y = e^{-\ln \cos x} \int e^{\ln \cos x} e^{\sin x}\,dx = \sec x \int (\cos x) e^{\sin x}\,dx =$ $(\sec x)(e^{\sin x} + C)$.

13. The equation is equivalent to $\frac{dy}{dt} + \frac{1}{t} y = \sin t^2$, for which $P(t) = \frac{1}{t}$ and $Q(t) = \sin t^2$. Since $\ln t$ is an antiderivative of P for $t > 0$, $S(t) = \ln t$, so (3) implies that $y = e^{-\ln t} \int e^{\ln t} \sin t^2\,dt = \frac{1}{t} \int t \sin t^2\,dt = \frac{1}{t}(-\frac{1}{2} \cos t^2 + C) =$ $-\frac{1}{2t} \cos t^2 + \frac{C}{t}$.

14. The equation is equivalent to $\frac{dy}{dt} + \frac{1}{t} y = \sin t^2 + 5$, for which $P(t) = \frac{1}{t}$ and $Q(t) = \sin t^2 + 5$. Since $\ln t$ is an antiderivative of P for $t > 0$, $S(t) = \ln t$, so (3) implies that $y = e^{-\ln t} \int e^{\ln t}(\sin t^2 + 5)\,dt = \frac{1}{t} \int t(\sin t^2 + 5)\,dt =$ $\frac{1}{t}(-\frac{1}{2} \cos t^2 + \frac{5}{2} t^2 + C) = -\frac{1}{2t} \cos t^2 + \frac{5}{2} t + \frac{C}{t}$.

15. $P(x) = 5$ and $Q(x) = -4e^{-3x}$. Since $5x$ is an antiderivative of P, $S(x) = 5x$, so (3) implies that $y = e^{-5x} \int e^{5x}(-4e^{-3x})\,dx = -4e^{-5x} \int e^{2x}\,dx = -4e^{-5x}(\frac{1}{2} e^{2x} + C)$. If $y(0) = -4$, then $-4 = -4e^{-5(0)}(\frac{1}{2} e^{2(0)} + C)$, so that $C = \frac{1}{2}$. Therefore the particular solution with $y(0) = -4$ is $y = -4e^{-5x}(\frac{1}{2} e^{2x} + \frac{1}{2}) = -2e^{-3x} - 2e^{-5x}$.

16. The equation is equivalent to $\frac{dy}{dx} - \frac{4}{x} y = 1$, so that $P(x) = -\frac{4}{x}$ and $Q(x) = 1$. Since $-4 \ln|x|$ is an antiderivative of P, $S(x) = -4 \ln|x|$, so (3) implies that $y = e^{4 \ln|x|} \int e^{-4 \ln|x|}\,dx = x^4 \int x^{-4}\,dx = x^4(-\frac{1}{3} x^{-3} + C) =$ $-\frac{1}{3} x + Cx^4$. If $y(1) = 1$, then $1 = -\frac{1}{3} + C$, so that $C = \frac{4}{3}$. Therefore the particular solution with $y(1) = 1$ is $y = -\frac{1}{3} x + \frac{4}{3} x^4$.

17. The equation is equivalent to $\frac{dy}{dx} + \frac{1}{\cos x} y = \frac{1}{\cos x}$, so that $P(x) = \frac{1}{\cos x} = \sec x = Q(x)$. Since $\ln(\sec x + \tan x)$ is an antiderivative of P for $0 < x < \frac{\pi}{2}$, $S(x) = \ln(\sec x + \tan x)$, so (3) implies that

$$y = e^{-\ln(\sec x + \tan x)} \int e^{\ln(\sec x + \tan x)} \sec x\,dx$$

$$= \frac{1}{\sec x + \tan x} \int (\sec x + \tan x) \sec x\,dx$$

$$= \frac{1}{\sec x + \tan x} \int (\sec^2 x + \tan x \sec x)\,dx$$

$$= \frac{1}{\sec x + \tan x} (\tan x + \sec x + C) = 1 + \frac{C}{\sec x + \tan x}.$$

If $y(\frac{\pi}{4}) = 2$, then $2 = 1 + \frac{C}{\sqrt{2} + 1}$, so that $C = \sqrt{2} + 1$. Therefore the particular solution with $y(\frac{\pi}{4}) = 2$ is $y = 1 + \frac{\sqrt{2} + 1}{\sec x + \tan x}$.

18. $P(x) = -2x$ and $Q(x) = x$. Since $-x^2$ is an antiderivative of P, $S(x) = -x^2$, so (3) implies that $y = e^{x^2} \int e^{-x^2} x\,dx = e^{x^2}(-\frac{1}{2} e^{-x^2} + C) = -\frac{1}{2} + Ce^{x^2}$. If $y(0) = 0$, then $0 = -\frac{1}{2} + Ce^{0^2}$, so that $C = \frac{1}{2}$. Therefore the particular solution

with $y(0) = 0$ is $y = -\frac{1}{2} + \frac{1}{2} e^{x^2}$.

19. The equation is equivalent to $\frac{dI}{dt} + \frac{R}{L} I = \frac{1}{L} e^t$, so $P(t) = \frac{R}{L}$ and $Q(t) = \frac{1}{L} e^t$. Since $\frac{R}{L} t$ is an antiderivative of P, $S(t) = \frac{R}{L} t$, so (3) implies that $I = e^{-Rt/L} \int e^{Rt/L} (\frac{1}{L} e^t) dt$

$= \frac{1}{L} e^{-Rt/L} \int e^{(R/L+1)t} dt = \frac{1}{L} e^{-Rt/L} (\frac{1}{R/L + 1} e^{(R/L+1)t} + C_1)$

$= \frac{1}{R + L} e^t + Ce^{-Rt/L}$.

20. The equation is equivalent to $\frac{dI}{dt} + \frac{R}{L} I = \frac{1}{L} \cos t$, so $P(t) = \frac{R}{L}$ and $Q(t) = \frac{1}{L} \cos t$. Since $\frac{R}{L} t$ is an antiderivative of P, $S(t) = \frac{R}{L} t$, so (3) implies that $I = \frac{1}{L} e^{-(R/L)t} \int e^{(R/L)t} \cos t \, dt$. Integrating twice by parts, we find that

$\int e^{(R/L)t} \cos t \, dt = e^{(R/L)t} \sin t - \frac{R}{L} \int e^{(R/L)t} \sin t \, dt =$

$e^{(R/L)t} \sin t + \frac{R}{L} e^{(R/L)t} \cos t - \frac{R^2}{L^2} \int e^{(R/L)t} \cos t \, dt$. Combining integrals involving $\cos t$, we obtain

$\int e^{(R/L)t} \cos t \, dt = \frac{L^2}{L^2 + R^2} (e^{(R/L)t} \sin t + \frac{R}{L} e^{(R/L)t} \cos t)$

$+ C_1 = \frac{L}{L^2 + R^2} e^{(R/L)t} (L \sin t + R \cos t) + C_1$. Therefore the general solution is

$I = \frac{1}{L} e^{-(R/L)t} [\frac{L}{L^2 + R^2} e^{(R/L)t} (L \sin t + R \cos t) + C_1]$

$= \frac{1}{L^2 + R^2} (L \sin t + R \cos t) + Ce^{-(R/L)t}$.

21. If $I(0) = \frac{R}{L^2 + R^2}$ for the solution of the differential equation in Exercise 20, then

$\frac{R}{L^2 + R^2} = \frac{1}{L^2 + R^2} (L \sin 0 + R \cos 0) + Ce^{-(R/L)0} =$

$\frac{R}{L^2 + R^2} + C$, so that $C = 0$. Therefore the particular solution is

$I = \frac{1}{L^2 + R^2} (L \sin t + R \cos t)$.

22. a. $P(t) = \frac{p}{m}$ and $Q(t) = g$. Since $\frac{p}{m} t$ is an antiderivative P, $S(t) = \frac{p}{m} t$, so (3) implies that $v =$

$e^{-pt/m} \int e^{pt/m} g \, dt = ge^{-pt/m} (\frac{m}{p} e^{pt/m} + C_1) = \frac{gm}{p} + Ce^{-pt/m}$

If $v(0) = v_0$, then $v_0 = \frac{gm}{p} + Ce^0 = \frac{gm}{p} + C$, so that $C = v_0 - \frac{gm}{p}$, and thus $v = \frac{gm}{p} + (v_0 - \frac{gm}{p}) e^{-pt/m}$.

b. $\lim_{t\to\infty} v(t) = \lim_{t\to\infty} [\frac{gm}{p} + (v_0 - \frac{gm}{p}) e^{-pt/m}] = \frac{gm}{p}$.

Section 16.5

1. The characteristic equation is $s^2 - 5s - 14 = 0$, with roots $s = 7$ and $s = -2$, so Case 1 applies. By (6) the general solution is $y = C_1e^{7x} + C_2e^{-2x}$.

2. The characteristic equation is $s^2 - 25 = 0$, with roots $s = 5$ and $s = -5$, so Case 1 applies. By (6) the general solution is $y = C_1e^{5x} + C_2e^{-5x}$.

3. The characteristic equation is $s^2 + 2s - 24 = 0$, with roots $s = -6$ and $s = 4$, so Case 1 applies. By (6) the general solution is $y = C_1e^{-6x} + C_2e^{4x}$.

4. The characteristic equation is $s^2 - 6s + 9 = 0$, with root $s = 3$, so Case 2 applies. By (8) the general solution is $y = C_1e^{3x} + C_2xe^{3x}$.

5. The characteristic equation is $s^2 + 10s + 25 = 0$, with root $s = -5$, so Case 2 applies. By (8) the general solution is $y = C_1e^{-5x} + C_2xe^{-5x}$.

6. The characteristic equation is $s^2 + 2\sqrt{2}s + 2 = 0$, with root $s = -\sqrt{2}$, so Case 2 applies. By (8) the general solution is $y = C_1e^{-\sqrt{2}x} + C_2xe^{-\sqrt{2}x}$.

7. The characteristic equation is $s^2 + 9 = 0$, so $b = 0$ and $c = 9$, and thus $b^2 - 4c = -36 < 0$. Therefore Case 3 applies. If $u = -b/2 = 0$ and $v = \frac{1}{2}\sqrt{4c - b^2} = \frac{1}{2}\sqrt{4\cdot 9} = 3$, then by (11) the general solution is $y = C_1 \sin 3x + C_2 \cos 3x$.

8. The characteristic equation is $s^2 + 2 = 0$, so $b = 0$ and $c = 2$, and thus $b^2 - 4c = -8 < 0$. Therefore Case 3 applies. If $u = -b/2 = 0$ and $v = \frac{1}{2}\sqrt{4c - b^2} = \frac{1}{2}\sqrt{4\cdot 2} = \sqrt{2}$, then by (11) the general solution is $y = C_1 \sin\sqrt{2}\,x + C_2 \cos\sqrt{2}\,x$.

9. The characteristic equation is $s^2 + 3s + 3 = 0$, so $b = 3 = c$, and thus $b^2 - 4c = 3^2 - 4 \cdot 3 = -3 < 0$. Therefore Case 3 applies. If $u = -b/2 = -3/2$ and $v = \frac{1}{2}\sqrt{4c - b^2} = \frac{1}{2}\sqrt{4\cdot 3 - 3^2} = \frac{1}{2}\sqrt{3}$, then by (11) the general solution is $y = C_1e^{-3x/2} \sin \frac{1}{2}\sqrt{3}\,x + C_2e^{-3x/2} \cos \frac{1}{2}\sqrt{3}\,x$.

10. The characteristic equation is $s^2 + 2s + 5 = 0$, so $b = 2$ and $c = 5$, and thus $b^2 - 4c = 2^2 - 4\cdot 5 = -16 < 0$. Therefore Case 3 applies. If $u = -b/2 = -1$ and $v = \frac{1}{2}\sqrt{4c - b^2} = \frac{1}{2}\sqrt{4\cdot 5 - 2^2} = 2$, then by (11) the general solution is $y = C_1e^{-t} \sin 2t + C_2e^{-t} \cos 2t$.

11. Dividing by 6, we obtain $\frac{d^2y}{dt^2} - \frac{4}{6}y = 0$, or $\frac{d^2y}{dt^2} - \frac{2}{3}y = 0$, whose characteristic equation is $s^2 - \frac{2}{3} = 0$. Its roots are $s = \sqrt{2/3}$ and $s = -\sqrt{2/3}$, so Case 1 applies. By (6) the general solution is $y = C_1e^{\sqrt{2/3}\,t} + C_2e^{-\sqrt{2/3}\,t}$.

12. Dividing by 2, we obtain $\frac{d^2y}{dt^2} + \frac{5}{2}\frac{dy}{dt} + y = 0$, whose characteristic equation is $s^2 + \frac{5}{2}s + 1 = 0$. By the quadratic formula,

$$s = \frac{-\frac{5}{2} \pm \sqrt{\frac{25}{4} - 4}}{2} = \frac{-\frac{5}{2} \pm \sqrt{\frac{9}{4}}}{2} = \frac{-5 \pm 3}{4},$$

so the roots are $s = -2$ and $s = -\frac{1}{2}$, and thus Case 1 applies. By (6) the general solution is $y = C_1e^{-2t} + C_2e^{-t/2}$.

13. Dividing by 4, we obtain $\frac{d^2y}{dx^2} + 3\frac{dy}{dx} + \frac{9}{4}y = 0$, whose characteristic equation is $s^2 + 3s + \frac{9}{4} = 0$, or $4s^2 + 12s + 9 = 0$, or $(2s + 3)^2 = 0$. The root is $s = -\frac{3}{2}$, and thus Case 2 applies. By (8) the general solution is $y = C_1e^{-3x/2} + C_2xe^{-3x/2}$.

14. Dividing by 2, we obtain $\frac{d^2y}{dx^2} + 2\frac{dy}{dx} + \frac{5}{2}y = 0$, whose characteristic equation is $s^2 + 2s + \frac{5}{2} = 0$, so $b = 2$ and $c = \frac{5}{2}$, and thus $b^2 - 4c = 2^2 - 4\cdot\frac{5}{2} = -6$. Therefore Case 3 applies.

If $u = -b/2 = -1$ and $v = \frac{1}{2}\sqrt{4c - b^2} = \frac{1}{2}\sqrt{4(\frac{5}{2}) - 2^2} = \frac{1}{2}\sqrt{6}$, then by (11) the general solution is $y = C_1 e^{-x} \sin \frac{1}{2}\sqrt{6}\,x + C_2 e^{-x} \cos \frac{1}{2}\sqrt{6}\,x$.

15. The characteristic equation is $s^2 - 2s - 15 = 0$, with roots $s = 5$ and $s = -3$, so Case 1 applies. By (6) the general solution is $y = C_1 e^{5x} + C_2 e^{-3x}$. If $y(0) = 1$ and $y'(0) = -1$, then $1 = y(0) = C_1 + C_2$. Since $\frac{dy}{dx} = 5C_1 e^{5x} - 3C_2 e^{-3x}$, we have $-1 = y'(0) = 5C_1 - 3C_2$. Therefore $C_1 = 1 - C_2$, so $-1 = 5(1 - C_2) - 3C_2 = 5 - 8C_2$, and thus $C_2 = \frac{3}{4}$, so that $C_1 = 1 - \frac{3}{4} = \frac{1}{4}$. Consequently the particular solution is $y = \frac{1}{4}e^{5x} + \frac{3}{4}e^{-3x}$.

16. The characteristic equation is $s^2 + 16 = 0$, so $b = 0$ and $c = 16$, and $b^2 - 4c = -64 < 0$. Therefore Case 3 applies. If $u = -b/2 = 0$ and $v = \frac{1}{2}\sqrt{4c - b^2} = \frac{1}{2}\sqrt{4\cdot 16 - 0} = 4$, then by (11) the general solution is $y = C_1 \sin 4x + C_2 \cos 4x$. If $y(0) = 3$ and $y'(0) = 12$, then $3 = y(0) = C_2$. Since $\frac{dy}{dx} = 4C_1 \cos 4x - 4C_2 \sin 4x$, we have $12 = y'(0) = 4C_1$. Therefore $C_1 = 3$. Consequently the particular solution is $y = 3 \sin 4x + 3 \cos 4x$.

17. The characteristic equation is $s^2 - 10s + 25 = 0$, with root $s = 5$, so Case 2 applies. By (8) the general solution is $y = C_1 e^{5x} + C_2 x e^{5x}$. If $y(1) = 0$ and $y'(1) = e^5$, then $0 = y(1) = C_1 e^5 + C_2 e^5$, so $C_1 + C_2 = 0$. Since $\frac{dy}{dx} = 5C_1 e^{5x} + C_2 e^{5x} + 5C_2 x e^{5x}$, we have $e^5 = y'(1) = 5C_1 e^5 + C_2 e^5 + 5C_2 e^5$, so $1 = 5C_1 + 6C_2$. Therefore $C_1 = -C_2$, so $1 = 5(-C_2) + 6C_2 = C_2$, and thus $C_1 = -1$. Consequently the particular solution is $y = -e^{5x} + xe^{5x}$.

18. Dividing by 4, we obtain $\frac{d^2y}{dx^2} - \frac{dy}{dx} + \frac{1}{4}y = 0$, whose characteristic equation is $s^2 - s + \frac{1}{4} = 0$, or $(s - \frac{1}{2})^2 = 0$. Its root is $s = \frac{1}{2}$, so Case 2 applies. By (8) the general solution is $y = C_1 e^{x/2} + C_2 x e^{x/2}$. If $y(0) = 0$ and $y'(0) = 1$, then $0 = y(0) = C_1$. Since $\frac{dy}{dx} = \frac{1}{2}C_1 e^{x/2} + C_2 e^{x/2} + \frac{1}{2}C_2 x e^{x/2}$, we have $1 = y'(0) = \frac{1}{2}C_1 + C_2$. Therefore $1 = \frac{1}{2}\cdot 0 + C_2 = C_2$. Consequently the particular solution is $y = xe^{x/2}$.

19. Dividing by 3, we obtain $\frac{d^2y}{dx^2} + \frac{8}{3}\frac{dy}{dx} - y = 0$, whose characteristic equation is $s^2 + \frac{8}{3}s - 1 = 0$, or $3s^2 + 8s - 3 = 0$. By the quadratic formula, $s = \frac{-8 \pm \sqrt{64 + 36}}{6} = \frac{-8 \pm 10}{6}$, so the roots are $s = -3$ and $s = \frac{1}{3}$, and thus Case 1 applies. By (6) the general solution is $y = C_1 e^{-3x} + C_2 e^{x/3}$. If $y(0) = 2$ and $y'(0) = -2$, then $2 = y(0) = C_1 + C_2$. Since $\frac{dy}{dx} = -3C_1 e^{-3x} + \frac{1}{3}C_2 e^{x/3}$, we have $-2 = y'(0) = -3C_1 + \frac{1}{3}C_2$. Therefore $C_1 = 2 - C_2$, so that $-2 = -3(2 - C_2) + \frac{1}{3}C_2 = -6 + \frac{10}{3}C_2$, and thus $C_2 = \frac{6}{5}$, and $C_1 = 2 - C_2 = 2 - \frac{6}{5} = \frac{4}{5}$. Consequently the particular solution is $y = \frac{4}{5}e^{-3x} + \frac{6}{5}e^{x/3}$.

20. The characteristic equation is $s^2 + 4s + 5 = 0$, so $b = 4$ and $c = 5$, and thus $b^2 - 4c = -4 < 0$. Therefore Case 3 applies. If $u = -b/2 = -2$ and $v = \frac{1}{2}\sqrt{4c - b^2} = \frac{1}{2}\sqrt{4\cdot 5 - 4^2} = 1$, then by (11) the general solution is $y = C_1 e^{-2x} \sin x + C_2 e^{-2x} \cos x$. If $y(0) = 1$ and $y'(0) = 0$, then $1 = C_2$, so $y = C_1 e^{-2x} \sin x + e^{-2x} \cos x = e^{-2x}(C_1 \sin x + \cos x)$. Since $\frac{dy}{dx} = -2e^{-2x}(C_1 \sin x + \cos x) + e^{-2x}(C_1 \cos x - \sin x)$, we have $0 = y'(0) = -2 + C_1$, so that $C_1 = 2$. Consequently the particular solution is $y = 2e^{-2x} \sin x + e^{-2x} \cos x$.

21. If $y = C_1 y_1 + C_2 y_2$ with y_1 and y_2 solutions, then

$\frac{d^2y}{dx^2} + b\frac{dy}{dx} + cy = (C_1\frac{d^2y_1}{dx^2} + C_2\frac{d^2y_2}{dx^2}) + b(C_1\frac{dy_1}{dx} + C_2\frac{dy_2}{dx}) +$ $c(C_1y_1 + C_2y_2) = C_1(\frac{d^2y_1}{dx^2} + b\frac{dy_1}{dx} + cy_1) + C_2(\frac{d^2y_2}{dx^2} + b\frac{dy_2}{dx} +$ $cy_2) = 0 + 0 = 0$. Thus $C_1y_1 + C_2y_2$ is also a solution.

22. By the hypotheses and (12) we have $0.05\frac{d^2q}{dt^2} + 15\frac{dq}{dt} + \frac{1}{0.001}q = 0$, or equivalently, $\frac{d^2q}{dt^2} + 300\frac{dq}{dt} + 20{,}000\,q = 0$. The characteristic equation is $s^2 + 300s + 20{,}000 = 0$, with roots $s = -100$ and $s = -200$, so Case 1 applies. By (6), the general solution is $q = C_1e^{-100t} + C_2e^{-200t}$. By hypothesis, $q(0) = 5$ and $q'(0) = -200$. It follows that $5 = q(0) = C_1 + C_2$. Since $\frac{dq}{dt} = -100C_1e^{-100t} - 200C_2e^{-200t}$, we have $-200 = q'(0) = -100C_1 - 200C_2$. Thus $C_1 = 5 - C_2$, so that $-200 = -100(5 - C_2) - 200C_2 = -500 - 100C_2$. Therefore $C_2 = -3$, so that $C_1 = 5 - (-3) = 8$. Consequently the charge is given by $q = 8e^{-100t} - 3e^{-200t}$ for $t \geq 0$.

23. By the hypotheses and (12) we have $0.01\frac{d^2q}{dt^2} + 2\frac{dq}{dt} + \frac{1}{0.005}q = 0$, or equivalently, $\frac{d^2q}{dt^2} + 200\frac{dq}{dt} + 20{,}000\,q = 0$. The characteristic equation is $s^2 + 200s + 20{,}000 = 0$, so $b = 200$ and $c = 20{,}000$, and $b^2 - 4c = (200)^2 - 80{,}000 < 0$. Therefore Case 3 applies. If $u = -b/2 = -100$ and $v = \frac{1}{2}\sqrt{4c - b^2} = \frac{1}{2}\sqrt{4(20{,}000) - (200)^2} = 100$, then by (11) the general solution is $q = C_1e^{-100t}\sin 100t + C_2e^{-100t}\cos 100t$. By hypothesis, $q(0) = 1$ and $q'(1) = 100$. It follows that $1 = q(0) = C_2$, so $q = e^{-100t}(C_1 \sin 100t + \cos 100t)$. Since $\frac{dq}{dt} = -100e^{-100t}(C_1\sin 100t + \cos 100t) + e^{-100t}(100C_1\cos 100t - 100\sin 100t)$, we have $100 = q'(0) = -100 + 100C_1$, so that $C_1 = 2$. Consequently the charge is given by $q = 2e^{-100t}\sin 100t + e^{-100t}\cos 100t$ for $t \geq 0$.

Section 16.6

1. The homogeneous equation is $\frac{d^2y}{dx^2} + 5\frac{dy}{dx} + 4y = 0$, with characteristic equation $s^2 + 5s + 4 = 0$, whose roots are $s = -1$ and $s = -4$. Thus $y_1 = e^{-x}$ and $y_2 = e^{-4x}$. Next $g(x) = 3$, so by (9) and (10),

$$u_1'(x) = \frac{-e^{-4x}(3)}{e^{-x}(-4e^{-4x}) - (-e^{-x})(e^{-4x})} = e^x$$

$$u_2'(x) = \frac{e^{-x}(3)}{e^{-x}(-4e^{-4x}) - (-e^{-x})(e^{-4x})} = -e^{4x}$$

Therefore $u_1(x) = e^x$ and $u_2(x) = -\frac{1}{4}e^{4x}$, so that by (5), $y_p = e^xe^{-x} + (-\frac{1}{4}e^{4x})e^{-4x} = 1 - \frac{1}{4} = \frac{3}{4}$. By (4), the general solution is $y = \frac{3}{4} + C_1e^{-x} + C_2e^{-4x}$.

2. The homogeneous equation is $\frac{d^2y}{dx^2} - 4y = 0$, with characteristic equation $s^2 - 4 = 0$, whose roots are $s = 2$ and $s = -2$. Thus $y_1 = e^{2x}$ and $y_2 = e^{-2x}$. Next, $g(x) = e^{3x}$, so by (9) and (10),

$$u_1'(x) = \frac{-e^{-2x}e^{3x}}{e^{2x}(-2e^{-2x}) - 2e^{2x}e^{-2x}} = \frac{1}{4}e^x$$

$$u_2'(x) = \frac{e^{2x}e^{3x}}{e^{2x}(-2e^{-2x}) - 2e^{2x}e^{-2x}} = -\frac{1}{4}e^{5x}$$

Therefore $u_1(x) = \frac{1}{4}e^x$ and $u_2(x) = -\frac{1}{20}e^{5x}$, so that by (5), $y_p = \frac{1}{4}e^xe^{2x} - \frac{1}{20}e^{5x}e^{-2x} = \frac{1}{5}e^{3x}$. By (4), the general solution is $y = \frac{1}{5}e^{3x} + C_1e^{2x} + C_2e^{-2x}$.

3. The homogeneous equation is $\frac{d^2y}{dx^2} - 2\frac{dy}{dx} - 3y = 0$, with characteristic equation $s^2 - 2s - 3 = 0$, whose roots are $s = 3$ and $s = -1$. Thus $y_1 = e^{3x}$ and $y_2 = e^{-x}$. Next, $g(x) = e^x$, so by (9) and (10),

$$u_1'(x) = \frac{-e^{-x}e^{x}}{e^{3x}(-e^{-x}) - 3e^{3x}e^{-x}} = \frac{1}{4}e^{-2x}$$

$$u_2'(x) = \frac{e^{3x}e^{x}}{e^{3x}(-e^{-x}) - 3e^{3x}e^{-x}} = -\frac{1}{4}e^{2x}$$

Therefore $u_1(x) = -\frac{1}{8}e^{-2x}$ and $u_2(x) = -\frac{1}{8}e^{2x}$, so that by (5), $y_p(x) = -\frac{1}{8}e^{-2x}e^{3x} - \frac{1}{8}e^{2x}e^{-x} = -\frac{1}{4}e^{x}$. By (4), the general solution is $y = -\frac{1}{4}e^{x} + C_1e^{3x} + C_2e^{-x}$.

4. The homogeneous equation is $\frac{d^2y}{dx^2} + 8\frac{dy}{dx} + 15y = 0$, with characteristic equation $s^2 + 8s + 15 = 0$, whose roots are $s = -5$ and $s = -3$. Thus $y_1 = e^{-5x}$ and $y_2 = e^{-3x}$. Next, $g(x) = e^{-x}$, so by (9) and (10),

$$u_1'(x) = \frac{-e^{-3x}e^{-x}}{e^{-5x}(-3e^{-3x}) + 5e^{-5x}e^{-3x}} = -\frac{1}{2}e^{4x}$$

$$u_2'(x) = \frac{e^{-5x}e^{-x}}{e^{-5x}(-3e^{-3x}) + 5e^{-5x}e^{-3x}} = \frac{1}{2}e^{2x}$$

Therefore $u_1(x) = -\frac{1}{8}e^{4x}$ and $u_2(x) = \frac{1}{4}e^{2x}$, so that by (5), $y_p = -\frac{1}{8}e^{4x}e^{-5x} + \frac{1}{4}e^{2x}e^{-3x} = \frac{1}{8}e^{-x}$. By (4), the general solution is $y = \frac{1}{8}e^{-x} + C_1e^{-5x} + C_2e^{-3x}$.

5. The homogeneous equation is $\frac{d^2y}{dx^2} - \frac{dy}{dx} = 0$, with characteristic equation $s^2 - s = 0$, whose roots are $s = 0$ and $s = 1$. Thus $y_1 = 1$ and $y_2 = e^x$. Next, $g(x) = 2x - 3$, so by (9) and (10),

$$u'(x) = \frac{-e^{x}(2x-3)}{1\cdot e^{x} - 0\cdot e^{x}} = -2x + 3$$

$$u_2'(x) = \frac{1(2x-3)}{1\cdot e^{x} - 0\cdot e^{x}} = (2x-3)e^{-x}$$

Therefore $u_1(x) = -x^2 + 3x$, and since $\int(2x-3)e^{-x}dx = 2\int xe^{-x}dx - 3\int e^{-x}dx \overset{\text{parts}}{=} 2(-xe^{-x} + \int e^{-x}dx) + 3e^{-x} = -2xe^{-x} - e^{-x} + 3e^{-x} + C = -2xe^{-x} + 2e^{-x} + C$, we have $u_2(x) = -2xe^{-x} + 2e^{-x}$. By (5), $y_p = (-x^2 + 3x)1 + (-2xe^{-x} + 2e^{-x})e^{x} = -x^2 + 3x - 2x + 2 = -x^2 + x + 2$. By (4), the general solution is $y = -x^2 + x + 2 + C_1 + C_2e^{x}$.

6. The homogeneous equation is $\frac{d^2y}{dx^2} + 4\frac{dy}{dx} + 4y = 0$, with characteristic equation $s^2 + 4s + 4 = 0$, whose root is $s = -2$. Thus $y_1 = e^{-2x}$ and $y_2 = xe^{-2x}$. Next, $g(x) = e^{-x}$, so by (9) and (10),

$$u_1'(x) = \frac{-xe^{-2x}e^{-x}}{e^{-2x}(e^{-2x} - 2xe^{-2x}) - (-2e^{-2x})xe^{-2x}} = -xe^{x}$$

$$u_2'(x) = \frac{e^{-2x}e^{-x}}{e^{-2x}(e^{-2x} - 2xe^{-2x}) - (-2e^{-2x})xe^{-2x}} = e^{x}$$

Since $\int -xe^{x}dx \overset{\text{parts}}{=} -xe^{x} + \int e^{x}dx = -xe^{x} + e^{x} + C$, we take $u_1(x) = -xe^{x} + e^{x}$; also $u_2(x) = e^{x}$. By (5), $y_p = (-xe^{x} + e^{x})e^{-2x} + e^{x}(xe^{-2x}) = e^{-x}$. By (4), the general solution is $y = e^{-x} + C_1e^{-2x} + C_2xe^{-2x}$.

7. The homogeneous equation is $\frac{d^2y}{dx^2} + y = 0$, with characteristic equation $s^2 + 1 = 0$. This falls under Case 3, with $b = 0$ and $c = 1$. Since $u = -\frac{b}{2} = 0$ and $v = \frac{1}{2}\sqrt{4c - b^2} = \frac{1}{2}\sqrt{4\cdot 1 - 0^2} = 1$, it follows that the general solution of the homogeneous equation is $y = C_1 \sin x + C_2 \cos x$. Thus $y_1 = \sin x$ and $y_2 = \cos x$. Next, $g(x) = \csc x \cot x$, so by (9) and (10),

$$u_1'(x) = \frac{-\cos x \csc x \cot x}{\sin x(-\sin x) - \cos x \cos x} = \cot^2 x = \csc^2 x - 1$$

$$u_2'(x) = \frac{\sin x \csc x \cot x}{\sin x(-\sin x) - \cos x \cos x} = -\cot x$$

Therefore $u_1(x) = -\cot x - x$ and $u_2 = -\ln \sin x$, so that by (5), $y_p = (-\cot x - x)\sin x - (\ln \sin x)\cos x = -\cos x - x\sin x - \cos x \ln \sin x$. By (4) the general solution is

$y = -\cos x - x \sin x - \cos x \ln \sin x + C_1 \sin x + C_2' \cos x =$
$-x \sin x - \cos x \ln \sin x + C_1 \sin x + C_2 \cos x.$

8. The homogeneous equation is $\frac{d^2y}{dx^2} + y = 0$, so as in the solution of Exercise 7 we obtain $y_1 = \sin x$ and $y_2 = \cos x$. Next, $g(x) = \cos x$, so by (9) and (10),

$$u_1'(x) = \frac{-\cos x \cos x}{\sin x(-\sin x) - \cos x \cos x} = \cos^2 x = \frac{1}{2} + \frac{1}{2}\cos 2x$$

$$u_2'(x) = \frac{\sin x \cos x}{\sin x(-\sin x) - \cos x \cos x} = -\sin x \cos x = -\frac{1}{2}\sin 2x$$

Thus $u_1(x) = \frac{1}{2}x + \frac{1}{4}\sin 2x$ and $u_2(x) = \frac{1}{4}\cos 2x$, so that by (5), $y_p = (\frac{1}{2}x + \frac{1}{4}\sin 2x)\sin x + (\frac{1}{4}\cos 2x)(\cos x)$. By (4), the general solution is $y = (\frac{1}{2}x + \frac{1}{4}\sin 2x)\sin x + \frac{1}{4}\cos 2x \cos x + C_1 \sin x + C_2 \cos x$.

9. The homogeneous equation is $\frac{d^2y}{dt^2} + 9y = 0$, with characteristic equation $s^2 + 9 = 0$. This falls under Case 3, with $b = 0$ and $c = 9$. Since $u = -b/2 = 0$ and $v = \frac{1}{2}\sqrt{4c - b^2} = \frac{1}{2}\sqrt{4 \cdot 9 - 0^2} = 3$, it follows that the general solution of the homogeneous equation is $y = C_1 \sin 3t + C_2 \cos 3t$. Thus $y_1 = \sin 3t$ and $y_2 = \cos 3t$. Next $g(t) = 3t$, so by (9) and (10),

$$u_1'(t) = \frac{-(\cos 3t)(3t)}{\sin 3t(-3\sin 3t) - 3\cos 3t \cos 3t} = t \cos 3t$$

$$u_2'(t) = \frac{(\sin 3t)(3t)}{\sin 3t(-3\sin 3t) - 3\cos 3t \cos 3t} = -t \sin 3t$$

By integration by parts we have $\int t \cos 3t\, dt = \frac{1}{3}t \sin 3t - \int \frac{1}{3}\sin 3t\, dt = \frac{1}{3}t \sin 3t + \frac{1}{9}\cos 3t + C'$ and $\int -t \sin 3t\, dt = \frac{1}{3}t \cos 3t - \int \frac{1}{3}\cos 3t\, dt = \frac{1}{3}t\cos 3t - \frac{1}{9}\sin 3t + C''$. Thus we take $u_1(t) = \frac{1}{3}t \sin 3t + \frac{1}{9}\cos 3t$ and $u_2(t) = \frac{1}{3}t \cos 3t - \frac{1}{9}\sin 3t$, so that by (5), $y_p = (\frac{1}{3}t \sin 3t + \frac{1}{9}\cos 3t)\sin 3t + (\frac{1}{3}t\cos 3t - \frac{1}{9}\sin 3t)\cos 3t = \frac{1}{3}t \sin^2 3t + \frac{1}{3}t\cos^2 3t = \frac{1}{3}t$. By (4), the general solution is $y = \frac{1}{3}t + C_1 \sin 3t + C_2 \cos 3t$.

10. The homogeneous equation is $\frac{d^2y}{dt^2} - 9y = 0$, with characteristic equation $s^2 - 9 = 0$, whose roots are $s = 3$ and $s = -3$. Thus $y_1 = e^{3t}$ and $y_2 = e^{-3t}$. Next, $g(t) = \sin t$, so by (9) and (10),

$$u_1'(t) = \frac{-e^{-3t}\sin t}{e^{3t}(-3e^{-3t}) - 3e^{3t}e^{-3t}} = \frac{1}{6}e^{-3t}\sin t$$

$$u_2'(t) = \frac{e^{3t}\sin t}{e^{3t}(-3e^{-3t}) - 3e^{3t}e^{-3t}} = -\frac{1}{6}e^{3t}\sin t$$

Since $\int e^{at}\sin bt\, dt = \frac{e^{at}}{a^2 + b^2}(a \sin bt - b\cos bt) + C$ by Exercise 52(a) in Section 7.1 (with t replacing x), we take $u_1(t) = \frac{1}{6}\frac{e^{-3t}}{10}(-3\sin t - \cos t)$ and $u_2(t) = -\frac{1}{6}\frac{e^{3t}}{10}(3\sin t - \cos t)$. By (5), $y_p = \frac{e^{-3t}}{60}(-3\sin t - \cos t)e^{3t} - \frac{e^{3t}}{60}(3\sin t - \cos t)e^{-3t} = \frac{1}{60}(-3\sin t - \cos t - 3\sin t + \cos t) = -\frac{1}{10}\sin t$. By (4), the general solution is $y = -\frac{1}{10}\sin t + C_1 e^{3t} + C_2 e^{-3t}$.

11. The homogeneous equation is $\frac{d^2y}{dt^2} + 9y = 0$, with characteristic equation $s^2 + 9 = 0$. This falls under Case 3, with $b = 0$ and $c = 9$. Since $u = -b/2 = 0$ and $v = \frac{1}{2}\sqrt{4c - b^2} = \frac{1}{2}\sqrt{4 \cdot 9 - 0^2} = 3$, it follows that the general solution of the homogeneous equation is $y = C_1 \sin 3t + C_2 \cos 3t$. Thus $y_1 = \sin 3t$ and $y_2 = \cos 3t$. Next, $g(t) = \sin 3t$, so by (9) and (10),

$$u_1'(t) = \frac{-\cos 3t \sin 3t}{\sin 3t(-3\sin 3t) - (3\cos 3t)(\cos 3t)} = \frac{1}{3}\sin 3t \cos 3t = \frac{1}{6}\sin 6t$$

$$u_2'(t) = \frac{\sin 3t \sin 3t}{\sin 3t(-3\sin 3t) - (3\cos 3t)(\cos 3t)} = -\frac{1}{3}\sin^2 3t = -\frac{1}{3}(\frac{1}{2} - \frac{1}{2}\cos 6t)$$

Thus $u_1(t) = -\frac{1}{36}\cos 6t$ and $u_2(t) = -\frac{1}{6}t + \frac{1}{36}\sin 6t$, so that by (5), $y_p = (-\frac{1}{36}\cos 6t)\sin 3t + (-\frac{1}{6}t + \frac{1}{36}\sin 6t)\cos 3t = -\frac{1}{6}t\cos 3t + \frac{1}{36}\sin 3t$. By (4), the general solution is

$$y = -\frac{1}{6} t \cos 3t + \frac{1}{36} \sin 3t + C_1' \sin 3t + C_2 \cos 3t =$$
$$-\frac{1}{6} t \cos 3t + C_1 \sin 3t + C_2 \cos 3t.$$

12. The homogeneous equation is $\frac{d^2y}{dx^2} - y = 0$, with characteristic equation $s^2 - 1 = 0$, whose roots are $s = 1$ and $s = -1$. Thus $y_1 = e^x$ and $y_2 = e^{-x}$. Next, $g(x) = xe^x$, so by (9) and (10),

$$u_1'(x) = \frac{(-e^{-x})(xe^x)}{e^x(-e^{-x}) - e^x(e^{-x})} = \frac{1}{2} x$$

$$u_2'(x) = \frac{e^x(xe^x)}{e^x(-e^{-x}) - e^x(e^{-x})} = -\frac{1}{2} xe^{2x}$$

Thus $u_1(x) = \frac{1}{4} x^2$, and since $\int -\frac{1}{2} xe^{2x} dx \overset{\text{parts}}{=} -\frac{1}{4} xe^{2x} + \int \frac{1}{4} e^{2x} dx = -\frac{1}{4} xe^{2x} + \frac{1}{8} e^{2x} + C$, it follows that $u_2(x) = -\frac{1}{4} xe^{2x} + \frac{1}{8} e^{2x}$. By (5), $y_p = \frac{1}{4} x^2 e^x + (-\frac{1}{4} xe^{2x} + \frac{1}{8} e^{2x})e^{-x} = \frac{1}{4} x^2 e^x - \frac{1}{4} xe^x + \frac{1}{8} e^x$. By (4), the general solution is $y = \frac{1}{4} x^2 e^x - \frac{1}{4} xe^x + \frac{1}{8} e^x + C_1 e^x + C_2 e^{-x}$.

13. The homogeneous equation is $\frac{d^2y}{dx^2} - 2\frac{dy}{dx} + y = 0$, with characteristic equation $s^2 - 2s + 1 = 0$, whose root is $s = 1$. Thus $y_1 = e^x$ and $y_2 = xe^x$. Next, $g(x) = \frac{1}{x} e^x$, so by (9) and (10),

$$u_1'(x) = \frac{-(xe^x)(\frac{1}{x} e^x)}{(e^x)(e^x + xe^x) - (e^x)(xe^x)} = \frac{-e^{2x}}{e^{2x}} = -1$$

$$u_2'(x) = \frac{(e^x)(\frac{1}{x} e^x)}{(e^x)(e^x + xe^x) - (e^x)(xe^x)} = \frac{\frac{1}{x} e^{2x}}{e^{2x}} = \frac{1}{x}$$

Therefore $u_1(x) = -x$ and $u_2(x) = \ln|x|$, so that by (5), $y_p = (-x)(e^x) + (\ln|x|)(xe^x) = -xe^x + xe^x \ln|x|$. By (4), the general solution is $y = -xe^x + xe^x \ln|x| + C_1 e^x + C_2' xe^x = xe^x \ln|x| + C_1 e^x + C_2 xe^x$.

14. The homogeneous equation is $\frac{d^2y}{dx^2} + 6\frac{dy}{dx} + 9y = 0$, with characteristic equation $s^2 + 6s + 9 = 0$, whose root is $s = -3$. Thus $y_1 = e^{-3x}$ and $y_2 = xe^{-3x}$. Next, $g(x) = e^{-4x}$, so by (9) and (10),

$$u_1'(x) = \frac{-xe^{-3x}e^{-4x}}{e^{-3x}(e^{-3x} - 3xe^{-3x}) - (-3e^{-3x})xe^{-3x}} = -xe^{-x}$$

$$u_2'(x) = \frac{e^{-3x}e^{-4x}}{e^{-3x}(e^{-3x} - 3xe^{-3x}) - (-3e^{-3x})xe^{-3x}} = e^{-x}$$

Since $\int -xe^{-x} dx \overset{\text{parts}}{=} xe^{-x} - \int e^{-x} dx = xe^{-x} + e^{-x} + C$, we take $u_1(x) = xe^{-x} + e^{-x}$. Also, $u_2(x) = -e^{-x}$. By (5), $y_p = (xe^{-x} + e^{-x})e^{-3x} + (-e^{-x})(xe^{-3x}) = e^{-4x}$. By (4), the general solution is $y = e^{-4x} + C_1 e^{-3x} + C_2 xe^{-3x}$.

15. The homogeneous equation is $\frac{d^2y}{dx^2} - 5\frac{dy}{dx} + 6y = 0$, with characteristic equation $s^2 - 5s + 6 = 0$, whose roots are $s = 2$ and $s = 3$. Therefore $y_1 = e^{2x}$ and $y_2 = e^{3x}$. Next, $g(x) = x^3 e^{2x}$, so by (9) and (10),

$$u_1'(x) = \frac{-e^{3x}(x^3 e^{2x})}{e^{2x}(3e^{3x}) - (2e^{2x})e^{3x}} = \frac{-x^3 e^{5x}}{e^{5x}} = -x^3$$

$$u_2'(x) = \frac{e^{2x}(x^3 e^{2x})}{e^{2x}(3e^{3x}) - (2e^{2x})e^{3x}} = \frac{x^3 e^{4x}}{e^{5x}} = x^3 e^{-x}$$

Thus $u_1(x) = -\frac{1}{4} x^4$. By successive integrations by parts, we obtain $\int x^3 e^{-x} dx = -x^3 e^{-x} + \int 3x^2 e^{-x} dx = -x^3 e^{-x} - 3x^2 e^{-x} + \int 6xe^{-x} dx = -x^3 e^{-x} - 3x^2 e^{-x} - 6xe^{-x} + \int 6e^{-x} dx = -x^3 e^{-x} - 3x^2 e^{-x} - 6xe^{-x} - 6e^{-x} + C$, so it follows that $u_2(x) = -(x^3 + 3x^2 + 6x + 6)e^{-x}$. Therefore by (5), $y_p = -\frac{1}{4} x^4 e^{2x} - (x^3 + 3x^2 + 6x + 6)e^{-x}(e^{3x}) = -\frac{1}{4} x^4 e^{2x} - (x^3 + 3x^2 + 6x + 6)e^{2x}$. By (4) the general solution is $y = -(\frac{1}{4}x^4 + x^3 + 3x^2 + 6x + 6)e^{2x} + C_1' e^{2x} + C_2 e^{3x} = -(\frac{1}{4}x^4 + x^3 + 3x^2 + 6x)e^{2x} + C_1 e^{2x} + C_2 e^{3x}$.

16. The homogeneous equation is $\frac{d^2y}{dx^2} + 5\frac{dy}{dx} - 6y = 0$, with characteristic equation $s^2 + 5s - 6 = 0$, whose roots are $s = -6$ and $s = 1$. Thus $y_1 = e^{-6x}$ and $y_2 = e^x$. Next, $g(x) = 7e^x$, so by (9) and (10),

$$u_1'(x) = \frac{-e^x(7e^x)}{e^{-6x}(e^x) - (-6e^{-6x})e^x} = -e^{7x}$$

$$u_2'(x) = \frac{e^{-6x}(7e^x)}{e^{-6x}(e^x) - (-6e^{-6x})e^x} = 1$$

Therefore $u_1(x) = -\frac{1}{7}e^{7x}$ and $u_2(x) = x$, so that by (5), $y_p(x) = -\frac{1}{7}e^{7x}e^{-6x} + xe^x = -\frac{1}{7}e^x + xe^x$. By (4) the general solution is given by $y = -\frac{1}{7}e^x + xe^x + C_1e^{-6x} + C_2'e^x = xe^x + C_1e^{-6x} + C_2e^x$.

17. We have $(0.04)\frac{d^2q}{dt^2} + 5\frac{dq}{dt} + \frac{1}{0.01}q = E(t)$, so that $\frac{d^2q}{dt^2} + 125\frac{dq}{dt} + 2500q = E(t)$. The characteristic equation is $s^2 + 125s + 2500 = 0$, so $(s + 100)(s + 25) = 0$. Thus $q_1 = e^{-100t}$ and $q_2 = e^{-25t}$.

a. Here $g(t) = E(t) = e^{-50t}$, so that by (9) and (10),

$$u_1'(t) = \frac{(-e^{-25t})(e^{-50t})}{(e^{-100t})(-25e^{-25t}) - (-100e^{-100t})(e^{-25t})} = \frac{-e^{-75t}}{75e^{-125t}} = -\frac{1}{75}e^{50t}$$

$$u_2'(t) = \frac{(e^{-100t})(e^{-50t})}{(e^{-100t})(-25e^{-25t}) - (-100e^{-100t})(e^{-25t})} = \frac{e^{-150t}}{75e^{-125t}} = \frac{1}{75}e^{-25t}$$

Thus $u_1(t) = -\frac{1}{3750}e^{50t}$ and $u_2(t) = -\frac{1}{1875}e^{-25t}$, so by (5), $q_p = (-\frac{1}{3750}e^{50t})(e^{-100t}) + (-\frac{1}{1875}e^{-25t})(e^{-25t}) = -\frac{1}{1250}e^{-50t}$. By (4), the general solution is $q = -\frac{1}{1250}e^{-50t} + C_1e^{-100t} + C_2e^{-25t}$ for $t \geq 0$.

b. Here $g(t) = E(t) = \sin 50t$, so that by (9) and (10),

$$u_1'(t) = \frac{(-e^{-25t})\sin 50t}{(e^{-100t})(-25e^{-25t}) - (-100e^{-100t})(e^{-25t})} = \frac{-e^{-25t}\sin 50t}{75e^{-125t}} = -\frac{1}{75}e^{100t}\sin 50t$$

$$u_2'(t) = \frac{(e^{-100t})\sin 50t}{(e^{-100t})(-25e^{-25t}) - (-100e^{-100t})(e^{-25t})} = \frac{e^{-100t}\sin 50t}{75e^{-125t}} = \frac{1}{75}e^{25t}\sin 50t$$

By Exercise 52 (a) in Section 7.1,

$u_1(t) = -\frac{1}{75}\int e^{100t}\sin 50t\,dt = -\frac{1}{75}\left[\frac{e^{100t}}{100^2 + 50^2}(100\sin 50t - 50\cos 50t)\right] = \frac{1}{18,750}e^{100t}(\cos 50t - 2\sin 50t)$ and

$u_2(t) = \frac{1}{75}\int e^{25t}\sin 50t\,dt = \frac{1}{75}\left[\frac{e^{25t}}{25^2 + 50^2}(25\sin 50t - 50\cos 50t)\right] = \frac{1}{9375}e^{25t}(\sin 50t - 2\cos 50t)$.

Consequently by (5),

$q_p = \frac{1}{18,750}(\cos 50t - 2\sin 50t) + \frac{1}{9375}(\sin 50t - 2\cos 50t)$
$= -\frac{1}{6250}\cos 50t$.

By (4), the general solution is $q = -\frac{1}{6250}\cos 50t + C_1e^{-100t} + C_2e^{-25t}$ for $t \geq 0$.

18. The homogeneous equation is $\frac{d^2x}{dt^2} + \frac{p}{m}\frac{dx}{dt} = 0$, with characteristic equation $s^2 + \frac{p}{m}s = 0$, whose roots are $s = 0$ and $s = -\frac{p}{m}$. Thus $x_1 = 1$ and $x_2 = e^{-pt/m}$. Next, $g(t) = g$, so by (9) and (10),

$$u_1'(t) = \frac{-e^{-pt/m}g}{1(-\frac{p}{m}e^{-pt/m})} = \frac{mg}{p}$$

$$u_2'(t) = \frac{1(g)}{1(-\frac{p}{m}e^{-pt/m})} = -\frac{mg}{p}e^{pt/m}$$

Therefore $u_1(t) = \frac{mg}{p} t$ and $u_2(t) = -\frac{m^2 g}{p^2} e^{pt/m}$, so by (5), $x_p = \frac{mg}{p} t - (\frac{m^2 g}{p^2} e^{pt/m}) e^{-pt/m} = \frac{mg}{p} t - \frac{m^2 g}{p^2}$. By (4), the general solution is $x = \frac{mg}{p} t - \frac{m^2 g}{p^2} + C_1' + C_2 e^{-pt/m} = \frac{mg}{p} t + C_1 + C_2 e^{-pt/m}$.

Section 16.7

1. As in Example 1, we obtain the differential equation $\frac{d^2x}{dt^2} + 64x = 0$, which has the solution $x = C_1 \sin 8t + C_2 \cos 8t$ for appropriate C_1 and C_2. By hypothesis, $x(0) = \frac{1}{6}$, so that $\frac{1}{6} = C_1 \sin 0 + C_2 \cos 0 = C_2$. Also $dx/dt = 8C_1 \cos 8t - 8C_2 \sin 8t$, so that since $x'(0) = 0$ by hypothesis, we have $0 = 8C_1 \cos 0 - 8C_2 \sin 0 = 8C_1$, so $C_1 = 0$. Thus $x = \frac{1}{6} \cos 8t$.

2. By Exercise 1, $x = C_1 \sin 8t + C_2 \cos 8t$ for appropriate C_1 and C_2. As in Exercise 1, $C_2 = \frac{1}{6} = x(0)$. But this time $x'(0) = \frac{1}{12}$ by hypothesis, so that since $dx/dt = 8C_1 \cos 8t - 8C_2 \sin 8t$, we have $\frac{1}{12} = 8C_1 \cos 0 - 8C_2 \sin 0 = 8C_1$, so that $C_1 = \frac{1}{96}$. Thus $x = \frac{1}{96} \sin 8t + \frac{1}{6} \cos 8t$.

3. We change the solution of Exercise 2 only in having $x'(0) = -\frac{1}{6}$, so that $-\frac{1}{6} = 8C_1 \cos 0 - 8C_2 \sin 0 = 8C_1$. Thus $C_1 = -\frac{1}{48}$. Since $C_2 = \frac{1}{6}$ by Exercise 2, the solution is $x = -\frac{1}{48} \sin 8t + \frac{1}{6} \cos 8t$.

4. We have $m = \text{weight}/g = \frac{1.6}{32} = \frac{1}{20}$, $k = \frac{1}{4}$, and $p = 0.2 = \frac{1}{5}$. Therefore (8) becomes $\frac{d^2x}{dt^2} + \frac{1/5}{1/20} \frac{dx}{dt} + \frac{1/4}{1/20} x = 0$, that is, $\frac{d^2x}{dt^2} + 4 \frac{dx}{dt} + 5x = 0$. The characteristic equation is $s^2 + 4s + 5 = 0$, which falls under Case 3 of Section 16.5 with $b = 4$ and $c = 5$. Since $u = -\frac{b}{2} = -2$ and $v = \frac{1}{2}\sqrt{4c - b^2} = \frac{1}{2}\sqrt{4 \cdot 5 - 4^2} = \frac{1}{2}\sqrt{4} = 1$, we conclude from (11) of Section 16.5 that $x = C_1 e^{-2t} \sin t + C_2 e^{-2t} \cos t$ for appropriate C_1 and C_2. By hypothesis, $x(0) = -\frac{1}{12}$, so that $-\frac{1}{12} = C_1 e^0 \sin 0 + C_2 e^0 \cos 0 = C_2$. Also $dx/dt = -2C_1 e^{-2t} \sin t + C_1 e^{-2t} \cos t - 2C_2 e^{-2t} \cos t - C_2 e^{-2t} \sin t = -(2C_1 + C_2) e^{-2t} \sin t +$

$(C_1 - 2C_2)e^{-2t}\cos t$, so that since $x'(0) = 0$ by hypothesis, we have $0 = -(2C_1 + C_2)e^0 \sin 0 + (C_1 - 2C_2)e^0 \cos 0 = C_1 - 2C_2$, so $C_1 = 2C_2 = -\frac{1}{6}$. Thus $x = -\frac{1}{6}e^{-2t}\sin t - \frac{1}{12}e^{-2t}\cos t$.

5. As in Exercise 4, $x = C_1e^{-2t}\sin t + C_2e^{-2t}\cos t$ for appropriate constants C_1 and C_2. As in Exercise 4, $C_2 = -\frac{1}{12}$ and $dx/dt = -(2C_1 + C_2)e^{-2t}\sin t + (C_1 - 2C_2)e^{-2t}\cos t$. But since $x'(0) = -\frac{1}{6}$ by hypothesis, we have $-\frac{1}{6} = -(2C_1 + C_2)e^0 \sin 0 + (C_1 - 2C_2)e^0 \cos 0 = C_1 - 2C_2$, so $C_1 = -\frac{1}{6} + 2C_2 = -\frac{1}{6} + 2(-\frac{1}{12}) = -\frac{1}{3}$. Thus $x = -\frac{1}{3}e^{-2t}\sin t - \frac{1}{12}e^{-2t}\cos t$.

6. We have $m = \text{weight}/g = \frac{0.96}{32} = \frac{3}{100}$, $k = \frac{1}{4}$, and $p = 0.2 = \frac{1}{5}$. Therefore (8) becomes $\frac{d^2x}{dt^2} + \frac{1/5}{3/100}\frac{dx}{dt} + \frac{1/4}{3/100}x = 0$, that is, $\frac{d^2x}{dt^2} + \frac{20}{3}\frac{dx}{dt} + \frac{25}{3}x = 0$. The characteristic equation is $s^2 + \frac{20}{3}s + \frac{25}{3} = 0$, so that $s = \dfrac{-\frac{20}{3} \pm \sqrt{\frac{400}{9} - \frac{100}{3}}}{2} = \frac{-20 \pm 10}{6}$, so $s = -5, -\frac{5}{3}$. Thus by (6) in Section 16.5, $x = C_1e^{-5t} + C_2e^{-5t/3}$ for appropriate C_1 and C_2. By hypothesis, $x(0) = -\frac{1}{12}$, so that $-\frac{1}{12} = C_1e^0 + C_2e^0 = C_1 + C_2$. Also $dx/dt = -5C_1e^{-5t} - \frac{5}{3}C_2e^{-5t/3}$, so that since $x'(0) = 0$ by hypothesis, we have $0 = -5C_1e^0 - \frac{5}{3}C_2e^0 = -5C_1 - \frac{5}{3}C_2$. Now we solve for C_1 and C_2. First, $C_2 = -C_1 - \frac{1}{12}$, so that $0 = -5C_1 - \frac{5}{3}(-C_1 - \frac{1}{12})$, so that $C_1 = \frac{1}{24}$. Then $C_2 = -C_1 - \frac{1}{12} = -\frac{1}{24} - \frac{1}{12} = -\frac{1}{8}$. Therefore $y = \frac{1}{24}e^{-5t} - \frac{1}{8}e^{-5t/3}$.

7. We first calculate the mass m, which must satisfy $p^2 = 4\,km$. Here $p = \frac{1}{5}$ and $k = \frac{1}{4}$ from Exercise 4, so that $\frac{1}{25} = 4(\frac{1}{4})m = m$. Since weight $= g\,(\text{mass}) = 32(\frac{1}{25}) = 1.28$, a weight of 1.28 pounds must be attached to achieve critical damping.

8. We must calculate p from the equation $p^2 = 4\,km$. Here $k = 0.25 = \frac{1}{4}$, and $m = \frac{8}{32} = \frac{1}{4}$. Thus $p^2 = 4(\frac{1}{4})(\frac{1}{4}) = \frac{1}{4}$, so $p = \frac{1}{2}$.

9. a. Since $e^{r_1t} > 0$ and $e^{r_2t} > 0$ for all t, it follows that if $C_1 > 0$ and $C_2 > 0$, then $f(t) = C_1t^{r_1t} + C_2e^{r_2t} > 0$, whereas if $C_1 < 0$ and $C_2 < 0$, then $f(t) = C_1e^{r_1t} + C_2e^{r_2t} < 0$. Either way, $f(t) \neq 0$ for all t.

   b. If C_1 and C_2 have opposite signs, then $-C_2/C_2 > 0$. Now $f(t) = 0$ provided that $0 = C_1e^{r_1t} + C_2e^{r_2t}$, so that $C_1e^{r_1t} = -C_2e^{r_2t}$, and thus $e^{(r_1-r_2)t} = -C_2/C_1$, which means that $(r_1 - r_2)t = \ln(-C_2/C_1)$, and finally, $t = \dfrac{\ln(-C_2/C_1)}{r_1 - r_2}$.

10. a. $f(t) = 0$ if $(C_1 + C_2t)e^{rt} = 0$, so that since $e^{rt} > 0$, we have $C_1 + C_2t = 0$, or $t = -C_1/C_2$.

   b. From part (a) we need to determine under what conditions $-C_1/C_2 > 0$, which happens if C_1 and C_2 have opposite signs.

Section 16.8

1. Let $y = \sum_{n=0}^{\infty} c_n x^n$. Then $\frac{dy}{dx} = \sum_{n=1}^{\infty} n c_n x^{n-1} = \sum_{n=0}^{\infty} (n+1)c_{n+1}x^n$.

Since $dy/dx - 5y = 0$, this means that

$$\sum_{n=0}^{\infty} (n+1)c_{n+1}x^n - 5\sum_{n=0}^{\infty} c_n x^n = 0$$

so that $\sum_{n=0}^{\infty} [(n+1)c_{n+1} - 5c_n]x^n = 0$. By Corollary 9.26, $(n+1)c_{n+1} - 5c_n = 0$, that is, $c_{n+1} = \frac{5}{n+1}c_n$. This yields

$$c_1 = \frac{5}{1}c_0 \qquad c_3 = \frac{5}{3}c_2 = \frac{5^3}{3!}c_0$$

$$c_2 = \frac{5}{2}c_1 = \frac{5^2}{1\cdot 2}c_0 \qquad c_4 = \frac{5}{4}c_3 = \frac{5^4}{4!}c_0$$

In general for any positive integer n we have $c_n = \frac{5^n}{n!}c_0$.

Thus a series solution is $y = c_0\sum_{n=0}^{\infty}\frac{5^n}{n!}x^n$.

2. Let $y = \sum_{n=0}^{\infty} c_n x^n$. Then $\frac{dy}{dx} = \sum_{n=1}^{\infty} n c_n x^{n-1}$. Since $dy/dx + 4xy = 0$, this means that

$$\sum_{n=1}^{\infty} n c_n x^{n-1} + 4\sum_{n=0}^{\infty} c_n x^{n+1} = 0$$

or equivalently,

$$(c_1 + \sum_{n=0}^{\infty} (n+2)c_{n+2}x^{n+1}) + \sum_{n=0}^{\infty} 4c_n x^{n+1} = 0$$

or

$$c_1 + \sum_{n=0}^{\infty} [(n+2)c_{n+2} + 4c_n]x^{n+1} = 0$$

By Corollary 9.26, $c_1 = 0$ and $(n+2)c_{n+2} + 4c_n = 0$, that is, $c_{n+2} = -\frac{4}{n+2}c_n$ for all n. Thus $c_n = 0$ for all odd positive integers n. For even n we have

$$c_2 = -\frac{4}{2}c_0 \qquad c_6 = -\frac{4}{6}c_4 = \frac{(-1)^3 4^3}{2\cdot 4\cdot 6}$$

$$c_4 = -\frac{4}{4}c_2 = \frac{(-1)^2 4^2}{2\cdot 4}c_0 \qquad c_8 = -\frac{4}{8}c_6 = \frac{(-1)^4 4^4}{2\cdot 4\cdot 6\cdot 8}$$

In general for any positive integer n we have

$$c_{2n} = \frac{(-1)^n 4^n}{2\cdot 4\cdot 6\cdots(2n)}c_0 = \frac{(-1)^n 2^n}{n!}c_0$$

Thus a series solution is $y = c_0\sum_{n=0}^{\infty}\frac{(-1)^n 2^n}{n!}x^{2n}$.

3. Let $y = \sum_{n=0}^{\infty} c_n x^n$. Then $\frac{dy}{dx} = \sum_{n=1}^{\infty} n c_n x^{n-1}$ and $\frac{d^2y}{dx^2} = \sum_{n=2}^{\infty} n(n-1)c_n x^{n-2}$. Since $d^2y/dx^2 + y = 0$, this means that $\sum_{n=2}^{\infty} n(n-1)c_n x^{n-2} + \sum_{n=0}^{\infty} c_n x^n = 0$, or equivalently, $\sum_{n=0}^{\infty}(n+2)(n+1)c_{n+2}x^n + \sum_{n=0}^{\infty} c_n x^n = 0$, so that $\sum_{n=0}^{\infty}[(n+2)(n+1)c_{n+2} + c_n]x^n = 0$. By Corollary 9.26, $(n+2)(n+1)c_{n+2} + c_n = 0$, that is, $c_{n+2} = -\frac{1}{(n+2)(n+1)}c_n$ for $n \geq 0$. Thus

$$c_2 = -\frac{1}{2\cdot 1}c_0 \qquad c_4 = -\frac{1}{4\cdot 3}c_2 = (-1)^2\frac{1}{4\cdot 3\cdot 2}c_0$$

$$c_3 = -\frac{1}{3\cdot 2}c_1 \qquad c_5 = -\frac{1}{5\cdot 4}c_3 = (-1)^2\frac{1}{5\cdot 4\cdot 3\cdot 2}c_1$$

In general for any positive integer n we have $c_{2n} = (-1)^n\frac{1}{(2n)!}c_0$ and $c_{2n+1} = (-1)^n\frac{1}{(2n+1)!}c_1$. Consequently a series solution is $y = c_0\sum_{n=0}^{\infty}\frac{(-1)^n}{(2n)!}x^{2n} + c_1\sum_{n=0}^{\infty}\frac{(-1)^n}{(2n+1)!}x^{2n+1}$.

4. Let $y = \sum_{n=0}^{\infty} c_n x^n$. Then $\frac{dy}{dx} = \sum_{n=1}^{\infty} n c_n x^{n-1}$ and $\frac{d^2y}{dx^2} = \sum_{n=2}^{\infty} n(n-1)c_n x^{n-2} = \sum_{n=0}^{\infty}(n+2)(n+1)c_{n+2}x^n$. Since $d^2y/dx^2 - 16y = 0$, this means that

$$\sum_{n=0}^{\infty}(n+2)(n+1)c_{n+2}x^n - \sum_{n=0}^{\infty}16c_n x^n = 0$$

or equivalently,

$$\sum_{n=0}^{\infty}[(n+2)(n+1)c_{n+2} - 16c_n]x^n = 0$$

By Corollary 9.26, $(n+2)(n+1)c_{n+2} - 16c_n = 0$, that is, $c_{n+2} = \frac{16}{(n+2)(n+1)} c_n$.

Thus

$$c_2 = \frac{16}{2\cdot 1} c_0 \qquad c_4 = \frac{16}{4\cdot 3} c_2 = \frac{16^2}{4!} c_0$$

$$c_3 = \frac{16}{3\cdot 2} c_1 \qquad c_5 = \frac{16}{5\cdot 4} c_3 = \frac{16^2}{5!} c_1$$

In general for any positive integer n we have

$$c_{2n} = \frac{16^n}{(2n)!} c_0 \quad \text{and} \quad c_{2n+1} = \frac{16^n}{(2n+1)!} c_1$$

Therefore a series solution is $y = c_0 \sum_{n=0}^{\infty} \frac{16^n}{(2n)!} x^{2n} + c_1 \sum_{n=0}^{\infty} \frac{16^n}{(2n+1)!} x^{2n+1}$.

5. Let $y = \sum_{n=0}^{\infty} c_n x^n$. Then $\frac{dy}{dx} = \sum_{n=1}^{\infty} n c_n x^{n-1}$ and $\frac{d^2y}{dx^2} = \sum_{n=2}^{\infty} n(n-1)c_n x^{n-2}$. Since $\frac{d^2y}{dx^2} + x\frac{dy}{dx} + y = 0$, this means that

$$\sum_{n=2}^{\infty} n(n-1)c_n x^{n-2} + x \sum_{n=1}^{\infty} n c_n x^{n-1} + \sum_{n=0}^{\infty} c_n x^n = 0$$

or equivalently,

$$\sum_{n=0}^{\infty} (n+2)(n+1)c_{n+2}x^n + \sum_{n=1}^{\infty} n c_n x^n + \sum_{n=0}^{\infty} c_n x^n = 0$$

so that

$$2c_2 + c_0 + \sum_{n=1}^{\infty} [(n+2)(n+1)c_{n+2} + (n+1)c_n] x^n = 0$$

By Corollary 9.26,

$$2c_2 + c_0 = 0, \quad \text{that is,} \quad c_2 = -\frac{1}{2} c_0$$

and

$$(n+2)(n+1)c_{n+2} + (n+1)c_n = 0, \quad \text{that is,} \quad c_{n+2} = -\frac{1}{n+2} c_n \quad \text{for } n \geq 1$$

Thus

$$c_2 = -\frac{1}{2} c_0 \qquad c_4 = -\frac{1}{4} c_2 = (-1)^2 \frac{1}{4\cdot 2} c_0$$

$$c_3 = -\frac{1}{3} c_1 \qquad c_5 = -\frac{1}{5} c_3 = (-1)^2 \frac{1}{5\cdot 3} c_1$$

In general for any positive integer n we have $c_{2n} = (-1)^n \frac{1}{(2n)(2n-2)\cdots 4\cdot 2} c_0 = (-1)^n \frac{1}{2^n n!} c_0$ and $c_{2n+1} = (-1)^n \frac{1}{(2n+1)(2n-1)\cdots 5\cdot 3} c_1 = (-1)^n \frac{(2n)(2n-2)\cdots 4\cdot 2}{(2n+1)!} c_1 = \frac{(-1)^n 2^n n!}{(2n+1)!} c_1$. Therefore a series solution is $y = c_0 \sum_{n=0}^{\infty} (-1)^n \frac{1}{2^n n!} x^{2n} + c_1 \sum_{n=0}^{\infty} (-1)^n \frac{2^n n!}{(2n+1)!} x^{2n+1}$.

6. Let $y = \sum_{n=0}^{\infty} c_n x^n$. Then $\frac{dy}{dx} = \sum_{n=1}^{\infty} n c_n x^{n-1}$ and $\frac{d^2y}{dx^2} = \sum_{n=2}^{\infty} n(n-1)c_n x^{n-2}$. Since $x^2 \frac{d^2y}{dx^2} + x\frac{dy}{dx} - 49y = 0$, this means that

$$x^2 \sum_{n=2}^{\infty} n(n-1)c_n x^{n-2} + x \sum_{n=1}^{\infty} n c_n x^{n-1} - 49 \sum_{n=0}^{\infty} c_n x^n = 0$$

or equivalently,

$$\sum_{n=2}^{\infty} n(n-1)c_n x^n + \sum_{n=1}^{\infty} n c_n x^n - 49 \sum_{n=0}^{\infty} c_n x^n = 0$$

so that

$$-49c_0 - 48c_1 x + \sum_{n=2}^{\infty} [n(n-1)c_n + n c_n - 49c_n] x^n = 0$$

By Corollary 9.26, $c_0 = 0$, $c_1 = 0$, and $n(n-1)c_n + n c_n - 49c_n = 0$, that is, $n^2 c_n = 49c_n$. Thus either $n = 7$ or $c_n = 0$. Consequently $y = c_7 x^7$ is a series solution.

7. Let $y = \sum_{n=0}^{\infty} c_n x^n$. Then $\frac{dy}{dx} = \sum_{n=1}^{\infty} n c_n x^{n-1}$. Since $dy/dx = xy$, this means that $\sum_{n=1}^{\infty} n c_n x^{n-1} = x \sum_{n=0}^{\infty} c_n x^n$, or equivalently, $\sum_{n=0}^{\infty} (n+1)c_{n+1}x^n - \sum_{n=1}^{\infty} c_{n-1} x^n = 0$, so that $c_1 + \sum_{n=1}^{\infty} [(n+1)c_{n+1} - c_{n-1}]x^n = 0$. By Corollary 9.26, $c_1 = 0$, and $(n+1)c_{n+1} - c_{n-1} = 0$ for $n \geq 1$, which means that

$c_{n+2} = \frac{1}{n+2} c_n$ for $n \geq 0$. Since $c_1 = 0$, this implies that $c_n = 0$ for any odd positive integer n. Also

$$c_2 = \frac{1}{2} c_0 \qquad c_6 = \frac{1}{6} c_4 = \frac{1}{6\cdot 4\cdot 2} c_0$$

$$c_4 = \frac{1}{4} c_2 = \frac{1}{4\cdot 2} c_0 \qquad c_8 = \frac{1}{8} c_6 = \frac{1}{8\cdot 6\cdot 4\cdot 2} c_0$$

In general for any positive integer n we have

$$c_{2n} = \frac{1}{(2n)(2n-2)\cdots 4\cdot 2} c_0 = \frac{1}{2^n n!} c_0$$

Therefore a series solution is $y = c_0 \sum_{n=0}^{\infty} \frac{1}{2^n n!} x^{2n}$. If $y(0) = 1$, then $c_0 = 1$, so the particular solution is $y = \sum_{n=0}^{\infty} \frac{1}{2^n n!} x^{2n}$.

8. Let $y = \sum_{n=0}^{\infty} c_n x^n$. Then $\frac{dy}{dx} = \sum_{n=1}^{\infty} n c_n x^{n-1}$. Since $\frac{dy}{dx} = x^2 y$, this means that $\sum_{n=1}^{\infty} n c_n x^{n-1} = x^2 \sum_{n=0}^{\infty} c_n x^n$, or equivalently, $\sum_{n=0}^{\infty} (n+1)c_{n+1}x^n = \sum_{n=2}^{\infty} c_{n-2}x^n$, so that $c_1 + 2c_2 x + \sum_{n=2}^{\infty} [(n+1)c_{n+1} - c_{n-2}]x^n = 0$. By Corollary 9.26, $c_1 = 0$, $2c_2 = 0$, and $(n+1)c_{n+1} - c_{n-2} = 0$, that is, $c_{n+1} = \frac{1}{n+1} c_{n-2}$ for $n \geq 2$, or equivalently, $c_{n+3} = \frac{1}{n+3} c_n$ for $n \geq 0$. Since $c_1 = 0 = c_2$, we deduce that $c_{3n+1} = 0 = c_{3n+2}$ for all positive integers n. Also

$$c_3 = \frac{1}{3} c_0 \qquad c_9 = \frac{1}{9} c_6 = \frac{1}{9\cdot 6\cdot 3} c_0$$

$$c_6 = \frac{1}{6} c_3 = \frac{1}{6\cdot 3} c_0 \qquad c_{12} = \frac{1}{12} c_9 = \frac{1}{12\cdot 9\cdot 6\cdot 3} c_0$$

In general for any positive integer n we have

$$c_{3n} = \frac{1}{(3n)(3n-3)\cdots 9\cdot 6\cdot 3} c_0 = \frac{1}{3^n n!} c_0$$

Thus a series solution is $y = c_0 \sum_{n=0}^{\infty} \frac{1}{3^n n!} x^{3n}$. If $y(0) = 2$, then $c_0 = 2$, so that the particular solution is $y = 2\sum_{n=0}^{\infty} \frac{1}{3^n n!} x^{3n}$.

9. Let $y = \sum_{n=0}^{\infty} c_n x^n$. Then $\frac{dy}{dx} = \sum_{n=1}^{\infty} n c_n x^{n-1}$ and $\frac{d^2y}{dx^2} = \sum_{n=2}^{\infty} n(n-1)c_n x^{n-2}$. Since $x^2 \frac{d^2y}{dx^2} - 6y = 0$, this means that $x^2 \sum_{n=2}^{\infty} n(n-1)c_n x^{n-2} - 6\sum_{n=0}^{\infty} c_n x^n = 0$, or equivalently, $\sum_{n=2}^{\infty} n(n-1)c_n x^n - 6\sum_{n=0}^{\infty} c_n x^n = 0$, so that $-6c_0 - 6c_1 x + \sum_{n=2}^{\infty} [n(n-1)c_n - 6c_n]x^n = 0$. By Corollary 9.26, $c_0 = 0$, $c_1 = 0$, and $[n(n-1) - 6]c_n = 0$ for $n \geq 2$. Since $n(n-1) - 6 = 0$ only if $n = 3$, it follows that $c_n = 0$ for $n = 2$ and $n \geq 4$. Thus a series solution is $y = c_3 x^3$. If $y(1) = 5$, then $5 = y(1) = c_3(1)^3 = c_3$, so that the particular solution is $y = 5x^3$.

10. Let $y = \sum_{n=0}^{\infty} c_n x^n$. Then $\frac{dy}{dx} = \sum_{n=1}^{\infty} n c_n x^{n-1}$ and $\frac{d^2y}{dx^2} = \sum_{n=2}^{\infty} n(n-1)c_n x^{n-2}$. Since $\frac{d^2y}{dx^2} - 2x\frac{dy}{dx} - 2y = 0$, this means that $\sum_{n=2}^{\infty} n(n-1)c_n x^{n-2} - 2x\sum_{n=1}^{\infty} n c_n x^{n-1} - 2\sum_{n=0}^{\infty} c_n x^n = 0$, or equivalently, $\sum_{n=0}^{\infty} (n+2)(n+1)c_{n+2}x^n - \sum_{n=1}^{\infty} 2n c_n x^n - \sum_{n=0}^{\infty} 2c_n x^n = 0$, so that $2c_2 - 2c_0 + \sum_{n=1}^{\infty} [(n+2)(n+1)c_{n+2} - 2(n+1)c_n]x^n = 0$. By Corollary 9.26, $2c_2 - 2c_0 = 0$ and $(n+2)(n+1)c_{n+2} - 2(n+1)c_n = 0$, so that $c_2 = c_0$ and $c_{n+2} = \frac{2(n+1)c_n}{(n+2)(n+1)} = \frac{2c_n}{n+2}$. Thus

$$c_2 = c_0 \qquad c_4 = \frac{1}{2} c_2 = \frac{1}{2} c_0 \qquad c_6 = \frac{1}{3} c_4 = \frac{1}{3\cdot 2} c_0$$

$c_3 = \frac{2}{3} c_1 \qquad c_5 = \frac{2}{5} c_3 = \frac{2^2}{5\cdot 3} c_1 \qquad c_7 = \frac{2}{7} c_5 = \frac{2^3}{7\cdot 5\cdot 3} c_1$

In general for any positive integer n we have

$c_{2n} = \frac{1}{n!} c_0$ and $c_{2n+1} = \frac{2^n}{(2n+1)(2n-1)\cdots 7\cdot 5\cdot 3} c_1 =$

$\frac{2^n(2n)(2n-2)\cdots 4\cdot 2}{(2n+1)!} c_1 = \frac{4^n n!}{(2n+1)!} c_1$.

Therefore a series solution is $y = c_0 \sum_{n=0}^{\infty} \frac{1}{n!} x^{2n} +$

$c_1 \sum_{n=0}^{\infty} \frac{4^n n!}{(2n+1)!} x^{2n+1}$. If $y(0) = 1$, then $c_0 = y(0) = 1$.

Next, $\frac{dy}{dx} = c_0 \sum_{n=1}^{\infty} \frac{2n}{n!} x^{2n-1} + c_1 \sum_{n=0}^{\infty} \frac{4^n n!(2n+1)}{(2n+1)!} x^{2n}$. Thus if

$y'(0) = 0$, then $c_1 = 0$. Consequently the particular solution

is $y = \sum_{n=0}^{\infty} \frac{1}{n!} x^{2n}$.

11. Let $y = \sum_{n=0}^{\infty} c_n x^n$. Then $\frac{dy}{dx} = \sum_{n=1}^{\infty} n c_n x^{n-1}$ and $\frac{d^2y}{dx^2} =$

$\sum_{n=2}^{\infty} n(n-1)c_n x^{n-2}$. Since $\frac{d^2y}{dx^2} - x\frac{dy}{dx} - y = 0$, this means

that $\sum_{n=2}^{\infty} n(n-1)c_n x^{n-2} - x \sum_{n=1}^{\infty} n c_n x^{n-1} - \sum_{n=0}^{\infty} c_n x^n = 0$, or

equivalently, $\sum_{n=0}^{\infty} (n+2)(n+1)c_{n+2}x^n - \sum_{n=1}^{\infty} n c_n x^n - \sum_{n=0}^{\infty} c_n x^n = 0$, that

is, $2c_2 - c_0 + \sum_{n=1}^{\infty} [(n+2)(n+1)c_{n+2} - (n+1)c_n]x^n = 0$. By

Corollary 9.26, $c_2 = \frac{1}{2} c_0$ and $(n+2)(n+1)c_{n+2} - (n+1)c_n$

$= 0$, so that $c_{n+2} = \frac{1}{n+2} c_n$ for $n \geq 0$. Thus

$c_3 = \frac{1}{3} c_1 \qquad c_5 = \frac{1}{5} c_3 = \frac{1}{5\cdot 3} c_1$

$c_4 = \frac{1}{4} c_2 = \frac{1}{4\cdot 2} c_0 \qquad c_6 = \frac{1}{6} c_4 = \frac{1}{6\cdot 4\cdot 2} c_0$

In general for any positive integer n we have

$c_{2n} = \frac{1}{(2n)(2n-2)\cdots 4\cdot 2} c_0 = \frac{1}{2^n n!} c_0$ and

$c_{2n+1} = \frac{1}{(2n+1)(2n-1)\cdots 5\cdot 3} c_1 = \frac{(2n)(2n-2)\cdots 4\cdot 2}{(2n+1)!} c_1 =$

$\frac{2^n n!}{(2n+1)!} c_1$. Thus a series solution is $y = \sum_{n=0}^{\infty} c_{2n}x^{2n} +$

$\sum_{n=0}^{\infty} c_{2n+1}x^{2n+1} = c_0 \sum_{n=0}^{\infty} \frac{1}{2^n n!} x^{2n} + c_1 \sum_{n=0}^{\infty} \frac{2^n n!}{(2n+1)!} x^{2n+1}$. If

$y(0) = 1$, then $c_0 = 1$. Next, $\frac{dy}{dx} = c_0 \sum_{n=1}^{\infty} \frac{2n}{2^n n!} x^{2n-1} +$

$c_1 \sum_{n=0}^{\infty} \frac{2^n n!(2n+1)}{(2n+1)!} x^{2n}$. Thus if $y'(0) = 0$, then $c_1 = 0$.

Consequently the particular solution is $y = \sum_{n=0}^{\infty} \frac{1}{2^n n!} x^{2n}$.

12. By the result of Exercise 11, $y = c_0 \sum_{n=0}^{\infty} \frac{1}{2^n n!} x^{2n} +$

$c_1 \sum_{n=0}^{\infty} \frac{2^n n!}{(2n+1)!} x^{2n+1}$. If $y(0) = 2$, then $c_0 = 2$. Next,

$\frac{dy}{dx} = c_0 \sum_{n=1}^{\infty} \frac{2n}{2^n n!} x^{2n-1} + c_1 \sum_{n=0}^{\infty} \frac{2^n n!(2n+1)}{(2n+1)!} x^{2n}$, so that if

$y'(0) = 1$, then $c_1 = 1$. Thus the particular solution is

$y = 2 \sum_{n=0}^{\infty} \frac{1}{2^n n!} x^{2n} + \sum_{n=0}^{\infty} \frac{2^n n!}{(2n+1)!} x^{2n+1}$.

Section 16.9

1. $2y + 5 = 0$ if $y = -5/2$. Thus $y = -5/2$ is the constant solution.

2. $2y(4 - 3y) = 0$ if $y = 0$ or $y = 4/3$. Thus $y = 0$ and $y = 4/3$ are the constant solutions.

3. $y^2 - 2y - 15 = 0$ if $(y - 5)(y + 3) = 0$, so that $y = 5$ or $y = -3$. Thus $y = 5$ and $y = -3$ are the constant solutions.

4. $4y^2 - y = 0$ if $y(4y - 1) = 0$, so that $y = 0$ or $y = 1/4$. Thus $y = 0$ and $y = -1/4$ are the constant solutions.

5. $y^2e^{-y} = 0$ if $y = 0$. Thus $y = 0$ is the constant solution.

6. $\sin y = 0$ if $y = n\pi$ for some integer n. Thus $y = n\pi$ is a constant solution for any integer n.

7. $f(y) = 1 - y$; $f'(y) = -1$; $f'(y(t))\frac{dy}{dt} = (-1)\frac{dy}{dt}$

Constant solution: $y = 1$.

If $y(0) = 2$ then $f(y(0)) = f(2) = -1$, so y is strictly decreasing,

By (5), the graph is concave upward.

If $y(0) = -2$ then $f(y(0)) = f(-2) = 3$, so y is strictly increasing.

By (5), the graph is concave downward.

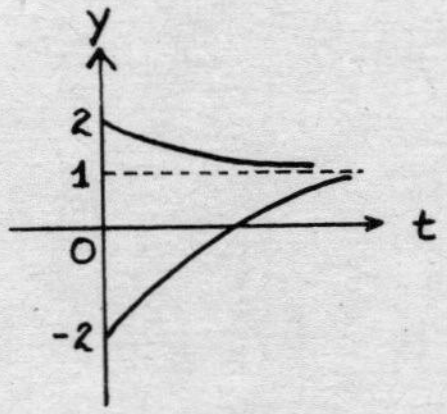

8. $f(y) = y + 2$; $f'(y) = 1$; $f'(y(t))\frac{dy}{dt} = 1\frac{dy}{dt} = \frac{dy}{dt}$

Constant solution: $y = -2$. If $y(0) = -\frac{3}{2}$ then $f(y(0)) = f(-\frac{3}{2}) = \frac{1}{2}$, so y is strictly increasing. By (5), the graph is concave upward.

If $y(0) = -3$ then $f(y(0)) = f(-3) = -1$, so y is strictly decreasing.

By (5), the graph is concave downward.

If $y(0) = -2$ then $f(y(0)) = f(-2) = 0$, and y is the constant solution $y = -2$.

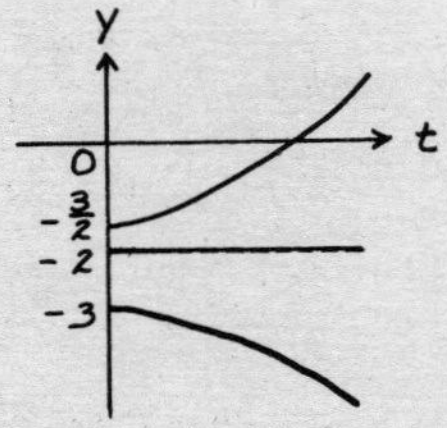

9. $f(y) = y^2 - 2y = y(y - 2)$; $f'(y) = 2y - 2 = 2(y - 1)$; $f'(y(t))\frac{dy}{dt} = 2(y(t) - 1)\frac{dy}{dt}$

Constant solutions: $y = 0$ and $y = 2$.

If $y(0) = \frac{5}{2}$ then $f(y(0)) = f(\frac{5}{2}) = \frac{5}{4}$, so y is strictly increasing.

By (5), the graph is concave upward.

If $y(0) = \frac{3}{2}$ then $f(y(0)) = f(\frac{3}{2}) = -\frac{3}{4}$, so y is strictly decreasing.

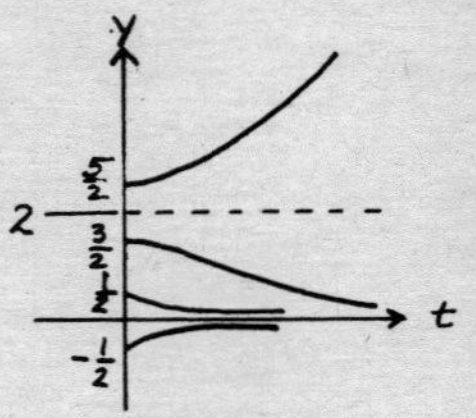

By (5), the graph is concave downward above the line $y = 1$ and concave upward below the line $y = 1$.

If $y(0) = \frac{1}{2}$ then $f(y(0)) = f(\frac{1}{2}) = -\frac{3}{4}$, so y is strictly decreasing. By (5), the graph is concave upward.

If $y(0) = -\frac{1}{2}$ then $f(y(0)) = f(-\frac{1}{2}) = \frac{5}{4}$, so y is strictly increasing. By (5) the graph is concave downward.

10. $f(y) = -y^2 + 2y = -y(y - 2)$; $f'(y) = -2y + 2 = -2(y - 1)$; $f'(y(t))\frac{dy}{dt} = -2(y(t) - 1)\frac{dy}{dt}$

Constant solutions: $y = 0$ and $y = 2$.

If $y(0) = \frac{5}{2}$ then $f(y(0)) = f(\frac{5}{2}) = -\frac{5}{4}$, so y is strictly decreasing.

By (5), the graph is concave upward.

If $y(0) = \frac{3}{2}$ then $f(y(0)) = f(\frac{3}{2}) = \frac{3}{4}$, so y is strictly increasing.

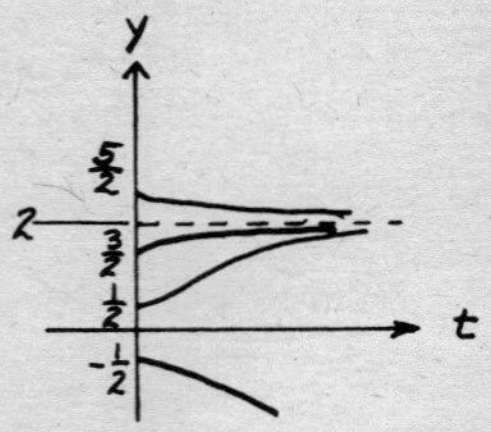

By (5), the graph is concave downward.

If $y(0) = \frac{1}{2}$ then $f(y(0)) = f(\frac{1}{2}) = \frac{3}{4}$, so y is strictly increasing. By (5), the graph is concave upward below the line $y = 1$ and concave downward above the line $y = 1$.

If $y(0) = -\frac{1}{2}$ then $f(y(0)) = f(-\frac{1}{2}) = -\frac{5}{4}$, so y is strictly decreasing. By (5), the graph is concave downward.

11. $f(y) = y^2 + 2y + 4 = (y + 1)^2 + 3;$

$f'(y) = 2y + 2 = 2(y + 1);\ f'(y(t))\,\frac{dy}{dt} = 2(y(t) + 1)\,\frac{dy}{dt}$

No constant solutions.

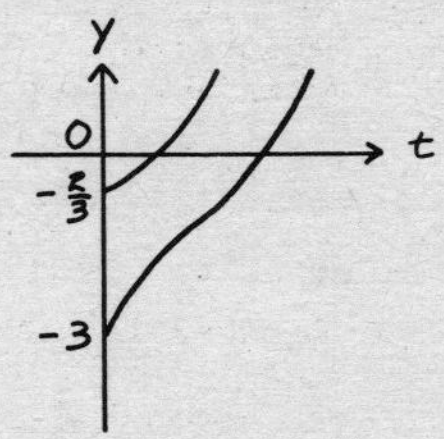

If $y(0) = -\frac{2}{3}$ then $f(y(0)) = f(-\frac{2}{3})$ $= \frac{28}{9}$, so y is strictly increasing.

By (5), the graph is concave upward.

If $y(0) = -3$ then $f(y(0)) = f(-3)$ $= 7$, so y is strictly increasing.

By(5), the graph is concave downward below the line $y = -1$ and concave upward above the line $y = -1$.

12. $f(y) = 2y^2 - y - 1 = (2y + 1)(y - 1);$

$f'(y) = 4y - 1;\ f'(y(t))\,\frac{dy}{dt} = (4y(t) - 1)\,\frac{dy}{dt}$

Constant solutions: $y = -\frac{1}{2}$ and $y = 1$.

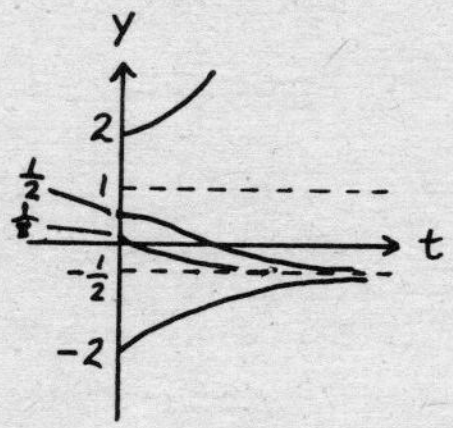

If $y(0) = 2$ then $f(y(0)) = f(2)$ $= 5$, so y is strictly increasing.

By (5), the graph is concave upward.

If $y(0) = \frac{1}{2}$ then $f(y(0)) = f(\frac{1}{2}) =$ -1, so y is strictly decreasing. By (5), the graph is concave downward above the line $y = \frac{1}{4}$ and concave upward below the line $y = \frac{1}{4}$.

If $y(0) = \frac{1}{8}$ then $f(y(0)) = f(\frac{1}{8}) = -\frac{35}{32}$, so y is strictly decreasing. By (5), the graph is concave upward.

If $y(0) = -2$ then $f(y(0)) = f(-2) = 9$, so y strictly increasing. By (5), the graph is concave downward.

13. $f(y) = y^3;\ f'(y) = 3y^2;\ f'(y(t))\,\frac{dy}{dt} = 3[y(t)]^2\,\frac{dy}{dt}$

Constant solution: $y = 0$.

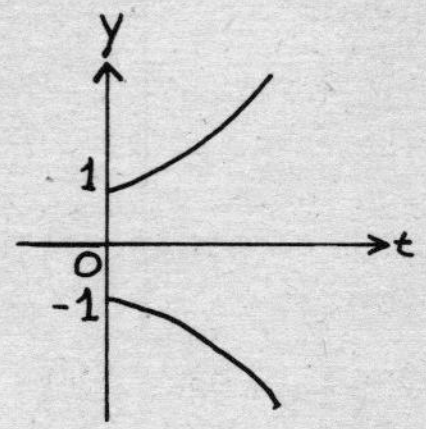

If $y(0) = 1$ then $f(y(0)) = f(1) =$ 1, so y is strictly increasing.

By (5), the graph is concave upward.

If $y(0) = -1$ then $f(y(0)) = f(-1)$ $= -1$, so y is strictly decreasing.

By (5), the graph is concave downward.

14. $f(y) = \frac{1}{y};\ f'(y) = -\frac{1}{y^2};\ f'(y(t))\,\frac{dy}{dt} = -\frac{1}{[y(t)]^2}\,\frac{dy}{dt}$

No constant solutions.

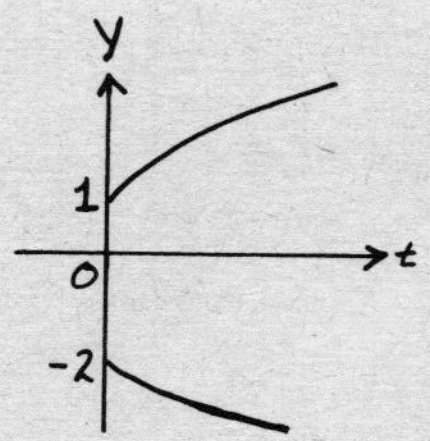

If $y(0) = 1$ then $f(y(0)) = f(1) =$ 1, so y is strictly increasing.

By (5), the graph is concave downward.

If $y(0) = -2$ then $f(y(0)) = f(-2)$ $= -\frac{1}{2}$, so y is strictly decreasing.

By (5), the graph is concave upward.

15. $f(y) = y^2(y - 1);\ f'(y) = 3y^2 - 2y =$ $3y(y - \frac{2}{3});\ f'(y(t))\,\frac{dy}{dt} = 3y(t)(y(t) - \frac{2}{3})\,\frac{dy}{dt}$

Constant solutions: $y = 0$ and $y = 1$.

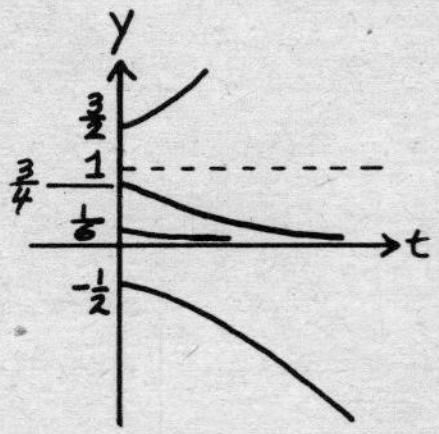

If $y(0) = \frac{3}{2}$ then $f(y(0)) = f(\frac{3}{2}) =$ $\frac{9}{8}$, so y is strictly increasing.

By (5), the graph is concave upward.

If $y(0) = \frac{3}{4}$ then $f(y(0)) = f(\frac{3}{4}) =$ $-\frac{9}{64}$, so y is strictly decreasing.

By (5), the graph is concave downward above the line $y = \frac{2}{3}$ and concave upward below the line $y = \frac{2}{3}$.

If $y(0) = \frac{1}{6}$ then $f(y(0)) = f(\frac{1}{6}) = -\frac{5}{216}$, so y is strictly decreasing. By (5), the graph is concave upward.

If $y(0) = -\frac{1}{2}$ then $f(y(0)) = f(-\frac{1}{2}) = -\frac{3}{8}$, so y is strictly decreasing. By (5), the graph is concave downward.

16. $f(y) = y^2(y - 2)^2$; $f'(y) = 2y(y - 2)^2 + 2y^2(y - 2) = 4y(y - 1)(y - 2)$; $f'(y(t)) \frac{dy}{dt} = 4y(t)(y(t) - 1)(y(t) - 2) \frac{dy}{dt}$

Constant solutions: $y = 0$ and $y = 2$.

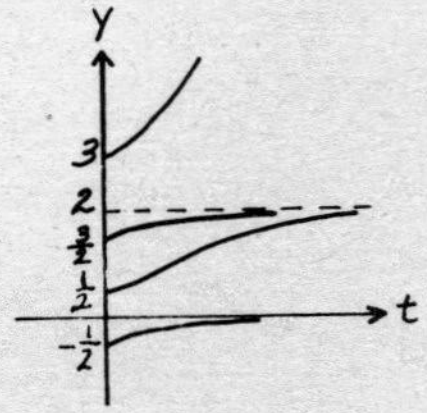

If $y(0) = 3$ then $f(y(0)) = f(3) = 9$, so y is strictly increasing. By (5), the graph is concave upward.

If $y(0) = \frac{3}{2}$ then $f(y(0)) = f(\frac{3}{2}) = \frac{9}{16}$, so y is strictly increasing. By (5), the graph is concave downward.

If $y(0) = \frac{1}{2}$ then $f(y(0)) = f(\frac{1}{2}) = \frac{9}{16}$, so y is strictly increasing. By (5), the graph is concave upward below the line $y = 1$ and concave downward above the line $y = 1$.

If $y(0) = -\frac{1}{2}$ then $f(y(0)) = f(-\frac{1}{2}) = \frac{25}{16}$, so y is strictly increasing. By (5), the graph is concave downward.

17. $f(y) = y^3(y - 2)^3$; $f'(y) = 3y^2(y - 2)^3 + 3y^3(y - 2)^2 = 6y^2(y - 1)(y - 2)^2$; $f'(y(t)) \frac{dy}{dt} = 6(y(t))^2(y(t) - 1)(y(t) - 2)^2 \frac{dy}{dt}$

Constant solutions: $y = 0$ and $y = 2$.

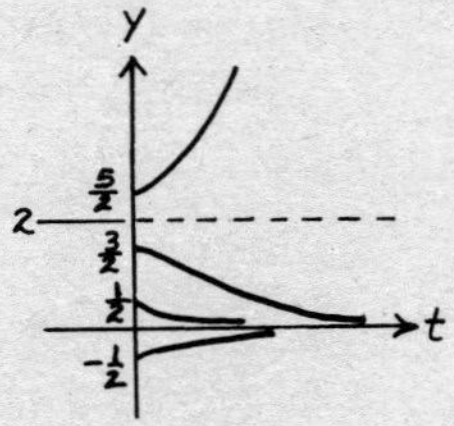

If $y(0) = \frac{5}{2}$ then $f(y(0)) = f(\frac{5}{2}) = \frac{125}{64}$, so y is strictly increasing. By (5), the graph is concave upward.

If $y(0) = \frac{3}{2}$ then $f(y(0)) = f(\frac{3}{2}) = -\frac{27}{64}$, so y is strictly decreasing. By (5), the graph is concave downward above the line $y = 1$ and concave upward below the line $y = 1$.

If $y(0) = \frac{1}{2}$ then $f(y(0)) = f(\frac{1}{2}) = -\frac{27}{64}$, so y is strictly decreasing. By (5), the graph is concave upward.

If $y(0) = -\frac{1}{2}$ then $f(y(0)) = f(-\frac{1}{2}) = \frac{125}{64}$, so y is strictly increasing. By (5), the graph is concave downward.

18. $f(y) = \sin y$; $f'(y) = \cos y$; $f'(y(t)) \frac{dy}{dt} = (\cos y(t)) \frac{dy}{dt}$

Constant solution: $y = n\pi$ for any integer n.

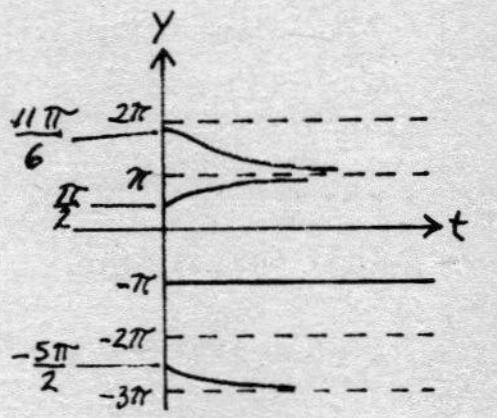

If $y(0) = \frac{\pi}{2}$ then $f(y(0)) = f(\frac{\pi}{2}) = \sin \frac{\pi}{2} = 1$, so y is strictly increasing. By (5), the graph is concave downward.

If $y(0) = \frac{11\pi}{6}$ then $f(y(0)) = f(\frac{11\pi}{6}) = \sin \frac{11\pi}{6} = -\frac{1}{2}$, so y is strictly decreasing. By (5), the graph is concave downward above the line $y = \frac{3\pi}{2}$ and concave upward below the line $y = \frac{3\pi}{2}$.

If $y(0) = -\pi$ then y is a constant solution.

If $y(0) = -\frac{5\pi}{2}$ then $f(y(0)) = f(-\frac{5\pi}{2}) = \sin(-\frac{5\pi}{2}) = -1$, so y is strictly decreasing. By (5), the graph is concave upward.

19. $f(y) = \sin^2 y$; $f'(y) = 2 \sin y \cos y = \sin 2y$; $f'(y(t)) \frac{dy}{dt} = (\sin 2y(t)) \frac{dy}{dt}$

Constant solutions: $y = n\pi$ for any integer n.

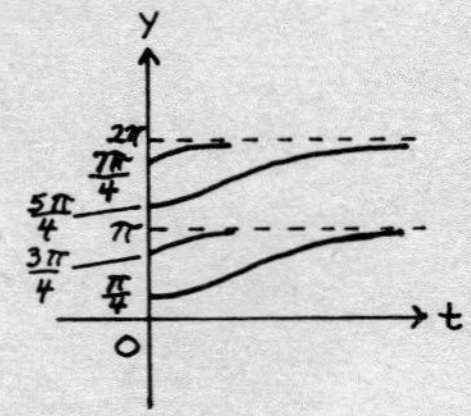

If $y(0) = \frac{\pi}{4}$ then $f(y(0)) = \sin^2(\frac{\pi}{4}) = \frac{1}{2}$, so y is strictly increasing. By (5), the graph is concave upward below the line $y = \frac{\pi}{2}$ and concave downward above the line $y = \frac{\pi}{2}$.

If $y(0) = \frac{3\pi}{4}$ then $f(y(0)) = f(\frac{3\pi}{4}) = \sin^2(\frac{3\pi}{4}) = \frac{1}{2}$, so y is strictly increasing. By (5), the graph is concave downward.

If $y(0) = \frac{5\pi}{4}$ then $f(y(0)) = f(\frac{5\pi}{4}) = \sin^2(\frac{5\pi}{4}) = \frac{1}{2}$, so y is strictly increasing. By (5), the graph is concave upward below the line $y = \frac{3\pi}{2}$ and concave downward above the line $y = \frac{3\pi}{2}$.

If $y(0) = \frac{7\pi}{4}$ then $f(y(0)) = f(\frac{7\pi}{4}) = \sin^2(\frac{7\pi}{4}) = \frac{1}{2}$, so y is strictly increasing. By (5), the graph is concave downward.

20. $f(y) = e^{-y}$; $f'(y) = -e^{-y}$; $f'(y(t))\,\frac{dy}{dt} = -e^{-y(t)}\,\frac{dy}{dt}$

No constant solutions.

If $y(0) = 0$ then $f(y(0)) = f(0)$ $= e^{-0} = 1$, so y is strictly increasing. By (5), the graph is concave downward.

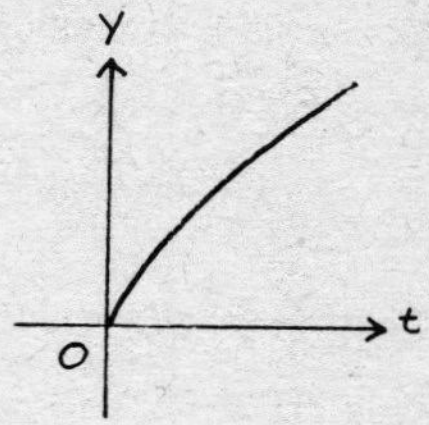

21. a.

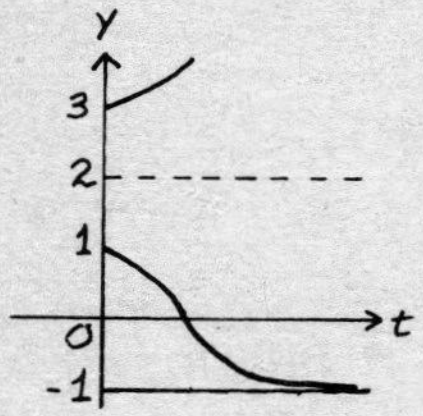

b.

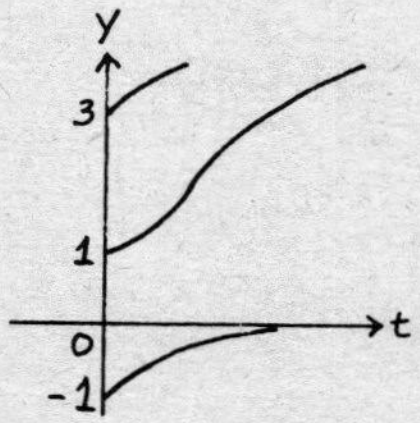

c.

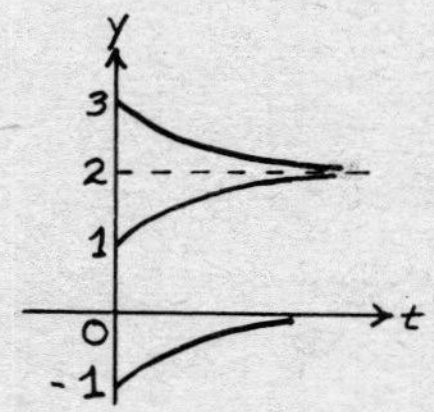

22. $f(T) = -k(T - 10)$; $f'(T) = -k$; $f'(T(t))\,\frac{dT}{dt} = -k\,\frac{dT}{dt}$

Constant solution: $T = 10$.

a. If $T(0) = 15$ then $f(T(0)) =$ $f(15) = -k(15 - 10) = -5k < 0$, so y is strictly decreasing. By (5), the graph is concave upward.

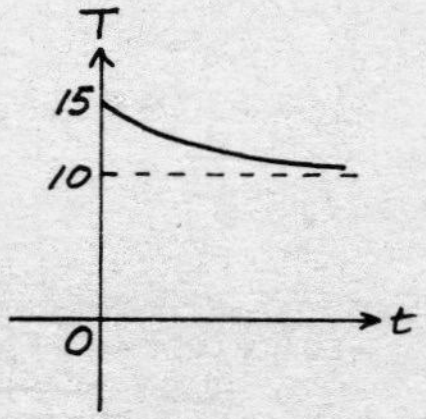

b. If $T(0) = 5$ then $f(T(10)) =$ $f(5) = -k(5 - 10) = 5k > 0$, so y is strictly increasing. By (5), the graph is concave downward.

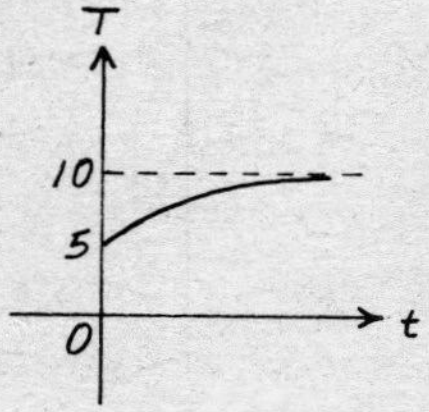

23. $f(y) = ky(a - y)$; $f'(y) = k(a - y) - ky = k(a - 2y)$; $f'(y(t))\,\frac{dy}{dt} = k(a - 2y(t))\,\frac{dy}{dt}$

Constant solutions: $y = 0$ and $y = a$.

a. If $0 < y(0) < a/2$ then $f(y(0)) = ky(0)(a - y(0)) > 0$, so y is strictly increasing. By (5), the graph is concave upward below the line $y = a/2$ and concave downward above the line $y = a/2$.

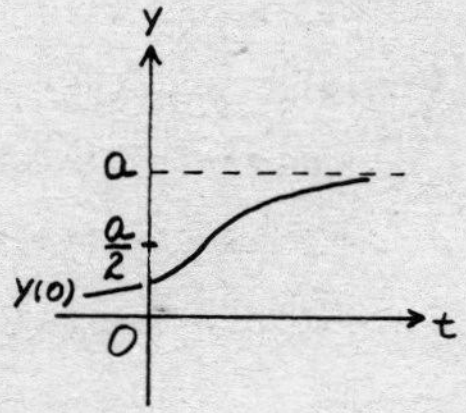

b. If $a/2 < y(0) < a$ then $f(y(0)) = ky(0)(a - y(0)) > 0$, so y is strictly increasing. By (5), the graph is concave downward.

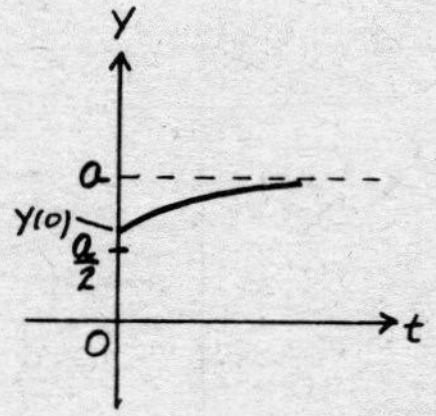

24. $f(y) = k(a - y)(b + y)$; $f'(y) = -k(b + y) + k(a - y) = k(a - b - 2y)$; $f'(y(t))\frac{dy}{dt} = k(a - b - 2y(t))\frac{dy}{dt}$

Constant solutions: $y = a$ and $y = -b$.

Notice that $f'(y) = k(a - b - 2y) = 0$ if $y = \frac{a-b}{2}$. Moreover, $f'(y) > 0$ if $y < \frac{a-b}{2}$, and $f'(y) < 0$ if $y > \frac{a-b}{2}$. Since $a>b>0$ by hypothesis, we have $\frac{a-b}{2} < a$. However, $\frac{a-b}{2} \le b$ only if $a \le 3b$.

If $y(0) = b$ and $a \le 3b$, then $f(y(0)) = f(b) = k(a-b)(2b) > 0$, so y is strictly increasing. By (5) and the preceding comments, the graph is concave downward.

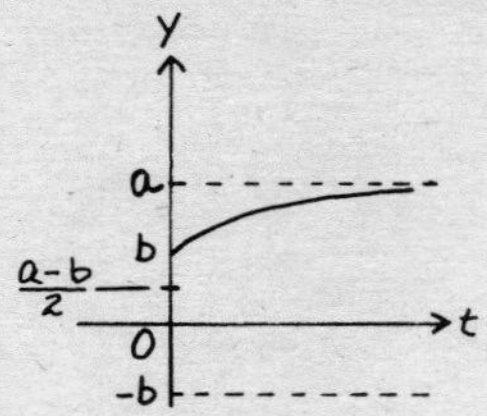

If $y(0) = b$ and $a > 3b$, then $f(y(0)) > 0$ as before, and y is strictly increasing. By (5) and the preceding comments, the graph is concave upward below the line $y = \frac{a-b}{2}$ and concave downward above the line $y = \frac{a-b}{2}$.

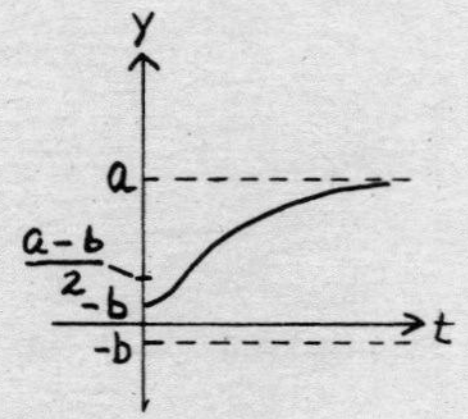

Chapter 16 - Review

1. $P(x) = \frac{2}{x}$ and $Q(x) = x^2 + 6$. Since $2 \ln x$ is an antiderivative of P for $x > 0$, $S(x) = 2 \ln x$, so by (3) in Section 16.4, the general solution is $y = e^{-2 \ln x}\int e^{2 \ln x}(x^2 + 6)\,dx$ $= \frac{1}{x^2}\int x^2(x^2 + 6)\,dx = \frac{1}{x^2}\int (x^4 + 6x^2)\,dx = \frac{1}{x^2}(\frac{1}{5}x^5 + 2x^3 + C)$ $= \frac{1}{5}x^3 + 2x + \frac{C}{x^2}$.

2. The characteristic equation is $s^2 + 6s + 2 = 0$. By the quadratic formula, $s = \frac{-6 \pm \sqrt{36 - 8}}{2} = -3 \pm \sqrt{7}$, so the roots are $s = -3 + \sqrt{7}$ and $s = -3 - \sqrt{7}$. Thus by (6) in Section 16.5, the general solution is $y = C_1 e^{(-3+\sqrt{7})x} + C_2 e^{(-3-\sqrt{7})x}$.

3. Since $\frac{\partial}{\partial x}\frac{y}{\sqrt{x^2 + y^2}} = \frac{-xy}{(x^2 + y^2)^{3/2}} = \frac{\partial}{\partial y}\frac{x}{\sqrt{x^2 + y^2}}$, the differential equation is exact. Thus there is a function f such that $\frac{\partial f}{\partial x} = \frac{x}{\sqrt{x^2 + y^2}}$ and $\frac{\partial f}{\partial y} = \frac{y}{\sqrt{x^2 + y^2}}$. Then $f(x,y) = \sqrt{x^2 + y^2} + g(y)$, for a suitable function g, so that $\frac{\partial f}{\partial y} = \frac{y}{\sqrt{x^2 + y^2}} + \frac{dg}{dy}$. Since $\frac{\partial f}{\partial y} = \frac{y}{\sqrt{x^2 + y^2}}$, it follows that $\frac{dg}{dy} = 0$, so that $g(y) = C_1$. Consequently the general solution is $\sqrt{x^2 + y^2} = C_2$, or $x^2 + y^2 = C$. (This solution could also be obtained by first multiplying both sides of the given equation by $\sqrt{x^2 + y^2}$ and then finding the function f.)

4. $x\sqrt{1 - y^2} + y\sqrt{1 - x^2}\frac{dy}{dx} = 0$, so $\frac{x}{\sqrt{1 - x^2}}dx = -\frac{y}{\sqrt{1 - y^2}}dy$, a separable differential equation. By integration we obtain the general solution $-\sqrt{1 - x^2} = \sqrt{1 - y^2} + C$.

5. The characteristic equation is $s^2 - 4s + 8 = 0$, so $b = -4$ and $c = 8$, and thus $b^2 - 4c = 16 - 32 < 0$. Therefore Case 3 of Section 16.5 applies. If $u = -b/2 = 2$ and $v = \frac{1}{2}\sqrt{4c - b^2} = \frac{1}{2}\sqrt{32 - 16} = 2$, then by (11) of Section 16.5 the general

solution is $y = C_1 e^{2x} \sin 2x + C_2 e^{2x} \cos 2x$.

6. $P(x) = -\cot x$ and $Q(x) = \csc x$. Since $-\ln \sin x$ is an antiderivative of P on $(0,\pi)$, $S(x) = -\ln \sin x$, so by (3) in Section 16.4, the general solution is $y = e^{\ln \sin x} \int e^{-\ln \sin x} \csc x \, dx = \sin x \int \frac{\csc x}{\sin x} \, dx = \sin x \int \csc^2 x \, dx = \sin x \, (-\cot x + C) = -\cos x + C \sin x$.

7. $P(x) = \cot x$ and $Q(x) = \csc x$. Since $\ln \sin x$ is an antiderivative of P on $(0,\pi)$, $S(x) = \ln \sin x$, so by (3) in Section 16.4, the general solution is $y = e^{-\ln \sin x} \int e^{\ln \sin x} \csc x \, dx = \frac{1}{\sin x} \int \sin x \csc x \, dx = \frac{1}{\sin x} \int 1 \, dx = \frac{1}{\sin x} (x + C)$.

8. Since $\frac{\partial}{\partial x} [x(\cos y + \sin y)] = \cos y + \sin y = \frac{\partial}{\partial y} (x + \sin y - \cos y)$, the differential equation is exact. Thus there is a function f such that $\frac{\partial f}{\partial x} = x + \sin y - \cos y$ and $\frac{\partial f}{\partial y} = x(\cos y + \sin y)$. Then $f(x,y) = \frac{1}{2} x^2 + x \sin y - x \cos y + g(y)$, for a suitable function g, so that $\frac{\partial f}{\partial y} = x \cos y + x \sin y + \frac{dg}{dy}$. Since $\frac{\partial f}{\partial y} = x(\cos y + \sin y)$, it follows that $\frac{dg}{dy} = 0$, so that $g(y) = C_1$. Consequently the general solution is $\frac{1}{2} x^2 + x \sin y - x \cos y = C$.

9. Since $\frac{\partial}{\partial x} (\sinh 2x \sinh 2y) = 2 \cosh 2x \sinh 2y = \frac{\partial}{\partial y} (\cosh 2x \cosh 2y)$, the differential equation is exact. Thus there is a function f such that $\frac{\partial f}{\partial x} = \cosh 2x \cosh 2y$ and $\frac{\partial f}{\partial y} = \sinh 2x \sinh 2x$. Then $f(x,y) = \frac{1}{2} \sinh 2x \cosh 2y + g(y)$ for a suitable function g, so that $\frac{\partial f}{\partial y} = \sinh 2x \sinh 2y + \frac{dg}{dy}$. Since $\frac{\partial f}{\partial y} = \sinh 2x \sinh 2y$, it follows that $\frac{dg}{dy} = 0$, so that $g(y) = C_1$. Consequently the general solution is $\frac{1}{2} \sinh 2x \cosh 2y = C_2$, and thus $\sinh 2x \cosh 2y = C$.

10. The characteristic equation is $s^2 + 8s + 16 = 0$, with root $s = -4$. By (8) of Section 16.5, the general solution is $y = C_1 e^{-4x} + C_2 x e^{-4x}$.

11. The differential equation is equivalent to the separable differential equation $\frac{1}{x^2} dx + y e^{-y^2} dy = 0$. By integration we obtain the general solution $-\frac{1}{x} - \frac{1}{2} e^{-y^2} = C_1$, or $\frac{1}{x} + \frac{1}{2} e^{-y^2} = C$.

12. The homogeneous equation is $\frac{d^2y}{dx^2} + y = 0$, with characteristic equation $s^2 + 1 = 0$. This falls under Case 3 of Section 16.5 with $b = 0$ and $c = 1$. Since $u = -\frac{b}{2}$ and $v = \frac{1}{2}\sqrt{4c - b^2} = \frac{1}{2}\sqrt{4} = 1$, it follows from (11) in Section 16.5 that the general solution of the homogeneous equation is $y = C_1 \sin x + C_2 \cos x$. Thus $y_1 = \sin x$ and $y_2 = \cos x$. Next, $g(x) = \sec^2 x$, so by (9) and (10) of Section 16.6,

$$u_1'(x) = \frac{-\cos x \sec^2 x}{\sin x(-\sin x) - \cos x(\cos x)} = \sec x$$

$$u_2'(x) = \frac{\sin x \sec^2 x}{\sin x(-\sin x) - \cos x(\cos x)} = \frac{\sin x}{\cos^2 x}$$

Therefore $u_1(x) = \ln|\sec x + \tan x|$ and $u_2(x) = -\frac{1}{\cos x} = -\sec x$, so that by (5) in Section 16.6, the particular solution y_p is given by $y_p = \sin x \ln|\sec x + \tan x| - \cos x \sec x = \sin x \ln|\sec x + \tan x| - 1$. Consequently by (4) in Section 16.6 the general solution is $y = \sin x \ln|\sec x + \tan x| - 1 + C_1 \sin x + C_2 \cos x$.

13. The homogeneous equation is $\frac{d^2y}{dx^2} + 4y = 0$, with characteristic equation $s^2 + 4 = 0$. This falls under Case 3 of Section 16.5 with $b = 0$ and $c = 4$. Since $u = -b/2 = 0$ and $v = \frac{1}{2}\sqrt{4c - b^2} = \frac{1}{2}\sqrt{16} = 2$, it follows from (11) in Section 16.5 that the general solution of the homogeneous equation is

$y = C_1 \sin 2x + C_2 \cos 2x$. Thus $y_1 = \sin 2x$ and $y_2 = \cos 2x$. Next, $g(x) = \cos 2x$, so by (9) and (10) of Section 16.6,

$$u_1'(x) = \frac{-\cos 2x \cos 2x}{\sin 2x(-2 \sin 2x) - 2 \cos 2x(\cos 2x)} = \frac{1}{2}\cos^2 2x$$
$$= \frac{1}{4} + \frac{1}{4}\cos 4x$$

$$u_2'(x) = \frac{\sin 2x \cos 2x}{\sin 2x(-2 \sin 2x) - 2 \cos 2x(\cos 2x)} = -\frac{1}{2}\sin 2x \cos 2x$$
$$= -\frac{1}{4}\sin 4x$$

Therefore $u_1(x) = \frac{1}{4}x + \frac{1}{16}\sin 4x$ and $u_2(x) = \frac{1}{16}\cos 4x$, so that by (5) in Section 16.6, a particular solution y_p is given by $y_p = (\frac{1}{4}x + \frac{1}{16}\sin 4x)\sin 2x + \frac{1}{16}\cos 4x \cos 2x = \frac{1}{4}x \sin 2x + \frac{1}{16}(\cos 4x \cos 2x + \sin 4x \sin 2x) = \frac{1}{4}x \sin 2x + \frac{1}{16}\cos(4x - 2x) = \frac{1}{4}x \sin 2x + \frac{1}{16}\cos 2x$. Consequently by (4) in Section 16.6, the general solution is given by $y = \frac{1}{4}x \sin 2x + \frac{1}{16}\cos 2x + C_1 \sin 2x + C_2' \cos 2x = \frac{1}{4}x \sin 2x + C_1 \sin 2x + C_2 \cos 2x$.

14. The homogeneous equation is $\frac{d^2y}{dx^2} - \frac{dy}{dx} - 2y = 0$, with characteristic equation $s^2 - s - 2 = 0$, whose roots are $s = 2$ and $s = -1$. Thus $y_1 = e^{2x}$ and $y_2 = e^{-x}$. Next, $g(x) = 2e^{-x}$, so by (9) and (10) of Section 16.6,

$$u_1'(x) = \frac{-e^{-x}(2e^{-x})}{e^{2x}(-e^{-x}) - 2e^{2x}e^{-x}} = \frac{2}{3}e^{-3x}$$

$$u_2'(x) = \frac{e^{2x}(2e^{-x})}{e^{2x}(-e^{-x}) - 2e^{2x}e^{-x}} = -\frac{2}{3}$$

Therefore $u_1(x) = -\frac{2}{9}e^{-3x}$ and $u_2(x) = -\frac{2}{3}x$, so that by (5) in Section 16.6, a particular solution y_p is given by $y_p = (-\frac{2}{9}e^{-3x})(e^{2x}) + (-\frac{2}{3}x)(e^{-x}) = -\frac{2}{9}e^{-x} - \frac{2}{3}xe^{-x}$. Consequently by (4) in Section 16.6, the general solution is given by $y = -\frac{2}{9}e^{-x} - \frac{2}{3}xe^{-x} + C_1e^{2x} + C_2'e^{-x} = -\frac{2}{3}xe^{-x} + C_1e^{2x} + C_2e^{-x}$.

15. The differential equation is equivalent to the separable differential equation $2x\,dx = \frac{y}{y+1}dy$. Since $\frac{y}{y+1} = \frac{y+1-1}{y+1} = 1 - \frac{1}{y+1}$, we obtain the general solution by integration: $x^2 = y - \ln|y + 1| + C$. If $y(0) = -2$, then $0 = -2 - \ln|-2 + 1| + C$, so that $C = 2$, and thus the particular solution is given by $y - \ln|y + 1| = x^2 - 2$.

16. The differential equation is equivalent to $\frac{dy}{dx} - xy = x$, so $P(x) = -x$ and $Q(x) = x$. Since $-\frac{1}{2}x^2$ is an antiderivative of P, $S(x) = -\frac{1}{2}x^2$, so by (3) in Section 16.4 the general solution is $y = e^{x^2/2}\int e^{-x^2/2}x\,dx = e^{x^2/2}(-e^{-x^2/2} + C) = -1 + Ce^{x^2/2}$. If $y(1) = 2$, then $2 = -1 + Ce^{1/2}$, so $C = 3e^{-1/2}$. Therefore the particular solution is $y = -1 + 3e^{-1/2}e^{x^2/2} = -1 + 3e^{(x^2-1)/2}$. (The given differential equation is also separable.)

17. The characteristic equation is $s^2 - 2s + 3 = 0$, so $b = -2$ and $c = 3$, and thus $b^2 - 4c = 4 - 12 < 0$. Therefore Case 3 of Section 16.5 applies. If $u = -b/2 = 1$ and $v = \frac{1}{2}\sqrt{4c - b^2} = \frac{1}{2}\sqrt{12 - 4} = \sqrt{2}$, then by (11) of Section 16.5 the general solution is $y = C_1e^x \sin\sqrt{2}x + C_2e^x \cos\sqrt{2}x$. If $y(0) = 1$, then $1 = y(0) = C_2$. Next, $\frac{dy}{dx} = C_1e^x \sin\sqrt{2}x + \sqrt{2}C_1e^x \cos\sqrt{2}x + C_2e^x \cos\sqrt{2}x - \sqrt{2}C_2e^x \sin\sqrt{2}x$, so if $y'(0) = 3$ then $3 = y'(0) = \sqrt{2}C_1 + C_2 = \sqrt{2}C_1 + 1$, and thus $C_1 = \frac{2}{\sqrt{2}} = \sqrt{2}$. Consequently the particular solution is $y = \sqrt{2}e^x \sin\sqrt{2}x + e^x \cos\sqrt{2}x$.

18. The characteristic equation is $s^2 + 2s - 3 = 0$, with roots $s = -3$, $s = 1$. By (6) of Section 16.5, the general solution is $y = C_1e^{-3x} + C_2e^x$. If $y(0) = 1$, then $1 = y(0) = C_1 + C_2$. Next, $\frac{dy}{dx} = -3C_1e^{3x} + C_2e^x$, so if $y'(0) = 3$ then $3 = y'(0) = -3C_1 + C_2$. Therefore $3 = -3(1 - C_2) + C_2 = -3 + 4C_2$, so that $C_2 = \frac{3}{2}$, and thus $C_1 = 1 - C_2 = 1 - \frac{3}{2} = -\frac{1}{2}$. Consequently the particular solution is $y = -\frac{1}{2}e^{-3x} + \frac{3}{2}e^x$.

19. $y(1 + x^2)dy + (y^2 + 1)dx = 0$, so $\frac{y}{y^2 + 1}\,dy = -\frac{1}{1 + x^2}\,dx$, a separable differential equation. By integration we obtain the general solution $\frac{1}{2}\ln(y^2 + 1) = -\arctan x + C$. If $y(0) = \sqrt{3}$ then $\frac{1}{2}\ln(3 + 1) = 0 + C = C$, so $C = \frac{1}{2}\ln 4 = \frac{1}{2}\ln 2^2 = \ln 2$, and thus the particular solution is $\frac{1}{2}\ln(y^2 + 1) + \arctan x = \ln 2$.

20. Since $\frac{\partial}{\partial x}(xe^y + \sin x + 1) = e^y + \cos x = \frac{\partial}{\partial y}(e^y + y\cos x)$, the differential equation is exact. Thus there is a function f such that $\frac{\partial f}{\partial x} = e^y + y\cos x$ and $\frac{\partial f}{\partial y} = xe^y + \sin x + 1$. Then $f(x,y) = xe^y + y\sin x + g(y)$, for a suitable function g, so that $\frac{\partial f}{\partial y} = xe^y + \sin x + \frac{dg}{dy}$. Since $\frac{\partial f}{\partial y} = xe^y + \sin x + 1$, it follows that $\frac{dg}{dy} = 1$, so that $g(y) = y + C_1$. Consequently the general solution is $xe^y + y\sin x + y = C$. If $y(3\pi/2) = -1$, then $\frac{3\pi}{2}e^{-1} + (-1)\sin\frac{3\pi}{2} - 1 = C$, so that $C = \frac{3\pi}{2e}$. Consequently the particular solution is $xe^y + y\sin x + y = \frac{3\pi}{2e}$.

21. $P(x) = \tan x$, and $Q(x) = \sec x$. Since $-\ln\cos x$ is an antiderivative of P on $(-\pi/2, \pi/2)$, $S(x) = -\ln\cos x$, so by (3) in Section 16.4, the general solution is $y = e^{\ln\cos x}\int e^{-\ln\cos x}\sec x\,dx = \cos x\int\frac{1}{\cos x}\sec x\,dx = \cos x\int\sec^2 x\,dx = \cos x(\tan x + C) = \sin x + C\cos x$. If $y(0) = \pi/4$, then $\frac{\pi}{4} = \sin 0 + C\cos 0 = C$, so the particular solution is $y = \sin x + \frac{\pi}{4}\cos x$.

22. The characteristic equation is $s^2 - 2 = 0$, with roots $s = \sqrt{2}$ and $s = -\sqrt{2}$. By (6) of Section 16.5, the general solution is $y = C_1e^{\sqrt{2}x} + C_2e^{-\sqrt{2}x}$. If $y(0) = \frac{1}{2}\sqrt{2}$ then $\frac{1}{2}\sqrt{2} = y(0) = C_1 + C_2$. Next, $\frac{dy}{dx} = \sqrt{2}\,C_1e^{\sqrt{2}x} - \sqrt{2}\,C_2e^{-\sqrt{2}x}$, so if $y'(0) = -\frac{1}{2}$, then $-\frac{1}{2} = y'(0) = \sqrt{2}\,C_1 - \sqrt{2}\,C_2$. Therefore $-\frac{1}{2} = \sqrt{2}(\frac{1}{2}\sqrt{2} - C_2) - \sqrt{2}\,C_2$, so $C_2 = \frac{3}{8}\sqrt{2}$. Thus $C_1 = \frac{1}{2}\sqrt{2} - C_2 = \frac{1}{2}\sqrt{2} - \frac{3}{8}\sqrt{2} = \frac{1}{8}\sqrt{2}$. Consequently the particular solution is $y = \frac{1}{8}\sqrt{2}\,e^{\sqrt{2}x} + \frac{3}{8}\sqrt{2}\,e^{-\sqrt{2}x}$.

23. $(\frac{3}{2}x^2 - 3y)dy = x(x^4 - 3y)dx$, so $x(x^4 - 3y)dx - (\frac{3}{2}x^2 - 3y)dy = 0$. Since $\frac{\partial}{\partial x}[-(\frac{3}{2}x^2 - 3y)] = -3x = \frac{\partial}{\partial y}[x(x^4 - 3y)]$, this differential equation is exact. Thus there is a function f such that $\frac{\partial f}{\partial x} = x(x^4 - 3y) = x^5 - 3xy$ and $\frac{\partial f}{\partial y} = -\frac{3}{2}x^2 + 3y$. Then $f(x,y) = \frac{1}{6}x^6 - \frac{3}{2}x^2y + g(y)$, for a suitable function g, so that $\frac{\partial f}{\partial y} = -\frac{3}{2}x^2 + \frac{dg}{dy}$. Since $\frac{\partial f}{\partial y} = -\frac{3}{2}x^2 + 3y$, it follows that $\frac{dg}{dy} = 3y$, so that $g(y) = \frac{3}{2}y^2 + C_1$. Consequently the general solution is $\frac{1}{6}x^6 - \frac{3}{2}x^2y + \frac{3}{2}y^2 = C$. If $y(-1) = 2$, then $C = \frac{1}{6}(-1)^6 - \frac{3}{2}(-1)^2(2) + \frac{3}{2}(2^2) = \frac{19}{6}$.

24. The characteristic equation is $s^2 - 5s + 6 = 0$, with roots $s = 2$ and $s = 3$. Thus $y_1 = e^{2x}$ and $y_2 = e^{3x}$. Next, $g(x) = 8e^x$, so by (9) and (10) of Section 16.6,

$$u_1'(x) = \frac{-e^{3x}(8e^x)}{(e^{2x})(3e^{3x}) - (2e^{2x})(e^{3x})} = -8e^{-x}$$

$$u_2'(x) = \frac{e^{2x}(8e^x)}{(e^{2x})(3e^{3x}) - (2e^{2x})(e^{3x})} = 8e^{-2x}$$

Therefore $u_1(x) = 8e^{-x}$ and $u_2(x) = -4e^{-2x}$, so that by (5) in Section 16.6, the particular solution y_p is given by $y_p = (8e^{-x})(e^{2x}) + (-4e^{-2x})(e^{3x}) = 4e^x$. Thus the general solution of the given differential equation is $y = 4e^x + C_1e^{2x} + C_2e^{3x}$. If $y(0) = 0$, then $0 = y(0) = 4 + C_1 + C_2$. Next, $\frac{dy}{dx} = 4e^x + 2C_1e^{2x} + 3C_2e^{3x}$, so if $y'(0) = 0$ then $0 = y'(0) = 4 + 2C_1 + 3C_2$. Thus $C_1 = -4 - C_2$, so that $0 = 4 + 2(-4 - C_2) + 3C_2$, and therefore $C_2 = 4$. Then $C_1 = -4 - C_2 = -4 - 4 = -8$. Consequently the particular solution is $y = 4e^x - 8e^{2x} + 4e^{3x}$.

25. Let $y = \sum_{n=0}^{\infty} c_n x^n$. Then $\frac{dy}{dx} = \sum_{n=1}^{\infty} n\, c_n x^{n-1}$ and $\frac{d^2y}{dx^2} =$ $\sum_{n=2}^{\infty} n(n-1)c_n x^{n-2}$. Since $\frac{d^2y}{dx^2} - 3x\frac{dy}{dx} - 3y = 0$, this means that

$$\sum_{n=2}^{\infty} n(n-1)c_n x^{n-2} - 3x\sum_{n=1}^{\infty} n\, c_n x^{n-1} - 3\sum_{n=0}^{\infty} c_n x^n = 0$$

or equivalently,

$$\sum_{n=0}^{\infty} (n+2)(n+1)c_{n+2}x^n - 3\sum_{n=1}^{\infty} n\, c_n x^n - 3\sum_{n=0}^{\infty} c_n x^n = 0$$

so that

$$2c_2 - 3c_0 + \sum_{n=1}^{\infty} [(n+2)(n+1)c_{n+2} - 3(n+1)c_n]x^n = 0$$

By Corollary 9.26, $2c_2 - 3c_0 = 0$, that is, $c_2 = \frac{3}{2}c_0$, and for $n \geq 1$ we have $(n+2)(n+1)c_{n+2} - 3(n+1)c_n = 0$, that is, $c_{n+2} = \frac{3}{n+2}c_n$. Thus

$$c_3 = \frac{3}{3}c_1 = c_1 \qquad c_5 = \frac{3}{5}c_3 = \frac{3^2}{5\cdot 3}c_1$$

$$c_4 = \frac{3}{4}c_2 = \frac{3}{4}\frac{3}{2}c_0 = \frac{3^2}{4\cdot 2}c_0 \qquad c_6 = \frac{3}{6}c_4 = \frac{3^3}{6\cdot 4\cdot 2}c_0$$

In general for any positive interger n we have

$$c_{2n} = \frac{3^n}{(2n)(2n-2)\cdots 4\cdot 2}c_0 = \frac{3^n}{2^n n!}c_0 \quad \text{and}$$

$$c_{2n+1} = \frac{3^n}{(2n+1)(2n-1)\cdots 5\cdot 3}c_1 = \frac{3^n(2n)(2n-2)\cdots 4\cdot 2}{(2n+1)!}c_1$$

$$= \frac{3^n 2^n n!}{(2n+1)!}c_1 = \frac{6^n n!}{(2n+1)!}c_1$$

Therefore the general series solution is $y =$ $c_0\sum_{n=0}^{\infty}\frac{3^n}{2^n n!}x^{2n} + c_1\sum_{n=0}^{\infty}\frac{6^n n!}{(2n+1)!}x^{2n+1}$.

26. Let $y = \sum_{n=0}^{\infty} c_n x^n$. Then $\frac{dy}{dx} = \sum_{n=1}^{\infty} n\, c_n x^{n-1}$ and $\frac{d^2y}{dx^2} =$ $\sum_{n=2}^{\infty} n(n-1)c_n x^{n-2}$. Since $x^2\frac{d^2y}{dx^2} - x\frac{dy}{dx} + y = 0$, this means that

$$x^2\sum_{n=2}^{\infty} n(n-1)c_n x^{n-2} - x\sum_{n=1}^{\infty} n\, c_n x^{n-1} + \sum_{n=0}^{\infty} c_n x^n = 0$$

or equivalently, $\sum_{n=2}^{\infty} n(n-1)c_n x^n - \sum_{n=1}^{\infty} n\, c_n x^n + \sum_{n=0}^{\infty} c_n x^n = 0$

so that $c_0 + \sum_{n=2}^{\infty} [n(n-1) - n + 1]c_n x^n = 0$,

or $c_0 + \sum_{n=2}^{\infty} (n-1)^2 c_n x^n = 0$.

By Corollary 9.26, $c_0 = 0$, and $(n-1)^2 c_n = 0$ for $n \geq 2$. Thus $c_n = 0$ for $n \geq 2$. Consequently $y = c_1 x$. Then $y(0) =$ 0 automatically. If $y'(0) = -7$, then $c_1 = -7$, so the particular solution is $y = -7x$.

27. $f(y) = 2y^2 - 7y + 5 = (2y-5)(y-1)$; $f'(y) = 4y - 7$;
$f'(y(t))\frac{dy}{dt} = (4y(t) - 7)\frac{dy}{dt}$
Constant solutions: $y = \frac{5}{2}$ and $y = 1$.

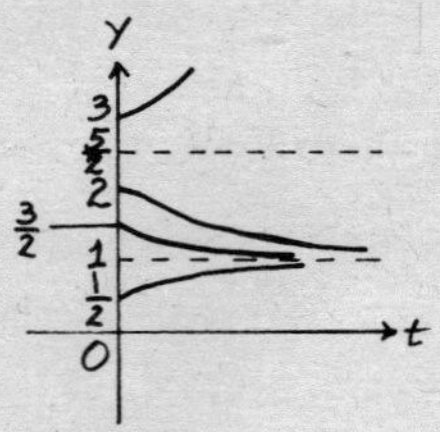

If $y(0) = \frac{1}{2}$ then $f(y(0)) = f(\frac{1}{2}) =$ 2, so y is strictly increasing. By (5) in Section 16.9, the graph is concave downward.
If $y(0) = \frac{3}{2}$ then $f(y(0)) = f(\frac{3}{2}) =$ -1, so y is strictly decreasing. By (5) in Section 16.9, the graph is concave upward.
If $y(0) = 2$ then $f(y(0)) = f(2) = -1$, so y is strictly decreasing. By (5) in Section 16.9, the graph is concave downward above the line $y = \frac{7}{4}$ and concave upward below the line $y = \frac{7}{4}$.
If $y(0) = 3$ then $f(y(0)) = f(3) = 2$, so y is strictly

increasing. By (5) in Section 16.9, the graph is concave upward.

28. $f(y) = y^3(y - 2)$; $f'(y) = 3y^2(y - 2) + y^3 = 4y^2(y - \frac{3}{2})$;

$f'(y(t))\frac{dy}{dt} = 4(y(t))^2(y(t) - \frac{3}{2})\frac{dy}{dt}$

Constant solutions: $y = 0$ and $y = 2$.

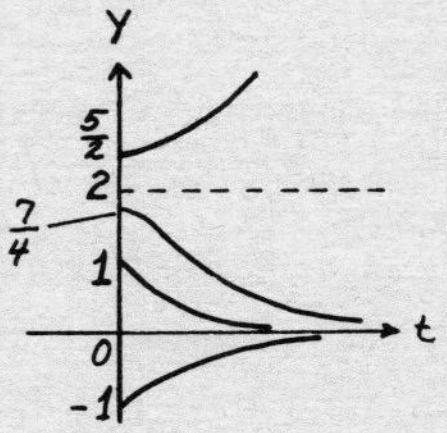

If $y(0) = -1$ then $f(y(0)) = f(-1) = 3$, so y is strictly increasing. By (5) in Section 16.9, the graph is concave downward.

If $y(0) = 1$ then $f(y(0)) = f(1) = -1$, so y is strictly decreasing. By (5) in Section 16.9, the graph is concave upward.

If $y(0) = \frac{7}{4}$ then $f(y(0)) = f(\frac{7}{4}) = -\frac{343}{256}$, so y is strictly decreasing. By (5) in Section 16.9, the graph is concave downward above the line $y = \frac{3}{2}$ and concave upward below the line $y = \frac{3}{2}$.

If $y(0) = \frac{5}{2}$ then $f(y(0)) = f(\frac{5}{2}) = \frac{125}{16}$, so y is strictly increasing. By (5) in Section 16.9, the graph is concave upward.

29. $f(y) = ye^y$; $f'(y) = e^y + ye^y = (1 + y)e^y$;

$f'(y(t))\frac{dy}{dt} = (1 + y(t))e^{y(t)}\frac{dy}{dt}$

Constant solution: $y = 0$.

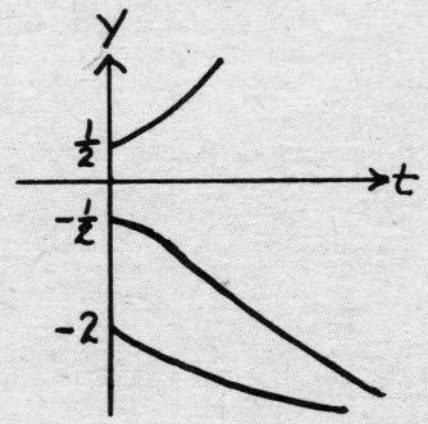

If $y(0) = -2$ then $f(y(0)) = f(-2) = -2e^{-2}$, so y is strictly decreasing. By (5) in Section 16.9, the graph is concave upward.

If $y(0) = -\frac{1}{2}$ then $f(y(0)) = f(-\frac{1}{2}) = -\frac{1}{2}e^{-1/2}$, so y is strictly decreasing. By (5) in Section 16.9, the graph is concave downward above the line $y = -1$ and concave upward below the line $y = -1$.

If $y(0) = \frac{1}{2}$ then $f(y(0)) = f(\frac{1}{2}) = \frac{1}{2}e^{1/2}$, so y is strictly increasing. By (5) in Section 16.9, the graph is concave upward.

30. $f(y) = \cos y$; $f'(y) = -\sin y$; $f'(y(t))\frac{dy}{dt} = -(\sin y(t))\frac{dy}{dt}$

Constant solutions: $y = \frac{\pi}{2} + n\pi$ for any integer n.

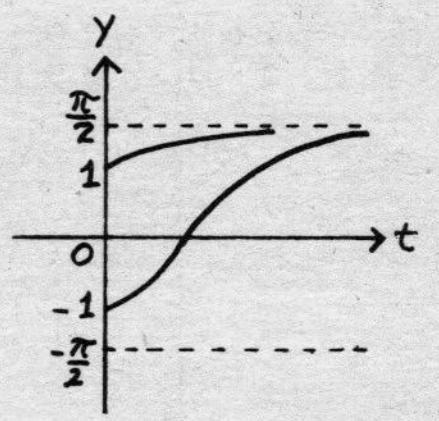

If $y(0) = 1$ then $f(y(0)) = f(1) = \cos 1 > 0$, so y is strictly increasing. By (5) of Section 16.9, the graph is concave downward.

If $y(0) = -1$ then $f(y(0)) = f(-1) = \cos(-1) > 0$, so y is strictly increasing. By (5) in Section 16.9, the graph is concave upward below the line $y = 0$ and concave downward above the line $y = 0$.

31. By (2) in Section 16.7, we have $\frac{k}{m} = \frac{g}{e}$, and by hypothesis $e = 1/2$. Thus $\frac{k}{m} = \frac{32}{1/2} = 64$. Therefore by (4) in Section 16.7, $\frac{d^2x}{dt^2} + 64x = 0$, which falls under Case 3 of Section 16.5 with $b = 0$ and $c = 64$.

If $u = -\frac{b}{2} = 0$ and $v = \frac{1}{2}\sqrt{4c - b^2} = \frac{1}{2}\sqrt{256 - 0} = 8$, it follows from (11) in Section 16.5 that the general solution is $x = C_1 \sin 8t + C_2 \cos 8t$. By hypothesis $x(0) = \frac{1}{12}$, so that $\frac{1}{12} = C_2$. Next, $\frac{dx}{dt} = 8C_1 \cos 8t - 8C_2 \sin 8t$. By hypothesis, $x'(0) = \frac{1}{24}$, so that $\frac{1}{24} = x'(0) = 8C_1$, and thus $C_1 = \frac{1}{192}$.

Consequently $x = \frac{1}{192}\sin 8t + \frac{1}{12}\cos 8t$.

32. We have $m = \frac{8}{32} = \frac{1}{4}$, $e = \frac{1}{6}$ and $p = 4.1$, so by (2) of Section 16.7, $k = \frac{mg}{e} = 48$. Thus $p^2 - 4km = (4.1)^2 - 4(48)(\frac{1}{4}) < 0$, so by Table 16.1 the vibration will be underdamped.

APPENDIX

1. The least upper bound is 1; the greatest lower bound is -1.
2. The least upper bound is 100; the greatest lower bound is 1/2.
3. The least upper bound is π; the greatest lower bound is 0.
4. The least upper bound is $\sqrt{2}$; the greatest lower bound is -9.9.
5. The least upper bound is 5; the greatest lower bound is 0.
6. The least upper bound is 4; the greatest lower bound is -1.
7. The least upper bound is 1; the greatest lower bound is 0.
8. The least upper bound is 1/3; the greatest lower bound is 3/10.
9. Assume that the set S of positive integers had an upper bound. By the Least Upper Bound Axiom S would then have a least upper bound M. For any number n in S, n + 1 is in S, so that by the definition of M, we have $n + 1 \leq M$. Thus $n \leq M - 1$, and consequently M - 1 is an upper bound of S. This contradicts the property of M that M is the least upper bound. Therefore S has no upper bound.
10. a. Assume that S had an upper bound. By the Least Upper Bound Axiom S would then have a least upper bound M. For any number na in S, (n + 1)a is in S, so that by the definition of M, we have $na + a = (n + 1)a \leq M$. Thus $na \leq M - a$, and it follows that M - a is an upper bound, and since $a > 0$ we deduce that M is not the least upper bound of S. Therefore S has no least upper bound.

    b. By part (a), b is not an upper bound of S, since S has no upper bounds. But this means that there is an element na in S such that $na > b$.
11. Let S be a set that is bounded below, and let T be the set of all numbers of the form -s, for s in S. Since S is bounded below, T is bounded above, so by the Least Upper Bound Axiom, there is a least upper bound M for T. If s is in S, then -s is in T, so $-s \leq M$, and thus $s \geq -M$. Consequently -M is a lower bound of S. If N is any lower bound of S, then -N is an upper bound of T, so $-N \geq M$ since M is the least upper bound of T. Therefore $N \leq -M$. Thus -M is the greatest lower bound of S.
12. Since $\frac{1}{n} > \frac{1}{n+1} > 0$ for all n, Theorem A.13 implies that $\left\{\frac{1}{n}\right\}_{n=1}^{\infty}$ converges to a number L, and $\frac{1}{n} \geq L \geq 0$ for all n. If $L \neq 0$, then $n \leq \frac{1}{L}$ for all n, which contradicts Exercise 9. Thus L = 0, and therefore $\lim_{n\to\infty} \frac{1}{n} = 0$.
13. Let $\varepsilon = 1$, and let δ be any positive number less than 1. If $x = \delta$ and $y = \frac{1}{2}\delta$, then $|x - y| = \frac{1}{2}\delta < \delta$, and $\left|\frac{1}{x} - \frac{1}{y}\right| = \left|\frac{1}{\delta} - \frac{2}{\delta}\right| = \frac{1}{\delta} > 1 = \varepsilon$. Thus $\frac{1}{x}$ is not uniformly continuous on (0, 1).